Publications of the

National Bureau of Economic Research, Inc.

Number 43

The Mining Industries, 1899–1939: A Study of

Output, Employment and Productivity

# The Mining Industries, 1899–1939

## *A Study of Output,*

## *Employment and Productivity*

by Harold Barger
and Sam H. Schurr

National Bureau of
Economic Research, Inc.

NEW YORK 1944

80738

# RELATION OF THE DIRECTORS TO THE WORK OF THE NATIONAL BUREAU OF ECONOMIC RESEARCH

1. The object of the National Bureau of Economic Research is to ascertain and to present to the public important economic facts and their interpretation in a scientific and impartial manner. The Board of Directors is charged with the responsibility of ensuring that the work of the Bureau is carried on in strict conformity with this object.

2. To this end the Board of Directors shall appoint one or more Directors of Research.

3. The Director or Directors of Research shall submit to the members of the Board, or to its Executive Committee, for their formal adoption, all specific proposals concerning researches to be instituted.

4. No report shall be published until the Director or Directors of Research shall have submitted to the Board a summary drawing attention to the character of the data and their utilization in the report, the nature and treatment of the problems involved, the main conclusions and such other information as in their opinion would serve to determine the suitability of the report for publication in accordance with the principles of the Bureau.

5. A copy of any manuscript proposed for publication shall also be submitted to each member of the Board. For each manuscript to be so submitted a special committee shall be appointed by the President, or at his designation by the Executive Director, consisting of three Directors selected as nearly as may be one from each general division of the Board. The names of the special manuscript committee shall be stated to each Director when the summary and report described in paragraph (4) are sent him. It shall be the duty of each member of the committee to read the manuscript. If each member of the special committee signifies his approval within thirty days, the manuscript may be published. If each member of the special committee has not signified his approval within thirty days of the transmittal of the report and manuscript, the Director of Research shall then notify each member of the Board, requesting approval or disapproval of publication, and thirty additional days shall be granted for this purpose. The manuscript shall then not be published unless at least a majority of the entire Board and a two-thirds majority of those members of the Board who shall have voted on the proposal within the time fixed for the receipt of votes on the publication proposed shall have approved.

6. No manuscript may be published, though approved by each member of the special committee, until forty-five days have elapsed from the transmittal of the summary and report. The interval is allowed for the receipt of any memorandum of dissent or reservation, together with a brief statement of his reasons, that any member may wish to express; and such memorandum of dissent or reservation shall be published with the manuscript if he so desires. Publication does not, however, imply that each member of the Board has read the manuscript, or that either members of the Board in general, or of the special committee, have passed upon its validity in every detail.

7. A copy of this resolution shall, unless otherwise determined by the Board, be printed in each copy of every National Bureau book.

*(Resolution adopted October 25, 1926, and revised*
*February 6, 1933, and February 24, 1941)*

# Director's Note

THIS report is one of several dealing with the trends of production and productivity in American industry since the opening of the twentieth century. Other volumes already published are *The Output of Manufacturing Industries, 1899–1937*, by Solomon Fabricant (1940); *Employment in Manufacturing, 1899–1939: An Analysis of Its Relation to the Volume of Production*, by the same author (1942); and *American Agriculture, 1899–1939: A Study of Output, Employment and Productivity*, by Harold Barger and Hans H. Landsberg (1942).

The study upon which this volume is based was made possible by funds granted by the Maurice and Laura Falk Foundation of Pittsburgh. The Falk Foundation is not, however, the author, publisher, or proprietor of this publication, and is not to be understood as approving or disapproving by virtue of its grant any of the statements made or views expressed herein.

William J. Carson
*Executive Director*

National Bureau of Economic Research, Inc.
December 1943

# Preface

As ITS subtitle indicates, this book is concerned with the output of the mining industries, with the draft upon the labor force which this output involved, and with the changing relationship between output and employment. Like others published by the National Bureau, this volume deals with a segment of the American economy and reports upon the progress that has been made in physical efficiency since the beginning of the present century. The studies in the series form a complement to other types of statistical inquiry—for example, those concerned with national income and the standard of living. Like such inquiries, the study of productivity changes touches one aspect of the general topic of economic progress. It affords an opportunity of examining the results of technological change, of new production methods, of the shortening of the workday, and of other factors which have influenced the productiveness of the individual worker.

The extraction of minerals from the earth is an activity of interest to many different kinds of specialist—the geologist, the engineer, the metallurgist, the geographer, the economist. Since the standpoint we have chosen is that of the economist or economic historian, and since we have further limited ourselves to certain aspects of all those which might appeal even to the economist, it follows that many features of the history of mining are scarcely mentioned in this volume or not discussed at all. Developments on the engineering or metallurgical side of mineral extraction are treated only insofar as they seem to the authors to have had a bearing upon productivity levels. Again, systems of wage payment, labor relations, and public policy toward the mineral industries, are mentioned only incidentally where they appear to have affected more immediately relevant aspects of mining history. Since we are interested chiefly in rather long run tendencies, the cyclical and other fluctuations to which most forms of mining are peculiarly subject will receive but the barest mention.

An inquiry such as the present one has two aspects. First there are problems of measurement, conceptual and statistical. For the period chosen, the data on mining output are fairly satisfactory and did not cause serious difficulty. The record of employment, on the other hand, had frequently to be pieced together from materials assembled for purposes quite different from our own— for instance, the computation of accident rates. As a result, figures for mining employment are for the most part clearly inferior to similar figures for, e.g., manufacturing or railroad transportation. Technical questions of industrial classification, and of the measurement of output and employment have, so far as possible, been excluded from the text of the report and reserved for appendix treatment.

The second part of the task had to do with the interpretation of the changes that occurred over the period in the effectiveness of labor in producing ouput—changes which were usually large enough to survive all doubts concerning the accuracy or comparability of the underlying data. In most branches of mining one may observe striking increases in output per manday; but in some industries these increases were much larger than in others, and in some productivity actually declined for periods as long as one or two decades. The authors believe that these developments and contrasts can be referred to the interaction of changing technology and resource conditions. For the mineral industries are peculiar in that their resources are subject to depletion, a phenomenon which it has in part been the function of technological advance to offset. This theme will recur at more than one point in the book.

The structure of the volume is briefly as follows: In Part One, Chapter 1 describes the field of study and clears the ground of certain preliminary matters. Chapters 2 and 3 review the course of output and employment, respectively, over four decades. Chapter 4 offers a summary view of changes in productivity, and contrasts the experience of different branches of mining.

Part Two treats technological changes in all mineral industries except petroleum and natural gas (the technology of the latter, radically different from that of other industries, is postponed until Chapter 10). Chapter 5 describes the progressive elaboration of mining methods, both underground and open pit, and the trend toward nonselective or mass mining. Chapter 6 examines the contribution that mechanization has made to this development.

Chapter 7 discusses coal preparation and ore concentration and the relation of these techniques to mining method.

In Part Three, Chapters 8 through 13, the relations between productivity levels, technological change and resource conditions are studied for each of the principal mining industries.

Part Four, which consists of Chapter 14, summarizes the results of the study and relates them to certain broad questions of economic theory and policy.

The five appendices are devoted to the presentation of statistics and to technical questions of measurement. The book concludes with a glossary of minerals and mining terms.

Harold Barger
Sam H. Schurr

# Authors' Acknowledgments

THROUGHOUT the study helpful advice and criticism were given by a National Bureau staff committee consisting of Thor Hultgren, Frederick C. Mills (chairman) and Leo Wolman; in addition we are heavily indebted to Solomon Fabricant for counsel and advice. The manuscript was read, in whole or in part, and useful comments were made, by other members of the National Bureau staff: Jacob M. Gould, Wesley C. Mitchell and George J. Stigler; by several Directors of the National Bureau; by Fred E. Berquist of the Department of Justice; and by Victor Paschkis and Thomas T. Read of Columbia University.

We are indebted to the following for the use of unpublished material and for numerous suggestions during the course of the study: W. W. Adams, Oliver Bowles and Paul M. Tyler of the Bureau of Mines; O. E. Kiessling, Vivian Eberle Spencer and Nicholas Yaworski of the Bureau of the Census; Harry S. Kantor of the Wage and Hour Division of the Department of Labor; Frederick Laist of the Anaconda Copper Company; H. H. Anderson of the Shell Pipe Line Corporation; and Fred Van Covern of the American Petroleum Institute.

We are grateful to several coworkers who assisted us in different phases of the study. Many of the computations were performed by Corolynn L. Lee and Céleste N. Medlicott. In the laborious tasks of checking the manuscript and reading proof, assistance was rendered by Melvin I. White and Robert C. Cohen respectively. The charts were drawn by H. Irving Forman who gave freely of his time and skill. Bettina Sinclair edited the manuscript and suggested numerous improvements.

Finally, the senior author is indebted to the President and Trustees of Columbia University for granting him leave of absence from his University duties in order to conduct the study.

H. B.
S. H. S.

# Contents

# Text Tables

# Appendix Tables

# Charts

# Part One

# Output and Employment

"There is not a single mineral substance of which the quantity used in the past century is less than the total of all the centuries that preceded." T. T. READ

# Chapter 1

# Introduction

THE DEGREE to which our material wants are satisfied from day to day, and the possibility of improving the physical equipment of the community for future use, alike depend upon the kind and quantity of things produced in the economy. Our interest in physical output proceeds from two related standpoints. We may inquire what changes have occurred in the aggregate size of the flow of goods and services: this is the task of index number construction. Or we may be more concerned with the composition of this output: the emphasis is then upon the expansion or contraction of particular kinds of production, and the share of each in the total. In discussing the mining industries of this country we shall adopt both types of approach.

Measurement of the volume of output tells us something of the growth or decline of the economy, or of segments of it, but it yields at best an inadequate picture of changes in the efficiency of the productive system from one period to another. For it takes no account of the draft made upon the economic resources of the nation in turning out goods and services. To carry the analysis a step further we need to measure the input of factors of production. The input of resources—human and material—cannot be aggregated with the facility with which we can total the things emerging from a productive process. Partly for this reason, and partly because human resources are of special interest, we shall confine our measurements of input to labor, i.e., we shall measure only the volume of employment. Consequently our figures of productivity will be derived only in terms of labor, and will neglect the input of capital and other factors. But we should not lose sight of the fact that such figures tell us only part, if perhaps the most interesting and important part, of the story of industrial efficiency.

A study of production and productivity, such as that about to be undertaken for the mining industries, offers interesting material for the writing of economic history. It affords opportunity for an assessment of the results of technological progress and the application of scientific knowledge to industrial ends. It provides data which may inform us concerning the effects of public policy in economic matters, such as labor legislation, conservation and the tariff. It reflects changes in ways of living and of getting a living, in consumption standards and in working habits. And it points a signpost toward achievement in the future.

## THE MINING INDUSTRIES

For the purpose of this report, the mining industries include not only mining proper but also the quarrying of stone and the production of crude petroleum and natural gas. The operations in which we are interested cover every form of mineral extraction, and are carried on both beneath and above the ground. Although the geographic distribution of mining activity is extremely wide, the production of individual minerals is often concentrated in a single area: anthracite coal in Pennsylvania, phosphate rock in Florida, mercury in California, gold and silver in the western states. For obvious reasons the mining of a given mineral is more rigidly restricted topographically than any other form of economic activity.

Many more mineral deposits are known to exist than are in fact exploited at the present time; and doubtless still further deposits lie buried in the earth, undiscovered. Only the richer, the more easily worked, or the more accessible minerals are actively exploited in any given era. The profitability of working a particular ore body may change radically from one period to another because of variations in the market price of the product and for other reasons as well. For example, new concentrating techniques may lessen the advantage of the richer ore bodies, as has been found in copper mining. Improvements in transportation may render accessible certain deposits which formerly could not be worked: thus the extension of the railroad network was a prior condition for the development of base metal mines in the West. As the nineteenth century advanced there occurred a geographic redistribution of mining activity which was not unlike the shift experienced by staple agriculture. Just as the wheat fields of New England could not compete with the wheat fields of Kansas, so the iron mines of the Atlantic Coast gave place to the iron mines of

Minnesota. A prime characteristic of mineral deposits is their exhaustibility: ghost towns of the mountain states bear silent witness to the departure of metals for which they were once a source. Mines close because the good ore is worked out, so that if any deposits are left they are in poorer, narrower seams which must be worked at greater depths, or because newer, richer deposits are discovered elsewhere. Mining continues, but under other skies, perhaps with other methods.

As a source of livelihood the mining industries (including stone quarries and oil and gas wells) are of relatively minor importance in the United States. In recent years they have employed about 2 percent of the working population, and have produced somewhat less than 2 percent of the national income. One occupied person in five is engaged in manufacturing, and one in six tills the soil or cares for livestock, but only one in fifty is a miner, quarryman or oil-well operative. Yet the mining industries furnish practically all of our fuel (solid and otherwise), and satisfy the major part of our need for metals and building materials. By value more than half of the output of the extractive industries consists of fuels, with metallic ores accounting for most of the remainder.

Some mining industries are much older than others. The length of time during which deposits have been worked has an important influence upon the technological state of the industry today and upon the degree to which depletion of its resources has already occurred. Small amounts of coal and iron were extracted for the use of blacksmiths even in Colonial times; lead was probably the first nonferrous metal to be produced domestically in any quantity. But we are concerned rather with the age of the mining industry as we now know it, the length of time during which today's deposits have been worked, and the date when modern technological problems first had to be faced.[1]

We know, for example, that anthracite has been mined continuously in Pennsylvania since 1820, and bituminous coal in Virginia at least since 1800. As for iron, bog ores were smelted in Massachusetts during the eighteenth century, and ironstone was mined and smelted in Maryland and Virginia before 1800. During

[1] The remainder of this section is based largely upon J. D. Whitney, *The Metallic Wealth of the United States* (Lippincott, Grambo and Co., Philadelphia, 1854); Albert S. Bolles, *Industrial History of the United States* (Henry Bill Publishing Co., Norwich, Conn., 1878); and U. S. Bureau of the Census, *Special Reports*, "Mines and Quarries, 1902."

the first half of the nineteenth century each of the New England states and a number of others had a local iron industry, and it was around 1825 that iron ore mining as we now know it had its beginnings in Pennsylvania. In 1840, 300,000 tons of iron ore were produced, mainly in Pennsylvania; scarcely any came from the Lake Superior region until the following decade. Gold was obtained by washing in Colonial times, but apparently it was not until 1825 that the first mining of gold-bearing quartz occurred, in North Carolina. Almost no silver was produced in this country until it appeared as a byproduct of California gold mining after 1848. Silver mining began with the discovery of the fabulous Comstock lode in Nevada in 1859. During the eighteenth century copper was worked rather spasmodically in New Jersey and Connecticut; even the extensive workings started at Bristol in the latter state in 1836 seem not to have been profitable. The establishment of regular copper mining in this country dates only from the opening of the Lake Superior region of Michigan in 1843. Lead mining has a somewhat longer continuous history. First exploited by the French in 1720, the lead mines of Missouri have apparently been worked consistently since 1798, when underground mining was started and a reverberatory furnace constructed. In 1819 the state boasted 45 lead mines in operation. By 1854 fears were already heard that the Missouri lead mines would soon be exhausted: up to the present, however, this has not yet occurred. In Wisconsin, which was less accessible than Missouri, lead mining did not begin until 1823. Although zinc is often found in association with lead, serious efforts to mine that metal in this country were slow to develop. Writing in 1854, Whitney observes that zinc ores "have, as yet, hardly begun to be worked": New Jersey, the sole producer, yielded less than 1,000 tons in 1852. Mercury was first mined in California about 1850.

The quarrying of stone followed the first settlements only at a distance, for lumber and imported brick were the initial building materials. By the middle of the eighteenth century, however, there were a number of important quarries in existence, so that stone quarrying stands out as one of the older forms of mineral extraction on this continent. Salt mining also has a long history, dating from the latter part of the eighteenth century. Most other forms of nonmetallic mineral production are relatively young. The petroleum industry had its start in western Pennsylvania as recently as 1859, and phosphate rock was not mined until 1867.

It does not follow, as we shall see, that because an industry is old, and has faced the same problems for many decades, its technological state is correspondingly more advanced than that of a newer industry. It may happen that mining tradition or the original layout of the mine makes mechanization a more difficult undertaking than it would be in a newer enterprise. It is in the younger industries or in the relocation of old industries, as with the development of the porphyry coppers of the West, that the real technological revolutions are to be found. Age does, however, exert a more direct influence upon resource depletion. In anthracite mining, one of the oldest of the extractive industries, depletion has considerably increased the difficulty of obtaining the coal, although exhaustion is still a long way off.

## THE DISTINCTION BETWEEN MINING AND MANUFACTURING

The actual separation of a mineral from the earth is usually a small part of the business of mining. The product must be broken, more or less, at the pit face, must be transported to the surface, and must then be cleaned, crushed or purified. The latter operations may be performed either in the vicinity of the mine or at some distance, in which case further transportation is necessary. Finally, there is usually a series of processes at the end of which the mineral, or part of it, is burnt up or emerges as a constituent of some finished commodity. At what point, then, do mining operations cease and manufacturing processes begin? Output and employment in manufacturing are treated in other volumes in this series,[2] and it was naturally desirable, in writing the present report, to avoid duplication between mining and manufacturing as far as possible. Censuses of Mining have been by no means consistent in this respect,[3] but we have tried to arrange the data so that, within practical limits, a uniform definition might apply in measuring output and employment, and that this definition might

[2] Solomon Fabricant, *The Output of Manufacturing Industries, 1899–1937* (National Bureau of Economic Research, 1940), and *Employment in Manufacturing, 1899–1939: An Analysis of Its Relation to the Volume of Production* (National Bureau of Economic Research, 1942).

[3] For example the Census of 1909 admitted significant overlapping of its results with those of the Census of Manufactures of the same year. See *Thirteenth Census of the United States, 1910*, Vol. XI, pp. 15-17. In the 1902, 1919 and later Censuses greater pains apparently were taken to prevent duplication of the sort indicated.

include all processes up to, but not beyond, the point where operations of a kind covered by the Census of Manufactures begin. Accordingly, in the case of metallic ores, we regard as mining not only the physical separation of the mineral from the earth, but also milling, concentration, or other processes of beneficiation. We include the crushing of stone, but not the sawing or shaping of dimension stone; the mining, but not the calcining, of gypsum.

Practical decisions of this kind receive statistical application at two points in a study such as this one. First, in reference to *output*, our indexes use prices as weights, that is, they represent comparisons in dollar terms, constant unit values being employed for each comparison. Thus, the valuation of a mineral is intended to occur at the point at which it leaves the mining operation as defined above: this is what we mean by the "mine value" of minerals. Second, the *employment* included represents the labor expended up to this same point of division between mining, as we have defined it, and subsequent economic processes. The resulting relationship between output and employment reflects changes in the productivity of mining proper and beneficiating, of quarrying and stone crushing; but it is unaffected by changes in the technology of smelting,[4] of the dressing of dimension stone, or of petroleum refining, for these we regard as manufacturing processes.

## THE MEASUREMENT OF OUTPUT AND EMPLOYMENT

In accordance with the plan adopted in other studies in this series, our indexes of output combine the physical quantities of different products, with unit mine values serving as weights. They therefore offer comparisons between dollar aggregates reckoned in constant prices. A description of the precise method of construction of these indexes, together with the data on which they are based, is presented in Appendix A. At this point it is necessary merely to discuss briefly the physical units chosen for measuring the output of individual minerals, and the related concepts of gross and net output.

Ideally we should seek to assemble separate production data for

4 However, we measure the output of most ores of the nonferrous metals in terms of recoverable content. An improvement in smelting techniques may raise the ratio of recoverable to actual content, and thus affect our measures of output and productivity. Changes in smelter recovery during the period appear, at least in the case of copper, to have been slight (see Appendix Table D-1).

every grade of ore or concentrate, weighting each by an appropriate price, for only by such a procedure could we take full account of changes in the quality of the mineral product whose output we are assessing. In the case of iron and manganese we have treated different grades of ore as separate commodities, combining the output of each with appropriate unit values as weights. In the case of petroleum, too, a breakdown is available to distinguish Pennsylvania grade from other crude oil, with appropriate prices for each. But in other instances lack of data made it impossible for us to follow this course, and the difficulty had to be surmounted in a different fashion. For the nonferrous metals (other than manganese) we do not have a breakdown of ore and concentrates which can be matched with a similar breakdown of their prices. Instead, we measure the mineral product of these industries in terms of its metallic content, using a single price or mine value for each metal.[5] In the case of anthracite, bituminous coal, natural gas and other minerals, we have for each a single output series which affords no means of allowing for such changes in the quality, or shifts in the composition, of output as may have occurred.

From this discussion it will be seen that our measures of mineral production are indexes of the *gross* physical output of the various mining industries, not of their *net* output. This distinction is important. No deduction to take account of fuel or other materials consumed during the production process has been attempted. These should, of course, be deducted [6] in the interests of strict accuracy. Otherwise fuel consumed, for example, in the copper industry is counted twice, once in the coal industry and once in the copper industry. It is possible that the amount of materials consumed per unit of output has increased during the period spanned by this study, in part because of the need to use more elaborate supports and larger amounts of power in mining at greater depths. But there are also definite indications of a contrary tendency. In several industries less product is wasted than formerly: in the petroleum industry natural gas, once dissipated, is

[5] The principal nonferrous metal mines were classified as follows: (1) lead and zinc in the Mississippi Valley, (2) copper, and (3) gold, silver and miscellaneous metal mines. For the products produced within each of these three industries, market prices had to be used for weighting purposes. In combining the output indexes for the three industries, unit mine values were used as weights. The necessity of this treatment is explained in Appendices A and B.

[6] I.e., materials consumed should be included in the output indexes with negative weights.

now marketed; and in the nonferrous metal industries the higher recovery ratios of modern concentrating techniques afford another illustration. Further, the shift to open cut mining has reduced the need both for mine supports and for pumping. Fuel has probably been economized in power production. Such considerations suggest a fall rather than a rise in materials consumed per unit of output in the mining industries as a whole. It is difficult or impossible to subject this question to a statistical test. But if the consumption of materials per unit of output has altered, indexes for the *net* output of the mining industries, in which the physical volume of materials consumed was deducted, would naturally behave somewhat differently from the indexes for gross output which we present. If materials have, on balance, been economized, an index of net output would plainly rise more rapidly than does our index of gross output. So would an index of net output per worker.

Thus in the realm of production statistics we can only approximate that which we would most wish to measure. The same is true in the employment field. First, the exclusion of workers engaged in manufacturing operations is sometimes troublesome, particularly in the quarrying of dimension stone. Second, since we do not regard additions to mining equipment or facilities as part of current mining output, a case exists for the exclusion of construction employees. But employees engaged in construction and other nonproducing activities, such as exploration, cannot usually be segregated from those who are actually digging the mineral. Because the amount of construction and development work varies rather sharply from year to year, short run variations in our productivity measures are probably not significant: the problem is less important when periods of ten or twenty years are being considered. The third way in which our employment figures may err is in the coverage of employees working for contractors. We have tried to cover these employees but we may not have been entirely successful. This disturbance to the results affects chiefly oil and gas wells. A similar difficulty occurs in connection with lead and zinc mining, where labor employed in leased workings may not be completely covered.

To the numbers of workers employed in mining industries we have paid slight attention. Fluctuations in mining activity from year to year are for the most part so violent, and mining operations have such a strong tendency to be intermittent, that the size of the labor force gives a poor idea of labor input, or the amount of human effort consumed. We have therefore preferred to express employment in terms of mandays or manhours, wherever these alternative measures could be developed. The manhour is perhaps the more fundamental unit of employment, but we have generally been forced to treat the manday as the basic unit of labor input in measuring productivity. Our reliance upon the manday is in the nature of a compromise. The majority of employment statistics in mining are still collected in terms of men on the payroll, and are converted by the Bureau of Mines or the Census Bureau into derived totals for mandays or manhours. Consequently manday totals involve fewer adjustments and are closer to the crude data than figures for manhours. Moreover, they are available generally for longer periods of time. In many cases we have given both types of data.

The measures of productivity which result from a comparison of output and employment are thus subject to numerous qualifications, some of which will be explored in greater detail in chapters dealing with individual industries.

In the remainder of Part One, Chapters 2 to 4 cover mining activity as a whole and embody the main statistical results of the study. In Chapter 2, which deals with output, an attempt is made to explain why the production of some minerals has expanded much more rapidly than that of others: in particular the role of scrap in the metal industries, and the economy of fuel and the substitution of oil for coal as a source of power, receive consideration. Chapter 3 reviews the major changes which occurred between 1902 and 1939 in the volume of employment, in its composition, and in the length of the work day. Chapter 4 examines the relationship between changing output and changing employment, and makes some comparisons of the trend of productivity in different branches of mining.

In Part Two, Chapter 5 presents a review of technological developments in various mining industries (except oil and gas wells, whose technology is discussed in the chapter on petroleum); in particular the trend toward nonselective mining is noted. This discussion is continued in Chapter 6, where various phases of the mechanization of the mining process are explored. Chapter 7 is devoted to the subsequent preparation of the mineral, and especially to the concentration of metallic ores and its relation to mining method.

In Chapters 8 through 13, which constitute Part Three, we examine the relations between output, employment and technology in major individual industries—bituminous coal, anthracite, petroleum, iron ore, copper and the quarrying of stone.

Part Four consists of a single concluding chapter, embodying a summary of the results and some reflections on their significance. In addition to appendices, a glossary of minerals and mining terms will be found at the end of the book.

Chapter 2

# The Behavior of Mining Output

IN THE STUDY of changes in production and productivity in the mining industries the first phase of our inquiry must evidently be concerned with the measurement of physical output. We need to know what has been produced, how various minerals compare in importance, and what shifts have occurred in the positions they occupy. In accordance with the practice adopted in other reports in this series,[1] data on the physical output of as many minerals as possible have been combined, with values as weights, into group and total indexes. For the most part, the results are presented for each year from 1899 to 1939. For details of index number construction, and for the various minerals included in the over-all index in different years, the reader is referred to Appendix A. The new index of mining output is shown in Table 1 and in Charts 1, 2 and 3.

## MINING AND OTHER SECTORS OF THE ECONOMY

Our index of mining output may be compared with the familiar measure published by the Federal Reserve Board, and with other mining indexes. The Board's index of mineral production, for the period since 1919, is based upon nine series only—bituminous and anthracite coal, crude petroleum, iron ore, copper, lead, zinc, gold and silver—which together accounted for slightly less than 80 percent of the value of all mineral products reported by the Bureau of Mines for 1929. The National Bureau index of course includes many more items, and for the period since 1919 covers the output of more than 99 percent of all minerals for which value data are available. The most important items not covered by the Reserve Board index (but included in the index presented here) are natu-

[1] Solomon Fabricant, *The Output of Manufacturing Industries, 1899–1937* (National Bureau of Economic Research, 1940); Harold Barger and Hans H. Landsberg, *American Agriculture, 1899–1939: A Study of Output, Employment and Productivity* (National Bureau of Economic Research, 1942). The statistical methods employed in the present study resemble closely those followed in these reports.

## TABLE 1

INDEXES OF PHYSICAL OUTPUT FOR MINING, MANUFACTURING
AND AGRICULTURE, 1899–1939

*1899:100*

| Year | Mining* | | | | Manu-facturing^b | Agricul-ture* |
| | Metals | Fuels | Other Non-Metals | Total | | |
|---|---|---|---|---|---|---|
| 1899 | 100 | 100 | 100 | 100 | 100 | 100 |
| 1900 | 109 | 106 | 108 | 108 | 102 | 101 |
| 1901 | 111 | 116 | 105 | 114 | 115 | 99 |
| 1902 | 120 | 118 | 116 | 119 | 129 | 103 |
| 1903 | 120 | 141 | 128 | 134 | 132 | 104 |
| 1904 | 125 | 142 | 149 | 138 | 124 | 109 |
| 1905 | 141 | 157 | 184 | 154 | 148 | 108 |
| 1906 | 149 | 162 | 222 | 160 | 159 | 118 |
| 1907 | 145 | 188 | 231 | 173 | 161 | 110 |
| 1908 | 139 | 172 | 223 | 162 | 133 | 112 |
| 1909 | 170 | 187 | 255 | 184 | 158 | 111 |
| 1910 | 175 | 203 | 264 | 195 | 168 | 114 |
| 1911 | 166 | 204 | 261 | 192 | 161 | 117 |
| 1912 | 184 | 215 | 278 | 206 | 185 | 123 |
| 1913 | 192 | 230 | 281 | 217 | 198 | 119 |
| 1914 | 172 | 218 | 258 | 202 | 186 | 129 |
| 1915 | 212 | 226 | 253 | 220 | 218 | 129 |
| 1916 | 264 | 248 | 279 | 254 | 259 | 119 |
| 1917 | 259 | 276 | 281 | 268 | 257 | 124 |
| 1918 | 249 | 286 | 245 | 270 | 254 | 130 |
| 1919 | 184 | 259 | 235 | 234 | 222 | 125 |
| 1920 | 195 | 305 | 288 | 271 | 242 | 130 |
| 1921 | 99 | 268 | 247 | 222 | 194 | 118 |
| 1922 | 155 | 269 | 300 | 239 | 249 | 130 |
| 1923 | 214 | 374 | 383 | 329 | 280 | 132 |
| 1924 | 207 | 346 | 386 | 310 | 266 | 137 |
| 1925 | 226 | 352 | 422 | 321 | 298 | 138 |
| 1926 | 235 | 386 | 447 | 348 | 316 | 146 |
| 1927 | 223 | 401 | 475 | 357 | 317 | 141 |
| 1928 | 230 | 397 | 482 | 357 | 332 | 147 |
| 1929 | 252 | 434 | 507 | 389 | 364 | 144 |
| 1930 | 197 | 393 | 459 | 343 | 311 | 145 |
| 1931 | 136 | 346 | 344 | 286 | 262 | 150 |
| 1932 | 76 | 301 | 221 | 230 | 197 | 144 |
| 1933 | 88 | 327 | 223 | 249 | 228 | 140 |
| 1934 | 111 | 346 | 251 | 271 | 252 | 120 |
| 1935 | 144 | 365 | 265 | 293 | 301 | 133 |
| 1936 | 195 | 410 | 362 | 344 | 353 | 134 |
| 1937 | 251 | 449 | 396 | 387 | 376 | 153 |
| 1938 | 176 | 403 | 340 | 331 | 295 | 152 |
| 1939 | 224 | 430 | 382 | 366 | 374 | 159 |

*For footnotes see next page.*

14

ral gas and gasoline, crushed stone, and sand and gravel. According to our index mineral production in 1939 was significantly below that of 1929, whereas the Reserve Board index shows practically no change between these two years. This and other slight

Chart 1

INDEXES OF MINING OUTPUT

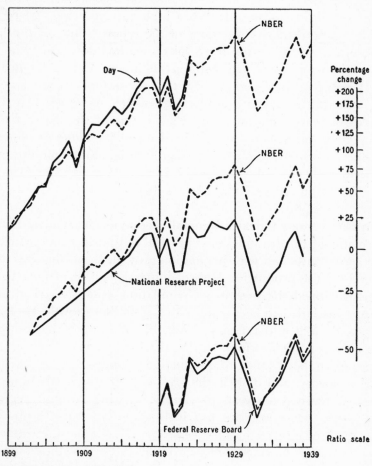

For source and notes see Appendix E

*Footnotes to Table 1.*

ª See Appendix Table A-7.
ᵇ Solomon Fabricant, *Employment in Manufacturing, 1899–1939: An Analysis of Its Relation to the Volume of Production* (National Bureau of Economic Research, 1942), p. 331.
ᶜ Harold Barger and Hans H. Landsberg, *American Agriculture, 1899–1939: A Study of Output, Employment and Productivity* (National Bureau of Economic Research, 1942), p. 21. The index refers to net output, and is based on crop year data in the case of crops, calendar year data in the case of livestock.

discrepancies are no larger than might be expected in view of the difference in coverage between the two indexes.

The index of mineral output for 1899–1923 constructed by Day [2] has a coverage (96 percent) comparable to that of our own index, and the two agree well. It employs fixed (value) weights instead of the modified chain method used in this study,[3] but otherwise is very similar in scope. The National Research Project index of mining output also has a high coverage—from 94 to 97 percent, according to the author of the report [4]—but for the last two decades of the period it exhibits a marked downward bias in comparison with the National Bureau index. This difference is attributable primarily to the fact that the authors of the former index used manhour instead of value weights. As we shall see, the output of petroleum and natural gas is one of the fastest rising component series included; but its share of the value of mineral products is far greater than its share of manhour employment. Consequently our index, based as it is on value weights, rises more rapidly during the 1920's and 1930's than does an index based on manhour weights.

In Chart 2 our index of mineral production is compared with the National Bureau indexes of physical output in manufacturing and agriculture, and with population growth. It will be seen that since 1899 the production both of minerals and of manufactures has outstripped the increase of population, whereas agricultural output has failed to keep pace with population growth. Between 1899 and 1929 mineral production, like manufacturing output, increased roughly fourfold. During the 1930's a sharp contraction occurred in both kinds of production, followed by an equally sharp recovery; and in 1939 the level of each was about equal to the peak reached ten years previously. Viewing the four decades as a whole, we should not feel inclined to say that the upward movement of either curve has ceased as yet. To be sure, there is in each case some evidence of retardation in the growth of output, for it is obvious that a parabola fitted to the logarithmic data in

[2] Edmund E. Day, "The Volume of Production of Basic Materials in the United States, 1909–21," *Review of Economic Statistics* (July 1922), and "The Physical Volume of Production in the United States for 1923," *Review of Economic Statistics* (July 1924).

[3] See Appendix A.

[4] Vivian E. Spencer, *The Mineral Extractive Industries, 1880–1938* (National Research Project, Philadelphia, 1940), p. 4. The arithmetic index with 1929 weights (*ibid.*, p. 9) is the one shown in Chart 1.

Chart 2

OUTPUT OF MINING, MANUFACTURING AND AGRICULTURE

National Bureau Indexes

(1899 : 100)

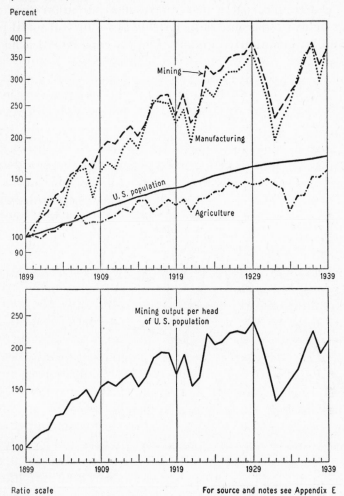

Ratio scale                                     For source and notes see Appendix E

Chart 2 would be convex upward, both for manufacturing and for mining. It does not appear, however, that such slackening of growth much exceeds the similar slackening apparent in the rate of population increase.

That mineral production should have kept pace with manufacturing output is at first sight surprising, particularly when we recall that in recent decades the nation's factories have achieved striking economies in the use of mineral raw materials. Moreover, in the case of many extractive industries output has shown little sign of growth or has actually contracted during the last twenty years. For example, coal, which receives more attention than many mining industries because of its fertility as a source of social problems and its quantitative importance, has experienced a marked

Chart 3

MINING: GROUP INDEXES OF OUTPUT

(1899 : 100)

Percent

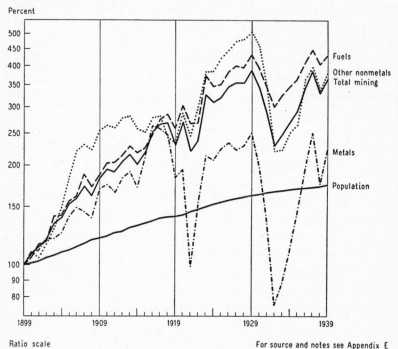

Ratio scale                          For source and notes see Appendix E

contraction in output. Indeed, it would be accurate to conclude that mining as a whole has reached a declining stage of its development were it not for the sensational growth of petroleum and natural gas production. It is the expansion in the output of these two commodities which has largely compensated for the retardation, or more than outweighed the actual decline, of the older forms of mineral extraction.

## GROUP INDEXES OF OUTPUT

Mineral production falls naturally into three rather unequal divisions. Fuels ranked first in importance in 1937, the latest year for which we have appropriate data, with a mine value of $2¾ billion, not quite two thirds of which consisted of oil products, and the remainder of coal.[5] Second in importance came metals, with a value of $640 million, one third of this being accounted for by iron ore. The remaining group, which comprises nonmetals other than fuels, was valued in 1937 at slightly less than $400 million. Among these, crushed limestone, sand and gravel, and sulfur were the most important; this third group includes also numerous minor minerals, from marl to ground soapstone.

Indexes for the output of each of these three groups of minerals, and for total output and population, will be found in Chart 3. Here the failure of the metals to grow as rapidly as the other groups is clearly evident. While the output of metallic minerals barely kept pace with the growth of population, indexes for both the fuels and the other nonmetals rose considerably faster than population. An important element in the slower growth of the metals is undoubtedly the increased availability of scrap: [6] metal once mined may be used again, but fuel burned is gone forever. Besides growing less rapidly than the other groups, the metals appear to fluctuate more violently. The amplitude of fluctuation for mineral output as a whole is very similar to that for manufacturing output (Chart 2). However, among different types of mineral the metals are much more sensitive to business cycle influences than the nonmetals. The extremely low levels of the metals index in 1921 and 1932 are especially noticeable (Chart 3). The very low level of this group in 1921 is associated with the liquidation of inventories accumulated during the war, and the short-lived post-war boom. The low point in 1932 reflects, in turn, the extreme decline of the important iron ore component, which fell by almost nine tenths from 1929 to 1932; as Chart 4 shows, iron ore output in 1932 was less than half as great as it had been at the turn of the century.

[5] The value of individual minerals for 1899, 1909, 1919, 1929 and 1937 will be found in Appendix Table A-2.

[6] Our indexes relate to ore mined and do not include the recovery of secondary metal.

## METALS

We estimate the mine value of all metals produced in 1937 at $642 million.[7] Of this total, $608 million was accounted for by the combined value of iron ore ($207 million) and the major nonferrous and precious metals, copper, lead, zinc, gold and silver (together $400 million [8]). As for the remainder, $34 million, molybdenum was valued at $20 million, and antimony, bauxite, chromite, manganese, mercury, platinum, tungsten, uranium, vanadium and ti-

Chart 4

COPPER, LEAD AND ZINC, AND IRON ORE: OUTPUT
(1899 : 100)

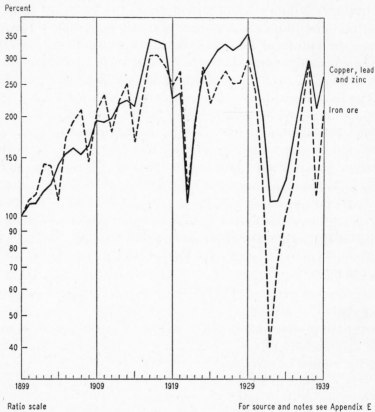

Ratio scale                                    For source and notes see Appendix E

[7] The value of individual minerals for 1899, 1909, 1919, 1929 and 1937 will be found in Appendix Table A-2.

[8] Included in this sum is the value of a small amount of (nonmetallic) fluorspar which appears as a byproduct of lead and zinc.

tanium—no one of which accounted for as much as $5 million separately—made up the other $14 million. It should be remembered that a substantial fraction of this country's consumption of copper, bauxite (aluminum), manganese and mercury, and virtually its entire supply of nickel and tin, are imported either as concentrates or as metal.[9] Domestic production, with which we are here concerned exclusively, is therefore a poor gauge of the relative importance of different metals from the standpoint of consumption.

Chief among the industrially important metals of domestic origin are iron, copper, lead and zinc. In 1937 the value of the output of iron ore was about half that of copper, lead and zinc combined; however, the former weighed, in terms of metal, around twenty times the latter. Indexes for the output of iron ore and for copper, lead and zinc production are compared in Chart 4. It will be seen that, broadly speaking, the movements of the two series are similar. Between 1899 and 1916–18 the production of iron ore and of the three nonferrous metals tripled. Since the close of the first World War the trends of both series have been stationary or slowly declining. Both show marked cyclical fluctuations, and both fall to low levels in the depressions of 1921 and 1932. On the other hand the iron ore series fluctuates with greater violence than does the series for nonferrous metals. This difference in behavior may perhaps be related to differences in degree of diversification among the uses to which the two kinds of metal are put. It is probably attributable also to the great importance and continuous availability of iron and steel scrap, which in periods of depression is often substituted for iron ore in the manufacture of steel.

## Iron Ore

The demand for iron ore is derived primarily from the demand for steel. As we should expect, the short run fluctuations in the output of the former follow a pattern very similar to that shown by movements of the latter (Chart 5). It is obvious, however, that although the two curves resemble each other in shape, the production of iron ore has lagged behind the growth of steelmaking.

[9] In the case of copper, imports of ore and concentrates are usually offset, or more than offset, by exports of refined metal.

Chart 5

IRON ORE OUTPUT, STEEL PRODUCTION AND
CONSUMPTION OF SCRAP

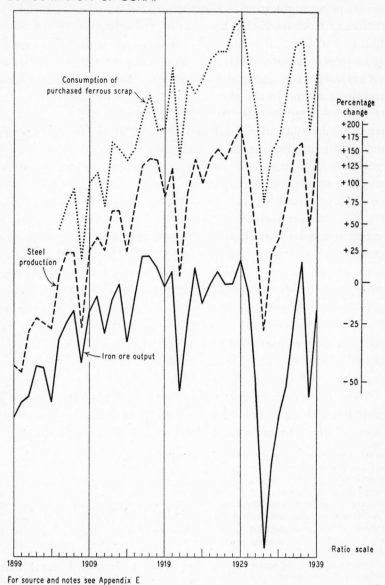

Consumption of
purchased ferrous scrap

Percentage
change
+200
+175
+150
+125
+100
+ 75
+ 50
+ 25

0

− 25

Steel
production

− 50

Iron ore output

Ratio scale

1899            1909            1919            1929            1939

For source and notes see Appendix E

The failure of iron mining to keep pace with steel production is to be explained by three separate factors whose relative importance is not easy to assess. In the first place the substitution of steel for cast or wrought iron—a substitution which began with the invention of steel itself—has continued: for example 28 percent of pig iron and ferro-alloy output went for other uses than steelmaking in 1899, compared with only 18 percent in 1937.[10] This means that relatively less and less ore has been used for other purposes than steelmaking. In the second place the steel industry, like other branches of manufacture, has made economies in the use of raw materials: in 1937 about 10 percent less ferrous materials were used in the production of a ton of steel than were required in 1909.[11] Perhaps still more important is a third factor—the substitution of scrap iron and steel for pig iron as a raw material in steelmaking. It will be seen from the uppermost curve in Chart 5 that the consumption of purchased scrap [12] by steelmakers increased at a faster rate than steel production and very much more rapidly than the production of iron ore. This increased use of scrap in steelmaking is to be explained partly by its greater availability, and partly by technical changes in the manufacture of steel. We should notice, in regard to the availability of scrap, the retardation which has occurred in the growth of steel production itself: the ratio of past steel output (i.e. at the time when currently available scrap was freshly manufactured) to present steel output has perhaps never been so high as it is today.[13]

Of the three factors mentioned, each of which has tended to retard the growth of iron ore production in comparison with the output of steel, the last would appear to be the most important at

[10] Fabricant, *The Output of Manufacturing Industries, 1899–1937*, p. 273.

[11] *Ibid.*, pp. 265-66.

[12] Substantial quantities of scrap are produced by the steelmakers themselves, and used by them as raw material (e.g., ingots too short to roll, and trimmings left in rolling or forging); data on the consumption of this scrap (which of course does not enter commercial channels) have been available only since 1935. In recent years purchased scrap has accounted for about half of total scrap consumption. Not quite all scrap is used for making steel; small amounts are consumed in the manufacture of iron products.

[13] The availability of scrap appears also to have been increased during recent decades by the obsolescence of reciprocating engines on the advent of the turbine, and the short life of the automobile in comparison with older forms of transportation equipment: see Erich W. Zimmerman, *World Resources and Industries* (Harper, 1933), pp. 600-05. In some uses, to be sure, technological advance may have lengthened rather than shortened the useful life of the metal, but this contrary tendency does not seem to have been important.

the present time, whatever has been the case in past eras. To the substitution of steel for iron, and to economy in the use of materials in steelmaking itself, there are definite limits which are already being approached. On the other hand, there is still considerable scope for further increases in the use of scrap. In the short run scrap and pig iron from ore are by no means perfect substitutes for the manufacture of steel, although with appropriate technical adaptation it is entirely possible to use either exclusively. It may be that in the future the requirements of the steel industry for pig iron will be further reduced: certainly the supply of scrap has grown steadily in recent decades and appears likely to increase still further.

### Alloy Metals

Steel is now the principal product for which iron ore is used, but by no means all steel is of the ordinary carbon or "tonnage" class. Increasing amounts of a great variety of alloy steels are manufactured for different purposes. Of all steel made, alloy steels rose from less than 1 percent in 1909 to 5 or 6 percent in the years immediately preceding the present war (Chart 6). These percentages are in terms of weight; by value they run much higher.

Among the metals used in ferro-alloys (in addition to iron) manganese is quantitatively the most important.[14] First added to Bessemer steel in 1856, it is employed to secure uniformity of structure and to lessen the effect of impurities. Variations in the production of manganese are shown in Chart 7. It will be seen that the fluctuations in manganese output are much more violent than in iron ore output, but the movements in the two series are usually in the same direction except for the years 1901–14. The low level of manganese compared with iron ore production during this period was apparently associated with increased dependence on imports of manganese. Since iron ore is bulky and low in value, imports are normally of negligible importance (Table 2). In contrast, a substantial fraction of our manganese requirements has always been supplied from abroad. A high level of imports during the decade preceding the first World War was followed after 1914

[14] The technical information in this section is largely taken from J. M. Camp and C. B. Francis, *The Making, Shaping and Treating of Steel* (5th ed., Carnegie-Illinois Steel Corp., 1940), pp. 908-1057.

by lessened dependence upon foreign
sources: since then imports and domestic production have usually expanded and contracted in unison.

Smaller quantities of many other
metals are used for making steel alloys.
Tungsten is a constituent of all high-
speed tool steels, and vanadium, molybdenum, nickel or cobalt are usually
added as well. Nickel steels not only
possess magnetic properties, but are
less brittle than ordinary carbon steels;
they are used for making high pressure
boilers and heavy duty gears. Chrome
steels are exceptionally hard; they appear in files, ball bearings, gears and
small tools. Chromium, moreover, has
become important recently because of
its ability, alone or in combination
with other alloy metals, to improve
the resistance of steel to high temperatures. Many industries using equipment made of steel have pushed temperatures and pressures to levels at
which ordinary steels would break
down; in this connection chrome steel
has improved the efficiency of the high
pressure steam boiler, of the internal
combustion engine, of apparatus for
cracking or hydrogenating petroleum,
and of many types of equipment in the
chemical industry. Chromium has
found further application in the man-

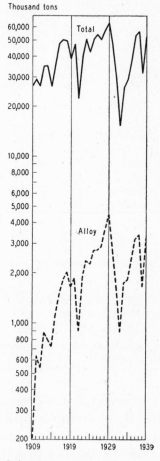

Chart 6

STEEL INGOTS AND
CASTINGS

Production, 1909–39

Ratio scale

For source and notes see Appendix E

ufacture of stainless steel, which may contain as much as 10 to 30
percent of the alloy metal; by contrast, most other special steels
contain only 1 to 4 percent of alloy metal.

Molybdenum steels, easily machined and particularly suitable
for welding, are used for structural plates and heavy welded pipe.
Vanadium steels make excellent forgings, and hence are employed
for crankshafts; also for tools, dies, taps and razor blades. So large

TABLE 2

IRON ORE AND ALLOY METALS
Value of Domestic Production and Imports, Averages for Years Shown
*Million dollars*

|  |  | 1899–1901 | 1914–16 | 1917–19 | 1927–29 | 1937–39 |
|---|---|---|---|---|---|---|
| Iron ore | *Production* | 49.4 | 118.4 | 226.6 | 168.0 | 146.9 |
|  | *Imports* | 1.3 | 4.4 | 3.2 | 6.5 | 5.7 |
| Manganese | *Production* | 1.0 | 1.3 | 8.2 | 4.8 | 3.1 |
|  | *Imports* | 1.7 | 4.4 | 12.2 | 7.4 | 8.6 |
| Tungsten | *Production* | b | 5.5 | 4.8 | .7 | 3.9 |
|  | *Imports* | c | 2.8 | 7.4 | 1.1 | 1.4 |
| Molybdenum | *Production* | b | .1 | .7 | 2.1 | 21.4 |
|  | *Imports* | c | c | .1$^d$ | b | b |
| Vanadium | *Production*$^a$ | c | .7 | 1.1 | c | 1.0$^e$ |
|  | *Imports* | c | c | b | .5 | .8 |
| Chromite | *Production* | b | .3 | 1.7 | b | b |
|  | *Imports* | .3 | 1.0 | 1.8 | 2.0 | 5.3 |
| Nickel | *Production* | b | .5 | .4 | .3 | c |
|  | *Imports* | 1.4 | 7.5 | 9.9 | 14.2 | 22.1 |
| Cobalt | *Production* | b | 0 | b | 0 | 0 |
|  | *Imports* | .1 | .3 | .6 | 2.0 | 2.6 |

*Source:* Annual issues of *Mineral Resources* and its successor, *Minerals Yearbook* (U. S. Bureau of Mines).
$^a$ Includes uranium.
$^b$ Less than $50,000.
$^c$ Not available.
$^d$ Annual average for July 1918 to December 1919; data for remainder of period not available.
$^e$ Average 1938 and 1939; data for 1937 not available.

a variety of steels contain more than one alloy metal that only a few illustrations can be given here: manganese-nickel and manganese-molybdenum alloys are common in railroad equipment, where resistance to fatigue and to sharp impacts is important; manganese-chromium-molybdenum steels are used for chisels and punches, chromium-molybdenum for large springs and forgings, nickel-molybdenum for axles, shafts and armor plate, and other purposes requiring high tensile properties and high fatigue resistance; nickel-chromium steels, being easily machined yet wear-resistant, are particularly suited for gears and oil well bits.

Fluctuations in the output of the alloy metals are so erratic that we have not thought it worth while to chart them, except in the case of manganese (Chart 7). Such output data as can be assembled

for individual minerals will be found in Appendix Table A-1 and
have been included in our indexes. Variations in domestic production and in imports are reflected in Table 2, which presents
value data for iron ore, and for the seven principal metals used in

Chart 7

IRON ORE AND MANGANESE: OUTPUT

(1899 : 100)

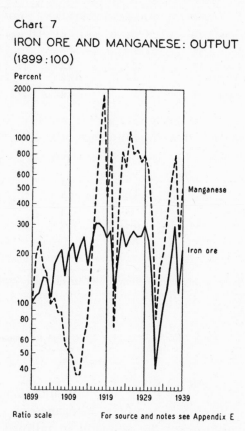

Percent

Ratio scale              For source and notes see Appendix E

steel alloys. Here it is shown that although none of these metals
compares in importance with iron ore itself, the two most significant in value terms are nickel and molybdenum. Particularly impressive is the increasing importance of molybdenum, the only
one of the seven alloy metals of which the United States has an
adequate domestic supply. In normal times there is no domestic
production of cobalt; output of chromite is insignificant, and of
nickel very small. As for manganese, tungsten and vanadium, domestic production is sufficient to fill a substantial part, but by no
means all, of our needs.

*Nonferrous Metals*

It is difficult to devise a satisfactory industrial classification of non-ferrous-metal mines. If we adopt the most convenient treatment, a fourfold division into lead-zinc mines, copper mines, gold-silver mines and placer workings, we must bear in mind that while mines in the first group yield lead and zinc almost exclusively, copper mines also produce gold and silver, and gold-silver mines provide some lead and zinc in addition to the precious metals. Placer operations produce gold and a little silver. Since employment is associated with a mine, rather than with the production of a single metal from that mine, we have had to use the industrial classification just described in order to measure productivity (Chapter 4, below). In the present chapter, however, we are interested rather in the individual metals for their own sake: copper from a gold or silver mine is just as good for most purposes as copper from a copper mine. For each metal, therefore, the outputs from different types of mine have been aggregated, and in Chart 8 the total for each is shown, irrespective of the type of mine from which it came.[15]

There are striking contrasts in the behavior of the five metals. During the first two decades of the present century the three metals for which the demand is primarily industrial, copper, lead and zinc, increased their output substantially in comparison with the two precious metals, gold and silver. Thereafter the trends of the five metals were less dissimilar. In 1939 the output of gold and silver was only 10 to 20 percent above the 1899 level, whereas lead output had doubled, copper output had more than doubled, and zinc output had quadrupled. In amplitude of fluctuation, and especially in cyclical behavior, equally sharp contrasts may be observed. The widest variations in output are to be seen in copper, and after copper in zinc and silver. Cyclical movements in lead are somewhat less marked, and in gold they scarcely show at all.

In the case of gold, the lack of positive correlation with the business cycle accords with expectation, and is due to its fixed selling price; indeed, one can observe here an inverse correlation with general movements in business. The sharp decline in gold output from 1915 to 1920 must be ascribed to the rising monetary costs

[15] The classification of nonferrous metal mines is considered further in Appendix B.

of its production, the equally sharp recovery from 1933 to 1939 to the devaluation of the dollar. As for silver, its greater sensitivity to movements in business seems at first sight surprising, for its industrial applications are not much more important than are

Chart 8

NONFERROUS METALS

Output of Individual Minerals

(1899 : 100)

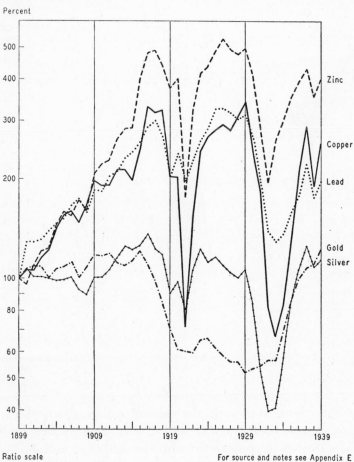

Percent

Ratio scale                                    For source and notes see Appendix E

those of gold. However, silver is to a large extent a byproduct of other nonferrous metals, so that changes in its output result chiefly from fluctuations in the demand for these metals. The sharp rise in silver output after 1933 is obviously connected with the silver-buying policy of the United States Treasury—a policy which must also have affected indirectly the production of gold and copper, with which it is jointly produced.

Copper, lead and zinc may be considered together. Each is—at least in some of its uses—a substitute for the other, and the prices

Chart 9

COPPER, LEAD AND ZINC: PRICES

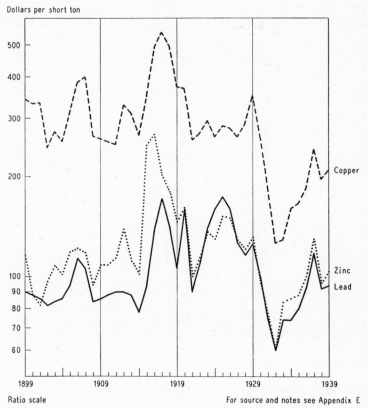

Dollars per short ton

Ratio scale                                    For source and notes see Appendix E

of all three tend to move in the same direction (Chart 9). Copper is more expensive than either lead or zinc, a fact which probably restricts its uses in comparison with the other two metals; for this reason either lead or zinc, if equally applicable, will be preferred to copper (especially in building construction). The premium in the price of copper appears, however, to be steadily diminishing. This development is difficult to explain. It can hardly be attributed to an expansion in copper output in relation to the supply of the other metals, for copper production in this country has lagged behind that of zinc, and has shown scarcely any increase as compared with lead. Increased output in Chile and in Africa no doubt played a part. At any rate it is noteworthy that during 1922–28 the price of copper was about the same as before the first

Chart 10

COPPER

Primary and Secondary Output, 1907 – 39

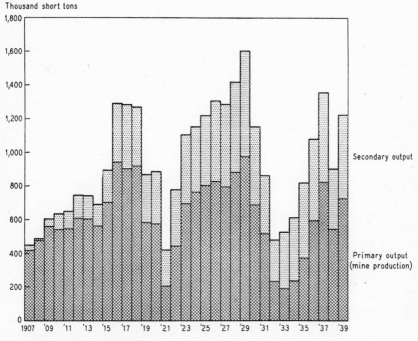

Thousand short tons

For source and notes see Appendix E

World War, whereas lead and zinc were both considerably more expensive than in the pre-war era. Except for a period of dear copper during 1928–30, this decline in the premium of the copper price over the prices of lead and zinc has persisted. Some substitution of copper for the other two metals must have taken place.[16]

[16] "It is evident that the low selling price of copper in recent years has encouraged consumption, discouraged the search for substitutes, and resulted in the finding of many new uses for the metal. Undoubtedly substitutes would have been employed for some uses had prices been higher, whether or not such substitutes could have met requirements quite as well as copper." C. E. Julihn and Helena M. Meyer, "Copper," *Mineral Resources of the United States, 1925* (U.S. Bureau of Mines), Part I, p. 351.

The three metals show differences in trend which are not to be explained entirely by the relations among their prices. Zinc output grew from 1908 to 1917 at an appreciably faster rate than either copper or lead, and since then the corresponding increase in the relative importance of zinc has persisted. The price of zinc,

Chart 11

LEAD

Primary and Secondary Output, 1907 – 39

Thousand short tons

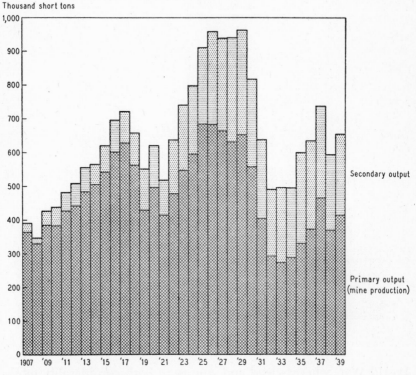

For source and notes see Appendix E

which was comparatively high during 1915–16, has declined no more rapidly than the price of copper, and has fallen only slightly in relation to lead. Lead is distinguished from the other two metals considered here by the fact that it is apparently much less sensitive to business cycle fluctuations: in 1921, for example, lead output was only slightly below its level for the two preceding years, whereas zinc and copper dropped precipitously, numerous copper mines closing down completely. In 1929–32 the contrast

is less marked, for lead declined as much as zinc, though not so
sharply as copper. Finally, while the three metals show slight sign
of positive growth since the peaks reached in 1916–18, lead alone
appears to have begun a definite downward trend. During 1937–

Chart 12
ZINC
Primary and Secondary Output, 1909 – 39

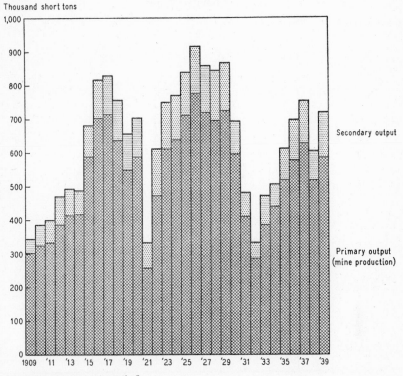

Thousand short tons

For source and notes see Appendix E

39—the most recent peacetime years—the output of all three metals
was lower than it had been ten years previously: zinc had declined
19 percent, copper 21 percent, but lead as much as 36 percent.
Perhaps business in general was not as good in 1937–39 as it had
been in 1927–29, but the comparison seems a fair one, for the two
periods occupy roughly corresponding positions in the business
cycle. These differences in behavior appear to be due partly to the
relative availability of secondary sources of supply, and partly to
variations among the principal uses to which each metal is put.

Let us first consider the scrap situation. The only output included in the indexes presented in this volume of course consists
of new metal from the mines. But the actual supply of any metal
available for use at a given time consists only partly of mine out-

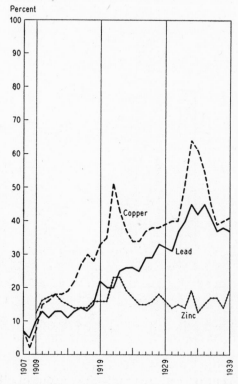

Chart 13

COPPER, LEAD AND ZINC
Ratio of Secondary Output to
Secondary plus Primary Output
1907 – 39

For source and notes see Appendix E

put: there is always available a larger or smaller amount of scrap,
either recovered during the manufacturing process or derived
from articles discarded by their users. The elasticity of supply of
secondary metal is very difficult to determine. Scrap recovered
from manufacturing processes is practically a byproduct, and
probably very inelastic in supply. The supply of old nonferrous

scrap turned in by large industrial enterprises, such as the railroads, must also be comparatively insensitive to the price it fetches.
Scrap from the ordinary junk pile or automobile graveyard, on
the other hand, is considerably more troublesome to collect and

Chart 14

COPPER

Consumption by Use, 1919 − 40

Thousand short tons

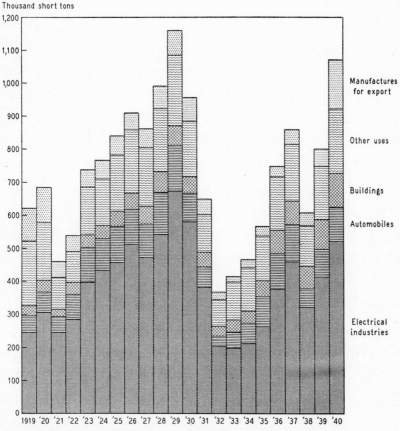

For source and notes see Appendix E

process, and hence must be much more elastic in supply. Unfortunately, statistics fail adequately to distinguish between these
various sources of scrap. If the supply of scrap were perfectly inelastic, we might regard mine output as determined—apart from
inventory changes—by the demand for the metal minus the supply

of scrap. The actual situation is so complicated, however, that this simple treatment cannot be employed.

That secondary output plays an important role in the total supply of each of the three metals under consideration is clearly apparent from an inspection of Charts 10, 11 and 12, in each of which secondary is superimposed upon primary output. Indeed,

Chart 15

LEAD

Consumption by Use, 1919 – 40

Thousand short tons

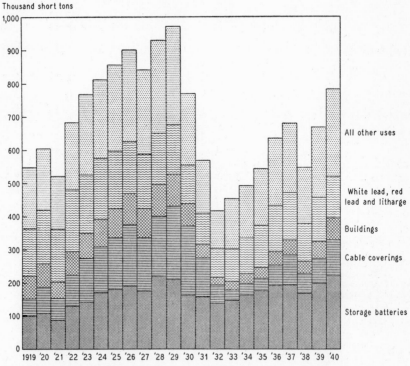

For source and notes see Appendix E

in the case of copper secondary exceeded primary production during several years of the period. Chart 13 summarizes the three preceding charts and shows the ratio of secondary output to total supply for each metal. For all three, but most notably for copper and lead, secondary appears through time to have grown in importance in relation to primary output. This is not surprising, for the stock pile of old metal in the hands of ultimate consumers (whether business firms, governmental agencies or private households), and so also potentialities of recovery, must continually have increased from decade to decade. In this connection we must not overlook the increasing quantities of lead used for storage batteries (Chart 15); unlike other applications of this metal, practically the whole amount used in batteries returns to the manufacturer as secondary material within a very few years. This probably

Chart 16

ZINC

Consumption by Use, 1908 – 40

Thousand short tons

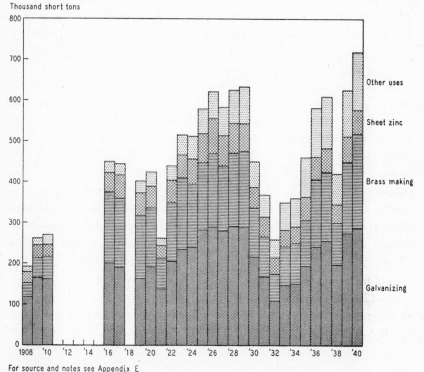

For source and notes see Appendix E

accounts for the large increase in secondary lead output (Chart 11), as well as for the decline in its mine production over the past fifteen years (Chart 8) which we have already noted.

About half the secondary output of copper is new rather than old metal, i.e., it is a byproduct of the casting and machining of copper and brass or other alloys.[17] The supply of this new scrap

[17] In 1939, 57 percent of secondary copper was old scrap; the remainder was new scrap. Corresponding ratios for old scrap were 87 percent for lead, but only 24 percent for zinc.

must obviously fluctuate, often subject to a time lag, with the consumption of copper by industries using the metal (Chart 14). The appearance of large supplies of secondary copper shortly after a period of great activity in these industries is therefore to be looked for. Something of the sort appears to have occurred during the sharp recession of 1920–21. The extremely violent fall in the output of primary copper in 1921, which no doubt reflected in part the cumulative effect of large inventories of the metal remaining from the period of hostilities and the brief post-war boom, appears also to have been attributable to large supplies of scrap.[18] The dependence of secondary output upon activity in the recent past is further suggested by the continued decline in the consumption of scrap copper during 1922, at a time when the output of primary metal had started to recover (Chart 10).

In the case of zinc also a substantial fraction of the secondary supply comes from the zinc-using industries rather than from the junk pile, and thus roughly parallels activity in metalworking. Indeed the junk pile is a less important source of zinc than of the other nonferrous metals. While some scrap zinc comes from old brass, zinc is peculiar among the three metals in that a high proportion of its output is entirely consumed and disappears permanently from circulation. Like lead paint, zinc paint completely dissipates the metal in use. But large amounts of zinc are employed also for galvanizing (Chart 16), and here again the metal is completely lost. This feature undoubtedly accounts for the rather minor importance of secondary as compared with primary output in the case of zinc (Charts 12 and 13), and the maintenance of the primary output of zinc in relation to that of lead and copper (Chart 8).

### Other Metals

The only remaining metallic minerals for which we have satisfactory output data are bauxite and mercury.[19] With products worth $2.4 and $1.5 million respectively in 1937, these two industries are the subject of Chart 17. The bauxite industry, which produces

[18] See N. E. Crump, *Copper* (William Rider, London, 1925), pp. 115-16.
[19] The various minor metals used for making ferrous alloys have already been discussed.

the raw material for aluminum, resembles mercury mining in that both are subject to competition from abroad: in neither metal is the United States self-sufficient in normal times. In 1939, 45 percent of bauxite and 83 percent of mercury consumption was supplied domestically. But there are also striking differences between the two industries, for bauxite is a new and mercury an old min-

Chart 17

BAUXITE AND MERCURY: OUTPUT

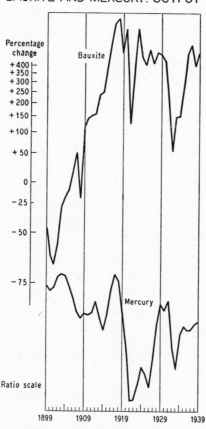

For source and notes see Appendix E

ing enterprise. Until a few decades ago, aluminum was a curiosity, and the bauxite mines of Arkansas have a very brief history. Thus for the first half of the period 1899–1939, bauxite output expanded with the rapidity characteristic of a very young industry.

Mercury, by contrast, has been mined in California continuously since about 1850. A number of the deposits are exhausted, and now, not infrequently, the poorer grades of ore have to be worked. The trend of output appears downward, despite something of a revival in recent years.

Chart 18
FUELS
Output of Individual Minerals
(1899 : 100)

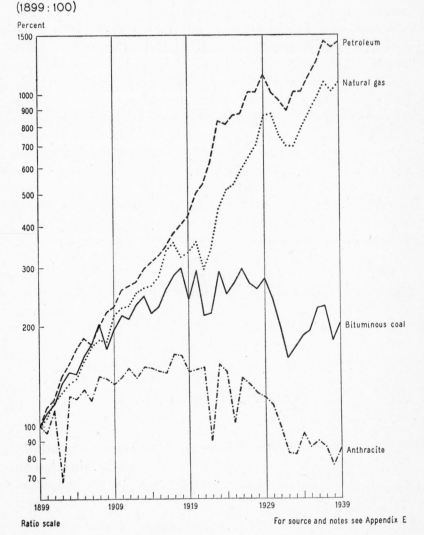

Percent

Petroleum

Natural gas

Bituminous coal

Anthracite

1899        1909        1919        1929        1939

Ratio scale                                    For source and notes see Appendix E

## FUELS

Valued in 1937 at about $2.8 billion, fuels account for nearly three quarters of the value of all minerals produced in the United States.[20] Of the total value of fuels, more than half was contributed by crude petroleum ($1,513 million), less than a third by bituminous coal ($831 million), and the remainder by Pennsylvania anthracite ($198 million), natural gas ($123 million) and natural gasoline ($97 million). On this basis petroleum is now nearly twice as important as bituminous coal, but it still furnishes substantially less total energy than the latter (Chart 19).

We have already seen (Chart 3) that the production of fuels rose during our forty-year period somewhat more rapidly than mineral output as a whole. An inspection of Chart 18 reveals that this result is attributable wholly to the sensational growth in the output of petroleum and natural gas, for bituminous coal gained only moderately and anthracite, in 1939, stood at a lower level than at the opening of the period. Compared with mineral output as a whole, which increased nearly fourfold, petroleum production was about fourteen times, and natural gas more than ten times, as large as in 1899. By contrast the output of bituminous coal, which tripled between 1899 and the peak year 1918, stood in 1939 at only twice the earlier level, while anthracite suffered a net decline of about 15 percent over the four decades.

TABLE 3

GROWTH OF THE ENERGY SUPPLY, 1889–1939[a]

| Year | Total Consumption (trillion BTU) | Per Capita Consumption (million BTU) |
|---|---|---|
| 1889 | 4,316 | 70 |
| 1899 | 7,426 | 99 |
| 1909 | 14,182 | 157 |
| 1919 | 18,883 | 180 |
| 1929 | 26,534 | 218 |
| 1939 | 24,620 | 188 |

[a] Minerals Yearbook, 1937, pp. 807-08, and 1941 (preprint). Water power is included with constant fuel equivalent.

Let us reduce these several fuels to a common denominator. Apart from a few minor uses, the purpose of each is to supply the

[20] The value of individual minerals for 1899, 1909, 1919, 1929 and 1937 will be found in Appendix Table A-2.

nation with energy.[21] According to Table 3 the consumption of
energy in all forms (coal, oil, gas and water power) jumped more
than threefold, and per capita consumption doubled, between

Chart 19

THE ENERGY SUPPLY
Distribution by Source, 1889 – 1939

BTU x 10$^{15}$

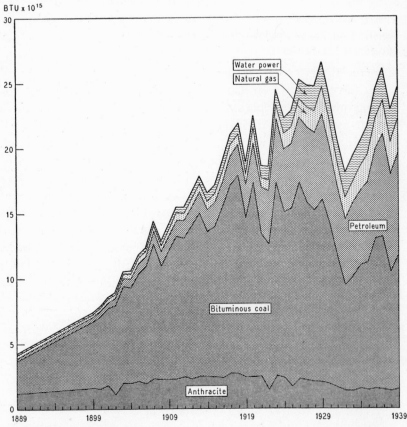

For source and notes see Appendix E

1899 and 1929—the latter year representing an all-time high. Then
there came a slump, followed by a revival which carried total (but
not per capita) energy consumption back to the 1929 level for the
first time in 1940. Economy in the use of fuel and the elimination

21 Energy is measured by engineers in British thermal units. One BTU is the quantity of heat required to raise the temperature of one pound of water one degree
Fahrenheit. The BTU value of a fuel is determined by complete combustion in a
calorimeter, and therefore represents the maximum energy obtainable if there were
no losses in consuming the fuel.

of energy waste have prevented total consumption from growing more rapidly in recent years, but it seems very unlikely that per capita consumption has reached the saturation point.

Even more interesting are the changes that have occurred in the sources from which the nation's energy supply is derived (Charts

Chart 20

THE ENERGY SUPPLY

Relative Contributions of Individual Sources, 1889 – 1939

Percent of total BTU equivalent

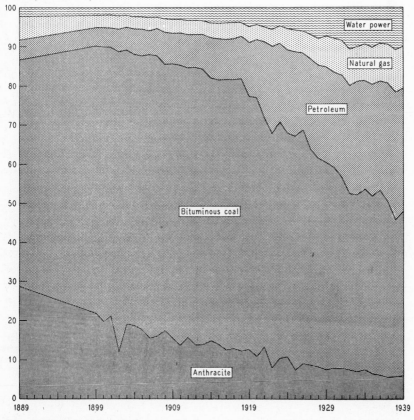

For source and notes see Appendix E

19 and 20). Today petroleum and natural gas together yield about as much energy as bituminous coal alone, yet they still supply substantially less than bituminous and anthracite in combination. Coal still provides about half the total energy used in the United States, even when allowance is made for water power.

*The Decline in Coal Consumption*

In its heyday anthracite was preeminently the domestic fuel of those northern and eastern states within easy reach of the mines. The decline in its importance derives partly from economies in the use of anthracite (the result of more efficient heating systems), but chiefly from the discovery that fuel oil provides greater efficiency and convenience. The present widespread use of oil for domestic heating is a development that dates from the middle 1920's. So far as is known, anthracite reserves greatly exceed oil reserves, and the day may come when we shall be forced to return to anthracite for domestic heating. But at present a single manhour of labor in the mining industries will produce several times as many BTU in the form of oil as in the form of coal (Table 14 below).

The case of bituminous coal, the consumption of which is shown in Chart 21, is more complicated. Its decline, both relative and absolute, may be traced to three types of influence: (1) substitution, direct or indirect, of other fuels or of water power; (2) a change in the manner in which the coal is utilized, resulting indirectly in fuel economy; (3) direct savings of coal in existing uses. All three have been important.

First, with regard to substitutes, we should note that bituminous coal has yielded some ground to natural gas for industrial purposes;[22] for most uses, however, petroleum products do not offer an acceptable substitute. Competition between the coal mine and the oil well is, for the most part, indirect. The demand for locomotive coal is reduced, not by a resort to oil for firing locomotives (though this has occurred), but through the development of the gasoline-driven highway vehicle.

Second, the manner in which coal is utilized has changed. The substitution of electricity, even when generated from coal, for the steam-driven prime mover has resulted in large economies of fuel. The small steam engine is notoriously inefficient, particularly if the load factor is adverse, whereas electric current can be generated in a large plant under optimum conditions of scale. A small-scale prime mover like the railroad locomotive may have a thermal efficiency of 10 percent; in a large central station, current can be generated, from the same coal the locomotive uses, perhaps

[22] For example in cement manufacture; see Nicholas Yaworski and others, *Fuel Efficiency in Cement Manufacture, 1909–35* (National Research Project, Philadelphia, 1938), pp. 17-18.

twice as efficiently.[23] Further, much electric power is produced by hydraulic means, without the consumption of any coal whatever. Where energy requirements are large and continuous, as in the production of aluminum and of fertilizer, it is more economical

Chart 21

BITUMINOUS COAL

Consumption by Use, 1917 – 40

Million short tons

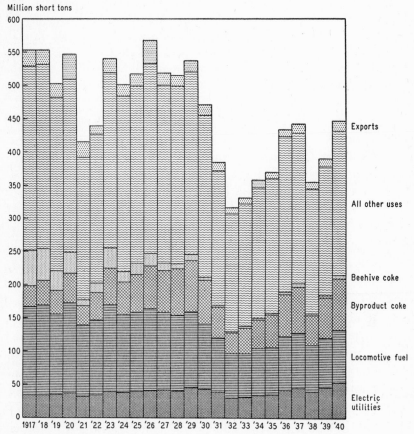

For source and notes see Appendix E

to use current generated from water power than from coal. In several instances this fact has become a decisive influence upon industrial location.

[23] National Resources Committee, *Energy Resources and National Policy* (1939), pp. 107-08.

Third, and perhaps most important, large declines in coal consumption have resulted from increased efficiency in the use of fuel. Quickened by the high price of coal during the first World War, interest in the subject of fuel economy became intense.

The runaway prices of 1917, 1920, and 1922 produced little effect at the time, but they set up influences which have persisted ever since. The electric utilities, especially, found themselves pinched between the rising price of coal and the fixed prices of their product. Efficiency in the use of coal was their only salvation. Fuel economy became the fashion. The route to promotion was seen to lead through the boiler room, and the best brains of the electric-power industry were directed to squeezing more and more kilowatt-hours out of the same ton of coal.[24]

The average amount of coal consumed by the electric light and power industry per kilowatt hour of current generated fell from 3.2 pounds in 1919 to 1.4 pounds in 1939, or by more than one half.[25] In spite of large increases in the output of coal-using electric plants, the consumption of coal for the generation of electricity has remained practically stationary for a quarter of a century (Chart 21). Lesser, but still large, economies were also achieved by other fuel-using industries. Between 1919 and 1939 the railroads cut coal consumption per passenger train car-mile by one fifth, per gross freight ton-mile by one third.[26] In the iron and steel industry the amount of coke needed to produce a ton of pig iron fell by one fifth, while more efficient use of coal in coking (especially with byproduct ovens) produced a like saving of energy in the coking process itself.[27] In addition, the substitution of scrap for iron ore as a raw material in steelmaking has further reduced the consumption of fuel, for scrap does not have to be smelted. Evidently it would be a mistake to think of the decline in coal consumption purely in terms of a shift toward other fuels.

These economies result partly from more efficient combustion

[24] F. G. Tryon, O. E. Kiessling and L. Mann, "Coal," in *Mineral Resources, 1926,* Part II, p. 446.

[25] Bituminous coal varies widely in energy content; in calculations of the kind indicated, a standard energy equivalent is to be understood, e.g., 13,100 BTU per pound (*Minerals Yearbook, Review of 1940,* p. 777).

[26] Gross ton-miles refer to the combined weight of load and equipment moved.

[27] Data quoted are from *Minerals Yearbook, Review of 1940,* p. 772.

and reduced heat losses, partly from mechanical improvements which diminish friction, and partly from improvement of the load factor (in power generation) and the recovery of byproducts (in the manufacture of coke). They seem likely to be intensified in the future. Much evidence, from the age distribution of steam locomotives still in service to the dispersion of thermal efficiencies among electric power stations,[28] assures us that a wide gap still exists between optimum and merely average practice in the fuel consumption field. As older is replaced by more modern equipment, further savings will doubtless accrue, even in the absence of technological developments in the future. Moreover, the most efficient plants now engaged in converting coal into mechanical energy do not have thermal efficiencies in excess of 30 percent, so that there would appear to be ample scope for technological progress as well.[29]

## Petroleum and Natural Gas

The vast increase in the output of crude petroleum, depicted in Chart 18 above, may be further analyzed with the help of the partial account of refinery output available since 1917 and shown in Chart 22. The products of the modern cracking process are numerous indeed: in addition to those listed they include especially wax, road surfacing materials and a variety of crude chemicals. The output of only the four most important items—gasoline, fuel oil, kerosene and lubricants—appears in Chart 22. While these are still to some extent joint products, this is much less true than formerly, for considerable latitude exists today in the proportions in which they come from the stills. Thus the extent to which the expansion of petroleum output has reflected a rise in the demand for gasoline is suggested by the much more rapid growth of gasoline production than of the output of the other

[28] Against the countrywide average of 1.4 pounds per kilowatt hour quoted above, we may contrast the performance of individual stations which, working with steam and mercury vapor at high temperatures and pressures, generate a kilowatt hour for as little as 0.7 pounds of coal. Again, in 1937 average pounds per kilowatt hour by states ranged from 1.1 to 3.6 (A. A. Potter, "The Production of Power," in *Technological Trends and National Policy*, National Resources Committee, 1937, p. 256; *Energy Resources and National Policy*, pp. 108-09). See also the wide dispersion of coal consumption per barrel of product at cement plants (Yaworski and others, *Fuel Efficiency in Cement Manufacture*, p. 61).

[29] *Energy Resources and National Policy*, p. 107.

Chart 22

PETROLEUM

Output of Principal Refined Products, 1917 – 40

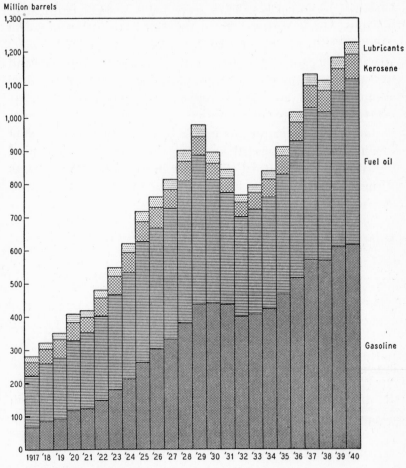

Million barrels

For source and notes see Appendix E

petroleum products shown in Chart 22. Between 1917 and 1939 gasoline output increased ninefold, fuel oil only fivefold.[30]

Let us summarize. Fuel oil has been substituted directly for anthracite, and natural gas for coal gas, in domestic heating. Similarly natural gas has sometimes superseded coal for industrial purposes, and gasoline has been substituted indirectly for

[30] See also Fabricant, *The Output of Manufacturing Industries, 1899–1937*, pp. 234–38.

bituminous coal through diversion of traffic from the railroad to the highway.[31] But the story is really more complicated than this simple statement would suggest. For on the one hand large economies have been effected in the use of solid fuels; and on the other the development of the automobile has led to an expansion in the use of transportation which would have been impossible had there been no escape from dependence upon the steam engine.

## OTHER NONMETALS

Nonmetals other than fuels had a value in 1937 of about $390 million, or slightly more than one tenth of mineral output as a whole. Among these minerals, stone accounted for $170 million, or nearly one half the total value of the group.

### Stone

Two principal kinds of stone are quarried—crushed stone and dimension or building stone. In value terms the former is now much the more important: in 1937 crushed stone output was worth $143 million, compared with $28 million for dimension. This disparity has not always been as great as it is today, for the output of dimension stone has tended downward, the output of crushed stone upward, in recent decades.

About one third of the output of dimension stone, measured by value, consists of granite; the remainder includes limestone, marble, slate and sandstone, in that order. Three quarters of all crushed stone produced is limestone; trailing far behind are the other varieties, basalt (or trap rock), granite, sandstone and slate. The types of stone used for building are also used for crushing, and crushed and dimension stone are often produced by the same quarry, for to some extent the former is a byproduct of the latter. Many of the largest crushed stone quarries, however, produce no dimension stone at all.

The indexes of output for dimension and for crushed stone, and for the stone industries as a whole, are shown in Chart 23. It will be observed that the trend in dimension stone is downward: by

[31] The latter development will be considered in detail in a forthcoming volume on *The Transportation Industries* by Harold Barger and Jacob M. Gould.

contrast, production of crushed stone, especially if noncommercial output is included, has expanded substantially during the period we cover in this study. No doubt the decline in dimension

Chart 23
STONE QUARRYING: OUTPUT, 1906–39
(1906:100)

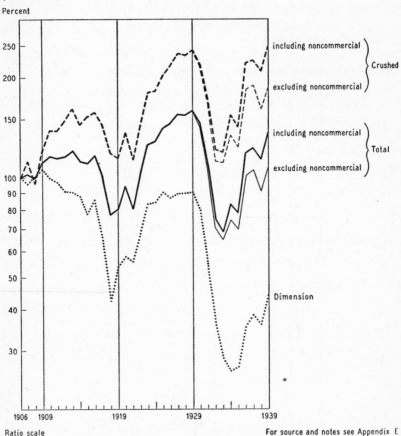

Percent

including noncommercial } Crushed
excluding noncommercial

including noncommercial } Total
excluding noncommercial

Dimension

1906   1909            1919            1929            1939
Ratio scale                              For source and notes see Appendix E

stone is to be explained partly by the low level of construction activity in recent years; but it has other causes also. In Chart 24 the output of dimension stone is compared with the best measure we could devise for the physical volume of building construction.[32] It will be seen that the consumption of building stone has

[32] See Appendix Table A-16.

not kept pace even with building activity, a fact which we must attribute mainly to the rising importance of steel and concrete construction. To a large extent this development has involved a substitution of crushed stone (in the form of cement rock, or of concrete aggregate) for traditional building stones. Even cheap

Chart 24

DIMENSION STONE OUTPUT AND
BUILDING CONSTRUCTION, 1915 – 39
(1915 : 100)

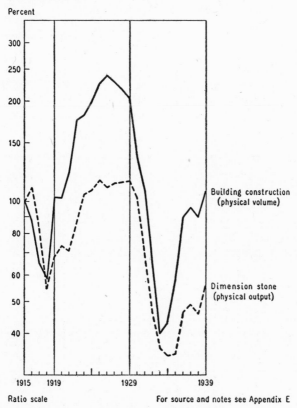

Ratio scale

For source and notes see Appendix E

varieties of building stone—for example, rubble, or stone with only one good face, formerly much used for foundations—have given way to concrete.

The output of individual varieties of dimension stone is shown in Chart 25. Among these varieties, granite is the principal monumental stone, mainly because of the sharp contrast in visual im-

pressions afforded by its polished and unpolished surfaces, a factor which favors its use for inscriptions. It is also used largely for
building, and to some extent for paving. Granite is widely distributed, being quarried in the Appalachian region and New

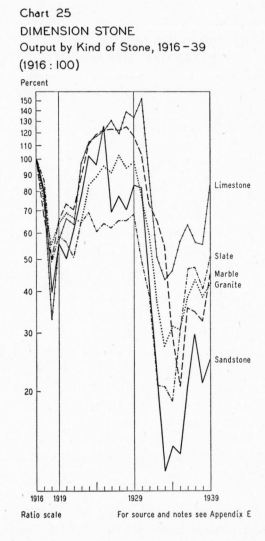

Chart 25
DIMENSION STONE
Output by Kind of Stone, 1916 – 39
(1916 : 100)

England, in Minnesota and Wisconsin, and in the Mountain and
Pacific states. Dimension limestone is used almost exclusively for
building: more than half its output comes from the single state
of Indiana, and much of the remainder from Alabama and Ken-

tucky. Marble is employed chiefly for building, and especially for interior work, because of its high polish and its ability to resist abrasion when laid as a floor or staircase. Most marble is quarried in the Appalachian belt, Tennessee and Vermont being the principal producing states. Slate, derived chiefly from Pennsylvania and Vermont, serves primarily as a roofing material, and is used to some extent also in the manufacture of electrical apparatus; in both these applications it has had to compete with numerous substitutes. The uses of sandstone are diversified: for exterior and interior building; for sea walls and dock facings (because of its resistance to erosion by water); for paving and curbing; and as an abrasive, in the form of grindstones, for sharpening tools or for grinding wood pulp. Sandstone is readily accessible, and is produced in most states.

In Chart 25 the output of the five varieties of dimension stone is shown on a 1916 base, the earliest year for which data for all five are available. In 1939 the production of dimension limestone was somewhat below the 1916 level; of slate, marble and granite about one half of the respective levels of that year; and of sandstone only about one quarter of its 1916 level. It is curious that sandstone, with uses at least as diversified as those of any other stone, should have suffered the largest decline.

Unlike the output of dimension stone, that of crushed stone has expanded during recent decades (Chart 23). In large measure the growing popularity of concrete, both for building and for highway construction, has been responsible for this expansion. All varieties of crushed stone are used for making concrete. For the manufacture of the cement itself, crushed limestone or cement rock is required, while as aggregate the most conveniently available local crushed stone can be employed. Much crushed stone is used also for road metal and railroad ballast. The rather close connection between the output of crushed stone for concrete aggregate and road metal (including noncommercial production) and the physical volume of highway construction is illustrated in Chart 26.[33] The lag of crushed stone behind highway construction during 1927–31 is probably to be explained by the use of concrete containing crushed stone aggregate for many purposes other than roadbuilding; it is to be observed also that crushed stone is used for highway repairs as well as for new construction.

[33] See also Appendix Table A-17.

During these years other uses probably lagged behind the construction of new highways.

A breakdown of crushed stone output by use (Table 4) shows that in 1939 about half the total went into concrete aggregate and road metal. About two thirds consisted of limestone; the remain-

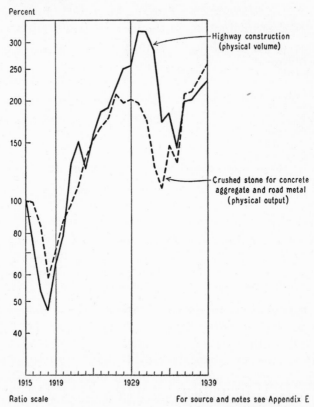

Chart 26

CRUSHED STONE OUTPUT AND
HIGHWAY CONSTRUCTION, 1915-39

(1915 : 100)

Percent

Highway construction (physical volume)

Crushed stone for concrete aggregate and road metal (physical output)

1915    1919         1929         1939

Ratio scale                          For source and notes see Appendix E

der comprised basalt, granite, sandstone, and a substantial fraction drawn from miscellaneous varieties. More than half of the stone used for railroad ballast and for refractory purposes in 1939 was also limestone. The outstanding position of limestone in other applications is less surprising. For making cement and lime, and in numerous minor industrial uses, stone is desired for its chemical rather than its physical properties, and limestone is the only variety that is technically satisfactory. For cement making an admixture of clay is an advantage, but pure limestone is necessary to produce lime. Most of the minor uses of limestone also require raw material of a high quality.[34]

TABLE 4

CRUSHED STONE
Consumption by Use, 1939[a]

| Type of Stone and Use | Thousand Short Tons | Percent of Total |
|---|---|---|
| Concrete aggregate and road metal | 96,894 | 52.5 |
| Limestone for cement manufacture | 30,463 | 16.5 |
| Metallurgical uses (mainly limestone) | 17,288 | 9.4 |
| Limestone for lime | 8,509 | 4.6 |
| Railroad ballast | 6,997 | 3.8 |
| Riprap | 5,812 | 3.2 |
| Limestone for agricultural use | 5,459 | 3.0 |
| Limestone for alkali works | 4,656 | 2.5 |
| Refractory uses | 1,492 | .8 |
| Limestone for sugar factories | 622 | .3 |
| Slate granules and flour | 352 | .2 |
| Limestone for paper mills | 303 | .2 |
| Limestone for calcium carbide works | 275 | .1 |
| Limestone for asphalt filler | 266 | .1 |
| Limestone for glass factories | 241 | .1 |
| Other uses | 4,845 | 2.6 |
| TOTAL | 184,473 | 100.0 |

[a] *Minerals Yearbook, 1940,* pp. 1178, 1184-86. Consumption of stone produced at noncommercial operations is included.

## Minor Nonmetals

Of the remaining nonmetals the following are the most important (values in 1937 in parentheses): sand and gravel ($79 million), sulfur ($49 million), clay ($18 million),[35] phosphate rock ($14 million), potash ($10 million), borates ($7 million), and bromine

[34] In alkali works the product is sodium carbonate; when obtained by the Solvay or ammonia soda process the calcium in limestone is replaced by sodium from common salt, ammonia being an intermediate reagent recoverable at the end of the process. In refining beet sugar, calcium hydroxide is used to remove all constituents except the cellulose. Calcium carbide is obtained by treating a mixture of limestone and coke in an electric furnace. In making glass, limestone is used to supply the calcium required in the final product. Limestone is also used in small quantities as a bone builder in animal feeding stuffs, to obtain carbon dioxide for refrigeration, and in the manufacture of mineral wool for insulation purposes. (See Oliver Bowles, *The Stone Industries,* McGraw-Hill, 1934, pp. 377-96.)

[35] Only fine clays are considered here, since satisfactory statistics for common clay (for brick making, etc.) are not available.

and gypsum ($5 million each). No other mineral had a product valued as high as $5 million in 1937.

The output history of these eight minerals is shown in Chart 27. Two of them—sand and gravel, and gypsum—are closely associated with the building industry. The output of both expanded rapidly during the first quarter of the present century, but within recent years levels of production—like construction activity itself —have failed to return to the peaks registered during the 1920's. Clay is used for pottery, oil refining, paper making and as a refractory material—the last being quantitatively the most important.[36] It is said that the life of blast furnace linings has doubled within the past ten years,[37] a fact which must account in part for the retardation in the growth of clay output. Phosphate rock, which is used almost entirely for the production of fertilizer, shows a slow but steady upward trend in volume.

Sulfur, boron minerals, potash and bromine compounds—the remaining four minerals with a value in 1937 in excess of $5 million—are essentially raw materials for one or another branch of the chemical industry. Sulfur production, a new industry, was negligible at the beginning of the century; virtually all its growth coincides with the period following 1899. As with all new industries, phenomenal growth rates are to be observed in the early stages. Thus sulfur output was multiplied by ten between 1900 and 1903, by ten again between 1903 and 1906, and by ten once more between 1906 and 1930. Over the past decade growth has been inappreciable, and the industry appears to have reached adulthood. Sulfur is used chiefly in the manufacture of sulfuric acid, which in turn is required for the production of superphosphates (fertilizer), the refining of petroleum, the processing of textiles, the manufacture of explosives, and as the starting point for the synthesis of a wide range of chemical substances. More than 99 percent of domestic sulfur comes from Texas or Louisiana.

The output of borax and other boron minerals has shown steady and consistent growth, stimulated by both foreign and domestic demand, for this industry produces more than 90 percent of the world's supply. Among numerous applications, the manufacture of heat-resisting glass and vitreous enamelware are the most important.

[36] Clay used for brick making is not included in the production statistics.
[37] Minerals Yearbook, Review of 1940, p. 1234.

Chart 27
MINOR NONMETALS: OUTPUT

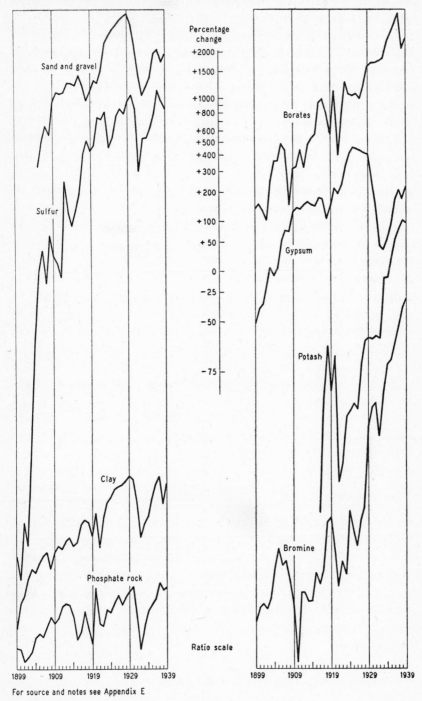

Percentage change

+2000
+1500

+1000
+800

+600
+500
+400

+300

+200

+100

+ 50

0

−25

−50

−75

Ratio scale

Sand and gravel

Sulfur

Clay

Phosphate rock

Borates

Gypsum

Potash

Bromine

1899    1909    1919    1929    1939

1899    1909    1919    1929    1939

The mining of potash dates only from the first World War; as one would expect, the rate of growth has been very rapid, and the expansion of output has thus far shown little, if any, sign of retardation. Potash is used principally as a fertilizer ingredient. Almost the entire supply comes from natural brine, or from bedded saline deposits in California and New Mexico.

Bromine compounds, long obtained from brine on a small scale, have expanded enormously in output during the past fifteen years as a result of the development of antiknock fuels for the automobile. In addition to brine from wells, sea water has been enlisted as a source of supply.

Besides data for the minerals already discussed, we have collected and incorporated in our indexes figures for a dozen or more minor nonmetals, none of which reached a value in 1937 of as much as $5 million (Appendix Table A-2). These are pyrites, fluorspar, salts of calcium, sodium and magnesium, silica abrasives, asbestos, asphalt, barite, feldspar, graphite, magnesite, mica, talc. Output data for these minerals will be found in Appendix Table A-1; a brief note on each appears in the glossary at the end of the volume.

# Chapter 3

# Employment in Mining

WE ARE NOW READY to proceed to the second phase in our investigation—the study of labor input. Once this has been completed, we shall be in a position to relate output to employment, and so to construct indexes of productivity for individual industries and for mining as a whole.

The extraction of minerals from the surface of the earth occupies but a small fraction of the nation's labor force. Of the entire working population, only about one person in fifty is engaged in mining, in quarrying or in operating oil wells. It should be remembered in this connection that the smelting of ores, the refining of oil and the dressing of stone are classed not as mining, but as manufacturing, operations. Consequently the employment statistics given in the present chapter and elsewhere in this volume are confined as closely as possible to the actual separation of minerals from the earth, to the simpler processing operations which are normally carried on at the mine or quarry (such as the milling of ore and the crushing of stone), and to development work undertaken in connection with the actual operation of the mine.

## THE SHARE OF THE LABOR FORCE ATTACHED TO MINING

The most comprehensive data we possess concerning the distribution of the labor force, among industries and occupations, are derived from the decennial Census of Population. The entire occupied population consists of all persons who report themselves as having a gainful occupation, whether or not they are actually working at the date of enumeration.

The distribution of the labor force among mining, manufacturing, agriculture, and other industries is given for Census years

TABLE 5

THE LABOR FORCE AND ITS INDUSTRIAL DISTRIBUTION, 1870-1940[a]
Gainfully Occupied Persons, 10 Years of Age and Over[b]

| Year | Total[c] (thousands) | Percentage Distribution[d] | | | |
|------|---------|---------|---------------|-------------|------------------|
|      |         | Mining  | Manufacturing[e] | Agriculture[c] | Other Industries[f] |
| 1870 | 12,925  | 1.5 | 16.8 | 53.0 | 28.6 |
| 1880 | 17,392  | 1.9 | 19.3 | 49.4 | 29.4 |
| 1890 | 23,318  | 2.1 | 20.3 | 42.6 | 35.0 |
| 1900 | 29,073  | 2.7 | 22.1 | 37.5 | 37.7 |
| 1910 | 37,371  | 2.9 | 23.1 | 31.0 | 42.9 |
| 1920 | 42,434  | 3.0 | 26.8 | 27.0 | 43.3 |
| 1930 | 48,830  | 2.5 | 24.2 | 21.4 | 51.9 |
| 1940 | 52,148  | 2.2 | 25.2 | 17.6 | 55.1 |

[a] All data are derived, directly or indirectly, from the Census of Population. The labor force includes persons unemployed as well as those in employment.

[b] Prior to 1940, occupational data were tabulated for all persons 10 years of age and over. In 1940, for the first time, the Bureau of the Census considered it no longer worth while to collect occupational data for persons below the age of 14. The vast majority of child workers today are to be found in agriculture. For 1940 the numbers of such workers in both agricultural and nonagricultural occupations were estimated by the Bureau of the Census and are included (see U. S. Bureau of the Census release, "Trends in the Proportion of the Nation's Labor Force Engaged in Agriculture: 1820 to 1940," March 28, 1942).

[c] Bureau of the Census release, March 28, 1942 (see preceding footnote). In 1940 the distribution between agricultural and nonagricultural occupations of persons employed on emergency work had to be estimated by the Census Bureau; also numbers of occupied persons aged 10 to 13 (see footnote b). Besides these adjustments to the data for 1940, revisions were made in some other years also (see U. S. Bureau of the Census release, "Industrial Distribution of the Nation's Labor Force: 1870 to 1930," October 23, 1938; also Harold Barger and Hans H. Landsberg, American Agriculture, 1899–1939: A Study of Output, Employment and Productivity, National Bureau of Economic Research, 1942, Chapter 6).

[d] The distribution between agricultural and nonagricultural workers was first obtained from the Bureau of the Census release, March 28, 1942 (see footnote b). Nonagricultural workers were then distributed among mining, manufacturing and other industries as follows. For 1870 to 1930 the distribution was carried out on the basis of figures compiled by Daniel Carson, "Labor Supply and Employment" (National Research Project, unpublished). For 1940 the distribution was based upon the Bureau of the Census release, "Industry Classification of Persons 14 Years Old and Over in the Labor Force, for the United States and for Regions: March 1940," November 11, 1942.

[e] Includes electric light and power and manufactured gas in addition to all activities ordinarily classed as manufacturing.

[f] Includes forestry, fishing, construction, transportation, communication, trade, finance, public service, professional service, domestic and personal service.

since 1870 in Table 5.[1] Here it is shown that mining approximately doubled its share of the total number occupied in all

[1] We are interested in the industrial, rather than the occupational, distribution of the occupied population; accordingly for years in which only the latter classification was available (1870 to 1900 and 1920), clerical and other industrially nondescript occupations have been distributed among the various industrial categories. The distribution in question was made by Daniel Carson ("Labor Supply and Employment," National Research Project, unpublished).

branches of the economy between 1870 and 1920. The proportion
of the nation's labor force attached to mining has always been
small as compared with manufacturing, but the trends in both
fields have been similar: as in the case of manufacturing, the contribution of mining to the occupied population as a whole appears to have reached a peak during the first quarter of the
present century, and to have begun to decline in recent years.

## NUMBERS OCCUPIED VERSUS EMPLOYMENT

The distribution of occupied persons, furnished by the decennial
Census of Population, provides a very comprehensive view of
the number of workers attached to an industry. This enumeration includes, in addition to workers actually engaged in production at the time of the Census, those who are unemployed, perhaps
even some who are retired. If, however, we were to use such
figures to measure labor input, we should be debiting the industry
with numerous individuals whose responsibility for current output is remote, or even nonexistent. This scarcely seems an appropriate procedure. Yet every person who reports himself as
occupied in a given industry—whether currently employed or
not—must be regarded, in some degree at least, as immobilized by
that industry. He is immobilized to the extent that his present
employment, his memories of past employment, his prospects of
future employment, his geographical location, or his peculiar
skills prevent him from becoming a candidate for a job in some
other industry. Thus his attachment to the industry in which he
claims to be occupied must be viewed, at least from the social
aspect, as part of the costs of operation of that industry. Nevertheless, it remains true that for purposes of measuring labor input
and productivity we are interested in employment rather than
in numbers occupied. The Census of 1940 was the first population count to report employment as well as occupational status.
These employment figures, which are strictly comparable with the
occupational data, appear in the center of Table 6. Unfortunately,
they cannot easily be used for precise comparisons with employment in any other year; at this writing they have not been released
with detailed breakdowns. Consequently we shall make no extensive use of them in the present report. The most detailed employment data we have been able to assemble relate to the year

1939, and are derived not from the Census of Population but from the Census of Mineral Industries. These figures, given fully in Table 7, are shown for comparison in summary form at the right hand side of Table 6.

The two sets of employment data shown in Table 6 differ because each is the product of a separate inquiry. The figures from

TABLE 6

PERSONS OCCUPIED AND EMPLOYED IN MINING, 14 YEARS OF AGE AND OVER, 1939–40

| | Population Census | | | | Census of Mineral Industries | |
| Industry | Occupied[a] March 1940 | | Employed[b] March 1940 | | Employed Average 1939[c] | |
| | Thousand | Percent | Thousand | Percent | Thousand | Percent |
|---|---|---|---|---|---|---|
| All Industries[d] | 48,163 | .. | 44,477 | .. | .. | .. |
| Mining | 1,044 | 100.0 | 913 | 100.0 | 887 | 100.0 |
| Metal mining | 132 | 12.6 | 117 | 12.8 | 102 | 11.5 |
| Coal mining | 611 | 58.5 | 527 | 57.7 | 491 | 55.3 |
| Oil and gas | 203 | 19.4 | 184 | 20.1 | 203 | 22.9 |
| Other | 98 | 9.4 | 85 | 9.3 | 91 | 10.3 |

[a] Numbers employed (column to right), plus workers seeking employment; U. S. Bureau of the Census release, "Industry Classification of Persons 14 Years Old and Over in the Labor Force, for the United States and for Regions: March 1940," November 11, 1942. The figures are derived from the Census of Population.

[b] Source same as for numbers occupied (column to left): see preceding footnote.

[c] These figures comprise wage earners (average of 12 monthly counts), salaried workers, and individual proprietors and firm members. See Table 7.

[d] Does not include 2,530 thousand persons employed on public emergency work, or 689 thousand persons who failed to specify the industry in which they were occupied.

the Census of Population result from a single count in March 1940, whereas the Census of Mineral Industries presents an average of employment for the year 1939. Apparently also there are differences in degree of coverage, though these are difficult to assess; not all persons canvassed by the population enumerators disclosed the industry in which they were occupied; similarly, the Census of Mineral Industries cannot be regarded as a complete record.[2] Finally, employment in the mining industries as a whole

[2] For example, the absence of any reference to bootleg operations, at least in the preliminary releases, suggests that this sector of the anthracite industry was not covered by the Census of Mineral Industries; but presumably bootleg operators would report themselves in the Population count as employed in coal mining.

was higher in March 1940 than it was on the average during 1939.[3] Despite these and other divergences, it is broadly true that the data in Table 6 confirm each other and afford a consistent picture. Judged by input of labor, coal mining is still over-whelmingly the most important form of extraction; between one half and two thirds of all miners are coal miners. Oil and gas wells employ about one fifth of the nation's miners, metal mines another tenth, and the remaining industries together less than one tenth.

## CHANGES IN THE DISTRIBUTION OF EMPLOYMENT AMONG MINING INDUSTRIES

A complete view of employment in the nation's mines is possible only for the years in which a Census of the industry was taken. The best conspectus of the changing composition of employment in mining over our period is to be obtained by comparing 1939 with 1902. Accordingly, data for 1939 are shown at the right hand side of Table 7. The column "total engaged" affords a break-down of material already given in Table 6. Unfortunately, how-ever, we have not been able to present in comparable form em-ployment data from the Census of Mines and Quarries taken in 1902. Figures for wage earners in that Census are presented (for the most part) in the form of 300-day averages: that is to say, where an enterprise worked fewer than 300 days in 1902, the number of workers reported for that year was written down pro-portionately during the process of editing the schedules.[4] At this late date these results cannot be unscrambled; nor can we de-termine what the 1902 figures would have looked like had the Census refrained from applying this averaging procedure. We cannot compute other kinds of average from the 1902 Census, but it is fairly easy in a rough way to convert 1939 employment figures to a 300-day basis. In fact the "300-day workers" shown for 1939 in Table 7 are simply the mandays reported (by the Bureau of Mines or by the Census of Mineral Industries; see note b to Table 7) divided by 300. These figures for 1939 are as comparable

---

[3] Bureau of Labor Statistics indexes report that mining employment was 7 percent higher; the rise suggested by Table 6 is only 2 percent.
[4] U. S. Bureau of the Census, *Special Reports*, "Mines and Quarries, 1902," p. 1123.

# TABLE 7

## EMPLOYMENT IN MINING, 1902 AND 1939[a]

| Industry | 300-Day Workers[b] 1902 | | 300-Day Workers[b] 1939 | | Wage Earners, Census Average[c] 1939 | | Total Engaged, Census[d] 1939 | | Active Period Average, Bureau of Mines[e] 1939 |
|---|---|---|---|---|---|---|---|---|---|
| | Number | Percent of Total | Number | Percent of Total | Number | Percent of Total | Number | Percent of Total | Number |
| Metal mining, total | 120,583 | 20.3 | 91,232 | 14.7 | 90,671 | 11.6 | 101,858 | 11.5 | ... |
| Iron ore | 40,027 | 6.7 | 16,204 | 2.6 | 20,456 | 2.6 | 22,680 | 2.6 | 21,859 |
| Copper | 27,920 | 4.7 | 22,553 | 3.6 | 23,840 | 3.0 | 26,744 | 3.0 | 23,153 |
| Other metal mining, except placers | 49,486 | 8.3 | 49,104 | 7.9 | 43,147 | 5.5 | 48,469 | 5.5 | 59,954 |
| Gold and silver, lode | ... | ... | ... | ... | 21,822 | 2.8 | 24,486 | 2.8 | ... |
| Lead and zinc | ... | ... | ... | ... | 15,613 | 2.0 | 17,166 | 1.9 | ... |
| Manganese | ... | ... | ... | ... | 494 | .1 | 530 | .1 | ... |
| Mercury | ... | ... | ... | ... | 652 | .1 | 951 | .1 | ... |
| Bauxite | ... | ... | ... | ... | 732 | .1 | 831 | .1 | ... |
| Molybdenum | ... | ... | ... | ... | 940 | .1 | 1,103 | .1 | ... |
| Tungsten | ... | ... | ... | ... | 714 | .1 | 936 | .1 | ... |
| Vanadium and uranium | ... | ... | ... | ... | 391 | r | 493 | .1 | ... |
| Other[f] | ... | ... | ... | ... | 1,789 | .2 | 1,973 | .2 | ... |
| Placer mining | 3,150 | .5 | 3,371 | .5 | 3,228 | .4 | 3,965 | .4 | ... |
| Fuels, total | 410,917 | 69.2 | 479,266 | 77.1 | 612,200 | 78.2 | 693,629 | 78.2 | 704,872 |
| Pennsylvania anthracite | 94,937[q] | 16.0 | 56,793 | 9.1 | 82,890 | 10.6 | 88,646 | 10.0 | 93,138 |
| Bituminous coal[g] | 283,710 | 47.8 | 263,133 | 42.3 | 373,225 | 47.7 | 401,886 | 45.3 | 444,953 |
| Oil and gas wells[h] | 32,270 | 5.4 | 159,340 | 25.6 | 156,085 | 19.9 | 203,097 | 22.9 | 166,781 |
| Other nonmetal mining, total | 62,599 | 10.5 | 51,297 | 8.2 | 58,570 | 7.5 | 65,665 | 7.4 | ... |
| Stone quarrying[i] | 49,837 | 8.4 | 33,473 | 5.4 | 36,339 | 4.6 | 40,230 | 4.5 | 48,329 |
| Phosphate rock | 5,991 | 1.0 | 2,749 | .4 | 3,372 | .4 | 3,753 | .4 | ... |
| Gypsum | 823 | .1 | 1,040 | .2 | 1,327 | .2 | 1,424 | .2 | ... |

*For footnotes see pp. 66-68.*

TABLE 7—(concluded)

| Industry | 300-Day Workers[b] 1902 | | 300-Day Workers[b] 1939 | | Wage Earners, Census Average[c] 1939 | | Total Engaged, Census[d] 1939 | | Active Period Average, Bureau of Mines[e] 1939 |
|---|---|---|---|---|---|---|---|---|---|
| | Number | Percent of Total | Number | Percent of Total | Number | Percent of Total | Number | Percent of Total | Number |
| **Other nonmetal mining (cont.)** | | | | | | | | | |
| Abrasive materials[j] | 729 | .1 | 720 | .1 | 804 | .1 | 931 | .1 | .. |
| Asbestos | 23 | r | 134 | r | 151 | r | 160 | r | .. |
| Asphalt | 156 | r | 541 | .1 | 730 | .1 | 853 | .1 | .. |
| Barite | 336 | .1 | 606 | .1 | 792 | .1 | 870 | .1 | .. |
| Borates | 153 | r | 446 | .1 | 533 | .1 | 638 | .1 | .. |
| Clay[k] | 2,547 | .4 | 5,846 | .9 | 7,742 | 1.0 | 8,578 | 1.0 | .. |
| Feldspar | 252 | r | 412 | .1 | 512 | .1 | 605 | .1 | .. |
| Mica | 98 | r | 150 | r | 190 | r | 221 | r | .. |
| Monazite | 88 | r | 0 | 0 | 0 | 0 | 0 | 0 | .. |
| Sand[l] | 335 | .1 | 1,869 | .3 | 2,375 | .3 | 2,833 | .3 | .. |
| Sulfur[m] | .. | .. | 1,351 | .2 | 1,503 | .2 | 2,010 | .2 | .. |
| Talc and soapstone | 779 | .1 | 862 | .1 | 970 | .1 | 1,137 | .1 | .. |
| All other nonmetals[n] | 452 | .1 | 1,098 | .2 | 1,230 | .2 | 1,422 | .2 | .. |
| Total, comparable industries[o] | 594,099 | 100.0 | 621,795 | 100.0 | 761,441 | 97.2 | 861,152 | 97.1 | .. |
| **Industries not canvassed in 1902:** | | | | | | | | | |
| Common clay and shale | .. | .. | .. | .. | 2,906 | .4 | 3,044 | .3 | .. |
| Potash | .. | .. | .. | .. | 1,516 | .2 | 1,800 | .2 | .. |
| Rock salt | .. | .. | .. | .. | 1,380 | .2 | 1,561 | .2 | .. |
| Sand and gravel | .. | .. | .. | .. | 14,584 | 1.9 | 17,740 | 2.0 | .. |
| General contract services[p] | .. | .. | .. | .. | 1,365 | .2 | 1,656 | .2 | .. |
| TOTAL, ALL INDUSTRIES | .. | .. | .. | .. | 783,192 | 100.0 | 886,953 | 100.0 | .. |

*For footnotes see pp. 66-68.*

*Footnotes to Table 7.*

ᵃ In addition to providing data on the distribution of employment among different branches of mining activity, this table is designed to contrast: (1) employment in 1902 and in 1939, in terms of 300-day workers (which alone allow such a comparison); (2) employment in 1939 in terms of 300-day workers and of active period average workers, for those industries for which such a comparison can be made; (3) employment in 1939 in terms of wage earners and of total engaged (wage earners, salaried employees, and individual proprietors and firm members). Data cover employment at mines, quarries or wells, and at mills or crushing plants. Employment in manufacturing operations, such as smelting metallic ores, dressing or cutting dimension stone, calcining gypsum or refining petroleum, is so far as possible excluded.

ᵇ Figures in these columns represent the number of workers who would have been required if each of them had worked 300 days or shifts during the year. The Census of 1902 adopted this concept in presenting its figures, and its results cannot now be adapted to allow of comparisons with later years on any other basis. In essence the number of 300-day workers in 1902 is obtained by multiplying the number of workers reported by the mine by the number of days the mine was active, and dividing the result by 300. For all mines reporting fewer than 300 days' operation this adjustment was performed in 1902 by the Bureau of the Census itself in the course of editing the schedules. (See U. S. Bureau of the Census, *Special Reports,* "Mines and Quarries, 1902," pp. 1122-23. The implication, in the second footnote on p. 90 of the same volume, that the method used was "practically the same" as that followed in the Report on Manufactures for the Twelfth Census, i.e., an average of 12 monthly counts, appears to be misleading. That the two methods lead to divergent results is admitted indirectly in the following quotation from the *Fifteenth Census,* "Mines and Quarries, 1929," p. 5: "The Census Bureau's figures for wage earners . . . are averages based on the number employed on the 15th of each month, and while representing the number, according to the pay rolls, to whom wages were paid on that date, they doubtless represent a larger number than would be required to perform the work in any industry if all were continuously employed during the year." This may now be confirmed by comparing, for 1939, mandays divided by 300 with average wage earners: the latter, an average of 12 monthly counts, nearly always exceeds the former, which approximates the number of 300-day workers.) In those few industries where more than 300 days were worked, a corresponding adjustment was roughly made by ourselves. In Pennsylvania anthracite and bituminous coal, where for 1902 mandays are available directly, these were divided by 300. For 1939 mandays reported by the Bureau of Mines, or manshifts reported by the Census, were uniformly divided by 300.

For iron ore, copper, gold and silver (lode), lead and zinc, mercury, bauxite, pyrites, manganese and stone, 1902 data come from the Census of that year. For Pennsylvania anthracite 1901 data, and for bituminous coal 1902 data, are from the U. S. Geological Survey. For all the above industries, data for 1939 are derived from the accident statistics collected by the Bureau of Mines. In these industries, technical, supervisory and other employees who actually work in and about the mines (but not office employees) are included in both years. For all other industries for which data are given the figures cover wage earners only, and (except for employment in gypsum mining and at oil and gas wells in 1902) rely in both years directly upon Census data. For gypsum, data for 1902 are derived from Robinson Newcomb and Knute Peterson, "Production, Employment and Output per Man in Gypsum Mining" (U. S. Bureau of Mines, Information Circular 7134, 1940), Table 1. For oil and gas wells, data for 1902 are from O. E. Kiessling and others, *Petroleum and Natural-Gas Production* (National Research Project, Philadelphia, 1939), p. 327. Many of the above data can readily be derived from Appendix Table A-3. Figures for "other metal mining, except placers" run slightly higher than corresponding data reported for mandays in Appendix Table A-3 because of the inclusion of tungsten, uranium and vanadium, chrome ore, magnesite, molybdenum, nickel and cobalt, and rutile in 1902; and tungsten, uranium and vanadium, titanium, magnesite, molybdenum, antimony ore and chromite in 1939. The coverage of these industries by "Metal-Mine Accidents" is in doubt; in Appendix Table A-3 they are not included for 1902, and we have assumed that they are not included there for 1939.

For oil and gas wells in 1939 employment is not available in mandays. However, for natural gasoline plants and for oil- and gas-well contract services, it was possible to estimate mandays by multiplying active period average employment by average number of days active. Mandays so obtained were then divided by 300. For petroleum and natural gas wells proper the number of 300-day wage earners was assumed to equal the Census average. Since wells generally operate throughout the year without interruption, this treatment probably introduces little distortion. The figures are derived in Appendix Table A-19.

ᶜ Data are uniformly from preliminary releases of the Census of Mineral Industries, 1939. The method of averaging employment over the year is the same as that followed in Censuses of Manufactures since 1899 (*Twelfth Census*), i.e., an average of twelve monthly figures for each enterprise, including inactive months (if any). Where enterprises operated for twelve months, but for fewer than 300 days in the aggregate, Census average wage earners tend to exceed the number shown for 300-day workers (see note b above). On the other hand, where the latter included numerous supervisory employees, 300-day workers tend to exceed in number Census average wage earners.

ᵈ Data are uniformly from preliminary releases of the Census of Mineral Industries, 1939. Figures include salaried employees, and individual proprietors and firm members, in addition to average wage earners.

ᵉ Except for oil and gas wells, the figures in this column are obtained from Bureau of Mines accident statistics, and represent the average number of employees during the active period of operation of each enterprise. Technical, supervisory and other employees who actually work in and about the mine (but not office employees) are included. The figure for oil and gas wells relates to wage earners only, and is taken from preliminary releases of the Census of Mineral Industries, 1939. Since in most industries for which data are shown in this column the mines worked fewer than 300 days on the average in 1939, active period average employment runs higher than the number of 300-day workers. The Census method of averaging (see note c) counts the number on the payroll as of the fifteenth of each month, and then averages these monthly figures over the entire year. Where idle days are uniformly distributed throughout the year, the active period average of the Bureau of Mines will tend to equal the Census average. But where shutdowns cover an entire month, the active period average will exceed the Census average: nevertheless it probably still falls short of the number of individuals who were employed by the industry, at one time or another during the year, for however brief a period. The figure for "other metal mining, except placers" exceeds the corresponding figure in Appendix Table A-3 for the reason given in note b above.

ᶠ Magnesite and brucite, chromite, antimony, titanium and pyrites. In 1902 also includes employment at sulfur mines (not separable from pyrites), and nickel and cobalt; and in 1939 at fluorspar mines in Illinois and Kentucky (not always separable from lead and zinc mining, and included for comparability with other columns).

ᵍ Includes peat and lignite; also anthracite outside Pennsylvania.

ʰ Covers employment at natural gasoline plants as well as at oil and gas wells; includes employment by contractors furnishing field services to producers, as well as by regular producers. Figures for 300-day workers, and for active period average workers, in this industry are for wage earners only, and do not include technical, supervisory and other salaried employees. For 1902 the source of the data is given in note b above. For 1939 all data are from the Census of Mineral Industries: their derivation, together with that of similar figures in Table A-3 for comparison, will be found in Appendix Table A-19.

ⁱ The industries covered are limestone (including that used for lime and cement), marble, sandstone (except when used for abrasive purposes), granite and slate. Employment at nondimension quarries and crushers, and at dimension quarries, is included; but not employment at plants engaged in dressing or cutting dimension stone.

ʲ Includes grindstones, millstones, oilstones and other abrasive stones; corundum and emery; pumice; garnet; crystalline quartz; infusorial earth, tripoli and diatomite; flint.

ᵏ Includes fire clay, kaolin, ball clay, bentonite and fuller's earth; but not common clay, such as that used for brick making, which was covered for the first time by the 1939 Census.

ˡ Includes glass sand and foundry sand; but not common sand or gravel.

ᵐ Employment data for sulfur in 1902 cannot be separated from those for pyrites. Apparently production consisted mainly of the latter, and the figure for both industries is therefore included in "other metal mining" above.

ⁿ Includes fluorspar (in 1939, only such mines outside Illinois and Kentucky: see note f above); lithium minerals; graphite; marl (greensand); vermiculite; kyanite,

*Footnotes to Table 7 continued on next page.*

with the corresponding figures for 1902 as it is possible to make them.[5]

Between 1902 and 1939 total employment in mining hardly changed, but there were sharp alterations in the relative importance of different minerals. A decline occurred in the percentage of workers engaged in metal mining, and particularly in iron mining: we shall see that technological advance has been especially rapid in the extraction of iron ore. The fraction of the working force engaged in mining fuel increased—but only because the large expansion of employment in oil and gas wells more than offset the decline in coal mining. Nonmetals other than fuels lost some ground as sources of employment, especially because of the decline of stone quarrying in this respect. Several minor industries, particularly clay and sand, employ, relatively, much more labor than formerly. On the other hand monazite (a thorium compound used for gas mantles) is no longer mined.

Changes in the number of 300-day workers between 1902 and 1939 are shown in index form in Table 8. While total employment in mining apparently rose some 5 percent,[6] the number of

[5] As explained, the figure for 300-day workers is essentially an estimate of the number of mandays worked divided by 300. Even in 1939 mandays were not always obtained by summing payroll records: they were sometimes derived by multiplying number of men by number of days that the mine was active (see, for example, *Minerals Yearbook, 1940*, pp. 799-800, for comment on methods of reporting employment at bituminous coal mines). This second method is almost certain to overstate the number of mandays worked, for not all the men will work every day the mine is active. However, the mandays implicit in the data for 1902 were uniformly derived by the second method, and must contain an even larger element of exaggeration. It seems probable, therefore, that the comparisons between 1902 and 1939 shown for 300-day workers in Tables 7 and 8 understate the rise, or overstate the decline, in employment between the two years.

Another way of making the same point would be to say that the number of men reported is not a true "active period" average. To yield an accurate manday figure when multiplied by number of days active, such an average would have to be derived by each mine from daily counts of its employees, but in fact in the majority of cases this is not the way in which the average in question is computed.

[6] This may be an understatement; see preceding footnote.

Footnotes to Table 7, concluded.
andalusite and dumortierite; and some miscellaneous varieties of stone.

[o] These totals exclude items shown below, because of lack of data for 1902; and precious stones (covered in 1902) for which data for 1939 are not available.

[p] Does not include contract services to oil and gas wells; see note h above. Other services were covered in 1939 for the first time by the Census: about one third were performed by companies engaged principally in loading and hauling activities; about one third by companies specializing in the stripping of overburden from mineral deposits; and the remainder by firms engaged in sinking mine shafts, driving tunnels, and performing miscellaneous maintenance and development work. Most of this employment can, if desired, be distributed among the industries serviced.

[q] Figure is for 1901; employment in 1902 was affected by the strike.

[r] Less than 0.05.

metal miners declined 24 percent, and of miners of nonmetals other than fuels, 18 percent. Numbers engaged in the production of fuels expanded 17 percent, but only because of the five-fold increase in employment at oil and gas wells.

TABLE 8

CHANGES IN MINING EMPLOYMENT, 1902–39[a]

| Industry | 1902 | 1939 |
|---|---|---|
| Metal mining, total | 100 | 76 |
| Iron ore | 100 | 40 |
| Copper | 100 | 81 |
| Other metal mining[c] | 100 | 100 |
| Fuels, total | 100[b] | 117 |
| Pennsylvania anthracite | 100[b] | 60 |
| Bituminous coal | 100 | 93 |
| Oil and gas wells | 100 | 494 |
| Other nonmetal mining, total[d] | 100 | 82 |
| Stone | 100 | 67 |
| All other nonmetals[d] | 100 | 140 |
| Total mining { including oil and gas | 100[b] | 105 |
| { excluding oil and gas | 100[b] | 82 |

[a] Data based upon the comparison for 300-day workers shown in Table 7.
[b] Because employment in Pennsylvania anthracite in 1902 was greatly affected by strike conditions, for this industry data for 1901 were substituted.
[c] Includes placer mining.
[d] Does not include common clay, potash, rock salt, sand and gravel, and general contract services; these industries were not canvassed in 1902.

## SALARIED WORKERS, WAGE EARNERS AND INDIVIDUAL PROPRIETORS

The Census of 1902 reported a total employment in mining of 620 thousand persons, of whom 582 thousand [7] were wage earners and 38 thousand salaried workers. This suggests a ratio of one salaried worker to every fifteen wage earners. In 1939 the corresponding ratio was one salaried employee to every ten wage earners. The relevant data are set forth in Table 9. It will be seen that salaried workers are relatively most important in the petroleum industry, and least important in coal mining, but that in each branch of extraction their share in labor input has expanded since the turn of the century. A similar picture is shown by manufacturing, which employed one salaried worker for every

[7] Since these are apparently 300-day workers, the number of jobs, or of active period average workers, would considerably exceed this figure. It differs from the total reported for 1902 in Table 7 for the reasons given in note a to Table 9.

TABLE 9

WAGE EARNERS AND SALARIED EMPLOYEES, 1902 AND 1939[a]

| | Total | Metal Mining[b] | Pennsyl-vania Anthracite | Bituminous Coal | Oil and Gas Wells | Other[c] |
|---|---|---|---|---|---|---|
| *1902* | | | | | | |
| Wage earners, average for year | 581,728 | 111,816 | 69,691 | 280,638 | 22,230 | 97,353 |
| Salaried employees | 38,128 | 8,300 | 3,014 | 14,413 | 4,956 | 7,445 |
| Ratio, wage earners to salaried employees | 15.3 | 13.5 | 23.1 | 19.5 | 4.5 | 13.1 |
| *1939* | | | | | | |
| Total engaged | 886,953 | 101,858 | 88,646 | 401,886 | 203,097 | 91,466 |
| Wage earners, average for year | 783,192 | 90,671 | 82,890 | 373,225 | 156,085 | 80,321 |
| Salaried employees | 81,849 | 9,815 | 5,469 | 19,828 | 37,704 | 9,033 |
| Individual proprietors and firm members | 21,912 | 1,372 | 287 | 8,833 | 9,308 | 2,112 |
| Performing manual labor | 12,250 | 992 | 159 | 7,030 | 3,247 | 822 |
| Ratio, wage earners to salaried employees | 9.6 | 9.2 | 15.2 | 18.8 | 4.1 | 8.9 |

[a] Data derived from U. S. Bureau of the Census, *Special Reports,* "Mines and Quarries, 1902," and from preliminary releases of the Census of Mineral Industries, 1939. Figures for wage earners in 1902 and 1939 as shown in this table are not really comparable. In 1902 the Census adjusted the average number of wage earners to a 300-day basis wherever an enterprise operated fewer than 300 days during the year. While it made no such adjustment in the case of enterprises operating more than 300 days, the figures shown for wage earners in 1902 approximate a 300-day average. In 1939, on the other hand, the number shown for wage earners represents the average of 12 monthly counts. If the 1939 figures had been obtained in the same manner as the figures for 1902, they would stand substantially below the level shown.

For 1902 figures for wage earners shown here differ from figures for the number of 300-day workers in Table 7 for the following reasons. (1) The latter include nonclerical salaried workers; and for wage earners have been adjusted by us to a 300-day basis in the case of enterprises working more than 300 days during the year (see note b to Table 7). (2) In obtaining the data in Table 7 we adjusted the Census totals upward to correct for undercoverage of employment in gold mines and at oil and gas wells, and downward to exclude employees engaged in processing dimension stone and gypsum (see notes to Appendix Table A-3). (3) In Table 7 figures for anthracite mining relate to 1901 instead of 1902, whereas here all data refer to 1902. (4) In Table 7 precious stones are omitted for 1902 because data for this industry are not available for 1939. No such adjustments were made in this table, and the figures shown here are unadjusted Census totals, both for 1902 and (in preliminary form) for 1939. Data on individual proprietors and firm members are not available for 1902.

[b] In 1902, gold, silver, copper, lead and zinc, iron ore, manganese, mercury, sulfur and pyrite, mineral pigments, bauxite, tungsten, uranium and vanadium, chrome ore, magnesite, molybdenum, nickel and cobalt, rutile (titanium). In 1939, gold, silver, copper, lead and zinc, iron ore, manganese, mercury, pyrites, bauxite, tungsten, uranium and vanadium, magnesite and brucite, molybdenum, titanium, fluorspar in Illinois and Kentucky, miscellaneous metallic minerals (antimony ore and chromite).

[c] In 1939 includes common clay, potash, rock salt, sand and gravel, and general contract services; these industries were not canvassed in 1902.

13 wage earners in 1899, and one for every 8 wage earners in 1939.[8]

It seems certain that this growth in the importance of salaried employees is to be attributed, not to a change in methods of remuneration, but to a genuine variation in the significance of different functions. On the whole, persons who receive salaries once or twice a month are white collar workers; if not office employees, their functions are predominantly of a technical or supervisory character. Persons who receive wages by the day or week for the most part perform manual work. The basic distinction here is between managerial functions (in the broadest sense) and the physical operations of production. Partly because of more rapid progress in mechanizing the work of the wage earner than that of the salary earner, partly because of the increasing complication, both economic and technical, of the modern productive process, the type of work performed by the salaried employee has risen in quantitative importance compared with that done by the wage earner.[9]

In 1939 the proportion of individual proprietors and firm members in the working force was somewhat greater in mining than in manufacturing: 2.5 percent in the former, 1.4 percent in the latter.[10] As in manufacturing, so also in the mining industries this percentage has declined with the years. The Census of 1902 did not collect data of the kind indicated, but in 1909 individual proprietors and firm members comprised 3 percent of all persons engaged in mining.

[8] Solomon Fabricant, *Employment in Manufacturing, 1899–1939* (National Bureau of Economic Research, 1942), Appendix B.

[9] That the change reflects a shift in the relative importance of different functions, and is not due merely to alterations in methods of remuneration, may be seen from an examination of the Census schedules. *Salaried employees* are defined as follows: "Principal officers of corporations; managers, superintendents, and other responsible administrative employees; technical employees, mining engineers, and chemists; clerks, stenographers, bookkeepers, and other clerical employees on salary." *Wage earners* are thus described: "Wage earners, including employees paid by the ton, car, yard, or other unit and miners and others compensated by share of product . . . DO NOT include persons who were not employed on manual or mechanical work." (See *Fifteenth Census*, "Mines and Quarries, 1929," p. 411.) The distinction is thus primarily one of function: see also Fabricant, *Employment in Manufacturing, 1899–1939*, pp. 179-80.

[10] Fabricant, *Employment in Manufacturing, 1899–1939*, Appendix B. However, the figure for manufacturing, at least, represents an understatement, owing to the exclusion by the Census of Manufactures since 1921 of establishments with products valued at less than $5,000.

## HOURS OF WORK

In constructing indexes of productivity we shall find it convenient to take output per manday as our basic measure. As already indicated, in many respects the manhour is preferable to the manday as a unit of employment. It is therefore important to discover, at least roughly, how the length of the working day has altered. We shall thus obtain some indication of the bias introduced into our figures through the use of mandays rather than manhours.

In Table 10 will be found data on the length of the work day in the more important mining industries. In 1939 the prevailing length of the shift was about eight hours, except in coal mining where it had been reduced to seven. The working day has been shorter in coal mining than in other industries at least since the close of the first World War. The length of the working week depends not only on the length of the day, but also upon the number of days worked per week. However, in most mining industries the basis on which wage earners are remunerated is the day or shift rather than the week; for this reason data on the number of hours worked per week are difficult to assemble and not very meaningful. Our discussion will therefore be confined for the most part to the length of the work day.

TABLE 10

HOURS PER SHIFT[a]

| Industry | 1902 | 1909[b] | 1919 | 1929 | 1939 |
|---|---|---|---|---|---|
| Metal mining, total | 9.4 | .. | 8.6 | 8.3 | 7.9 |
| Iron ore | 9.9 | 9.9 | 9.1 | 8.9 | 8.0 |
| Copper | 8.9 | 8.2 | 8.4 | 8.2 | 8.0 |
| Other metal mining | 9.2 | .. | 8.3 | 8.0 | 7.9 |
| Coal, total | 8.9 | 8.8 | 8.0 | 8.1 | 7.0 |
| Pennsylvania anthracite | 9.5 | 9.0 | 8.0 | 8.0 | 7.0 |
| Bituminous | 8.8 | 8.7 | 8.1 | 8.1 | 7.0 |
| Stone | 9.7 | .. | 9.5 | 9.3 | 7.9 |
| Phosphate rock | 10.3 | 10.5 | 10.1 | 10.2 | 8.1 |
| Gypsum | 10.0 | .. | 9.7 | 8.9 | 7.9 |
| AVERAGE, ABOVE INDUSTRIES | 9.1 | .. | 8.3 | 8.2 | 7.3 |

[a] Except for stone in 1902, and the figures shown for 1909, the data in this table may all be derived from Appendix Table A-3: for sources see notes to that table. For stone in 1902, and for all industries shown in 1909, figures are derived from Census data.

The absence from this table of data for oil and gas wells is explained in the text.

[b] Data on hours of work released by the Census of 1909 were less extensive than in the case of other Censuses. This fact explains the lack of data for some industries in 1909.

The reduction in the number of hours worked per shift undoubtedly antedates the period which is studied here. Even as late
as 1880 a work day in excess of ten hours was not uncommon in
American industry.[11] In 1902 the average length of the work day
in mining was apparently about 9 hours, and since 1902 it has
been further reduced by perhaps a fifth. This shortening of the
work day has been far from a steady process. Although the partial
data for 1909 reveal some decline in hours during the first decade
of the century, a much larger reduction evidently occurred during
the second decade, which of course includes the first World War.
Again, little change seems to have occurred during the 1920's,
except apparently in gypsum mining, but a further sharp fall
took place between 1929 and 1939.

Why the second and fourth decades of the century should have
been so much more productive of increased leisure for employed
workers than the first and third decades is by no means completely
clear. Certainly the forces operating during the first World War
were very different in character from those present during the
Great Depression. But the result in both periods was increased
unionization—during the war because of the shortage of labor, and
the enhanced bargaining power of the working force; during the
depression because of governmental policies followed after 1933.
To be sure it may be doubted, especially with regard to the 1930's,
how far labor union action was responsible, in any exclusive
sense, for the reduction in hours that occurred. Partly under the
influence of a movement to "share the work," there were numerous initiatives of a governmental or quasi-governmental character
which tended to shorten the work day, notably the National Industrial Recovery Act (1933) and the Wage and Hour Act (1938).
Clearly the reasons leading to success or failure of the movement
for a shorter work day are complex: they cannot be analyzed in
detail here. But it seems no accident that the periods of sharpest
contraction in the length of the shift—the second and fourth
decades of the century—were also periods of rapid social change
and serious economic dislocation.

Up to this point nothing has been said about the length of
the work day at petroleum and natural gas wells, an industry

[11] See, for example, David A. Wells, *Recent Economic Changes* (Appleton, 1889),
p. 415; A. S. Bolles, *Industrial History of the United States* (Henry Bill Publishing
Co., Norwich, Conn., 1878), pp. 889-90.

which accounts for about one fifth of all mining employment. Unfortunately it is not possible to present data for this industry in the same form as for other industries. Nevertheless it is certain that large reductions have occurred in the length of the work day here as they have elsewhere. According to the Census of 1902 a 12-hour shift was worked at the overwhelming majority of wells. The production of crude oil and gas is peculiar in that, if a well is flowing, it flows—and may need some degree of attention— 24 hours a day. In 1902 this need appears to have been met in general by two 12-hour shifts, much longer working hours than were common in any other kind of mineral production at that time.[12] Of course the burden imposed on the labor force depends partly also upon the number of such shifts worked: it might be no more onerous to work, for example, three 12-hour shifts a week than six 8-hour shifts. However, the long hours worked at oil and gas wells in 1902 do not seem to have been offset in any marked degree by a smaller number of shifts worked per week or month. Data based upon the 1902 Census suggest a figure of over 3,600 for the number of hours worked per year.[13] This means that in 1902 the full time worker must have worked something like 300 of these 12-hour shifts.

Certainly hours worked by full time workers at oil and gas wells declined in marked degree after 1902, as they did in other mining industries. The following figures relate to operations of oil and gas wells by regular producers only.[14]

[12] Of 133,810 oil and gas wells reporting, 127,270 operated 2 shifts a day, and 127,931 operated 12-hour shifts ("Mines and Quarries, 1902," p. 110). The evidence seems conclusive.

[13] O. E. Kiessling and others, *Petroleum and Natural-Gas Production* (National Research Project, Philadelphia, 1939), p. 327. The figure quoted is obtained by dividing 122,824 thousand manhours (derived from wage payments) by 33,400 wage earners. The latter are apparently full time wage earners; but if some of them did not work full time, the number of full time hours per year would be even higher than that suggested in the text.

[14] *Ibid.* Regular producers employ about three quarters of the labor force. The data were obtained by dividing manhours worked, measured by wage payments, by average numbers employed. It is possible that average employment does not take adequate account of inactive periods, in which case the figures quoted understate hours worked by full time employees. For example the Bureau of Mines reports average weekly hours in 1937 as 40.5 for oil wells and 49.6 for gas wells ("Recent Trends in Employment and Productivity in the Oil and Gas Fields," Mineral Market Reports No. 728, April 24, 1939). If these are weighted roughly by workers employed in 1935 (from the same source), the average hours per week for oil and gas wells is 41.2 in 1937. If we assume a full time wage earner works 50 weeks a year, a figure of 2,060 hours per year is indicated. Perhaps because their employment is intermittent, wage earners employed by contractors apparently work fewer hours per year than do those hired by regular producers (see note to Appendix Table A-3).

| Year | Hours per Year |
|------|----------------|
| 1902 | 3,558 |
| 1909 | 3,034 |
| 1919 | 2,471 |
| 1929 | 2,310 |
| 1937 | 1,977 |

For 1939 an apparently comparable figure of about 1,800 is obtainable for the number of hours worked in that year by full time wage earners.[15]

Evidently hours worked per year in oil and gas production have been reduced rather steadily, and now stand at about half their level at the beginning of the century. It is not certain, however, that hours worked per day have fallen more sharply in petroleum and natural gas than in other mineral enterprises, for we have no recent data on the length of the shift at oil and gas wells. In other mining industries the working day has been shortened by about one fifth. It would seem likely, particularly in view of the very long hours which we know were worked at oil and gas wells at the turn of the century, that the decline has been proportionately greater here than elsewhere.

In all branches of mining for which we have data very substantial additions were made during the forty year period to the leisure of those in full time employment. In the next chapter we shall find that over the same period significant increases occurred in output per manday in most of these industries. It is obvious that corresponding increases in output per manhour must have been even larger.

15 By dividing 190,674 thousand manhours by 105,505 wage earners (average for the year, including inactive periods). Data are from the 1939 Census and cover producing and nonproducing oil and gas operations, but not labor employed by contractors. This, too, may be an understatement because of inclusion of some wage earners who did not work a full year.

# Chapter 4

# The Relation between Output and Employment

IF WE RELATE a quantity of output to a unit of some particular kind of input, we obtain a measure of what is commonly called the *productivity* of that input. Obviously there exist as many different criteria of productive efficiency, or productivity, as there are factors of production. In the present report we shall regard all labor, regardless of its grade or rate of pay, as a single factor of production. And we shall confine our attention to the measurement of labor productivity. Accordingly, the treatment of output in Chapter 2 and the discussion of employment in Chapter 3 may now be brought together. Our indexes of output, it will be recalled, compare dollar volumes of product at constant prices. If these indexes are divided by comparable indexes of employment, the productivity indexes which result clearly measure changes in the dollar volume of product per worker, or per manday, also at constant prices. Thus our productivity indexes involve a weighting system which depends on money values, just as do our output indexes. However, we may still claim to treat physical quantities, inasmuch as the direct influence of price changes has been eliminated from both types of measure.

The present chapter will furnish a review of productivity changes in mining as a whole. In Part Two (Chapters 5-7) we shall endeavor to supply a background of technological information with which to interpret these changes. More detailed studies of output, employment and productivity, and of associated changes in technology, in individual mining industries, will be undertaken in Part Three (Chapters 8-13).

## OUTPUT, EMPLOYMENT AND PRODUCTIVITY

The various industries for which we have comparable output and employment data for the two years 1902 and 1939 are listed in Table 11. Judged by value of products in 1937 these industries

Table 11

INDEXES OF OUTPUT, EMPLOYMENT AND PRODUCTIVITY, 1902 AND 1939[a]

*1902:100*

| Industry | 1902 | 1939 | | | | |
|---|---|---|---|---|---|---|
| | All Quantities | Output | Employment Man-days | Employment Man-hours | Output per Man-day | Output per Man-hour |
| Metal mining, total | 100 | 183 | 73 | 62 | 251 | 296 |
| Iron ore | 100 | 146 | 40 | 33 | 362 | 446 |
| Copper | 100 | 216 | 81 | 72 | 268 | 300 |
| Other metals[b] | 100 | 169 | 95 | 81 | 178 | 207 |
| Fuels, total[c] | 100 | 332 | f | 83 | f | 398 |
| Pennsylvania anthracite | 100[g] | 76 | 60 | 44 | 128 | 172 |
| Bituminous coal | 100 | 151 | 93 | 74 | 163 | 204 |
| Oil and gas wells | 100 | 1,112 | f | 230 | f | 483 |
| Stone quarrying | 100[h] | 93 | 38 | f | 245 | f |
| Phosphate rock | 100 | 266 | 45 | 35 | 594 | 758 |
| Gypsum | 100 | 395 | 126 | 100 | 313 | 396 |
| TOTAL, EXCLUDING OIL AND GAS[d] | 100 | 141 | 79 | 64 | 178 | 219 |
| TOTAL, INCLUDING OIL AND GAS[e] | 100 | 283 | 101 | 77 | 280 | 367 |

[a] Based on Appendix A, especially Table A-5.

[b] Includes gold, silver, lead, zinc, manganese, tungsten, molybdenum, mercury, bauxite, pyrites, fluorspar (Illinois and Kentucky only), but not placer mining. The classification is on an industry basis: hence the output data exclude gold and silver originating in copper mines. For further explanation, see Appendix B.

[c] The comparison base for Pennsylvania anthracite is 1901. When 1902:100 for anthracite as for other items, the figures for 1939 are as follows: output, 366; man-hours, 92; output per manhour, 399.

[d] For the comparison of 1902 and 1911 the industries included are all those except stone. For comparisons between 1911 and 1939 stone quarrying is also included. The comparison base for Pennsylvania anthracite is 1901. When 1902:100 for anthracite as for other items, the figures for 1939 are as follows: output, 152; mandays, 86; manhours, 70; output per manday, 178; output per manhour, 217.

[e] For the comparison 1902 to 1911 the industries included are all those shown except stone: judged by value of products in 1937 they have a coverage of 89.7 percent of all minerals for which the Bureau of Mines reports value data. For comparisons between 1911 and 1939 stone quarrying is also included, and the coverage is 94.3 percent on the same basis. Mandays for petroleum were included on the assumption that men employed worked 300 days per year. The comparison base for Pennsylvania anthracite is 1901. When 1902:100 for anthracite as for other items, the figures for 1939 are as follows: output, 303; mandays, 101; manhours, 83; output per manday, 299; output per manhour, 366.

[f] Not available.

[g] Applies to 1901; figures for anthracite in 1902 are distorted by the five-month strike in that year. When 1902:100, the figures for 1939 are as follows: output, 124; mandays, 99; manhours, 73; output per manday, 126; output per manhour, 170.

[h] Applies to 1911; no adequate production data are available for stone in 1902.

cover nearly 90 percent of mineral production as a whole.[1] The resulting productivity indexes may therefore be accepted as representative of mining activity. Any reservations we may have relate rather to the comparability between 1902 and 1939 of the employment data for individual industries. These data have been adjusted in various ways, particularly for 1902: the adjustments we felt it necessary to make are described in footnotes to Appendix Table A-3.[2]

For mining as a whole, output nearly tripled; and output per manhour multiplied more than three and a half times (Table 11). This result, to be sure, stems largely from the dramatic expansion in the output and productivity of oil and gas wells. If we exclude the petroleum industry from the comparisons, the changes for the period 1902–39 are much more moderate: a 41 percent rise in output, and a somewhat greater increase in productivity —78 percent in terms of mandays (Chart 28), 119 percent in terms of manhours. For mining as a whole, labor input, measured in manhours, declined between 1902 and 1939, although total employment, in terms of mandays, may have increased slightly (see also

[1] For stone quarrying in 1902 we have employment data but no measure of physical output. In the indexes for mining as a whole in the last line of Table 11, the stone industries are included for comparisons subsequent to 1911. For these comparisons—i.e. for all but the first quarter of the period—the industrial coverage of our output and employment measures exceeds 94 percent.

[2] These adjustments were chiefly (1) to exclude employment at manufacturing or processing plants, (2) to secure 100 percent coverage where the original figures clearly did not provide it, (3) to standardize the basis for averaging employment over the year. The employment figures for recent years, and particularly for 1939, may be accepted as satisfactory. The possibility remains that our employment indexes suffer from an upward bias owing to incomplete coverage in early years. The same possibility exists in regard to our output indexes, but here any upward bias can hardly be significant. The fact that the series we present for employment are much more likely to be subject to upward bias than the series for output, means that any increases we report in productivity are likely to err, if at all, on the side of understatement.

Something should be said of the comparability of 1902 and 1939 in respect to the level of business activity. According to the National Bureau's chronology, 1902 marks the conclusion of a mild recession which started in 1900. 1939 was a more active year than 1938, though not as active as 1937. In terms of general business, 1939 may be considered a "better" year than 1902. Nevertheless the recession of 1900–02 appears scarcely to have affected mining activity, for output tended to expand rather steadily year by year during the first few years of the present century. So far as concerns mining, therefore, both years may be described as fairly active. In the case of Pennsylvania anthracite, comparability is distorted by the five-month strike which occurred in 1902. For this reason in Table 11 we use the years 1901 and 1939 for the comparisons of anthracite productivity.

Table 7 above). Total manhours in petroleum and natural gas production doubled, but this expansion was more than offset by reductions elsewhere.

The results shown in Table 11 for the mining industries differ in several respects from comparable measures reported in previous National Bureau studies [3] for manufacturing and for agriculture.

Chart 28

MINING, EXCLUSIVE OF OIL AND GAS·WELLS

Output, Employment and Productivity, 1902 – 39

(1902:100)

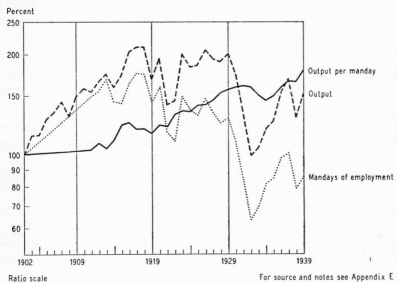

Ratio scale                                              For source and notes see Appendix E

As may be seen from Table 12, output tripled in mining and in manufacturing, but rose less than 50 percent in agriculture. However, if once again oil and gas wells are excluded, mining output expanded, like that of agriculture, by less than 50 percent. In terms of workers employed a given number of days a year, labor input was practically unchanged in mining (or declined about 20 percent if petroleum is excluded), rose 50 percent in manufactur-

[3] See Solomon Fabricant, *The Output of Manufacturing Industries, 1899–1937* (1940); the same author's *Employment in Manufacturing, 1899–1939: An Analysis of Its Relation to the Volume of Production* (1942); and Harold Barger and Hans H. Landsberg, *American Agriculture, 1899–1939: A Study of Output, Employment and Productivity* (1942).

TABLE 12

OUTPUT, EMPLOYMENT AND OUTPUT PER WORKER IN MINING, MANUFACTURING AND AGRICULTURE

| | Output | Employment[d] | Output per Worker |
|---|---|---|---|
| Mining, including oil and gas, 1939 (1902:100)[a] | 283 | 101 | 280 |
| Mining, excluding oil and gas, 1939 (1902:100)[a] | 141 | 79 | 178 |
| Manufacturing, 1939 (1902:100)[b] | 290 | 149 | 194 |
| Agriculture, 1937 (1900:100)[c] | 145 | 89 | 164 |

[a] See Table 11. The comparison base for Pennsylvania anthracite is 1901 instead of 1902.

[b] Solomon Fabricant, *Employment in Manufacturing, 1899–1939* (National Bureau of Economic Research, 1942), p. 331.

[c] Harold Barger and Hans H. Landsberg, *American Agriculture, 1899–1939* (National Bureau of Economic Research, 1942), p. 251. Comparisons are for five-year averages centered on years indicated.

[d] For mining, comparisons are made in terms of mandays or 300-day workers; for manufacturing, in terms of average wage earners; and for agriculture, in terms of gainfully occupied workers.

ing, and declined slightly in agriculture.[4] Output per worker (or per manday) tripled in mining, doubled in manufacturing, and increased somewhat more than 50 percent in agriculture. In this respect, again, the preeminence of mining results entirely from the inclusion of oil and gas wells: if they are excluded, output per worker rose about 80 percent only, i.e., more than in agriculture, but less than in manufacturing.

The preponderant effect exerted upon our results by the petroleum industry merits further examination. This influence has two aspects. Productivity at oil and gas wells rose more rapidly than elsewhere. In addition, a shift occurred which increased the relative importance of oil and gas wells—an industry in which the absolute level of productivity was higher than elsewhere throughout the period. By productivity in this context we mean of course the dollar value of product per worker (per manday or manhour) measured at constant prices. In this sense output per manhour in the petroleum industry was in 1902 nearly twice, and

[4] Strictly speaking, the comparison in Table 12 is made in terms of manyears containing a definite number of shifts only in the case of mining; in the other industries the comparisons are somewhat vaguer in character. The importance of using a worker employed a definite number of days a year as the unit of labor input is particularly great in mining because of the wide swings in degree of activity characteristic of this industry. In manufacturing wage earners represent the average of 12 monthly counts. In agriculture numbers occupied represent a single count for 1900 and an average of 12 monthly (sample) counts for 1937. For further details, the reader is advised to consult the sources mentioned for these industries.

in 1937 more than twice, the average for mining as a whole (Table 13). These two types of contribution to the productivity change in mining as a whole—which we may impute respectively to changes within industries and to shifts in their relative importance—are segregated for the comparison between 1902 and 1937 in Table 13.[5] It will be seen that about one third of the rise in output per manhour in mining as a whole can be traced to a shift in the relative weight of different industries in the total, and especially to a replacement of other forms of extraction by oil and gas wells.

TABLE 13

OUTPUT PER MANHOUR, BY INDUSTRIES, 1902 AND 1937

*At constant prices*[a]

| Industry | 1902 (dollars) | 1937 (dollars) | Change (dollars) | Ratio 1937 to 1902 |
|---|---|---|---|---|
| Metal mining[b] | .78 | 2.21 | +1.43 | 2.8 |
| Anthracite | .72 | 1.08 | +.36 | 1.5 |
| Bituminous coal | .52 | 1.00 | +.48 | 1.9 |
| Oil and gas wells | 1.00 | 4.11 | +3.11 | 4.1 |
| TOTAL, ABOVE INDUSTRIES | .65 | 1.95 | +1.31 | 3.0 |
| Part of change associated with: | | | | |
| Changes within industries[c] | .. | .. | +.92 | .. |
| Shifts between industries[c] | .. | .. | +.38 | .. |

[a] All money values in this table are expressed, for each industry, in terms of the average of unit values obtaining in 1902 and 1937. Consequently the data are merely a measure of physical output, and take no account of changes in prices between the two dates. Computed from Appendix Tables A-2 and A-5.

[b] Includes gold, silver, copper, lead, zinc, tungsten, molybdenum, mercury, bauxite, iron ore, manganese, pyrites, and fluorspar in Illinois and Kentucky.

[c] Let $x$ represent product per manhour in dollars (in constant prices), $y$ manhours, and suffixes 1902 and 1937 respectively. The part of the change associated with changes within industries may be written $\dfrac{\Sigma (x_2 - x_1) y_1}{\Sigma y_1}$, and the part associated with

shifts between industries $\dfrac{\Sigma x_2 \left( \dfrac{y_2}{p} - y_1 \right)}{\Sigma y_1}$, where $\Sigma$ denotes summation over all industries shown, and $p = \dfrac{\Sigma y_2}{\Sigma y_1}$.

A further aspect of the shift toward petroleum and natural gas, and away from other types of fuel, is illustrated in Table 14. If

[5] The comparisons in Table 13 are confined to the extraction of metals, coal and petroleum. However, the picture would scarcely be altered if minor industries, for many of which we do not have data, were included. We chose 1937 for the second year of the comparison because data for 1939 were not yet available when this computation was made.

the product of the fuel producing industries is measured in energy units (BTU), we find that output per manhour did not differ greatly among these industries in 1902, but that since then sharp divergence in movement has occurred. Today a worker produces in a given time two or three times as many BTU in the petroleum industry as he does in the coal industry. It should not be assumed from this that we can increase the national product by the simple

TABLE 14

COAL AND PETROLEUM: OUTPUT (IN BTU) PER MANHOUR, 1902 AND 1937[a]

*Million BTU per manhour*

| Industry | 1902 | 1937 | Change |
|----------|------|------|--------|
| Pennsylvania anthracite | 6.9 | 10.4 | +3.5 |
| Bituminous coal | 9.1 | 17.5 | +8.4 |
| Oil and gas wells | 7.0 | 32.6 | +25.6 |
| TOTAL, ABOVE INDUSTRIES | 8.5 | 21.0 | +12.5 |
| Part of change associated with: | | | |
|   Changes within industries[b] | .. | .. | +9.6 |
|   Shifts between industries[b] | .. | .. | +2.9 |

[a] Output, Appendix Table A-1; manhours, Appendix Table A-3; BTU from *Minerals Yearbook*, as follows: 27.2 mil. per short ton anthracite, 26.2 mil. per short ton bituminous, 6 mil. per barrel petroleum and natural gasoline, 1,075 per cubic foot of natural gas.

[b] Let $x$ represent BTU per manhour, $y$ manhours, and suffixes 1902 and 1937 respectively. The part of the change associated with changes within industries may be written $\dfrac{\Sigma (x_2 - x_1) y_1}{\Sigma y_1}$, and the part associated with shifts between industries $\dfrac{\Sigma x_2 \left(\dfrac{y_2}{p} - y_1\right)}{\Sigma y_1}$, where $\Sigma$ denotes summation over all industries shown, and $p = \dfrac{\Sigma y_2}{\Sigma y_1}$.

expedient of turning coal miners into oil well operatives. Energy content is not the only basis of economic valuation; besides transportation costs and capital investment, depletion prospects should be included in any rational accounting. Nor have we debited petroleum with the labor necessary to refine it, a cost which has no counterpart in the coal industry. Nevertheless, the rising relative efficiency of oil and gas production must have lowered the price of oil in relation to coal, and so stimulated the substitution of oil for coal as fuel which we noted in Chapter 2.[6]

[6] Measured at the point of production, the price of oil rose about 50 percent, the price of coal about 70 percent, between 1902 and 1937 (Appendix Table A-1). Probably the relative cheapening of oil to the ultimate consumer was greater than this, thanks to advances in transportation, processing and combustion techniques.

Measurement of the product in energy units provides us with a useful alternative way of judging output and productivity in the fuel producing industries. If we employ our standard methods of gauging physical output, i.e., weighting each product by its average price in the two years to be compared, we find that the output of these industries rose from 100 in 1902 to 343 in 1937. But if change over the same period is measured in BTU, the output of fuels expanded only from 100 to 269. This difference emerges despite the fact that we used constant ratios to convert tons of coal, barrels of oil and cubic feet of natural gas to BTU. It results from the displacement of coal by oil and gas, coupled with the higher monetary value (measured in dollars per BTU) at which the latter are sold. Again, output per manhour at coal mines and oil and gas wells combined was nearly four times as high at the end of the period as at the beginning, if gauged according to our standard practice. But measured in BTU per manhour, the productivity of the fuel producing industries was only about two and a half times as high in 1937 as in 1902. According to Table 14, nearly a third of this expansion may be traced to the shift from coal with a low, to petroleum and natural gas with a high, BTU output per manhour.

## MANDAY VERSUS MANHOUR MEASUREMENTS

For all mining industries except oil wells and stone quarries, figures for employment and productivity were given in Table 11 both in mandays and in manhours. Because of sizable reductions in the length of the shift (Table 10), manhours worked per year have declined in relation to mandays in all the industries for which data are given. For the same reason, output per manhour has in every case mounted more rapidly than output per manday (for details see Appendix Tables A-5 and A-6).

Despite the fact that all major branches of mining reported a larger output in 1939 than 1902,[7] only oil and gas wells increased their labor input in manhour terms; if the comparison is made for mandays, however, gypsum mining also used more labor in 1939 than in 1902. All other branches reduced their consump-

[7] Anthracite output was larger in 1939 than in 1902, but only because of the strike in 1902; output in 1939 was smaller than in 1901 or 1903. Anthracite employment, however, was smaller in 1939 than it was in any of the years 1901–03; this statement holds, both for manhours and for mandays, the strike notwithstanding.

tion of labor in manday terms, and still more in terms of manhours. Among the declines in employment, those in iron ore,
anthracite (adjusted for the strike in 1902), and phosphate rock
mining were particularly large.

Changes in output per manday range from a rise of 28 percent
for anthracite mining to the sixfold growth for phosphate rock.
The same two industries represent extremes of behavior with
respect to output per manhour: the one shows a rise of but 72
percent, the other a more than sevenfold increase in manhour
productivity.

Except in the case of oil wells, we know more about mandays
than about manhours worked in the mineral industries. For this
reason the emphasis in the remainder of this chapter, and in later
chapters (except that devoted to petroleum) will rest primarily
upon the behavior of output per manday. Throughout the discussion we should bear in mind, however, that the tendency has
been for the length of the workday to contract rather steadily. In
consequence—if we regard the manhour as the fundamental measure of labor input—we should remember that our indexes of output per manday (see, for example, Charts 28 to 32) understate
the rise or overstate the decline that has occurred in the productivity of labor.

## THE RELATION BETWEEN OUTPUT AND EMPLOYMENT

It cannot be said that there emerges from our results a clear picture which might be regarded as typical of all the mining industries. Instead a rather sharp contrast must be drawn between the
experience of different branches of extraction. In spite of the
fact that oil and gas wells show the second largest increase (following phosphate rock) in manhour productivity, this form of
enterprise has expanded both its output and its employment.
After petroleum, the output of gypsum has mounted more than
that of any other mineral studied; here again employment has
increased, at least in terms of mandays. But for the various metal
mining industries, for bituminous coal and for phosphate rock—
each of which increased its output substantially between 1902
and 1939—output per manhour or per manday rose more rapidly
than the volume of production, so that here there were declines
in employment. Productivity has risen least in anthracite mining,

the only major form of mineral production with an output lower in 1939 than at the beginning of the century.

There is some tendency, as one would expect, for employment to rise most or fall least in the industries with the largest increases in output. An outstanding exception to this rule is phosphate rock, which stands third in output growth, but which nevertheless cut down its employment more than any industry except iron ore and perhaps also stone quarrying. There is evidence, too—though rather slender evidence—to support the view that increases in productivity are correlated with increases in output. Phosphate rock again appears somewhat of an exception, for it ranks first in productivity increase but only third when measured by rise in output. Iron ore also departs from the general pattern; it had the third largest increase in productivity but expanded its output only moderately. Generalizations of this sort are difficult to make, not only because of the exceptions which immediately present themselves, but also because the industries for which we have data are small in number and heterogeneous in size and other characteristics.

Petroleum and natural gas now account for about half the value of all mineral products, but their contribution to employment, though substantial, is disproportionately small. We have seen that output and employment expanded much more rapidly in oil and gas production than in any other mineral industry, and output per manhour more rapidly than in any of the others except phosphate rock. The causes of these striking changes will be examined further in Chapter 10. For convenience, the remainder of this chapter will be confined to a discussion of the extraction of minerals other than petroleum and natural gas.

If we exclude oil and gas wells, and make a further exception in the case of gypsum, we find that in the remaining industries employment decreased. In metal mining, coal mining, stone quarrying and the mining of phosphate rock, that is to say, the rise in productivity exceeded the rise in output. The experience of these industries, which (apart from petroleum) account for the bulk of mineral production and employment, therefore resembles the course of affairs in agriculture rather than the history of manufacturing. We do not have exactly comparable data: possibly output and productivity increased a little more rapidly in these mining industries (taken together) than in agriculture. But the similarity of change over the period is striking (Table 12) as is the contrast of both these groups with manufacturing. Such comparisons suggest that the mining industries (excluding petroleum) and agriculture perhaps had something in common that they did not share with manufacturing—at least during the period under review.

The most obvious feature common to mining and to agriculture is that they are both extractive industries. They both obtain products from the ground with more or less difficulty and are therefore affected by changing resource conditions; and both yield raw products which usually have to be processed before they can be consumed. Again, the movement toward greater use of scrap and economy of materials has somewhat lessened the demand for raw products in comparison with the demand for finished goods. Finally, changes in quality or purity have been slight in the case of minerals and farm products, whereas a tendency toward a greater degree of fabrication has persisted in the case of manufactured goods.[8] These factors would lead us to expect a greater rise in the physical output of fabricated products than of raw minerals or agricultural commodities. On the other hand, the set of factors associated with the concept of diminishing returns—depletion of soil or minerals, declining grade of ore, the need to mine at greater depths—are encountered first and foremost in the extractive industries and have little if any application to manufacturing. The level of productivity in mining at any given time reflects the current phase of an enduring struggle between technological advance and resource depletion. To the degree that mining is affected by the operation of diminishing returns, and that technological innovation is unable fully to overcome the effects of depletion, one would expect output per worker in mining to lag behind its upward progress in manufacturing.

Considerations of this order would appear to explain the smaller rise in output and in output per worker in the mining in-

[8] In the case of minerals these changes are confined almost entirely to variations in the grade of coal mined, or in the grade of metallic concentrates as they leave the beneficiating plant. It is quite unlikely that alterations in quality are taken account of at all adequately in our indexes of output, whether of minerals, of farm products or of manufactures. This neglect is certainly most serious in the case of manufactured goods. If proper allowance could be made for changes in quality, the recorded increase in manufacturing relative to farm and mineral output would be even more marked than it appears from the data in Table 12. Some discussion of changes in the quality of mineral output, with special reference to copper mining, will be found in Appendix D.

dustries (again with the exception of petroleum) than in manufacturing. But they do not explain why employment itself has diminished. This last development is plainly a reflection of the fact that the first set of factors mentioned above—those which tend to restrain output—have been more powerful during our period than the second set of factors—those acting to curb the rise in output per worker. In other words technological advance has so far been sufficiently successful in its struggle with depletion to raise productivity more rapidly than output has expanded. This is about all that can be said in a general way. For a more detailed treatment of the relation between output and employment in the individual industries concerned, the reader is referred to the last section of this chapter and to the later chapters in this book. The concept of diminishing returns as it applies to mining is examined more fully, in the light of experience in the mineral industries, in the final chapter which constitutes Part Four.

The discussion has been confined to mineral industries other than the production of petroleum and natural gas. Plainly the oil and gas wells of the nation form an exception to the generalizations made above. Output, employment and productivity all expanded in a manner more reminiscent of some rapidly growing branch of manufacturing than of any of the other mineral industries. Petroleum is a young industry; as we saw in Chapter 2, it has invaded markets previously secured to other fuels; and resource depletion has been made good by frequent discovery of new fields. These and other factors which distinguish it from the older forms of mining are considered in Chapter 10 below.

## OUTPUT PER MANDAY IN INDIVIDUAL INDUSTRIES

As already explained, the relation between output and employment in the more important branches of mining will be the subject of separate chapters later in this volume. In any case a thoroughgoing account must consider changes in technology and their relation to resource depletion, and these have not yet been examined. The purpose of this section is to make some further comparisons between productivity changes in different mining industries. As in the preceding section, the discussion is confined to industries other than petroleum.

In Chart 29 our index for output per manday in mining and

quarrying is broken down into separate indexes for metal mining, coal mining, phosphate rock and gypsum.[9] The very large expansion of manday output in the mining of phosphate rock is further illustrated. Largely confined to Florida, the phosphate

Chart 29

COAL, METAL, GYPSUM AND PHOSPHATE ROCK MINING
Output per Manday, 1902 – 39
(1902 : 100)

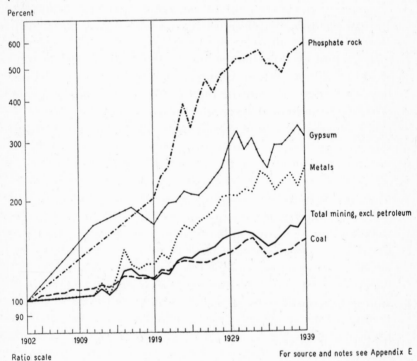

Percent

Ratio scale                                    For source and notes see Appendix E

rock industry is of course a comparatively small employer of labor. The greatest gains in productivity in this industry seem to have occurred before 1923, and to have been associated with the introduction of hydraulic methods of open pit mining soon after the beginning of the century.[10] In the case of gypsum much of the

[9] The separate indexes will be found in Appendix Table A-5. The breakdown in Chart 29 is exhaustive for 1902–11; thereafter the total includes data for stone quarrying. The latter, not distinguished in Chart 29, will be found in Chart 32.

[10] A. P. Haskell, Jr. and O. E. Kiessling, *Phosphate-Rock Mining, 1880–1937* (National Research Project, Philadelphia, 1938), pp. 13-16.

rise in output per manday seems to have occurred between 1902 and 1916: productivity appears almost to have doubled within 14 years. Too much confidence should not be placed in this result, for the mining of gypsum is often combined with calcining operations; it is possible that in 1911, and especially in 1902, the segregation, particularly of the employment data, was imperfect.[11] Since 1916 manday output in the gypsum industry has expanded at about the same rate as in metal mining.

Between 1902 and 1912 productivity apparently increased rather slowly, both in metal mining and in coal mining: on the average the rise was about 10 percent, or 1 percent yearly, for each of these series. For the remainder of the period, however, manday output in metal mining increased about twice as rapidly as in coal mining. This divergence may be attributable in part to the fact that coal mines are commonly older than metal mines. Age has two disadvantages. First, in an old mine it is mechanization which has to be adapted to the existing layout, instead of the other way round. Second, resource depletion is more likely to be felt: narrower seams or poorer ore must be worked, the mine must be deepened, the haul from the working face to the shaft must be lengthened. The more rapid rise of manday output in metal than in coal mining may result also in part from the superiority of open pit to underground mining, and in part from new techniques for beneficiating metallic ores. On the whole the advance of technique seems to have been more rapid in open pit mining: no single innovation in underground methods can compare with the introduction of the power shovel in stripping operations. This implement has had little application in the coal industry, still mainly carried on below ground. Again, such changes as selective flotation and new milling techniques, so important in metal mining, have left coal mining unaffected. It is to considerations of this order that we must look if we wish to explain the differing fortunes of these two groups of industries.

Contrasts of much the same sort may be discerned in Chart 30 where productivity changes are shown separately for individual metal and coal mining industries. As we have already noted, among the metal mining industries manday output increased most rapidly in the mining of iron ore. Preeminently an open pit in-

---

[11] As elsewhere, output and employment are intended to exclude manufacturing operations, of which calcining is an example.

dustry, iron ore mining has derived full benefit from the modern
power shovel; nor has it had, as yet, to combat serious depletion
of resources. Copper mining made little progress during the first
two decades of the century: deep mining, especially in Michigan,
was relatively more important than it is today, and grade of ore

Chart 30

COAL AND METAL MINING

Output per Manday, by Individual Industries, 1902 – 39

(1902 : 100)

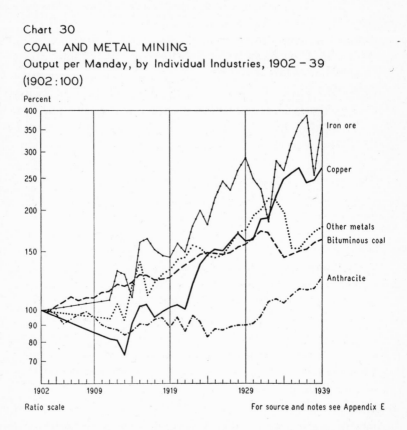

was of course declining.[12] After 1921 large scale open pit developments in the West, in conjunction with improved techniques for
concentrating low grade ores, appear to have asserted their influence, for manday output has more than doubled since that time.
The mining of "other metals" (especially gold, silver, lead and
zinc) is carried on mainly below ground,[13] and while productivity
has increased, it has risen little more rapidly than in the case of
bituminous coal. Among these "other metals" we may segregate

[12] See Table 22 below.
[13] Placer mining is excluded from the statistics in this chapter.

mercury mining, for which output per manday is shown in Chart
31. For the first three decades of the century the trend of productivity in mercury was steady or downward, but within the past
fifteen years it has risen rather rapidly. Over the period as a whole
the curve for mercury resembles that for anthracite (Chart 30).

Chart 31

MERCURY MINING AND RECOVERY

Output per Manday, 1902 – 39

(1902 :100)

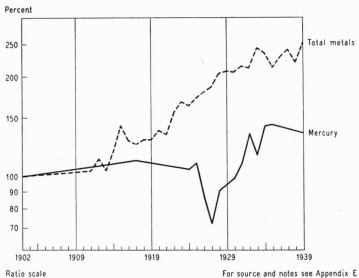

In these two industries the tendency for productivity to decline
during the early part of the period must be attributed to the
effects of depletion, but the reasons for the recovery both have
registered in output per manday in recent years appear to vary.
Thus the improvement in the efficiency of anthracite mining
seems rather definitely connected with the mechanization of loading operations (see Chapter 9 below). On the other hand the
recent rise of productivity in mercury mining is not susceptible
of any obvious explanation, but appears to have been occasioned
by general improvements in organization. The gain here is all the
more remarkable when we consider that despite a decline in the
average mercury content of domestic ores, from 0.54 percent in

1926 to 0.41 percent in 1933–34, the output of mercury per man-hour rose from 0.64 pounds in 1926 to 0.85 pounds in 1933.[14]

The experience of bituminous coal mining differs sharply from that of anthracite: productivity has risen steadily, if not sensationally, in soft coal production. In the latter industry mechanization has proceeded on a scale which narrow, inclined seams made impossible in anthracite mines.

Finally, in Chart 32 the course of events in stone quarrying is summarized. Because satisfactory physical output data for 1902

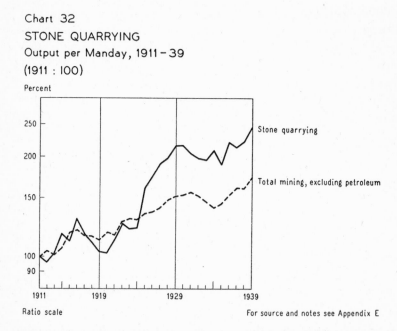

Chart 32
STONE QUARRYING
Output per Manday, 1911 – 39
(1911 : 100)

Percent

Stone quarrying

Total mining, excluding petroleum

Ratio scale                    For source and notes see Appendix E

are lacking, our productivity measures begin only with 1911. It will be seen that manday output moved somewhat erratically until the middle 1920's, but rose sharply thereafter. This rise is to be explained by the increasing importance of crushed stone, a product obtained almost exclusively from open pit workings with the aid of the power shovel. Modern techniques were introduced into crushed stone quarries somewhat later than in metal mining, but their effect is no less clear.

These summary comparisons represent all that can be said in the present context. We have seen that, if oil wells are included,

[14] *Minerals Yearbook, 1935,* p. 457.

productivity increased even more rapidly in mining than in manufacturing. Striking contrasts exist between the experience of different branches of the mineral industry. The effectiveness of labor increased much more rapidly in metal than in coal mining. Progress in extracting the nonmetals has occurred largely in the actual winning of the mineral; among metallic ores it has depended increasingly upon elaborate beneficiating techniques. In some fields open cut mining has increased its scope, proving a very efficient form of operation. The foundation for these changes has been mechanization of the mining process. In Part Two we turn to a review of technological development in the extraction of minerals from the earth. It is this development which has been responsible, in large measure, for the increases in the return to the miner's effort which we have noted. In subsequent chapters, in Part Three, the relation between output, employment and technology in some of the more important branches of mining will be further explored

Part Two

# Technological Change

"In order to mine the ore we must gain access
to it, then we must break it down without mixing
it with waste rock unnecessarily, and finally we
must transport the valuable mineralized material
to the surface. . . . Everywhere and for all time, the
essence of mining is the same; change occurs only
in the way of doing these simple, necessary things;
and the particular way of doing them is determined by what happens to be the state of knowledge and the physical means available at a given
time and place." C. E. JULIHN

# Chapter 5

# The Origins of Modern Mining Methods [1]

IF WE ARE to interpret intelligently the advances in productivity
reported in the preceding chapter, we must acquire at least the
indispensable minimum of information on technological developments in mining. There is much that is common to the methods
of the different industries we study here, and innovations have
frequently been carried over from one branch to another. For
this reason it is convenient first to sketch the technological picture for mining as a whole, before we turn, in Chapters 8 through
13, to the relation between productivity trends and technological
change in the more important individual industries.

There are many differences between contemporary American
mining and its earlier counterpart. The industry started as a
surface operation in which individuals, for the most part working independently, exploited rich outcroppings of coal or metallic
ore.[2] It has evolved, with the passage of time, into the large scale,
systematic exploitation of low grade mineral deposits, both underground and on the surface. Yet this change, so radical in scope,
has taken place almost entirely since the middle of the nineteenth
century.

This change, and the technological revolution which accompanied it, have affected the various branches of mining in greatly
differing degree. It is in metal mining that the transition from
the earlier small scale exploitation of rich mineral pockets to the
large scale nonselective methods of today has proceeded farthest.
Moreover, many problems were encountered first in this field,
and their solutions later adapted to other types of mining. Accordingly, we shall begin with a sketch of technological changes
in the mining of metallic ores, and then briefly review the history

[1] The scope of this and the two succeeding chapters in Part Two is confined to
the technology of the mining (including ore dressing) and quarrying of solid minerals. We do not treat here the technological aspects of petroleum and natural gas
production, since they are discussed separately in Chapter 10.

[2] For example, much of the copper mined during the eighteenth century was obtained in native form and did not even have to be smelted.

of coal mining. In Chapter 6 we shall investigate more particularly the forms which mechanization has taken in underground and open cut mining, and in stone quarrying. In Chapter 7 will be found a brief description of the methods employed in dressing and concentrating the mineral product, especially in the case of metallic ores, after it has been mined.

## MINING METHODS BEFORE 1899: METALLIC ORES

Descriptions of mining operations in this country prior to about 1850 uniformly report a very primitive type of endeavor. Gold, because of the unique geological character of its deposits, was more important in this early period of mining than the more common metals, including silver.[3] The surface mining of gold was a fairly simple business. The itinerant placer miner, who carried his own pick, shovel and pan, merely scooped up the gold-bearing gravel, washed it, and pocketed the residue, which was a relatively pure product requiring no further processing. Although with the passage of years his tools became somewhat more elaborate—for example, he acquired several devices to replace or supplement the pan in order to insure a more efficient recovery of fine gold particles [4]—modern small scale placer mining is still very much like that of a century or more ago.

Vein or quartz mining of gold developed from these simple beginnings. Quartz mining originally consisted of the exploitation of surface outcroppings which could easily be worked. The veins were inevitably followed somewhat deeper and operations on such deposits must soon have taken the form of open pits which

[3] Gold mining usually takes precedence in new regions because gold is very often found in the native state in deposits from which it may be recovered with very crude devices. No reduction process is necessary to free the metal. In addition, gold is so valuable that exploitation is possible in remote regions since the product, which is low in bulk in relation to its worth, can easily repay the otherwise prohibitive costs of primitive transportation.

[4] Among these devices were boxes which sloped gently and were mounted on rockers. The gold-bearing dirt was shoveled into the box (although perhaps first passed through a screen) and the rocking hastened the separation of the barren rock and its washing away. This device was later improved by transverse riffles or partitions which retained a larger percentage of the gold at the bottom of the box. (T. A. Rickard, *A History of American Mining*, McGraw-Hill, 1932, pp. 29-31; see also James H. Collins, "Mining Copper and the Nobler Metals" in Waldemar Kaempffert [ed.], *A Popular History of American Invention*, Scribner's, 1924, Vol. II, pp. 55-60.) Later improvements in recovery effected by the use of mercury and the amalgamation process are discussed in Chapter 7 below.

the miner attempted to work in the same manner as the familiar placers.[5]

Surface operations were by no means confined to gold mining. In the early workings of other minerals the tendency was also to proceed from the surface down, but this miniature open pit operation lacked all the economic and engineering features of contemporary large scale surface mining. Metal mining as practiced during the first half of the nineteenth century was a simple art, easily mastered. Often it consisted of nothing more than the gathering of loose outcrops. Or, in its more complex forms it might require the digging of trenches from which ore could be carried up inclined ways, as observed in Mississippi lead mining about 1820;[6] also drifting for some distance into the sidehills.[7] The men engaged in these activities could hardly be looked upon as skilled miners. Frequently they were primarily farmers; indeed, in the early days in the South, farming and small scale mining were often jointly pursued.[8] In any case, they were men without the technical experience one would then have found, for instance, among Cornish miners in England.[9]

Mining in this country was almost universally in the hands of individuals who, using simple tools and common sense, were able to obtain a mineral product easily convertible into cash. Even the extraction of the metal from its ore was largely performed by the miners themselves, and this was true not only of gold, which was relatively simple to recover, but even of lead, which required a pyrometallurgical operation.[10] The backward state of the arts of mining and metallurgy in the United States was actually attributable to the fact that rich mineral outcrops were readily available. Thus it was economically feasible to make a technically ineffi-

---

[5] Isaac Hourwich, writing in the 1902 Census, states: "The most natural method which suggested itself to the human mind for dealing with the gold-bearing rock was to reduce it to the same state in which the alluvial [placer] gold deposits were found and to separate the disseminated particles of gold from the pulverized mass by the familiar method of washing" (U. S. Bureau of the Census, *Special Reports*, "Mines and Quarries, 1902," p. 575).

[6] Rickard, *op. cit.*, p. 160. The author here refers to the observations of School-craft, an Indian agent of the Federal government, who visited the district.

[7] "Mines and Quarries, 1902," p. 460.

[8] Walter R. Crane, *Gold and Silver* (John Wiley and Sons, 1908), p. 343.

[9] This was less true of coal mining, however, for many of the early coal miners had learned their trade in Europe: see Carter Goodrich, *The Miner's Freedom* (Marshall Jones, Boston, 1925).

[10] Hourwich points out that up until the first quarter of the nineteenth century lead ore was crudely smelted by the miner ("Mines and Quarries, 1902," pp. 460-61).

cient recovery of metal from ore, or to abandon a rich operation of slight depth because water was encountered and could not be dealt with.[11] Pumps were available, but pumps required capital, and neither the demand for mineral raw material nor the imminent exhaustion of workings which did not require pumping had as yet called forth such investment. Similarly, the sinking of shafts was rare; where shafts were used the ore was raised by horse whim or windlass.[12] Power for all purposes was still provided by human muscle or brute force. Steam was not yet in common use, although in England during the eighteenth century it had been generally employed to actuate pumps. Even as late as about 1880 the following conditions seem to have prevailed in the Mississippi Valley lead district:

> Some storekeeper, farmer, or local capitalist furnished the small amount of money needed for tools; and the men who worked in the ground in winter usually engaged in farm work during the summer. The ore was generally raised to the surface by a windlass, and cleaned by hand with a "pickawee" hammer, or crushed with a "bucking iron" on a flat stone, or by an itinerant horsepower crusher, and was concentrated by sluicing and hand jigging.[13]

Important changes had, however, taken place before 1880, even though they had not permeated the entire structure of the metal mining industry. And as we might expect, gold and silver were in the vanguard. In placer mining the older methods of scooping and washing gravel began to be partially superseded by hydraulic mining around 1853. This advance was stimulated by conditions of climate and topography. Powerful streams of water were utilized to wash gravel banks down into trenches (ground sluices) in which recovery of the gold was effected. The earliest devices must have consisted of ordinary hose with an improvised nozzle (sometimes merely a tapering wooden box) attached to it.[14] In any case the method had a remarkable growth until conflict with California farming interests resulted in legislation virtually prohibiting the practice.[15] During the period of its greatest de-

---

[11] "Mines and Quarries, 1902," p. 460.

[12] Crane, *op. cit.*, p. 349.

[13] "Mines and Quarries, 1902," pp. 461-62.

[14] Crane, *op. cit.*, p. 344.

[15] The tailings from these operations were discharged into streams which, in turn, deposited them along their course, causing damage to adjacent farm lands ("Mines and Quarries, 1902," p. 572).

velopment (from about 1853 to 1875) huge sums of money are believed to have been invested in hydraulic equipment, and in the construction of ditches and canals for carrying water to centers of mining activity.[16] The chief result lay in the province of industrial organization with a shift from individual enterprise to operations of large companies, which alone were able to carry through the work on a sufficiently broad scale.[17] Placering did not die with the restrictions on hydraulic mining but developed in the direction of dredging—a technique utilized to tap deep-lying auriferous gravels. However, this is a development which began at about the turn of the century [18] and it was, at that time, no longer unique as a manifestation of large scale enterprise.

Of far greater significance in the evolution of mining technology was the development of a silver mining industry with the discovery of the fabulous Comstock lode near Virginia City, Nevada, in 1859. In broad terms it may be said that silver mining (beginning at Comstock) ended the poor man's day in mining and ushered in the era of the financier and the engineer.[19] Crude hand devices and common sense, so effective in the past, were now unable to cope with the depth and complexity of the vast silver workings, which required the adoption of methods hitherto unfamiliar in this country. Of these the most important was probably the system of square-set timbering, whereby timbers in rectangular sets replaced the ore as it was removed, so that the spaces between the timbers could be filled with waste rock to increase the strength of the support.[20] This method permitted the exploitation of large ore bodies with weak walls, which could not be handled under the older system of open stopes, i.e., stopes with only occasional artificial supports, if any.[21] Because it made possible the development of other large ore bodies, including the great copper

[16] Crane, op. cit., pp. 345, 347.

[17] Ibid., p. 347.

[18] "Mines and Quarries, 1902," p. 573.

[19] A succinct expression of the financial requirements of silver mining is found in an old Mexican adage, "It takes a gold mine to open a silver mine."

[20] E. D. Gardner, C. H. Johnson and B. S. Butler, "Copper Mining in North America," Bulletin 405 (U. S. Bureau of Mines, 1938), pp. 114-15. In reviewing the present manuscript, Professor Read observed that square-set mining was the first important application of the principles of engineering directly to mining, as contrasted with the adaptation to underground use of techniques originally developed elsewhere.

[21] C. F. Jackson and J. H. Hedges, "Metal Mining Practice," Bulletin 419 (U. S. Bureau of Mines, 1939), pp. 224-27. A stope is merely a room in which ore is mined.

lodes at Butte, Montana,[22] square-set timbering occupies an honored position in the development of the art of mining.[23] It still occupies an important place in those underground metal mines in which the newer shrinkage and caving methods (discussed below) cannot be employed.

Technology was forced, almost for the first time in this country, to adjust itself to new and unfamiliar geological conditions. Not only was the finest European machinery introduced, but mechanical and other innovations made Comstock for a time the "mining school of the world." [24] It may almost be said that the practicability of deep metal mining was demonstrated for the first time on the Comstock lode.

The further development of underground metal mining hinged on a number of factors which were coming into operation in the latter half of the nineteenth century. One was the constant expansion of the railroad system, now beginning to reach into regions hitherto virtually inaccessible. In many regions known to be rich in minerals, it was not feasible to undertake organized exploitation until the coming of the railroad lowered both the cost of materials needed for mining and the cost of marketing the mineral obtained. The influence of this factor is nowhere more clearly seen than in the opening of the western districts producing argentiferous lead ores. The existence of these deposits had been known to those who had earlier worked the same districts for placer gold, but large scale exploitation awaited the development of the railroads.[25] The expansion of the railroad network was bound up with the growth of the nation and the expanding industrialism which marked the post-Civil War period in American history. And it was the new industrialism, in turn, which created the demand for mineral raw materials. The need for metals could no longer be met by skimming the rich surface layer from mineral deposits. Mining had to be carried to greater and greater depths, and fortunately the initial step in this direction had already been taken.

[22] Robert M. LaFollette (ed.), *The Making of America*, Vol. 6 (Morris, Chicago, 1906), p. 27.

[23] Gardner, Johnson and Butler, *op. cit.*, p. 115.

[24] Crane, *op. cit.*, p. 350; see also LaFollette, *op. cit.*, p. 27.

[25] F. G. Tryon and Margaret H. Schoenfeld, "Mineral and Power Resources" in *Recent Social Trends* (McGraw-Hill, 1933), Vol. I, p. 66; also "Mines and Quarries, 1902," p. 460.

## MINING METHODS BEFORE 1899: COAL

Up to this point the discussion has been confined to the mining of metallic ores. We undertake a separate treatment of coal mining because the chronology of its technological development differs from that of metal mining. The extraction of anthracite in Pennsylvania reached a higher stage of technical efficiency during the first half of the nineteenth century than did other forms of mining. During the latter half of the century, however, the technology of metal mining advanced at so rapid a rate that it overtook coal mining, and at some point about midway in this period the two lines of development tended to converge. Thereafter metal mining technology led the field, but a pattern of development more or less common to both coal and metals can be traced.

An account of early nineteenth century coal mining would, in its significant aspects, read remarkably like the story of metal mining some decades later. Primitive tools, unskilled workmen, and lack of organized exploitation are as prominent here as they were in metal mining.[26] This resemblance is not surprising when we consider that the underlying factors were similar: in both cases the combination of easily accessible deposits and comparatively restricted demand explain the backward state of production techniques. But the point at which these circumstances ceased to apply was reached earlier in anthracite coal than in metals. Moreover, among the immigrants to this country there were many who were familiar with European coal mining techniques. As a result the utilization of more advanced methods emerged at an earlier date in coal than in metal mining.

Steam power was first employed in the mining of American anthracite as early as 1836. In that year a mine was sunk below the water level, a venture which depended on mechanized pumping.[27] Prior to that time all mines had been worked by tunneling from the water level upward,[28] but new deposits which lent themselves

---

[26] Peter Roberts, *The Anthracite Coal Industry* (Macmillan, 1901), p. 17.

[27] Eli Bowen, *Coal and the Coal Trade* (Peterson, Philadelphia, 1862), p. 27. Apparently the mining of bituminous coal continued for some time longer without benefit of steam powered pumps.

[28] Roberts, *op. cit.*, p. 18.

to natural drainage were becoming rarer.[29] The number of mines sunk below water level increased steadily; by about 1850 they added up to a fairly large segment of the anthracite industry—a segment in which steam power was essential to operations.[30] At about that time, too, the breaker was first used to prepare anthracite for the market, and steam power motivated the rolls and screens.[31]

Mechanical progress was accompanied by changes in the organization of the anthracite industry. The fields were orginally divided into small tracts of land that were operated successfully so long as simple production techniques were adequate. But as operations became more difficult and as expensive equipment became necessary, many small operators were unable to continue independently. Consolidation of small holdings into the hands of large companies soon began to spread, yet as late as the 1860's there existed no company able to organize production on a scale sufficiently large to utilize the most advanced production techniques of the day. This is clear from the writings of Eli Bowen, who argued that the universal use of slopes rather than perpendicular shafts for deep anthracite mining was retarding the development of the industry. The suggested remedy was to "organize companies with large capital, to sink enormously deep and permanent shafts." [32]

While anthracite production techniques moved ahead, bituminous coal remained for some time at a comparatively low technological level.[33] Resource conditions in bituminous fields were such that coal was easily worked by methods familiar in Europe.[34]

---

[29] However, it is noteworthy that the continued availability, even today, of small shallow deposits in the anthracite fields of Southern Pennsylvania has been a factor facilitating bootlegging operations (Commonwealth of Pennsylvania, *Report of the Anthracite Coal Industry Commission,* Harrisburg, 1938, p. 48). See also Chapter 9 below.

[30] Bowen, *op. cit.,* p. 27.

[31] Dever C. Ashmead, "How Greater Depth and Reduced Thickness of Coal Have Intensified Lackawanna Mine Problems," *Coal Age,* Vol. 23, pp. 324-25 (February 22, 1923). The preparation of coal for the market is discussed below in Chapter 7.

[32] Bowen, *op. cit.,* p. 31.

[33] However, the comparative backwardness of the bituminous industry was later to disappear. For when coal cutting machines and other mechanical devices were introduced into the bituminous fields, they were found unsuitable for mining anthracite. See below, Chapter 6, p. 124; and Chapter 8, Table 15.

[34] Shallow deposits and opportunities for natural drainage in late nineteenth century bituminous coal mining appear to have been peculiar to this country. Thus Jevons writes of Britain: "We have no extensive seams of coal now which can compare with those above described [i.e. in the United States] . . . four or five centuries

Technological adjustment to a changed geological environment, as in anthracite and metal mining, was not forced upon the industry until later in the century.[35] When the problems of deep development did arise, the result was mechanization of auxiliary functions such as pumping and ventilation. Thus by the end of the nineteenth century bituminous coal, anthracite and metal mining had developed a technology which—despite individual variations—had certain distinguishing features common to all three industries. We may now turn to a consideration of the characteristics of late nineteenth century mining.

## METAL MINING TECHNOLOGY IN 1899

The years following the inauguration of deep mining were marked by the discovery and exploitation of new mineral deposits, in many of which problems of deep development were encountered for the first time. By the opening of our period production of minerals came largely from these new underground mines.[36] Methods of shaft sinking, underground tunneling, and roof support had reached a high level of efficiency. Mechanical power, commonly steam, was in use for the vital auxiliary functions of hoisting, pumping and ventilation.

By now, too, the miner had developed into a highly skilled craftsman with a clearly defined function. The prodigality with which his predecessor had exploited rich deposits was, of neces-

---

ago it is supposed there were seams on the banks of the Tyne, and at Whitehaven, which could be worked by natural drainage. . . . But shallow coal has necessarily almost disappeared in England" (W. Stanley Jevons, *The Coal Question,* ed. by A. W. Flux, Macmillan, London, 1906, p. 342). The continued existence of shallow seams in this country must be credited partly to a comparatively greater initial abundance of such seams in relation to early rates of fuel consumption. It may also have been due in part to the use of wood for firing locomotives and of charcoal for smelting iron until a much later date than was possible in England, whose forests had all but disappeared by the end of the seventeenth century. It is worth noting, too, that prior to 1860 there was still a large demand by blacksmiths and other small scale fabricators for charcoal iron: they appear to have preferred this product because of the ease with which it could be fashioned for a wide variety of different uses. See Louis C. Hunter, "Influence of the Market upon Technique in the Iron Industry in Western Pennsylvania up to 1860," *Journal of Economic and Business History,* Vol. I, No. 2 (1929), pp. 241-81.

[35] Indeed, some would say that changing geological conditions have been less important in forcing mechanization than have rising wage rates.

[36] The leading exception was the large scale open cut exploitation of the Mesabi iron ore range, on which operations had begun in 1892. This operation introduced mechanical methods which did not become general until after 1899. The mechanization of large scale open cut mining is discussed below in Chapter 6.

sity, replaced by great care in working the mineralized area, for
the miner was charged with the responsibility of extracting as
much of the mineral with as little loss in waste as possible. In addition, the job of timbering for support and of maintaining the
working face was his. In spite of the larger scale on which mining
was now conducted, the actual separation of the mineral from
the ground was still predominantly a hand operation. This was
true in spite of the striking mechanical advances which had been
made in the auxiliary functions of mining. In metal mining, for
example, by 1899 compressed air drills were used for tunneling
to gain access to the ore, but hand drilling and hand picking were
still needed for mining the ore itself. And although dynamite had
replaced black powder, and thereby increased the efficiency and
safety of blasting, it was still utilized sparingly in mining operations. Commonly its use was confined to breaking the rock in approaching the ore body; often in winning the ore itself blasting
was entirely forbidden.[37]

This preference for methods apparently less efficient than
others that were readily available was the direct result of the
rationale of mining technology of that period. A miner using
hand tools will account for a much smaller tonnage per shift than
he would if he were using mechanized tools, but he can produce a
higher grade of product because he can exercise care in selection
and avoid waste. Whether the mine operator will choose tonnage
or quality is basically an economic decision, but this decision itself is shaped by external factors. On the one hand are geological
conditions, such as the richness of the ore. When a high grade
ore body is worked, the mine may be unable to afford such
mineral losses as would accrue, for example, through the introduction of mechanical breaking. As the ore declines in grade,
however, such losses may be counterbalanced by the increased
tonnage made possible through mechanization, coupled with subsequent concentration. The basic decision rests upon technological factors which determine the minimum grade of material that
can be sold or utilized in further processing. If a metallic ore, for
instance, is to go directly from the mine to the smelter, without
intermediate processing, the grade of ore is of great importance:

[37] C. E. Julihn, "Copper: An Example of Advancing Technology and the Utilization of Low Grade Ores," in *Mineral Economics,* ed. by F. G. Tryon and E. C. Eckel
(McGraw-Hill, 1932), pp. 127-28.

for smelting involves difficult and expensive pyrometallurgical processes which are very sensitive to the amount and character of the waste in which the metal is embedded. If, on the other hand, waste can be eliminated before shipment to the smelter, and particularly if the devices for this purpose are designed to operate cheaply and on a large scale, then a much lower grade of ore may profitably be mined. In the latter case an additional step in the production process will have been interposed between mining proper and smelting—a step which takes over a function previously performed by the miner himself. This is called beneficiating, and will be discussed below (Chapter 7).

Until close to the very end of the nineteenth century the grade of metallic ores worked was still high and the efficiency of bulk processes of mineral enrichment or beneficiation was low—circumstances which account for the popularity of the highly selective methods of hand mining already described. The first deviations from this type of mining, as on the Mesabi iron ore range, occurred late in the century. They may be considered to have ushered in the modern era of mineral exploitation. By 1899 the impact of these changes was beginning to be felt, but their full development belongs to the subsequent period.

## THE DEVELOPMENT OF NONSELECTIVE METAL MINING

The changes we associate with the transition to modern methods of metal mining first appeared in the extraction of copper ores. The emergence of modern methods of bulk or nonselective mining (as opposed to the older, selective methods) did not involve a distinct act of invention, but occurred rather gradually. In many mines the "pay streak," i.e. the richer part of the deposit from which production had so far been derived, approached exhaustion, or at least reached the stage where it alone was not sufficient for full utilization of the mine and mill facilities. Lower grades of ore were available, and their production involved only the additional cost of breaking, loading and transportation; the overhead costs associated with the auxiliary functions of pumping, hoisting and ventilation could, moreover, be spread over a larger production. Since the ores were of low grade they could be mined with less care, so that drilling and heavy blasting of the ore—which were avoided in the pay streak—could safely be applied. The results achieved were sufficient proof of the workability of low grade ores when mechanized methods were used. In some cases tonnage of ore per man-shift under nonselective techniques equaled the tonnage per man-week achieved with selective methods. Thereafter nonselective mining spread rapidly in underground metal mines fully a decade before it made its spectacular debut on the surface in open cut copper mining.[38]

The first step in the abandonment of selective mining consisted of the mechanization of functions which it had previously been thought necessary to perform by hand.[39] Thus breaking might profitably be mechanized if the grade of ore were low. But the constantly increasing use of nonselective methods at the turn of the century was associated also with the development of new techniques for concentrating metallic ores.[40] These new techniques contributed to the decline in the importance of selective methods at underground nonferrous metal mines, and made low grade surface development possible.[41] The foundation of modern methods of mining copper, for example, rests upon mechanization, but their essence lies in the integration of mining with ore dressing. When mining engineers first realized that the ability to concentrate the mineral product rapidly and efficiently had altered the relative advantages of different mining methods, and when they turned to the task of finding that combination of mining method and beneficiating technique which would insure the most effective utilization of a given mineral deposit, then modern mining began to take shape.

It is not easy to select a particular event in the history of mining as the turning point in this respect. We can, however, notice certain crucial steps, perhaps the plainest of which was the decision to exploit the steam shovel for the mining of Mesabi iron ore. Here was a clear case where the application of a mining method, then distinctly novel, was determined by extensive planning and exploration prior to the opening of the field. It was found that the ore body was particularly well adapted to open cut

[38] See Julihn, *op. cit.*, pp. 128-30.

[39] A more systematic treatment of the mechanization of the mining process will be found in Chapter 6 below.

[40] These are described in Chapter 7 below.

[41] On the other hand, the mass mining of iron ore at first owed little to processing techniques, but resulted rather from the peculiar geology of the Mesabi range.

exploitation, and thus began a type of mining which has since shown considerable adaptability and growth.

This kind of mining reached its full development in the first open cut copper mine at Bingham, Utah, where still another basic step was taken. The men who developed the Utah property were faced with a situation which differed from that on the Mesabi range in one very significant respect. Steam shovel mining alone was not the key to the development of the ore body. What was essential, in addition, was a concentrating technique able to take the steam shovel product—which was of exceedingly low grade—and convert it into a higher grade material which could be smelted. In other words, the ore body could be worked only by the combination of low cost mining and a bulk beneficiating process able to extract metal from a relatively large proportion of rock. In open cut copper mining there now developed a completely articulated technology of mining and beneficiating. The function of producing a pure or clean mineral product was completely separated from the function of breaking and extracting the ore. Bulk processes were utilized for both operations, and, as a result, overall efficiency was increased.

From our present perspective, nonselective mining appears to have been the mining industry's version of the process of specialization of functions which was occurring simultaneously in other industries. Ever since the introduction of open cut copper mining, nonselective mining methods have come to dominate the American mineral industry. Although metal mining—particularly copper—has produced the most complete expression of nonselective technique, its use is by no means confined to this portion of the mineral industry. Coal mining has developed in the same direction;[42] even the minor nonmetallic industries have not remained unaffected.[43] The latter group has been characterized in recent years by "wider adoption of bulk mining instead of highly selective mining, now that means have been found to remove admixed impurities mechanically." [44] Nevertheless the applica-

[42] Willard E. Hotchkiss and others, *Bituminous-Coal Mining* (National Research Project, Philadelphia, 1939), p. 11.

[43] Oliver C. Ralston, "Flotation and Agglomerate Concentration of Nonmetallic Minerals," U. S. Bureau of Mines, Report of Investigations, No. 3397 (May 1938), p. 2.

[44] Paul M. Tyler and Oliver Bowles, "Nonmetallic Mineral Industries in 1939," Information Circular 7106 (U. S. Bureau of Mines, 1940), p. 3.

tion of such techniques has not been universal. In the quick-silver industry, for instance, mass mining is notably absent.[45]

The fashion in which nonselective techniques manifest themselves in individual mines is, in good part, determined by resource conditions. When these lend themselves to open cut exploitation, that method is utilized. But resource conditions do not remain constant; and, with the exhaustion of ore bodies lying near the surface, the recent trend toward this particular method may be reversed, and a return to underground mining occur.[46] This does not mean an end of mass mining, for similar techniques are already widely used in underground exploitation.

The traditional methods of underground metal mining—cut-and-fill, and stoping with much square-set timbering—were developed in an age of hand shovel loading and the selective mining of rich ores. Still used in many mines where conditions do not permit of mass exploitation, these older techniques have given way increasingly to methods which employ shrinkage and caving. These methods, some of which break and load the ore by gravity, are nonselective in character. When they are used serious efforts to differentiate grades of ore, or to separate mineral from waste, within the mine itself are abandoned, and these functions are transferred to milling equipment on the surface.

Perhaps the three most characteristic examples of these newer methods of underground metal mining are shrinkage stoping, sub-level caving and block caving.[47] The choice of one or another of these, or of a variant or combination of them, is determined by the nature of the ore body. We have space here only to notice their most essential features. Shrinkage stoping (Chart 33) involves the least departure from traditional practice, for the ore

[45] C. N. Schuette, "Quicksilver," *Bulletin 335* (U. S. Bureau of Mines, 1931), p. 26. By the standards of other types of metal mining, mercury ores are lean, but their large scale exploitation by mechanical methods has not so far proved feasible.

[46] See National Resources Committee, *Technological Trends and National Policy* (1937), pp. 162-63. A case in point is the United Verde mine in Arizona where surface deposits are practically exhausted but large amounts of copper remain to be mined by underground methods.

[47] The description which follows is largely based upon Robert Peele and John A. Church, *Mining Engineers' Handbook* (3rd ed., John Wiley, 1941); Robert S. Lewis, *Elements of Mining* (2nd ed., John Wiley, 1941), Chapter IX; A. B. Parsons, *The Porphyry Coppers* (American Institute of Mining and Metallurgical Engineers, 1933), Chapter XIX; and Y. S. Leong and others, *Copper Mining* (National Research Project, Philadelphia, 1940), Chapter IV. For a lucid and concise account of these and other methods, see Professor Lewis' article on "Mining, Metalliferous" in the *Encyclopaedia Britannica*, 14th ed.

Chart 33
METAL MINING METHODS: SHRINKAGE STOPING
Sectional Diagram

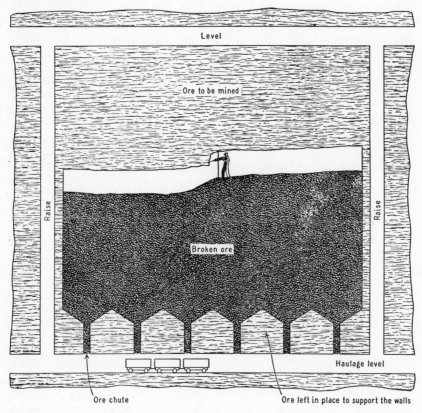

For source and notes see Appendix E

continues to be broken by drilling and blasting. Work proceeds upward as the miner stands on a floor composed of broken ore. The latter, since it occupies more space than the uncut mineral, must continually be drawn off through chutes to waiting cars below. As each section is mined out the remaining ore is drawn off. The method can be employed only where the walls are strong; its chief advantage over earlier practice is the use of gravity loading. Its nonselective character is shown by the fact that virtually the whole of the ore is removed, and no opportunity is given to the miner to prevent waste as well as ore from reaching the mine cars.

In sublevel caving (Chart 34) a number of sublevels are driven into the ore body at increasing vertical distances above the haulage level, and the ore remaining between the levels is mined from the top downward by caving. In this method, which is characteristic of underground iron mining in the Lake Superior region, gravity is used to break that part of the ore which is caved. Loading again takes place through a chute, but before this can occur

Chart 34
METAL MINING METHODS: SUBLEVEL CAVING
Sectional Diagram

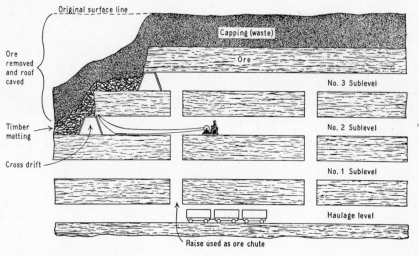

For source and notes see Appendix E

the ore must be trammed or scraped along the sublevel to the top of the chute. Sublevel caving is a development of a method known as top slicing, originally introduced in iron mining. In top slicing only the highest sublevel shown in Chart 34 is driven, and this is done immediately below the capping: mining proceeds downward, and the capping is allowed to cave.

The most advanced of the several techniques is block caving (Chart 35) in which the ore is broken and loaded almost entirely by gravity. A large mass of ore, perhaps 300 feet in height, is undercut except for supporting pillars. The latter are blasted away, so that the whole body of ore and overlying rock cave a short distance, in the course of which the ore is broken. As the ore is drawn off into mine cars through the chutes, the overlying rock

Chart 35

METAL MINING METHODS: BLOCK CAVING

Sectional Diagrams

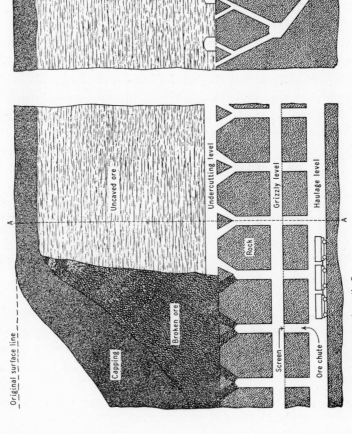

Original surface line

Capping

Uncaved ore

Broken ore

Rock

Undercutting level

Grizzly level

Haulage level

Screen

Ore chute

Capping

Uncaved ore

Rock

Section on A—A

For source and notes see Appendix E

continues to cave, until all the ore has been removed. Block caving has found its widest application in underground copper mining, and has been said to represent "probably the most important advance in underground copper mining methods since the invention of square-setting." [48] Originally introduced in Utah in 1906 as a development of sublevel caving, block caving requires soft or fractured ores for success, but it can be used with ores of grade so low that other gravity methods will not pay. It resembles open cut mining in that all material in the mineralized area is removed, waste as well as metallic ore.[49]

It is clear that the two main characteristics of the transition to nonselective mining—whether underground or open pit—have been, first, a decline in the grade of ore mined, and second, an elaboration of techniques of ore concentration. Thus we have already seen that nonselective mining was originally fostered by the decline in the grade of material mined. It was the industry's good fortune to be able to make a virtue of necessity. For the new techniques became so efficient that it is now often worth while deliberately to sacrifice quality for quantity in the mining process, and to achieve the former later, during concentration. The absence of new discoveries has no doubt contributed to the decline in the grade, for example, of copper ore during the past forty years. It has been estimated that as much as one half of the present copper production of the United States comes from deposits that were known in 1900 but were not then worked because of their low metal content.[50] This is, of course, an extreme illustration, but undoubtedly the same type of change (although less in magnitude) has characterized other mineral industries.[51] Where nonselective, i.e. large scale, operations are feasible, and the material mined can readily be concentrated, the grade of the ore has ceased—within wide limits—to exert upon costs the dominant in-

[48] Gardner, Johnson and Butler, *op. cit.*, p. 115.

[49] Tryon and Schoenfeld, *op. cit.*, p. 68.

[50] Andrew V. Corry and O. E. Kiessling, *Grade of Ore* (National Research Project, Philadelphia, 1939), p. 84.

[51] In the words of Professor Bucky of the Columbia University School of Mines: "Within the realm of our experience it is evident that the finding of ore bodies is being subordinated to economic extraction . . . improved practices [have] continually made available the ore bodies which at one time were not economic" (*Engineering and Mining Journal*, August 1941, p. 113). Further specific instances of the utilization of lower grade material, more or less directly attributable to advances in ore dressing techniques, are cited in Chapter 7.

fluence it formerly exercised. Where operations lend themselves
to mass exploitation, it may happen that low grade deposits can
be worked more cheaply than higher grade deposits which cannot
be thus exploited.[52]

It has been remarked, indeed, with reference to the newer techniques of large scale mining, that "The prospector stands aside;
the engineer steps forward." [53] It might also be noted, and with
almost equal validity, that the skilled miner stepped aside when
the engineer stepped forward. For when the engineer was called
upon to plan the large scale exploitation of minerals, the traditional technology based on the resourcefulness of the highly
skilled individual miner began to fall apart. No longer does the
success of the mining enterprise depend on the expertness with
which the miner breaks the mineral and separates it from the
waste; it is now a question of how well the engineer has designed
mining and beneficiating operations on the basis of his geological
data, and how carefully he has determined the geological structure and chemical nature of the ore deposits prior to the working out of suitable techniques.[54] This is patently true in open
cut workings and of underground mines where caving methods are
employed: here design is of the greatest importance. It is true also,
if sometimes in lesser degree, of all mechanized mining, where
maximum efficiency may depend on a reorientation of mining
method to the facts of mechanization. Meanwhile, the skilled crafts-

[52] This point emerges very clearly in an exchange between Cornelius Kelley,
president of the Anaconda Copper Company, and the chairman of the Temporary
National Economic Committee (*Hearings*, Part 25, Washington, 1940, p. 13203):

> Chairman: Of course it is common knowledge in mining regions that ore varies
> in content, that you have high-grade ore and low-grade ore, that ordi-
> narily the high-grade ore may be produced at a low cost, and the low-
> grade ore is produced at a higher cost. That is true, is it not?
> Mr. Kelley: No, sir.
> Chairman: It is not? What is the fact?
> Mr. Kelley: The fact is that the cheapest ore in the world is produced from
> the lower-grade ores where the character of the operation is such that it
> lends itself to great volume and mechanization. Those factors more than
> overcome a much higher grade of ore that has to be mined from a depth,
> transported underground and hoisted to the surface. Generally speaking,
> Senator, the lowest-cost copper is being produced from the lowest-grade
> ore.

[53] T. A. Rickard, "The Utah Copper Enterprise" (San Francisco, 1919), p. 9 (re-
printed from *Mining and Scientific Press*, Vol. 117, December 28, 1918, p. 848).

[54] Walter H. Voskuil, *Minerals in Modern Industry* (John Wiley, 1930), p. 7. It is
in exploratory drilling that churn drills, which allow the nature of the deposit to
be determined, have been of such enormous importance.

man has given place to the machine tender. Here, too, the position of the skilled worker has been subject to the same influences that have been operative in other industries.[55]

[55] See Y. S. Leong and others, *Copper Mining* (National Research Project, Phila-delphia, 1940), pp. 29-31. Even in coal mining, where craft traditions have survived best, similar tendencies have been at work: see Carter Goodrich, *The Miner's Free-dom*, pp. 108-10.

# Chapter 6

# The Mechanization of the Mining Process

As WITH OTHER less spectacular changes in the technique of extraction, the transition from selective to nonselective methods has involved a high degree of mechanization, both in the actual operation of winning the ore and in its subsequent processing. Although it has influenced other types of mining at numerous points, nonselective exploitation is primarily a characteristic of the metal mining industries—iron ore, copper, lead and zinc, and mixed metal mining. But mechanization is by no means confined to these industries. Even where—as in coal mining—resource conditions have not permitted a spectacular departure from older mining methods, mechanization has made striking advances. In many such mines the entire process, from drilling and blasting to loading and hauling, has been more or less completely mechanized. Such mechanization may be said to have produced a qualitative change in mining methods. When just one or two operations are mechanized, production is speeded but the method as a whole may remain essentially unchanged. As mechanization spreads, the integration of different processes, and the adjustment of the tempo of one to that of another, become more and more pressing, until eventually the whole interior of the mine may have to be redesigned.[1] In the case of many coal mines, when the last link in the chain of underground mechanization was forged with the introduction of mechanical loaders, a balanced cycle of operations became essential and many modifications of the traditional room-and-pillar method of mining were needed. In addition, the surface preparation plant assumed an increasingly important role, for once coal is loaded mechanically it can no longer be cleaned

[1] Albert L. Toenges, "Mining" in A. C. Fieldner and W. E. Rice, "Research and Progress in the Production and Use of Coal," Technical Paper No. 4 (National Resources Planning Board, 1941), p. 14. We shall find later that the apparent lag in bituminous and anthracite coal technology is in part attributable to the difficulty of redesigning these mines to accommodate new mechanical devices. This has been an outstanding cause of delay in the introduction of mechanical loading in particular. See below, pp. 124-29, and Chapters 8 and 9.

by the individual miner at the coal face. Changes of this kind in coal mining are less dramatic than those which accompanied the mechanization of copper and iron mines, but they are still considerable.

To the extent that mechanization involves a reorganization of mining methods, the mining industry alone may be credited with a substantial portion of its technological advance. We must not forget, however, that in the process of mechanization the mineral industry has been aided by technical advances achieved in other industries. Many of the early tools used in underground and open cut mining were originally devised for driving railroad tunnels,[2] and always the development of mining machinery has been dependent upon the "quality of construction materials such as alloy steels . . . and upon advances in the electrical and mechanical arts." [3] It is difficult, too, to overestimate the true importance of the development of electrically powered equipment, for without electricity "it would have been economically unfeasible, if not physically impossible, to mechanize many functions previously performed underground by hand labor or with animals" because of the difficulty of transmitting power by means of shafts, gears or belts to cramped underground workings.[4]

We must now examine in greater detail the forms mechanization has taken, both where nonselective methods are used and where resource conditions have not permitted their adoption. To do this it will be convenient first to consider underground mines, and thereafter to discuss open pit operations.

## UNDERGROUND MINING

There are three major steps in the process of mining ore underground. They are: (1) breaking the ore; (2) loading the broken ore; and (3) transporting the ore from the working face to the surface. It is most convenient to sketch technological change in underground mining in terms of these three steps in the mining process, for aside from changes in mining method proper, technological improvements have consisted mainly of the mechaniza-

[2] James H. Collins, "Mining Copper and the Nobler Metals," in Waldemar Kaempffert (ed.), *A Popular History of American Invention* (Scribner's, 1924), Vol. II, p. 65.

[3] Toenges, *op. cit.*, p. 6.

[4] Nicholas Yaworski and others, *Iron Mining* (National Research Project, Philadelphia, 1940), p. 24.

tion of these functions. We shall discuss the successive steps in the process of winning the ore, and shall finally devote a few paragraphs to parallel changes in such auxiliary functions as drainage and ventilation.

## Breaking the Mineral

Two distinct operations are usually required to break metallic ore: the drilling of holes for the insertion of explosives and the detonation of the explosives. In bituminous coal mining, additionally, the seam is undercut; this is to make the coal break into large pieces when the shot is fired, and cause it to fall forward so that it may conveniently be loaded. In the breaking down of bituminous coal seams, cutting occupies a position that corresponds in importance with drilling in metal mining. Actually, drilling is of secondary significance for such soft materials as are encountered in coal mines;[5] cutting, on the other hand, occurs only in the mining of coal.

By 1899, the year when our statistical series begin, mechanized drilling had already been introduced in metal mining. The first mechanical drill, a cumbersome device powered by steam, had been utilized some thirty odd years before to drive the Hoosac railroad tunnel in Massachusetts. A similar drill was adopted by Colorado metal miners before the completion of the tunnel (1875) and it had found its way into Lake Superior copper mining by 1876.[6]

These early drills were of the so-called piston variety. The drill steel was attached to a piston actuated back and forth within a cylinder, and compressed air was the usual source of power. The drill steel was not only driven back and forth, but was also rotated in the process. Before the device was perfected drilling was, of necessity, a difficult hand operation. Hand drilling required individuals of great brawn and considerable skill. In copper, at any rate, it was regarded as "an art that took years to learn."[7] It is not surprising, therefore, that the machine drill began to replace hand methods in copper quite early. In iron mining, on the other hand, machine drilling of soft ores was postponed until

[5] Willard E. Hotchkiss and others, *Bituminous-Coal Mining* (National Research Project, Philadelphia, 1939), p. 20.

[6] Y. S. Leong and others, *Copper Mining* (National Research Project, Philadelphia, 1940), p. 106.

[7] *Ibid.*, p. 110.

well into the twentieth century, although hard ores were machine drilled as early as the 1880's.[8] How far mechanical drilling
had spread in the metal mining industries at the turn of the century it is difficult to say, although the frequent mention of mechanical drills in such a contemporary account as the 1902 Census
report suggests that their use was not uncommon, especially for
copper, gold and silver.[9] In that volume data relating to mines
producing those three metals indicate that almost 75 percent of
the total quantity of gold and silver ore mined underground and
more than 85 percent of the copper ore came from mines using
power drills.[10]

The cutting of coal was characterized by advances similar to
those in drilling. For the greater part of the nineteenth century
coal cutting had been a hand task. Since the cut was usually made
under the coal seam, the miner was forced to lie on his side while
performing the operation. In this position, working with a pick,
he formed beneath the coal seam a wedge-shaped opening which
extended for two or three feet and tapered from a foot or more
at the front to several inches at the back. It may well be imagined
that the undercutting of coal was one of the most back-breaking
and time-consuming tasks the underground coal miner had to perform. Not until the cutting machine replaced the miner's pick—
a development which dates from about 1880 when mechanical
cutters were introduced—was this operation made less onerous.[11]
As we might expect, the first cutting machines simulated the
hand pick operations and relied on percussive action. This type
of machine was the dominant mechanized cutter for the remainder of the century; in 1899 it accounted for 22.7 percent
of the underground tonnage.[12] Since then it has been superseded
by various types of continuous chain instruments.

[8] Yaworski and others, *Iron Mining*, p. 140.
[9] U. S. Bureau of the Census, *Special Reports*, "Mines and Quarries, 1902," *pas-sim.*
[10] *Ibid.*, pp. 529-30, 476-78. The data on copper do not include Michigan, which
reported more than two thirds of all the horsepower used in copper mining and
accounted for 53.0 percent of the tonnage mined. It seems altogether likely that
the inclusion of Michigan would have resulted in a still higher percentage.
[11] This development was confined to the bituminous fields. See *Report of the Industrial Commission*, Vol. XII (Washington, 1901), pp. 54, 150, 177, 651. To this day
anthracite is still cut by hand.
[12] This paragraph and other references to machine cutting are based largely on
Hotchkiss and others, *Bituminous-Coal Mining*, Vol. I, pp. 13-19. For data on the
percentage of total bituminous coal production cut by machine, see below, Chapter
8, Table 15.

Improvements in breaking metallic ores in recent decades have followed two directions: first, faster and more efficient drilling, and second, greater reliance upon the force of gravity. The latter is epitomized in such a practice as block caving, but it has many less dramatic applications as well. Let us first consider advances in mechanized drilling.

The switch from the piston-type to the hammer-type drill early in this century marks the chief advance in drill models. In the hammer-type drill the piston is not attached to the drill steel, but instead delivers a rapid succession of light blows, with the bit remaining permanently in the hole. This type of drill was found to possess many advantages over the older piston type. It was able to drill "up" holes, which had been very difficult with the piston drill. In addition, different models of the drill could be constructed to suit varying conditions encountered in specific operations. Finally, hollow drill steel, through which a mixture of air and water could be forced in order to keep the hole clean, could now be utilized.[13]

The hammer drill was developed in the 1890's and introduced into copper mining about 1909. Since then it has gained ascendancy in metal mining generally, and the older types of hand and piston drills are by now obsolete.[14] With the years its design has been improved, new drill steels have been developed and the mobility and speed of the drill have been increased. A recent modification has been the use of detachable steel bits. Now the miner can be supplied with enough detachable bits for a day's work, so that sharpened drills need no longer be distributed.[15]

For the most part, modern drills are still powered by compressed air. Many attempts have been made to replace air by electricity,[16] but they have usually been unsuccessful because of the difficulty of converting the rotary motion of the electric motor to the reciprocating action essential in drilling any hard material.[17] Only where auger drills are used, as in the working of such

[13] Leong and others, *Copper Mining*, p. 109. See also C. W. Nicolson, "Compressed Air Drilling" in *Engineering and Mining Journal*, August 1941, p. 104. The reciprocating drill scoured the hole by its own movement, but water was found still more efficient for this purpose.

[14] Leong and others, *Copper Mining*, p. 109; Yaworski and others, *Iron Mining*, p. 140.

[15] Leong and others, *Copper Mining*, p. 112.

[16] Nicolson, *op. cit.*, p. 104.

[17] C. E. Nighman and O. E. Kiessling, *Rock Drilling* (National Research Project, Philadelphia, 1940), p. 38.

relatively soft materials as coal and limestone, has the electric
motor been widely utilized. In these drills the spiral drill steel is
attached to a rotating rod which can be actuated by an electric
motor.[18] It should be noted in connection with auger drilling in
coal that its expanded use in the period since about 1925 is directly attributable to the extension of mechanical loading, which
made necessary a balanced cycle of mining operations.[19]

Drilling advances alone cannot be credited with the entire improvement in breaking performance in underground mines.
Breaking efficiency is strongly influenced also by the nature of the
blasting agents utilized, and the period ushered in by the advent of mechanical drilling has, naturally enough, been marked
by progress in the manufacture and use of explosives.[20] The introduction of dynamite in copper mining occurred at almost the
same time as the adoption of mechanical drilling.[21] As the use of
the mechanical drill spread in metal mining, dynamite tended to
replace such explosives as black powder and nitroglycerine which
were less efficient and more hazardous to use.[22] In coal mining, on
the other hand, the continued resort to hand drilling until well
into the present century was matched by the retention of black
powder for blasting; prior to 1909 black blasting powder was
virtually the only explosive for blasting coal.[23] As in drilling, the
advances of the present century in blasting have consisted mainly
of a large number of small changes that have resulted in a variety
of explosives which yield any desired type of fragmentation and
are readily adapted to specific conditions.[24] However, progress in
drilling and blasting constitutes only one way of improving the
efficiency of breaking, and the least dramatic. Let us turn, therefore, to consider the mining methods that dispense with drilling
and blasting almost entirely.

In the preceding chapter we referred briefly to caving methods

[18] *Ibid.,* p. 35. Electric drills were already known in coal mining in 1899 (*Report
of the Industrial Commission,* Vol. XII, pp. 55, 177).

[19] Hotchkiss and others, *Bituminous-Coal Mining,* p. 20.

[20] Under some conditions liquid carbon dioxide or compressed air may be used to
bring down the coal, but for the most part explosives are still employed: *ibid.,*
p. 24.

[21] Leong and others, *Copper Mining,* pp. 112-13.

[22] Collins, in Kaempffert, *op. cit.,* pp. 70-71.

[23] Toenges, *op. cit.,* p. 8. Dynamite is not suitable for blasting coal, having too
violent a shattering effect; other blasting agents had yet to be developed.

[24] Leong and others, *Copper Mining,* pp. 112-13.

in underground metal mining.[25] It will be recalled that in block caving a thick block of ore is undercut and allowed to break through force of gravity. Besides block caving in its pure form, numerous related devices have been introduced, notably sublevel caving.[26] The latter also employs gravity to break the ore, and is used quite extensively in iron mining. Such caving methods have been fairly widely adopted in copper and iron mining, and to this extent the labor formerly involved in drilling and blasting has for the most part been rendered unnecessary. During the period 1929–37, 16 percent of underground iron ore was produced by sublevel caving,[27] and in 1936 block caving accounted for 18.9 percent of underground copper.[28] The use of improved drilling and blasting techniques with or without caving methods has resulted, in copper mining, in a reduction of the working force engaged in breaking ore from two thirds of the total underground labor, when hand drilling was used, to 20 to 30 percent of the underground labor today.[29]

In the case of bituminous coal, improvements in cutting machines have kept pace with changes in drilling and blasting. As with drills, the most important change in coal-cutting machinery occurred early in the century. The percussive puncher machine, which was the dominant mechanical cutter at the end of the nineteenth century, soon began to be displaced by a fundamentally different type of machine. The new device, known as the chain-breast machine, had a cutting element consisting of "a heavy plate about 44 inches wide, known as the cutter bar, which projects about 6 feet in front of the machine. Around the outer edge of the plate is an endless chain fitted with removable steel bits. When the machine is started the endless chain revolves, and

[25] See Chapter 5 above, pp. 111-14; especially Chart 35.

[26] See Chart 34 above. Sublevel caving is especially applicable in soft ore bodies which would cave prematurely over wider openings (C. F. Jackson and J. H. Hedges, "Metal Mining Practice," *Bulletin 419*, U. S. Bureau of Mines, 1939, pp. 238-42).

[27] Yaworski and others, *Iron Mining*, Table A-22, p. 240. In addition 9.4 percent of underground iron was produced by a combination of sublevel caving and other stoping methods.

[28] Leong and others, *Copper Mining*, Table A-13, p. 256. The percentage is based on the recoverable copper content of ore mined, not the tonnage of ore. The latter basis would yield a far higher percentage (42.0 percent to be exact) but is a less significant measure because of the lower tenor of caved ore. Data relating to the efficiency and relative importance of different methods of mining copper will be found in Chapter 12 below, Tables 23 and 24.

[29] *Ibid.*, p. 106.

the cutter bar is automatically fed forward against the coal." [30]

The changes instituted since the introduction of the chain-breast machine have not modified the fundamental design of the cutter mechanism, although they have enhanced the efficiency and ease with which the machine may be worked and moved about the mine. With the early machine, the full width of the working face could not be cut unless the machine were withdrawn after each cut and moved across the face to make another cut, and so on until the entire face had been covered. One of the first modifications permitted continuous operation for the full width of the working face. The short-wall machine, which embodied this feature, came into general use about 1910 and rapidly replaced the earlier types. Shortly thereafter, another important change enabled the machine to cut at any elevation in the coal face without being removed from the truck on which it was transported.

The major modifications in the machine were devised before the first World War. Since that time numerous further improvements have rendered the machine cutter more efficient. Among these may be listed such items as increase in the size of the cutter bar, improvement in cutter bits and increases in power. In 1938 the mechanical cutter was responsible for 87.5 percent [31] of total bituminous coal production, but it is still rarely employed in anthracite mines, where the nature of the deposits has obstructed mechanization in cutting.[32]

## Loading the Mineral

The loading of broken mineral is an operation that occurs midway between breaking and hauling. Although loading thus occupies a central position in the mining process, it remained a hand job in many mining industries long after breaking and hauling had been mechanized. Indeed the development of mechanized equipment to replace hand loading is strictly a post-World War phenomenon, in spite of the fact that hand loading was the most laborious of the underground miner's operations in the coal and iron ore industries.[33] It is not surprising, then, that during the

[30] Hotchkiss and others, *Bituminous-Coal Mining*, p. 15.

[31] See below, Chapter 8, for data on machine cutting of bituminous coal.

[32] Harry Jerome, *Mechanization in Industry* (National Bureau of Economic Research, 1934), p. 133.

[33] Yaworski and others, *Iron Mining*, p. 151; Hotchkiss and others, *Bituminous-Coal Mining*, p. 114.

period of its developing use mechanical loading has played an extremely important part in increasing efficiency in underground mining as a whole. In loading, more than in any other single function, mechanization fosters an increased tempo of mine operations in general. It may indeed be said that the balanced cycle of underground operations is a concomitant of the post-World War mechanization of the loading process.[34]

Of course, technological advance in loading did not begin with the introduction of mechanical loaders. Before this innovation the efforts of those who sought to make the operation more efficient were directed toward improving the means and methods of hand shoveling. Among other things, shovels were redesigned, lower mine cars were built, and miners were instructed in proper techniques of shoveling. Even these small changes made for sizable increases in labor efficiency.[35] In addition, the utilization of gravity methods of loading in many cases predated the mechanical loader. As in the case of breaking, the adoption of techniques which took advantage of the force of gravity succeeded in eliminating much hand labor formerly necessary. But gravity breaking and gravity loading did not necessarily go together. Thus in iron mining, where sublevel caving is widely used, gravity methods of loading are rather definitely confined to a few deposits. Here, therefore, mechanical loading was a great boon to mine efficiency.[36] On the other hand, gravity loading is used in copper even in some mines—for example in shrinkage stoping—where block caving is not practiced.[37]

More, perhaps, than any other device, the mechanical loader must be closely adapted to the peculiar physical circumstances of the individual mine.[38] In consequence loading equipment appears in a quite extraordinary range of design and type. This fact makes it impossible for us to discuss the mechanization of the loading

[34] Hotchkiss and others, *Bituminous-Coal Mining*, pp. 140-42.

[35] Leong and others, *Copper Mining*, p. 114.

[36] Yaworski and others, *Iron Mining*, p. 151.

[37] L. N. Plein, F. E. Berquist and F. G. Tryon, *Mechanization Trends in Metal and Nonmetal Mining as Indicated by Sales of Underground Loading Equipment* (National Research Project, Philadelphia, 1937), p. 3.

[38] "There is no universal loader and there never will be, because of the wide variations in underground conditions and requirements." Charles E. Van Barneveld, *Mechanical Underground Loading in Metal Mines* (University of Missouri: School of Mines and Metallurgy, Bulletin, Technical Series, Vol. VII, No. 3, Rolla, Mo., 1924, p. 75).

process with the thoroughness it deserves. We shall describe only a few leading types of loader in the more important industries.

The first World War may serve as a starting point for a discussion of the mechanization of underground loading, no matter what mining industry we consider. Although attempts at mechanization had been made before then, the real impetus was undoubtedly provided by the labor shortage during the first World War and early post-war period.[39] At that time two types of mechanical loaders were introduced into metal mining: the shovel loader and the scraper.

The shovel loader at first seemed the preferable device and was, therefore, adopted in many metal mines. This machine, which can best be described as a miniature power shovel, involved serious mechanical difficulties and was, in addition, essentially ill adapted to small, artificially supported workings such as are encountered in underground iron ore and nongravity copper mines.[40] Hence in copper and iron mining mechanical shovel loaders met with little success and were rapidly superseded by scraper mechanisms. The shovel loaders continued, however, to be utilized in development work where they are not handicapped by insufficient head room, and they have greatly increased the efficiency of drifting or tunneling.[41] It should be noted also that shovel loaders have been used with great success in the Southeast Missouri lead field, where underground workings are sufficiently roomy to accommodate the machines.[42] In recent years the introduction of a smaller power shovel has made for a renewed use of this machine in underground iron and nonferrous mining, but still largely for development work.[43]

A more successful loading device for use in underground metal mines is the scraper. Even in the Southeast Missouri lead district, where 100 percent mechanization of loading has been achieved in recent years, scrapers have to some extent replaced shovel load-

[39] Hotchkiss and others, *Bituminous-Coal Mining*, pp. 114-15; Yaworski and others, *Iron Mining*, p. 152; C. F. Jackson, in the Foreword to "Mechanical Shoveling in Underground Metal Mines," by McHenry Mosier and J. H. Steinmesch, *Bulletin 423* (U. S. Bureau of Mines, 1940).

[40] Yaworski and others, *Iron Mining*, p. 152; Leong and others, *Copper Mining*, p. 117.

[41] Leong and others, *Copper Mining*, p. 117.

[42] Andrew V. Corry and O. E. Kiessling, *Grade of Ore* (National Research Project, Philadelphia, 1938), p. 80.

[43] Plein, Berquist and Tryon, *op. cit.*, p. 12.

ers.[44] The scraper consists of little more than a scoop, pulled by a rope attached to a hoist, in which the ore is dragged along the floor. It is superior to the shovel loader in that it requires very little head room and can also be used for hauling. Actually the device does not load, but rather serves to drag the material to a convenient elevated point from which it can be discharged into a mine car or an ore chute. Initially, if we may generalize on the basis of iron mining experience, the scraper was operated by the timber hoists which were already available. But this provided only a mechanical means of dragging the scraper toward the hoist, with the return trip powered by hand. By 1923, however, double-drum hoists driven by compressed air were being introduced.[45] More recently, the increase in the capacity of hoisting equipment has favored the substitution of electric power.[46]

Up to this point we have discussed the loaders that eliminate hand shoveling entirely; these, as is clear from the references to their use, are found mainly in metal mining. In coal mining similar machines are coming into use, but before we treat the fully mechanized loading of coal it is well to consider another type of machine which merely reduces the labor involved in hand shoveling without eliminating the operation entirely. Such machines have been widely employed in coal mining in the past.

The most important device to reduce hand shoveling is the pit-car loader, essentially an elevating conveyor. With this type of machine the miner need lift the coal only a short distance from the floor of the mine onto the lower end of the conveyor, which in turn lifts the coal into the car. Thus the necessity for lifting the coal the entire height of the car is obviated, and much labor is thereby saved. This device was introduced in bituminous coal mines at about the same time that the shovel loader found its way into metal mining; it was taken up by the coal operators mainly because it did not require important changes in existing mine practice. Although it was of low capacity, it permitted hand separation of impurities and could, therefore, be readily fitted into the existing mine routine.[47]

[44] Corry and Kiessling, Grade of Ore, p. 80.

[45] Yaworski and others, Iron Mining, pp. 152-53.

[46] McHenry Mosier, "Underground Loading," Engineering and Mining Journal, August 1941, p. 107. The increase in the size of equipment may be appraised from the fact that in 1923 hoists of from 4 to 7½ horsepower were used, whereas today they range up to 150 horsepower (Plein, Berquist and Tryon, op. cit., p. 9).

[47] Hotchkiss and others, Bituminous-Coal Mining, p. 120.

The pit-car loader, which represents an intermediate stage between hand and fully mechanized loading, is still used in many mines.[48] Recently, however, there has been a tendency to replace it with the completely mechanical mobile loader. This loader is based either on the shovel principle or on the gathering principle.[49] The shovel type is similar to the machine already discussed in connection with metal mining. The gathering type uses claw-like arms which push the coal onto a conveyor.

Scraper mechanisms have not been widely used in coal mining mainly because resource conditions do not favor them. However, the combination of loading with hauling which the scraper offers in metal mines is found in coal in the hand loaded conveyor. This consists of an ordinary conveyor unit, which, in recent years, has been adapted to all systems of coal mining.[50] The conveyor is brought up to the working face and the coal is loaded onto it, to be carried either to mine cars or to a mainline conveyor system. This appears to be more of a haulage than a loading mechanism, yet it is of some importance in loading since it reduces the height to which the coal must be lifted by the miner and eliminates the need for bringing mine cars into the rooms where the mining is carried on.

Since mechanical loading is of comparatively recent origin, it is interesting to see how far its use has spread. The extent to which the various mechanical loaders have been adopted is more easily determined in coal mining than in other mining industries. Available data indicate that about 30 percent of the underground tonnage of bituminous and anthracite coal is mechanically loaded.[51] For other mining industries statistics on mechanized loading are lacking, but there are scattered facts which roughly indicate its extent. In iron mining, for instance, scraper mechanisms are known to be widely used in the Lake Superior region, the most important underground producing center. In copper mining, too, scraping has been widely applied in Michigan, where resource conditions are favorable.[52] For copper mining in general, however, the field for mechanized loading is definitely limited

---

[48] Toenges, *op. cit.*, p. 11.

[49] Hotchkiss and others, *Bituminous-Coal Mining*, p. 120.

[50] *Ibid.*, p. 125-30.

[51] For data on the mechanical loading of coal, see below, Chapter 8, Table 15, and Chapter 9, Table 17.

[52] Plein, Berquist and Tryon, *op. cit.*, p. 9.

because of the wide use in this industry of gravity methods of loading which render mechanical devices unnecessary, or of the square-set technique of mining [53] which involves timbering that is too close to permit mechanized loading.[54] As for lead and zinc mining, we have already noted the fact that loading in Southeast Missouri lead mines is 100 percent mechanized. This has contrasted markedly, at least until recently, with the adjacent Tri-State [55] lead and zinc producing district where loading has been done almost entirely by hand.[56]

With regard to the other metals, all that can be said is that mechanical loading is used in mining them all, though little is definitely known as to the amount of production for which such loading accounts. The indications are that the metals, as a group, do not yet use mechanical loading to as great a degree as do the nonmetals, especially coal. To be sure, mechanical devices are less necessary in loading metallic ores than in loading coal, owing to the greater scope for gravity methods in the former case.

There can be little doubt that the mechanization of loading has been of great importance in increasing productivity in underground mining in recent years. In many mines, loading was the last function to be mechanized, so that its adoption completed the chain of mechanized processes, with a resultant gain in over-all efficiency. In other mines—particularly coal—mechanization of loading replaced a hand process which had consumed the greatest portion of the underground mining crew's efforts. In addition, the use of mechanical loading called forth the mechanization of other functions to preserve the balance between different parts of the cycle of mining operations. In this sense its indirect effect on the productivity of underground mining has been potent indeed.[57]

[53] See above, Chapter 5, pp. 101-02.

[54] Plein, Berquist and Tryon, *op. cit.*, p. 3.

[55] The Tri-State area includes parts of Kansas, Missouri and Oklahoma.

[56] "These two districts, lying side by side, illustrate how largely the factors of size of operation and character of deposit affect the utilization of machinery. In the Tri-State area, the less regular character of the mineralization and of the underground workings, the smaller holdings, the prevalence of the leasing system, the use of small 'cans' instead of large-capacity cars in haulage, and other factors have worked to favor hand loading" (*ibid.*, p. 17). This quotation was written in 1937; we understand that since 1938 mechanical loading has developed rapidly in the Tri-State area, as it had already done in Southeast Missouri.

[57] For instance, we read that "by speeding up the mining process, scraper loading has permitted the concentration of work into fewer places, thereby reducing the amount of maintenance work and allowing more efficient utilization of transporta-

*Transporting the Mineral*

In most underground mines the transportation of minerals (as well as of men and supplies) involves two distinct operations: (1) horizontal movement from the working face to the mine shaft, or hauling; and (2) vertical movement from the underground level to the surface, or hoisting. Trends in the first of these operations include changes from hand to animal to mechanical haulage; and advances, not only in rail equipment, but also in the utilization of scrapers and conveyor systems (discussed above). As for hoisting, the second of these operations, we have already noted that along with pumping and ventilation, this function had to be mechanized in order that mining might be carried to greater depths in the late nineteenth century.

For the most part underground haulage systems were not mechanized until after the opening of the present century. Even though electric locomotives had been introduced into coal mines in 1887 [58] and into metal mines in the 1890's,[59] hand and animal traction were still chiefly employed in 1899.

In some cases, as in coal, such primitive methods were supplemented by rope or chain haulage on the mainline, but this was not a marked improvement, since the speed of rope haulage was usually no greater than that of the mule.[60] Of course both animal draft and rope haulage marked an advance over the use, at a still earlier date, of hand tramming underground, but even such modest improvements were not universally applied. They were widely adopted in coal mining, but for iron ore hand methods held sway until they were replaced by mechanical traction in the twentieth century.[61]

Hoisting, as we might expect, was more generally mechanized than haulage in the late nineteenth century. To the extent that

---

tion and other facilities. The two- or threefold increase in output per miner in the stopes has made it possible to maintain a specified production with one-half to one-third the number of stopes. This has permitted closer supervision of workings, easier distribution of supplies, simpler ventilation, easier drainage, and other economies" (Yaworski and others, *Iron Mining*, p. 158). This chain of developments has also occurred in coal mining.

[58] Van Barneveld, *op. cit.*, p. 40.

[59] Yaworski and others, *Iron Mining*, p. 144; Leong and others, *Copper Mining*, p. 122.

[60] Hotchkiss and others, *Bituminous-Coal Mining*, p. 25.

[61] Yaworski and others, *Iron Mining*, p. 144.

mineral production came from deep mines requiring vertical shafts, powerful hoisting units were essential. This was especially true of mines producing copper, gold and silver. Thus in the 1902 Census we find evidence of extensive use of hoists, usually powered by steam, in these industries.[62] As for coal, operations were usually not very deep, so that hoisting in general was less important here than in metal mining.

Electric locomotives, first introduced into mining operations toward the end of the nineteenth century, came into widespread use during the first decade and a half of the present century. Frequently they superseded mules directly, without the intervention of rope haulage. Their application, however, was confined almost entirely to mainline haulage. In newly-made drifts, mine rooms, and other small workings, hand and animal tramming remained predominant.[63] Such workings cannot easily accommodate overhead trolley wires; moreover the point where loading occurs is continually advancing. The difficulty was partially overcome by the cable-reel type of gathering locomotive.

A more recent development has been the introduction into underground mines of storage battery locomotives—self-contained units carrying their own source of power. This machine dispenses with wiring and is therefore well suited to the task of gathering haulage, i.e., transferring mine cars from small workings to the mainline. Reliable battery locomotives were apparently introduced into mining about the time of the first World War, and since then their use has expanded rapidly, so that today both mainline haulage and gathering are largely mechanized.[64] It should be noted, however, that in metal mining the most rapid extension of mechanized gathering haulage did not follow immediately upon the advent of the battery locomotive, but rather awaited the introduction of the small and compact 1½ ton battery locomotive in the early 1920's.[65]

Today both trolley and storage battery locomotives are used; the choice of one or the other depends upon the nature of the mine workings and the material being handled. However, because

[62] "Mines and Quarries, 1902," pp. 476-78, 526-30.

[63] Hotchkiss and others, *Bituminous-Coal Mining*, p. 26; Leong and others, *Copper Mining*, p. 123.

[64] F. G. Tryon and others, "The Mineral Industries" in *Technological Trends and National Policy* (National Resources Committee, 1937), p. 152; Leong and others, *Copper Mining*, p. 125.

[65] *Ibid.*, p. 125; Yaworski and others, *Iron Mining*, p. 146.

of the existence of both types, haulage can be mechanized in practically all workings. Hand and animal haulage still prevail in
many small mines.[66] An important illustration of such continued
use of hand and animal methods is found in the Tri-State lead
and zinc district, where mechanical hauling is still rare.[67]

Throughout the period, of course, there has been continuous
improvement in the construction of mine locomotives. In general,
weight and power have been increased, with the ratio of horsepower to weight constantly rising through a transfer of weight
from the frame to the motor.[68] There have also been marked
changes in the design of mine cars. These have resulted in larger
cars with less deadweight (because of the use of alloy steels in
construction) and in constantly improved dumping mechanims.
The most important among the latter group of changes has been
the switch from the end-dump car of hand-tramming days to the
bottom-dump and side-dump cars of today, which do not have to
be uncoupled for dumping.[69]

We have already discussed scrapers and conveyor systems in
connection with the mechanization of loading. For hauling,
scrapers are widely used in metal mines, but only for transportation over limited distances. Conveyor systems, on the other hand,
are adapted to relatively lengthy hauls, and in coal mines have
recently been used with mobile loaders.[70] In the last few years
conveyor systems have been installed in some iron mines, but
their application in metal mining is still unimportant.[71]

It is to be expected that improvements in the underground
haulage system have been matched by advances in hoisting. In the
1902 Census we find the following observation: "In a district
where it is cheaper to sink a new shaft than to tram ore 600 or
700 feet underground, central shafts of large capacity are out of
place." [72] Today a single, large, multiple-compartment shaft may
serve a huge underground copper mine; here is clear evidence
that improved underground haulage has exerted an influence on

[66] Jackson and Hedges, "Metal Mining Practice," pp. 169-72.
[67] "The Story of the Tri-State Zinc and Lead Mining District" (convention sou-
venir, American Institute of Mining and Metallurgical Engineers, Joplin, Mo., 1931),
p. 21.
[68] Yaworski and others, Iron Mining, p. 145.
[69] Ibid., p. 146.
[70] Hotchkiss and others, Bituminous-Coal Mining, p. 28.
[71] Jackson and Hedges, "Metal Mining Practice," pp. 173, 188-90.
[72] "Mines and Quarries, 1902," p. 462.

hoisting technique. Not only must improved haulage have made it cheaper to tram than to sink additional shafts, but it must also have induced more efficient hoisting to match the accelerated pace of underground transportation systems.

The change from small shafts to the larger shafts of today could not, of course, have been accomplished without continuous improvement in hoisting equipment. One of the most important of these advances has been the development of the system of hoisting in balance. Such a system utilizes a double drum which enables one cable to be wound and the other unwound simultaneously: one cage or skip is raised while another is lowered. This method was developed around 1900 and since then most installations in mining seem to have utilized balanced hoisting.[73]

Another significant change has been the increasing use of skips (or containers) rather than cages for hoisting.[74] Skips have been in use since about the turn of the century. Incidentally, the development of a satisfactory, self-dumping skip made possible the substitution of vertical for inclined shafts in the Lake Superior iron region.[75] Today hoisting by skip has largely replaced hoisting by cage in metal mining. Under certain circumstances, however, the use of cages may still be preferable.[76] Indeed, even such an old-fashioned device as the bucket—which gave way to the cage in the nineteenth century [77]—is still used in the Tri-State lead and zinc district, where relatively large tonnages are handled.[78]

Advances in hoisting have paralleled changes in other mechanized mine equipment. Speed and capacity have risen: in this advance the utilization of electric power has played a large part. Also, materials used in the construction of skips have been im-

---

[73] Yaworski and others, *Iron Mining*, p. 142; Leong and others, *Copper Mining*, p. 135.

[74] "Use of the cage involves loss of time both in loading the cars onto the cage and in removing them at the surface, requires labor to perform the loading and unloading, ties up mine cars in the process, and necessitates hoisting deadweight of the cars," while "adoption of the skip and skip pocket has brought about a considerable saving in labor and time. It has greatly reduced the labor previously engaged in loading and unloading, eliminated a considerable portion of the delay and congestion both at the shaft and the haulageways, and increased the capacity of the hoist by 25 to 40 percent by obviating the necessity of raising and lowering the deadweight of the mine cars." Leong and others, *Copper Mining*, pp. 135-36.

[75] Yaworski and others, *Iron Mining*, p. 141.

[76] Jackson and Hedges, *op. cit.*, p. 205.

[77] C. E. Julihn, "Copper: An Example of Advancing Technology and the Utilization of Low Grade Ores," in *Mineral Economics*, ed. by F. G. Tryon and E. C. Eckel (McGraw-Hill, 1932), p. 125.

[78] Jackson and Hedges, *op. cit.*, p. 203.

proved with a consequent reduction in deadweight. These and other such changes have operated to make possible concentration of hoisting in large single shafts in response to the pressure exercised by the faster tempo of underground mining operations. Indeed, the point has been reached where the efficiency of hoisting is no longer considered a limiting factor even when mining at much greater depths is contemplated. As Read points out,[79] ore can be successfully hoisted, without undue expense, from depths two or three times as great as the average for mines in the United States today.

## Auxiliary Functions

Technological change in underground mining has not been confined to advances in the primary functions of breaking, loading and transportation. Advances have been registered also in methods of mine drainage, ventilation, lighting, support and other so-called auxiliary functions. Improvements in these fields have rendered possible the working of seams or veins which in former times could not have been exploited. They must also have affected productivity levels, but mainly in ways which are indirect and difficult to evaluate. For this reason, and because drainage and ventilation, in particular, are highly specialized functions, an adequate treatment of them would of necessity be both prolix and technical. We shall confine ourselves, therefore, to a few general remarks.

The indirect operation of such improvements is well illustrated by changes in mine ventilation. For the greater part of the nineteenth century artificial ventilation was not used underground except in coal mines. Even here the natural draft was often considered sufficient, perhaps with the assistance of mechanical fans on the surface or of a pipe leading to a furnace in which the suction of the heated air drew the foul air from the mine.[80] Such devices were usually lacking in metal mines because of the belief among many mining men that only in coal mining was circulation of air at the working face necessary.[81] However, as metal mining was carried to greater depths, and as the working face receded farther from the shaft, mechanical ven-

[79] *Technological Trends and National Policy*, p. 164.
[80] Julihn, *op. cit.*, p. 125; Leong and others, *Copper Mining*, p. 151.
[81] *Ibid.*, p. 153.

tilation came to be recognized as a necessary condition for the continuation of operations. A description of the early days of the Comstock lode reveals how the lack of devices able to counteract the heat operated to reduce miners' efficiency to a very low level. Temperature in drifts sometimes went up to as high as 130°F., and although air pipes driven by powerful engines were placed close behind the men laboring at the face they could not work for more than a very few minutes in each hour, and were constantly driven to bathe their heads in streams of water.[82] This is, no doubt, an extreme example, but it serves to illustrate the deleterious effect of inadequate ventilating devices on labor efficiency.

Inventions of the twentieth century have succeeded in insuring adequate ventilation for underground mines. Improvements have been stimulated by increased knowledge of the relationship between labor efficiency and the temperature, humidity and cleanliness of the air. Physiology and engineering have in fact joined hands. The effect of such developments does not lend itself to measurement, but there can be no doubt that it must have been considerable.

So, too, improved systems of drainage must have exercised their effect on underground efficiency. With greater depth in mining the task which pumping machinery must perform becomes more considerable, if only because of the greater height to which water must be raised. Here again the difficulties created by water in underground workings must be overcome if miners are to be able to work efficiently.

Unlike ventilation and drainage, the task of illumination has not been burdened with increasing natural difficulties; hence any advance in the effectiveness with which it is provided constitutes a clear gain. That it has been more effectively provided is due mainly to the increasing use of electric lighting in underground mining. This has been a tremendous boon, particularly in coal mines. Prior to the use of electricity, portable devices which would give sufficient light and also provide the fullest safety against fire damp were not to be found.[83]

Finally we may consider the function of mine supports. The

[82] Robert M. LaFollette (ed.), *The Making of America*, Vol. 6 (Morris, Chicago, 1906), pp. 25-26.
[83] E. N. Zern, *The History of Mine Lighting*, College of Engineering, West Virginia University, Series 2, No. 1 (Morgantown, W. Va., 1916), p. 27.

effect of modifications in methods of support resembles that of changes in the primary mine functions, in that increased efficiency of support results in a reduction in the amount of time the miner must devote to this task, and enables him to spend more time in the primary functions associated with winning the mineral. The amount of the underground miner's time and effort that goes into timbering for support has been cut down in two ways. First, changes in mining methods have operated to reduce timbering for support to very minor proportions. Thus, the use of shrinkage stoping and caving methods [84] in modern iron and copper mining, in place of square-set timbering, has resulted in a great reduction in the number of artificial supports required, and hence the labor involved in their maintenance. By and large, however, support is still necessary, and the second type of improvement comprises means of reducing the time required in erecting and maintaining such supports. Among the most important of these are: (1) the use of preservatives which prolong the life of the timber, and (2) the standardization of timber sets, with a consequent transfer of preparation from the mine to a surface carpentry shop which may utilize machinery.[85]

## OPEN CUT MINING

As we have seen, the exploitation of this nation's mineral deposits has for the most part required underground operations. Yet where conditions are suitable, and the deposits do not occur too far below the surface, open pit methods of winning the mineral have proved very efficient. This is true especially of the quarrying of stone; but it applies also in many instances to the extraction of coal, copper, iron ore and other minerals. In both coal and metal mining, surface operations have increased in relative importance in recent decades, while the technology of open pit mining itself has made striking advances.[86]

---

[84] See above, pp. 110-14.

[85] Leong and others, *Copper Mining*, p. 150.

[86] Surface mining is probably the oldest form of mineral extraction since surface outcroppings of minerals were probably first to be exploited. In the United States, for instance, many early operations are known to have been of the surface variety, but these amounted to nothing more than gathering loose outcrops or digging with crude hand devices. This type of mining was superseded by underground workings when depth became too great for hand digging. In the present context we are interested not in these crude beginnings but rather in the present-day large-scale surface exploitation of iron, copper, and bituminous coal made possible by the devel-

In open cut mining the difficulties and hazards of underground mining are obviated. In this connection it is sufficient to note that such tasks as shaft sinking, tunneling, and timbering for support, all of which absorb a considerable amount of labor, are unnecessary in surface mining. Nor is it necessary to provide artificial lighting and ventilation, both of which are required in underground workings. Against these advantages must be set the disadvantage that considerable quantities of waste material, known as "overburden," have generally to be removed before the mineral can be reached. Consequently, the advantages of surface mining could not be realized to any great extent until equipment became available for moving material, chiefly in a horizontal direction, on a rather large scale. The development of such equipment—the mechanized means of breaking, loading and hauling ore and overburden—are considered in the remainder of this section. The history of open cut mining is largely the history of the power shovel.

In 1892, when operations began on the Mesabi iron ore range in Minnesota, the power shovel was already available in elementary form. Before this time it had been used for making railway cuts and for general excavation, and had even been employed, although not to any great extent, in stripping overburden in coal mining and in loading the mined product. Indeed, as early as 1877 a power shovel had been used in a coal strip pit; but this early machine had to be moved by block and tackle and could be propelled only in one direction.[87] It was not until 1890 that a shovel embodying backward and forward self-propulsion was introduced in strip mining.[88] This type of shovel, which was utilized in the first workings on the Mesabi range, was powered by steam and traveled on rails (the so-called railroad type steam shovel).[89]

opment of the power shovel (which may be dated roughly by the opening of the Mesabi iron ore range in 1892). Large-scale surface copper mining did not begin until 1906 and open cut coal operations, although undertaken quite early, were of slight importance until the World War period.

Since changes in crushed stone technology in the present century have paralleled those in open cut metal and coal mining they will be included in this discussion. Other minerals won by surface methods—notably dimension stone, phosphate rock, bauxite, and placer gold—utilize more individualized production techniques, some of which will be treated separately.

[87] F. E. Cash and M. W. von Bernewitz, "Methods, Costs, and Safety in Stripping and Mining Coal, Copper Ore, Iron Ore, Bauxite, and Pebble Phosphate," *Bulletin 298* (U. S. Bureau of Mines, 1929), p. 2.

[88] *Ibid.*, p. 3.

[89] Yaworski and others, *Iron Mining*, p. 89.

It was of relatively small dipper capacity and was able to swing only through a limited arc.[90]

The use of power shovels in loading implies a certain stage of technical evolution in the associated tasks of breaking and hauling the ore, for if these closely related jobs cannot be performed with sufficient speed for the shovel to function more or less continuously, the advantage of power loading is in good part lost. So far as concerns breaking, power machines were available for blast-hole drilling in the 1880's and were being successfully used in open cut iron mining in Pennsylvania, where they had been introduced in 1882.[91] But they made little headway in open cut iron mining elsewhere, and hand methods in fact held sway until well into the second decade of the present century. The superiority of the machine method over hand methods was apparently not very great, at least when relatively soft materials, such as those encountered in the Mesabi range, were worked.[92] The crushed stone industry, too, was dominated by hand drilling techniques during this early period.[93] As for haulage, we find steam locomotives used quite generally in open cut iron mines several years before the opening of the present century.[94] The crushed stone industry, on the other hand, which had not yet adopted the power shovel, was still utilizing in 1900 the primitive haulage methods already discarded in iron mining. Hand and animal haulage were widespread and only in relatively few cases had small steam dinkeys replaced horses in drawing the small wooden cars along narrow gauge tracks.[95]

The development of the power shovel typifies mechanical progress in open cut mining. The railroad-type steam shovel able

[90] Although the power shovel was used in coal and iron mining during the 1890's, it was not adopted in the crushed stone industry until the first decade of the present century. And even at this late date it was used mainly for stripping overburden, while loading remained essentially a hand operation. This lag is explained by the fact that the chief products of crushed stone operations at this time were limestone for flux and lime, both of which required hand sorting. Moreover, many crushed stone enterprises are small and operate only intermittently. Not until expanding industrialism created a demand for crushed stone in construction and road building was the industry able to adopt the power shovel and other mass production devices. See Harry S. Kantor and Geoffrey E. Saeger, *Crushed-Stone Industry* (National Research Project, Philadelphia, 1939), p. 27; also Nighman and Kiessling, *Rock Drilling*, p. 50.

[91] Yaworski and others, *Iron Mining*, p. 80.

[92] *Ibid.*, p. 81.

[93] See below, p. 142.

[94] Yaworski and others, *Iron Mining*, p. 101.

[95] Kantor and Saeger, *Crushed-Stone Industry*, p. 24.

to swing only through a limited arc, which was standard equipment in open cut operations until well into the decade following 1910, has been gradually modified until it has become the full revolving, caterpillar traction, electric shovel of today. The full revolving shovel was introduced during the period 1915–20,[96] although its practicability was not fully realized until the shovel was taken off railroad track.[97] In the early post-war period the shovels were first mounted on caterpillar treads,[98] an advance which one authority writing in 1930 called the "greatest in shovel practice during the past 20 years." [99] At about this time, too, the first electric shovels were introduced at a few operations.[100] The general adoption of each of these innovations has been a long, slow process, and one that is still continuing.[101]

It is obvious that the initial change from hand to machine stripping and loading must have resulted in a large increase in open cut productivity. Even with the first crude power shovels used in iron mining, the working crew of 10 men is estimated to have accomplished 6 to 12 times as much during a work shift as was possible with hand labor methods.[102] Efficiency was further

[96] Yaworski and others, *Iron Mining*, p. 92.

[97] Kantor and Saeger, *Crushed-Stone Industry*, p. 52.

[98] E. D. Gardner, C. H. Johnson and B. S. Butler, "Copper Mining in North America," *Bulletin 405* (U. S. Bureau of Mines, 1938), p. 136. It is interesting to note that the post-war use of caterpillar traction was stimulated by the development of equipment of this kind in World War military operations (A. B. Parsons, *The Porphyry Coppers*, American Institute of Mining and Metallurgical Engineers, 1933, pp. 379-81). It had also been used previously in agriculture.

[99] Quotation from A. Soderberg, cited in E. D. Gardner and McHenry Mosier, "Open Cut Metal Mining," *Bulletin 433* (U. S. Bureau of Mines, 1941), p. 8.

[100] *Ibid.*, p. 11; see also Leong and others, *Copper Mining*, p. 39.

[101] The gradual manner in which improvements in power shovel practice have been adopted is evident even in open cut copper mining, which represents the peak in large scale operations, as can be seen in this quotation from Leong and others, *Copper Mining*, p. 45:

> It should be pointed out, however, that there is always a time lag between the development of a new invention or the improvement of an old one and its general adoption. Thus there are only a few power shovels in service at open-pit copper mines that embody all the advanced features of electric shovels. The huge outlays already made for older types of loading equipment naturally limit the rate at which it appears economical to replace such equipment with more modern machines. In many instances operators have deemed it advisable to improve their existing machines by adopting some of the latest features instead of discarding the old for new equipment. With the advent of caterpillar traction, the old steam railroad-type shovels were modified by placing one tractor under each jack-arm and another in the rear. When the electric shovels proved their superiority over the steam machines, steam engines were replaced by electric motors.

[102] Yaworski and others, *Iron Mining*, p. 88.

increased by changes made after 1900. "Whereas the early Mesabi power shovel manned with a crew of from 7 to 12 men loaded 1,000 to 2,000 tons of ore in 10 hours, the largest and most efficient shovels now in use with 2- or 3-man crews can load ore at the rate of 1,000 tons in 1 hour." [103] Changes in loading performance resulting from more recent improvements are cited in the National Research Project's report on *Copper*:

> At the Utah copper mine the railroad-type steam shovels with 3½-yard dippers loaded, on the average, 2,350 tons of ore per 8-hour shovel-shift in 1923, compared with 5,200 tons loaded, on the average, in 1934 by electric shovels mounted on caterpillar crawlers and using 4½-yard dippers. The new full-revolving shovels equipped with 5-yard dippers which this mine has recently acquired have a maximum capacity of 8,000 tons per 8-hour shift and an average capacity well over 6,000 tons. At the Chino mine the cubic yards of material loaded per 8-hour shovel-shift increased gradually from 825 in 1923, when the old-type railroad steam shovels were in use, to 1,280 in 1931, when the loading machines were modernized.[104]

Improved loading performances would not have been possible unless advances in equipment used in related tasks matched the advance of loading machinery. Mechanical drilling, which was rare before the turn of the century, replaced hand drilling on a wide scale. Even in iron mining, the last stronghold of hand drills, power drilling was generally adopted after the first World War.[105] The trend in drilling tools since the start of open cut copper mining has been "toward heavier, more powerful and mobile" models of drills already in existence, and these improvements were "accompanied by gains of 200 to 300% in footage drilled per man-shift." [106] In recent years the substitution of other sources of power for steam—notably compressed air and electricity—the improvement in drilling bits, and the development of the self-propelled machine traveling on caterpillar treads, have contributed to increased efficiency.[107] A striking result of the increased depth to which drilling may economically be carried has been the development of higher benches in open cut metal mining, and

103 *Ibid.*, pp. 88-89.
104 Leong and others, *Copper Mining*, p. 47.
105 Yaworski and others, *Iron Mining*, p. 80.
106 Nighman and Kiessling, *Rock Drilling*, p. 107.
107 Gardner and Mosier, *op. cit.*, pp. 7, 108.

the shift from multiple-bench to single-bench operations in crushed stone quarries.[108] This has not only enabled operators to take advantage of larger shovels, but has greatly facilitated the transportation of the mined product.[109]

Improvements in haulage have followed the same general pattern. Here the increase in the size of locomotives and cars and the substitution of standard gauge for narrow gauge are indicative of a general tendency for standard railway practice to replace smaller scale mine railway practice.[110] In a few cases, too, the haulage system has been electrified, but steam is still the predominant source of power.[111] The productivity of open cut operations has also been increased by the substitution of mechanical track shifting for laborious hand methods. At the Utah Copper Company, for example, 5 or 6 times as many workers would be required for track shifting in the absence of the mechanical shifter.[112] A recent change which has been of importance in coal and crushed stone is the introduction of the motor truck.[113] The superiority of the truck derives mainly from its greater mobility and flexibility, which allow it to be placed in a position for loading with the least movement of the shovel.

## MECHANIZATION IN STONE QUARRYING

Although limestone and marble are sometimes produced from underground quarries, the stone industries offer an important example of open cut technique. In most respects the production of crushed stone, in particular, resembles other forms of open pit mining. Often the same problems are encountered, and similar equipment is used, as in the mining of coal or iron from surface deposits. Nevertheless, the stone industries possess sufficient peculiarities to justify separate consideration.

[108] Nighman and Kiessling, *Rock Drilling*, pp. 76, 95. A bench is a level of operations. Thus if a layer 100 feet high is removed in two equal stages, we should speak of the use of benches 50 feet high.

[109] Yaworski and others, *Iron Mining*, p. 88.

[110] Gardner and Mosier, *op. cit.*, p. 21.

[111] *Ibid.*, p. 17.

[112] Leong and others, *Copper Mining*, p. 56.

[113] Hotchkiss and others, *Bituminous-Coal Mining*, p. 91; also Kantor and Saeger, *Crushed-Stone Industry*, p. 58.

Trucks have been used in regular haulage at open cut metal mines only in small operations. Elsewhere, their use in metal mining has been confined to clean-up operations in pits that have become so deep that the remaining ore would not justify the cost of extending the track system (Gardner and Mosier, *op. cit.*, pp. 4, 16).

## Crushed Stone

The quarrying of stone has a longer continuous history than most other forms of surface exploitation. Consequently, it might be thought that the crushed stone industry should be the original and prototype of all open pit mining, but this is not the case. In matters of technical development open pit metal mines have usually been in advance of stone quarrying, and innovations—for example, the power shovel—have commonly spread from the former to the latter, rather than in the reverse direction. At the opening of our period, in 1900, when large scale power operations were already in progress on the Mesabi iron ore range, the quarrying of crushed stone was still predominantly a matter for hand labor and animal haulage.[114] The reason for this backwardness is not hard to find. Stone occurs in many places, and it is expensive to transport. Hence quarrying operations were, and to a large extent still are, conducted on a comparatively small scale: for quarries make up in number what they lack in size. Many of them operate only intermittently. To be sure, two developments have increased the scale, and have led to the mechanization, of quarrying operations in recent decades. One is the appearance of large, but highly localized, demands for crushed limestone, especially for cement plants. The other development is the demand for road material occasioned by the amplification and extension of the highway network.

For breaking, the crushed stone industry depends heavily upon the use of explosives, and for this reason extensive drilling is necessary. It has been estimated that in the days of hand drills as much as three quarters of the labor involved was occupied in drilling blast holes.[115] In 1900 hand drilling was still common.[116] By the first decade of the present century, however, piston drills, powered first by steam and then by compressed air, were making rapid headway.[117] Such drills were a great improvement over the hand drills formerly in use, but were rather slow in operation, and were limited to depths of 20 to 30 feet. Where deeper bodies of rock had to be broken, several benches were necessary.[118] To

---

[114] Kantor and Saeger, *Crushed-Stone Industry*, pp. 23-24.
[115] Nighman and Kiessling, *Rock Drilling*, p. 2.
[116] Kantor and Saeger, *Crushed-Stone Industry*, p. 34.
[117] See p. 119 above.
[118] I.e., the rock had to be removed in successive layers.

allow thicker layers of rock to be broken in a single operation, and
to furnish the new power loading equipment with an adequate
supply of broken stone, deeper drilling was needed. The answer
was the power churn drill, introduced about 1912.[119] This instrument was developed originally for drilling oil wells, and is still
known as the well drill. It requires a derrick, and can be used
only vertically, but will drill holes up to six inches in diameter
and several hundred feet deep if necessary. It consists essentially
of a heavy bar attached to a beam, the latter actuated in a seesaw
fashion by steam power. The power churn drill is cumbersome
and, like the piston drill, somewhat slow in operation. For deep
holes its use is still necessary, but for faces up to 40 feet in height.
the hammer or drifter drill, which is light in weight and rapid in
operation,[120] is now preferred. Hammer drills suitable for deep
drilling in stone are essentially a product of metallurgical advance;
they require long, hollow drill steels, which were not available
until about 1917.[121]

The next operation, blasting, often has to be carried out in two
stages. For if the primary blast fails to lead to a degree of fragmentation sufficient to allow of loading and crushing, then secondary
blasting must be undertaken to break down the larger pieces of
rock to an appropriate size. By using more explosive per ton of
rock, and drilling a larger number of holes, the amount of secondary blasting required can be reduced to a minimum. Thus a nice
choice exists between an elaborately prepared blast, in which almost complete fragmentation is achieved in a single operation,
and a less elaborate drilling and blasting program, after which
considerable secondary breaking may be necessary. In large crushed
stone operations the tendency has been in the direction of more
elaborate primary blasts and less secondary breaking. With a wide
range of explosives available, and a willingness to drill as many
as a thousand holes for a single blast, it has been found economical to break down several hundred thousand tons of rock
in a single operation. Naturally such projects are possible only
with the use of the power shovel and large capacity crushing
equipment. Nor would they be worth while in the absence of a
local demand for the stone on a scale unknown forty years ago.

[119] Nighman and Kiessling, *Rock Drilling*, p. 15.
[120] See above, p. 121.
[121] Nighman and Kiessling, *Rock Drilling*, p. 77.

Once the rock has been broken, it must be loaded for transportation to the crusher. Steam shovels, which were first used for stripping overburden, came into use for loading stone about the end of the first decade of the present century.[122] The early shovels, originally developed for iron ore mining and general excavation work, were of course of the railroad type. However, the lack of flexibility and the trouble and delay involved in shifting track were great disadvantages, and the potentialities of power loading were not fully realized until the full-revolving shovel mounted on caterpillar treads appeared during the second decade. Moreover, there was a continuous increase in the capacity of shovels. After 1920 electric power was applied to the shovel; occasionally even gasoline and Diesel engines have been used.

Haulage from quarry to crusher is still commonly a matter of rail transportation, and the tendency has been for narrow gauge to be replaced by standard railroad equipment. Within the last two decades the motor truck has sometimes been adopted because of its great flexibility.

Mechanical crushing was already standard practice in stone quarries at the opening of the present century. Since then there has been a marked rise in the capacity of crushing plants, apparently induced by the increased efficiency of loading and transportation systems. The amount of secondary breaking has also been reduced through the construction of crushers with larger openings.

### Dimension Stone

Dimension stone is a general term applied to all stone which is shaped or hewn, as for building, curbing, flagging, etc. Although underground marble and limestone quarries exist, most dimension stone comes from open pit enterprises. Overburden is removed by steam shovel or hydraulic methods and the rock is then cut layer by layer. Blasting is rarely employed because it tends to shatter the stone and produce undesired fragmentation. Where blasting is necessary, black powder rather than dynamite is used.

In marble, limestone and sandstone quarries the rock is cut in long rectangular blocks by a channeling machine. This piece of equipment is mounted on rails and driven by steam or electricity; it cuts a long vertical slit with a reciprocating three- or five-barred

[122] Kantor and Saeger, *Crushed-Stone Industry,* p. 50.

chisel-like steel.[123] Final separation from the solid rock is achieved by the driving of wedges.

Granite is too hard to be cut in this fashion, and for this rock other methods must be employed. Usually long rows of closely spaced holes are drilled, and wedges are then driven into the openings.

During the early part of the period we are discussing, slate was cut by channeling machines; these, however, are apt, even when specially designed, to produce cracks or undesired fragmentation. Since 1928 more and more slate has been quarried with the use of wire saws.[124] The wire saw consists of an endless steel cable three sixteenths to a quarter of an inch in diameter, composed of three strands, and ranging in length from a few hundred feet to half a mile. It is brought in contact with the rock face or stone to be cut by an elaborate system of pulleys, and its tension must be carefully regulated. The saw is commonly driven by electricity, and its cutting action is purely abrasive, so that there is no risk of undesired fragmentation. Often water and sand are injected into the cut to hasten the abrasive action of the saw. Essentially an innovation of the last two decades, the wire saw is used for dressing limestone, marble and sandstone, but in actual quarrying it has not yet superseded the channeling machine to any important extent, except in the case of slate.

The dressing of stone, sometimes carried on close to the quarry and sometimes at a distance, involves a great variety of processes which differ according to the type of stone and the use for which it is intended. Stone dressing, however, is a manufacturing operation, and falls outside the scope of this study.

---

[123] For a description, see Oliver Bowles, *The Stone Industries* (McGraw-Hill, 1934), pp. 46-52.
[124] *Ibid.*, pp. 255-60.

Chapter 7

# The Purification of the Mineral Product

A REVIEW OF technological changes in mineral extraction would be incomplete without some account of developments in ore dressing and other types of mineral beneficiation and concentration. Many minerals, even some coal, copper and iron ore, are shipped to the consumer or smelter as they come from the mine. But most coal is sized, and much of it cleaned, in a surface preparation plant; and most metallic ores are ground, concentrated, and sometimes separated from each other, before they leave the vicinity of the mine.

Changes in the technology of ore dressing and other types of processing can be appraised most satisfactorily in the light of developments in mining proper. As we have noted, mining has evolved since the end of the nineteenth century in the direction of techniques which may best be labeled nonselective. Open cut operations in general, and block caving methods of underground copper mining in particular, illustrate extreme forms of this development. But regardless of the mining method in vogue, wherever drilling, blasting and loading have been mechanized the product is apt to stand in need of after treatment. This is because the mechanically mined mineral has more waste mixed with it than it would have if hand picked and hand loaded. The need to purify the product, and to do this as a separate operation prior to shipment, is therefore partly the result of the mechanization of the mining process. The responsibility for producing a waste-free product of a marketable grade has been transferred, in the mechanized mine, from the individual miner to a processing plant on the surface.

In the case of many metallic ores the need for processing prior to shipment is traceable also to a desire to mine a lower grade of material, a product which, as it comes from the mine, is too lean to be smelted. By using suitable processing equipment, a 2 percent copper ore can be shipped to the smelter as a concentrate containing 30 or 40 percent of the metal. Finally, many complex ores cannot conveniently be smelted unless separated into their constituents. For this reason, if a silver ore contains lead or zinc it may sell for a lower price on that account; with suitable milling equipment separate concentrates, containing only silver, lead and zinc respectively, can be produced and a higher combined value realized.

Specialization of function has proceeded farthest, and the most elaborate processing techniques have been perfected, in concentrating the ores of the nonferrous metals. Meanwhile the producers of iron ore, coal, crushed stone, and many of the minor nonmetals have also evolved methods for mechanically sizing, grading and purifying their products in surface preparation plants. After briefly noting the methods used for processing coal and iron ore, we shall devote the balance of this chapter to a review of modern techniques for concentrating nonferrous ores.

## COAL [1]

Increased emphasis in recent years on the mechanical preparation of coal for market has resulted partly from the mechanization of loading, which prevents the miner from picking waste at the coal face, and partly from the growing interest of the consumer in grades of coal that have been cleaned as well as sized. Elementary forms of preparation have a long history, and in the case of anthracite date back almost to the beginning of mining. Partly because of initial difficulties in causing the coal to burn, partly because the character of the seams is such that a considerable admixture of refuse occurs, the producers of anthracite were faced with the problem of processing from the first. Crude sizing is known to have been practiced as early as 1830. A modern anthracite breaker screens the product, and may also crush it, into six or eight sizes, and includes an intricate array of jigs and picking tables for washing and cleaning the coal. The smaller sizes, particularly, are cleaned by hydraulic means. The jigs for this purpose make use of the fact that, while coal is only slightly heavier than water, rock and other impurities are usually much heavier. Coal is forced to the top of the jig by screens or by the upward flow of water, while the waste settles at the bottom. Such jigs recall those

[1] This section is adapted from A. T. Shurick, *The Coal Industry* (Little, Brown, 1924), Chapter IV; and Willard E. Hotchkiss and others, *Bituminous-Coal Mining* (National Research Project, Philadelphia, 1939), pp. 31-42.

used for concentrating metallic ores (see below); in this respect
the coal industry is said to have borrowed techniques from metal
mining.

What the breaker does for anthracite, the tipple does—usually
with less elaboration—for bituminous coal. Most bituminous
mines possess mechanical screening equipment, and most coal
from them is sold in screened sizes. But price differentials based
on size are less important for bituminous coal than for anthracite:
in consequence sizing is rough, and much bituminous coal, even
from mines with preparation plants, is still sold as run-of-the-
mine. Plants for cleaning bituminous coal are a rather recent
development: of the total output only about 5 percent was mechanically cleaned at the mine in 1915, about 12 percent in 1936.
Where there is no cleaning plant, hand picking of impurities is
often necessary at the time the coal is loaded onto railroad cars
for shipment. As with anthracite, washing in some form of jig
is the most common form of mechanical cleaning, although pneu-
matic devices also have been developed for the purpose.

## IRON ORE [2]

As with coal, the processing of iron ore before shipment from the
mine is a relatively simple matter. The purpose of such beneficiation, as it is called, may be to improve the physical structure of
the ore by crushing or sintering, to concentrate the ore into
smaller bulk through the removal of waste matter, or to do both
of these things. Most ore is still shipped in the form in which it is
mined, without beneficiation; but the need for such after treatment has increased rather steadily and is a function, in part at
least, of the depletion of rich direct-shipping ores. Lean ores may
be smelted directly, but an economy of fuel results if they are
concentrated first. The proportion of all iron ore shipments consisting of concentrates rose from a negligible amount in the years
before 1909 to a tenth in 1915, and nearly a fifth in 1935–37.[3]

The process, or combination of processes, used in a given bene-

[2] This section is based on Nicholas Yaworski and others, *Iron Mining* (National
Research Project, Philadelphia, 1940), Chapter VI.

[3] A rich iron ore may contain 50 percent, a lean ore 30 percent, of metal: the
ratio of concentration (ore to concentrates produced from it) runs 1½ or 2 to 1. By
contrast, a rich (direct smelting) copper ore may contain 5 percent, a lean (concentrating) ore 2 percent of metal: the ratio of concentration may be as high as 15
or 20 to 1.

ficiating plant depends mainly upon the characteristics of the ore to be treated. Some ores must be crushed and screened, i.e., broken to a uniform size. In other cases very fine ore is agglomerated through sintering into coarse porous lumps. The same treatment may be accorded finely ground concentrates. The operation is performed by heat, and when moisture and other volatile constituents are eliminated at the same time, sintering also yields some degree of concentration.

Washing is used extensively to concentrate Minnesota and Alabama ores in which the iron is found in coarser pieces mixed with finer particles of sand: after preliminary crushing, the sand is washed away. Jigging is a gravity concentration process applied to ores containing coarse particles of rock or other waste matter. When agitated under proper conditions, the lighter rock particles collect on the surface of a slowly moving mass of ore and are skimmed off. This operation, which resembles similar methods sometimes used in the cleaning of coal, is applied chiefly in Minnesota.

Magnetic methods have been used for many years to concentrate the magnetites of New York, New Jersey and Pennsylvania. These ores consist of oxides of iron having such pronounced magnetic characteristics that even large particles adhere to an ordinary horseshoe magnet, leaving the nonmagnetic waste material behind. The process cannot be employed to concentrate hematite ores, which are nonmagnetic; but methods are being developed to change hematite to magnetite. If these methods are successful, it may become possible to apply magnetic concentration indirectly to the hematites of Minnesota and Alabama. The improvement of concentration methods has received considerable attention in recent years. Vast reserves of lean ore susceptible of large scale open pit mining are known to exist, and the richer, direct-shipping, ores are steadily being depleted.

## NONFERROUS ORES [4]

Like coal and iron ore, the ores of the nonferrous metals can be separated to some extent from waste material or gangue by such

---

[4] See especially Y. S. Leong and others, *Copper Mining* (National Research Project, Philadelphia, 1940), Chapter V; A. B. Parsons, *The Porphyry Coppers* (American Institute of Mining and Metallurgical Engineers, 1933), Chapter XX; and T. A. Rickard, *History of American Mining* (McGraw-Hill, 1932), Chapter XVIII.

simple expedients as washing and hand sorting. The pan used by
the placer miner for treating gold-bearing gravel comes to mind
in this connection. But the mining of nonferrous metals is for
the most part distinguished by a high ratio of waste to mineral
(many copper ores assay less than 2 percent of metal), and by the
frequent presence, in intimate association, of more than one type
of ore. These circumstances have prompted the development of
increasingly elaborate techniques for processing nonferrous ores
characterized by high ratios of concentration and small losses in
recovery,[5] and for permitting the simultaneous separation of the
ores of one metal from those of another. The ore itself undergoes
no chemical change; it is merely separated from a large part of the
waste in which it is embedded, so that actual extraction of the
metal in smelting may be carried through with greater facility.
Since ores may be dressed close to the mine, but are often smelted
at a distance, an economy in freight charges also results. As already indicated, the successful concentration of the ore has frequently been a prior condition for the mechanization of mining
itself. The elimination of the need for hand sorting at vein mines
has facilitated the introduction of mechanical loading, while concentration of the ore has alone made possible the exploitation of
the low grade porphyry coppers of the West.[6]

Ore dressing involves two steps, each of which has many variants,
depending upon the particular type of ore to be processed. The
first consists of breaking, crushing or grinding; the second involves
the separation of particles containing metal from waste matter,
and perhaps of particles containing one metal from those containing another.[7] In a modern concentration plant both steps are

[5] The degree of concentration is measured by the ratio of ore treated to concentrates produced. The efficiency of recovery is indicated by the ratio of the metal content of concentrates to the metal content of ore from which they are derived. In
any appraisal of the effectiveness of concentration techniques both ratios must be
considered: see further discussion, with special reference to copper, in Appendix D.

[6] It is true that most nonferrous ores are first concentrated and then smelted.
There are, however, many exceptional cases. Direct smelting copper ores (containing
at least 3 to 4 percent of metal) may be smelted without prior concentration. Again,
the precious metals are recovered from their ores largely by mechanical or chemical
means which do not involve smelting. In addition, some copper is obtained from
oxide ores by leaching with a solvent such as sulfuric acid, the copper being subsequently precipitated: however, copper ores that can profitably be leached are not
very common.

[7] Why breaking the ore is an essential first step in the process of concentration is
clear from the following explanation which, although it relates specifically to copper
ore, is of general validity: "Essentially a copper ore is composed of minerals that

highly mechanized. In the first the ore passes through several different kinds of mill for successively finer grinding. In the second, water in combination with a variety of special reagents effects the desired separation.

## Separation of the Precious Metals

These methods have a long development which stems from the original introduction of Mexican grinding mills (arrastres) on the Comstock lode in Nevada to extract silver in the 1860's,[8] and the researches prompted by the difficulty experienced in reducing the complex ores [9] of the Leadville district of Colorado in the 1870's. A partial solution was found, particularly for treating argentiferous and auriferous ores, in the stamp mill. In this device a heavy cylinder of metal is made to fall on a die upon which the ore has been placed, both the ore and the die being covered with water. The resulting pulp is then treated for recovery of the mineral content.[10] The stamp mill in use at the turn of the century was generally constructed of steel and powered by steam—a marked improvement over earlier wooden devices actuated by gravity or water power.

Until the introduction of the cyanide process in 1890 the stamp mill product was washed over tables coated with mercury which caught the gold particles and held them in alloy. This process, known as amalgamation, was fairly successful in dealing with the

---

contain copper . . . such as chalcocite . . . , and copper-free minerals such as quartz and pyrite, called gangue. If a typical piece or particle in a given ton of ore is 1/4 chalcocite and 3/4 gangue, no mechanical device can possibly effect a separation— can concentrate it. If, however, each piece or particle is broken into 4 smaller particles, one of which is clean chalcocite and the other 3 clean gangue, it is physically possible to make two products: 1/4 ton of chalcocite concentrate and 3/4 ton of waste or tailing." Parsons, *op. cit.*, pp. 431-32.

[8] The arrastre or arrastra was still employed to some extent in 1902. In its simplest form the "arrastra . . . consists of a circular bed of rock from 6 to 10 feet in diameter, with walls of vertical planks, having an upright pivoted post in the center, from which extend 2 or 4 horizontal arms. Stone drags, weighing usually from 200 to 1,000 pounds each, are attached by ropes or chains to the extremities of the arms, and are slowly drawn around by the rotation of the latter. The depth is usually between 18 and 30 inches. The pavement and drags are of the hardest rock conveniently obtainable." (U. S. Bureau of the Census, *Special Reports*, "Mines and Quarries, 1902," pp. 575-76.)

[9] Complex ores contain more than one metal.

[10] "Mines and Quarries, 1902," p. 576. By 1900 arrastres had largely passed from the picture, but at the time the Census of 1880 was taken they outnumbered stamp mills.

so-called free milling ores in which gold occurs in metallic form, but it was entirely unable to cope with the much more plentiful refractory ores in which the gold occurs in intimate association with other minerals. The latter type of ore had to be smelted or treated by costly chemical processes. As a result, large bodies of low grade ore were rejected until cyanidation was discovered. Indeed, the adoption of the cyanide process led to the reopening of many abandoned gold mines containing large quantities of ore previously considered unworkable, as well as the reworking of gold-bearing tailings accumulated at stamp mills. These tailings resulted from the inability of amalgamation to capture very fine particles of gold even in free milling ore. The cyanide process, on the other hand, is applied to finely ground ore from which the gold is taken up by the sodium or potassium cyanide dissolved in water. This process, which still remains the chief method for the extraction of gold and silver from their ores, was one of the forces that served to foster the abandonment of selective mining.[11]

Improvements in the design of gravity concentration devices during the nineteenth century culminated in the shaking riffled tables introduced around 1875. Particles of ore were carried over several tables on a stream of water. The tables shook up, down and sideways, thereby causing the heavier metallic particles to sink lower than the lighter waste. The waste flowed off, and the metal was caught against the ridges of the table.[12] These tables effected such a satisfactory separation of sulfide minerals at so low a cost that they became an important factor—even before the development of modern methods for concentrating the base metals —in the shift to nonselective mining.[13] As the result of such improvements in the technique of ore dressing in the closing decades of the nineteenth century a decided fall occurred in the grade of gold and silver ores that could be treated economically.[14] Again,

11 *Ibid.*, pp. 594-95; C. E. Julihn, "Copper: An Example of Advancing Technology and the Utilization of Low-Grade Ores," in *Mineral Economics,* ed. by F. G. Tryon and E. C. Eckel (McGraw-Hill, 1932), p. 126.

12 James H. Collins, "Mining Copper and the Nobler Metals" in Waldemar Kaempffert (ed.), *A Popular History of American Invention* (Scribner's, 1924), Vol. II, pp. 71-76.

13 Julihn, *op. cit.,* p. 126.

14 Figures presented by Isaac Hourwich in the 1902 Census are of interest in this respect: "By the old amalgamation process not more than 70 percent, and usually not more than 60 percent, of the gold contents of the ore was saved. With the aid of modern processes [i.e. cyaniding and shaking riffled tables] more than 90 percent of the assay contents can be recovered" ("Mines and Quarries, 1902," p. 577). When

many complex ores, in which gold is found in union with silver, copper, iron, pyrites and other minerals, could not have been handled at all without the combination of improved concentration and cyanidation.

Thus methods for extracting the precious metals from their ores, principally by direct recovery (i.e. without the necessity of smelting), had already reached an advanced stage of development by the end of the nineteenth century. Judged by present day standards, techniques for concentrating and separating copper, lead-zinc, and complex ores had not, by 1900, made nearly so much progress. In the treatment of these ores in order to separate mineral from gangue, the various devices in use at the opening of the period we are studying relied upon a difference in specific gravity between the components of crushed ore. It was known that if particles of nearly equal size are agitated in water, the heavier metallic particles tend to sink to the bottom, while the waste material can be skimmed from the surface. In fact this technique —basic to all processes then employed—had already reached a high state of practicability more than a century earlier in the Harz jig, named for the German Harz mountains where it had been developed.[15] Since then no basic improvement had occurred. The çyanide process had proved a sort of philosopher's stone which "transmuted" waste material into gold: what this process had done for auriferous minerals, flotation techniques were to do for ores containing copper, lead and zinc.

## Concentration by Flotation

As with the ores of the precious metals, modern methods of treating copper, lead and zinc ores consist of two principal stages: first, milling, and second, concentration. In many cases, and especially in the treatment of the low grade porphyry ores of copper, crushing and grinding must produce particles no larger than a few thousandths of an inch in diameter: so intimately are

---

translated into monetary terms, the importance of the change is more easily grasped. In California in the early 1880's only gold ores yielding at least $100 to $200 per ton could be treated, and dumps were covered with large quantities of tailings ranging in content from $40 to $60 per ton. In 1900, with the improvement in recovery techniques, the rejected ore was considered exceptionally rich.

15 Julihn, *op. cit.*, pp. 118-19. The jig consisted essentially of a set of inclined screens moving up and down in boxes of water. The ore passed over the screens, and the heavier metallic particles gathered at the bottom of the box.

mineral and waste material associated that any coarser treatment
would fail to render separation possible. The ore to be crushed,
if it comes from an underground mine, is sometimes a foot in
diameter; from an open pit mine it may be even larger. No single
milling device is adequate. The coarser operations are performed
by jaw or gyratory crushers,[16] which reduce the lumps of ore to an
inch or two in size. These are then ground in ball or tube mills,
which utilize the abrasive action of steel balls or flint pebbles in
a revolving tube.[17]

Some of the simpler base metal ores can be successfully treated
by gravity methods, and jigs and shaking tables, familiar in the
technology of the precious metals, were the earliest devices used
for concentrating copper, lead and zinc ores. But today concentration, especially of low grade copper ores, depends heavily upon
flotation methods. The flotation process, introduced in 1912, may
be said to turn gravity concentration upside down. The metallic
content of the ore is made to float while the waste material sinks
to the bottom. This apparent interchange of physical properties
is accomplished by the addition of a minute quantity of oil to a
pulp consisting of water and ore. When the pulp is then agitated
—by the introduction of air from a blower at the bottom of the
flotation cell—the mineral particles attach themselves to the air
bubbles thus formed and may be scraped from the surface.[18] The
gangue particles, on the other hand, remain below. Parsons has
supplied a simplified explanation of the mechanics of the process
in the following passage: "A mutual attraction exists between a
bubble of air and a particle of mineral (either sulphide or gangue)
that is coated with a minute film of grease or oil. However, in the
presence of water, oil has a stronger tendency to film a particle of
sulphide . . . than a particle of gangue." [19]

In its tremendous impact on the copper, lead and zinc mining
industries, the flotation process matched the earlier changes

[16] As its name implies, the jaw crusher relies chiefly on compression. Gyratory
crushers consist usually of an eccentric cone revolving in a cylinder, and produce
both compression and abrasion.

[17] John Gross, "Crushing and Grinding," *Bulletin 402* (U. S. Bureau of Mines,
1938). The fine-grinding techniques used today in milling metallic ores were originally developed in the cement industry (Frederick Laist, "Developments in the
Metallurgy of Copper, 1880–1940," unpublished manuscript).

[18] Parsons, *op. cit.*, p. 442; also Laist, *op. cit.*

[19] *Op. cit.*, p. 443.

wrought by cyanidation in the mining of the precious metals. As in the case of amalgamation and cyanidation, the new process could profit by the very conditions that had affected the older method adversely. The chief difficulty of gravity concentration lies in its inability to effect a separation of metal from gangue when the material has been slimed (too finely ground). Yet with most ores of copper, lead and zinc, fine grinding is essential to liberate the metal from the gangue. For this reason, as much as 30 to 40 percent of the copper in porphyry ores [20] was wasted with gravity concentration, mostly in slimes which could not be concentrated.[21] This problem was solved by the flotation process, which in fact works best with finely ground ore. With such ores flotation not only achieves a higher recovery than gravity concentration, but also produces a cleaner concentrate, precisely because finer grinding liberates a higher percentage of the mineral from the gangue.[22]

The flotation process was originally developed in Australia about the year 1910 and was first applied in the United States in 1912 at a zinc concentrator.[23] Its use in copper concentrating dates from the period 1913–16, when it served merely as an accessory to gravity concentration. Usually it treated the slimed portion of the ground ore, to which gravity methods could not be applied. As grinding became increasingly fine, flotation gradually became the chief process, and the period 1923–27 witnessed the adoption of "all-flotation" methods at copper concentrators.[24]

The spread of flotation during this period was accelerated by a major refinement in the process. Although flotation recovered a higher percentage of the mineral in the ore than was possible with gravity methods, it could not distinguish adequately among the several minerals that might be found in the ore. If, for example, a copper ore included pyrite (iron sulfide) with the copper sulfide, the flotation concentrate was likely also to include the pyrite. Since the presence of pyrite meant greater difficulties in smelting and therefore served to augment costs, it was desirable to find a method that would eliminate pyrite from the concentrate. Such

[20] Porphyry ores are characterized by the fact that the mineral occurs in small particles finely disseminated through the rock, rather than in veins.

[21] Parsons, *op. cit.*, p. 441.

[22] Laist, *op. cit.*

[23] Parsons, *op. cit.*, p. 445; Rickard, *History of American Mining*, pp. 404-05.

[24] Thomas G. Chapman, "Concentration of Copper Ores in North America," *Bulletin 392* (U. S. Bureau of Mines, 1936), p. 5.

a technique, which came to be known as selective or differential flotation, was introduced around 1923.[25]

In selective flotation new reagents known as "collectors" and "depressants" are added to the mineral pulp. "These reagents are not oils but are chemical compounds. They do not take the place of oils, which still have to be used, but modify the surfaces of the sulphide particles in such a way that they become more receptive or less receptive to oiling, as the case may be." Thus, "the addition of a few ounces of sodium xanthate per ton of ore greatly accelerates the floatability of the minerals" and "a similar amount of sodium cyanide tends to keep iron pyrite from floating." [26] In this case the pyrite may be either removed with the gangue or recovered as a separate concentrate suitable for further processing.

Thus among the advantages of selective flotation is the fact that it facilitates the recovery of byproducts. For example, by earlier methods of concentration a lead-zinc ore would yield a lead concentrate containing some zinc (which not only interfered with smelting but was lost in the process) and a zinc concentrate containing enough lead to make smelting difficult (but not enough to be recovered). Moreover, both concentrates were often so lean that smelting became an expensive undertaking. The use of selective flotation now produces a lead concentrate practically free of zinc, and a zinc concentrate practically free of lead, both rich enough to be cheaply smelted.[27]

Since the introduction of selective flotation there has been no major change in concentration practice, although a number of modifications of the basic technique have increased recovery of metal and improved the grade of concentrate produced. Important among these changes has been the development of new chemical reagents which permit increasingly broader selective action in flotation.

The record of beneficiating plants—especially those working metallic ores—is impressive. In the face of a declining grade of material they have been able to recover ever higher percentages of the metal contained in the ore. Figures on percentage of recovery —the least ambiguous measure of increasing mill efficiency available to us—tell a story of remarkable achievement. In a sample of

[25] Parsons, *op. cit.*, pp. 456-57.
[26] Laist, *op. cit.*
[27] We are indebted to Professor Read for elucidating this example.

several of the leading copper concentrating plants, recovery rose from about 70 percent of the assay content in 1911 to about 90 percent in 1930.[28] These increased recoveries were accompanied by a marked improvement in the grade of concentrates produced. A smelter today need not treat as large a tonnage of concentrate to obtain a given amount of metal as was necessary some thirty years ago. In addition, the enhanced selective action of the flotation process has resulted in the elimination of many impurities that formerly rendered smelting difficult if not impossible.

The net result of all these changes has been not only an increase in the product obtainable from a given volume of raw material, but a greatly expanded scope of the methods of mass exploitation, which have been the distinctive contribution of the last five decades to mining technology.

[28] For source of data see below, Appendix D.

# Part Three

# Technological Change and Productivity in Individual Industries

"Mineral economics, therefore, is the record of struggle between opposing forces. On the one hand is the factor of exhaustion, with its burden of accumulating handicaps. On the other is mineral technology, aided by its allies, exploration and transport. Finding of new deposits gives the mining engineer new ground to work upon and expansion of the transportation network may open up deposits known but previously inaccessible. The result of the struggle differs from place to place. In thousands of individual mines and scores of districts depletion has the best of it. If the world were dependent on the copper mines of Cornwall, or the silver-lead of ancient Laurium, the best of its technology could not avert a huge increase in price and a curtailment of supply. But taking the world as a whole, technology and its allies have generally the best of it, and their victory has nowhere been more striking than in the United States."   F. G. TRYON

# Chapter 8

# Bituminous Coal Mining

IN THE preceding chapters we surveyed the mineral industry as a whole from the standpoint of physical efficiency. We investigated trends in output and employment during the past forty years, and made some comparisons between the experiences of different branches of mining. We sketched the history and development of the technique of mineral extraction and reviewed its present condition. The purpose of the more detailed studies in this and the following chapters is to round out the picture. The various minerals present quite different problems in their extraction, but in every case the physical conditions of their occurrence are of fundamental importance. Some minerals remain readily accessible and of excellent quality. In the case of others the highest grade or most easily mined deposits have long since been exhausted: here techniques unknown to the miners of the past must be used if workable material is to be obtained. We shall endeavor to appraise the results of the perennial conflict between resource depletion and advancing technology as it has affected the more important individual mining industries.

Among these industries coal deserves pride of place. Despite the substitution of other fuels, and the rise of water power, coal still furnishes about half of the nation's energy supply, and the mining of coal continues to employ more than half the workers engaged in mineral extraction. The production of solid fuel in this country falls naturally into two major divisions: (1) the bituminous coal industry, geographically scattered, and including all mines other than those in the Pennsylvania anthracite region, and (2) the Pennsylvania anthracite industry, concentrated in a rather small area within that state. We turn first to the larger of these two industries—that producing bituminous coal.

The bituminous industry, then, embraces all coal mines except those producing Pennsylvania anthracite. This peculiar definition has to be adopted because the industry's product is so diverse that no single positive criterion can serve as a convenient touchstone of classification. Diversity of product manifests itself in two forms: variations in rank [1] of coal, and variations in quality. Variations in rank range all the way from the sub-bituminous lignites of Texas and the Dakotas to the anthracites produced outside of Pennsylvania (notably in Arkansas and Virginia). However, the lignites and the non-Pennsylvania anthracites constitute a quantitatively unimportant segment of the bituminous industry's total output. Of greater significance are differences in quality of product, which cover such diverse factors as size, and content of ash, sulfur and moisture. These variations may, in fact, be but slightly disguised divergences in rank, which is greatly influenced by the amount of volatile matter contained in the coal.[2]

Despite variations in the product of the industry, output is generally measured by a single figure representing total tonnage produced. We have followed the customary usage in this respect; hence our index of physical output is a series of such figures expressed as relatives of a comparison base which is either 1899 or 1929. Whether any significant shifts in the internal composition of coal output have occurred during the period covered by our analysis we have no way of knowing with certainty.[3] If, as seems likely, the distribution of the output of coal with regard to rank has not shifted in any marked degree, our index is probably adequate on this score. It is possible, however, that the progressively greater acceptance of fine sizes over a period of years has led to an increase in their relative importance in the total picture, with a resultant upward bias in the movement of the index.[4] To a cer-

[1] By rank is meant the degree of metamorphism, or geological change, through which the coal has passed from its original deposition to the present.

[2] See *Report of the Committee on Prices in the Bituminous Coal Industry*, prepared for the Conference on Price Research (National Bureau of Economic Research, 1938), pp. 6-7.

[3] Ideally, in the absence of price changes, an index of output should vary directly with value of products, but it will not do so if shifts have occurred between differently priced varieties.

[4] It is important to note that our impression that some of the new sizes and varieties are of a relatively lower grade than the coal produced at the turn of the century is, in part at least, illusory, since their growing importance is a byproduct of technological advance both in the production and in the utilization of coal. Improvements in coal preparation techniques have made smaller sizes marketable because they have raised the quality of so-called fine coals. It is likely, then, that the "fines" of today are really something other than the "fines" of the early part of the century. Writing in 1927, F. G. Tryon concluded that since 1913 any change in the average quality of coal as a whole, measured in heat units per ton or otherwise, had been very slight (*Mineral Resources, 1926*, Part II, p. 445). In addition, there is the factor of increased efficiency in coal utilization, which has perhaps increased the efficiency of a ton of "poorer" coal to such a degree that it lessens appreciably the gap between the "high" grade coal of 1899 and the "low" grade coal of 1939.

tain extent, though, this putative bias must have been counteracted by the tendency of coal mines to pay more attention to the specialized needs of individual consumers, giving greater care to sizing, sorting, etc.

So much for the products of the industry. There remains the task of defining the limits of the production process that we call mining. Adjacent to the underground mine or open pit which yields the raw mineral is usually found a preparation plant where the run-of-the-mine coal is sized and perhaps cleaned. The functions performed by such a plant are generally considered as part of "mining." Hence, the industry, as defined for our purpose, is one that includes all processes preliminary to the movement of coal from the mining property for shipment to the consumer. Coking, like other forms of processing, we regard as manufacturing and exclude from the scope of this report.

## THE RELATION BETWEEN OUTPUT
## AND EMPLOYMENT

The peak in both production and employment [5] in bituminous coal mining came during the first World War, and that conflict may, therefore, be taken as a convenient dividing point in the history of the industry. Before the war one may trace a general upward movement in both series which culminated in their wartime peaks. Thereafter the direction of movement was reversed. The impression conveyed by Chart 36 is one of rapid rise, followed by gradual decline, in both production and employment.

Although the general direction of movement of output and employment is similar in both periods, it is clear that the relation between these two quantities underwent a gradual alteration. As the coal industry expanded, the growth of production outstripped the gain in employment: between 1899 and 1918 the increase in the former amounted to 200 percent, in the latter to only 140 percent. In like fashion, the post-war contraction was accompanied by a steeper fall in employment than in production: between 1918 and the low point in 1932 output declined 47 percent, employment 61 percent. During the period before the first World War output rose so rapidly in relation to advances in pro-

[5] As explained in Chapter 4, we shall regard the manday as the basic unit of employment.

ductivity that the level of employment also rose. After 1918 the trend of output was apparently downward, and in this period employment fell more rapidly than production. The decline reached its lowest point in 1932, when for the first (and as yet the only)

Chart 36

BITUMINOUS COAL

Output, Employment and Productivity, 1880 – 1939

(1899:100)

Percent

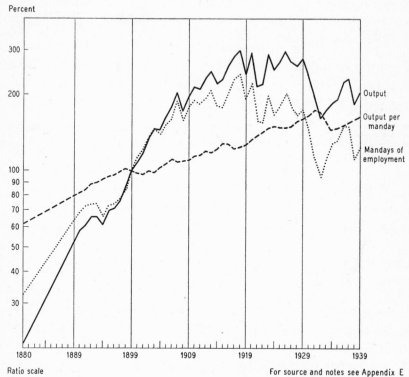

Ratio scale                    For source and notes see Appendix E

time since 1899 mandays worked fell below the 1899 level. Thereafter a recovery set in, but in 1936–37 employment was still no greater than it had been 30 years earlier in 1904–05. Thus the expansion in output per manday is seen to have been continuous in tendency, and to have proceeded at about the same rate, whether the trend of production was rising or falling.

As we saw in Chapter 2, the decline in bituminous coal mining from its peak in 1918 is in large degree the obverse of the meteoric rise of oil and gas wells as a source of fuel. Nevertheless, more people are still employed in mining bituminous coal than in any other mineral industry. In 1937 manhours of employment in this branch of activity were about equal to the composite of manhours at oil and gas wells, in the metal mining group, and in the dimension and crushed stone industries, with phosphate rock and gypsum mining thrown in for good measure. For this reason alone the factors that have determined the volume of the industry's employment would be worthy of close study. But there is an additional contrast, for in value of production this industry, with its extremely large labor force, has relinquished first place to the petroleum and natural gas industry, which in 1937 absorbed only about one half as many manhours of labor. Again, the group of industries listed above, whose composite of manhours was about equal to that of bituminous coal in 1937, had products with a combined value about three times as great as the worth of bituminous coal produced in that year. This contrast suggests that the extraction of coal, judged by its consumption of labor, is an extremely expensive business. So it is, in terms of dollar value of product, or of energy units produced, per manhour.[6] To be sure, we cannot conclude on this account alone that the technological state of the industry is backward. But these considerations may suggest either that the technological problems encountered by the industry are peculiar, or that its resource conditions are less favorable than those obtaining elsewhere. We shall find that there are elements of truth in both these suppositions.

Among the mining industries for which we have productivity measures, bituminous coal ranks low in the increase registered between 1902 and 1939. Output per manday increased 63 percent, output per manhour 104 percent (Table 11). Among the more important mining industries, only Pennsylvania anthracite failed to better this record. The metal group, the stone industries, and oil and gas wells all showed substantially larger increases in productivity over the period. When compared with the average change in productivity for mining as a whole (excluding oil and gas wells), the record of bituminous coal mining appears less unfavorable, but chiefly by reason of the relatively large part that the industry itself plays in the determination of this average.

The two coal industries—bituminous and anthracite—are the only branches of mining for which we have continuous annual

[6] See also Tables 13 and 14 above.

employment data back to 1902. In Chart 37 a comparison is made between man, manday and manhour productivity for bituminous coal. The divergence between output per manday and per manhour (plotted to intersect in 1902) reflects the shortening of the workday (from 8.8 hours in 1902 to 7 hours in 1939: see Table 10 above). Differences in movement between output per manday and output per man are a function of the number of days worked per

Chart 37

BITUMINOUS COAL
Productivity, 1902 - 39
(1902 : 100)

Percent

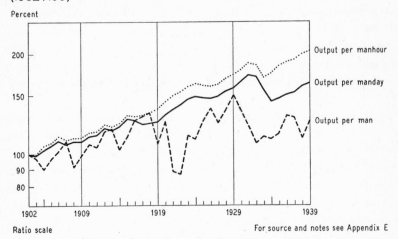

year. The latter curve reflects year-to-year variations in output which scarcely influence manday or manhour productivity. We must attribute the slower rise of output per man than of output per manday, and the tendency of these two curves to move farther apart as the period advances, to a decline in the number of working days per year, i.e., to more intermittent operation of the average mine than was formerly common. This change has been regarded by many as a symptom of overcapacity.

Among the complex factors which have influenced productivity in bituminous coal, as in other mining industries, are two that deserve special attention: (1) resource conditions, that is, the extent to which depletion has occurred, the circumstances wherein currently exploited deposits of the mineral are found, and the ease or difficulty of extraction; and (2) technology, considered broadly to include all mechanical and engineering, and even some managerial, aspects of coal mining. These two factors, in their joint and several operation, are commonly the most important influences upon the productivity of any mineral industry. Yet the manner in which they exert their influence differs markedly from one industry to another. Let us turn first to resource conditions, and then consider the part played by technology.

## RESOURCE CONDITIONS

In the mining of many minerals deterioration in the quality of resources over time may constitute a drag on the growth of industrial productivity. We should therefore seek to determine whether this basic factor, whose effect can be delayed only if exploitation of the mineral is renounced, has been at work in the bituminous coal industry.

To a certain extent all mineral industries are beset by natural difficulties which increase as extraction proceeds, for it usually happens that the most readily accessible and the highest grade deposits are brought into production early during the life of any branch of mining.[7] As these deposits become depleted (that is, decline in grade or become less readily accessible), and as demand continues and perhaps expands, it becomes necessary to bring other deposits—which in one way or another are inferior to the deposits first exploited—into production. And so, in broad outline, the process continues. However, for purposes of comparing one industry with another the broad outline is less important than the variations within its framework. Thus, in the present context, we are more interested in the deterioration of the country's bituminous coal resources compared with rates of depletion of other minerals than we are in the absolute change in the quality of workable bituminous coal deposits as such. Only then can we discover whether the relatively smaller rise in the industry's productivity is attributable, in part at least, to a greater deterioration of bituminous coal resources.

The quality and accessibility of our deposits of bituminous coal have not yet seriously declined. As recently as ten years ago, for example, Tryon and Berquist remarked: "There is such an abundance of thick and easily accessible coal that mining condi-

[7] See Chapter 5 above.

tions are nearly, if not entirely, as favorable today as they were 50 years ago." [8]

It is doubtful that such a statement could be made about any other major branch of extraction, with the possible exception of petroleum and natural gas. Certainly, since the beginning of mining, the deterioration of bituminous coal resources has been slight in comparison with the situation in the metal mining industries.[9] To be sure, the statement that 3 thousand billion tons of recoverable coal remain in the ground—enough to last perhaps 70 centuries at current rates of exploitation—conveys somewhat too favorable an impression. The supplies of high grade coking coal, for instance, are relatively much more limited: the Connellsville seam may be exhausted within a few decades, and supplies of coal of comparable quality for metallurgical purposes are not widely distributed. The best steam coal is somewhat more common, but it too forms only a small fraction of total coal reserves.[10]

Nevertheless, when all suitable qualifications have been made, the broad generalization seems justified that in the bituminous coal industry depletion has not yet led to appreciable deterioration in the physical conditions under which the mineral is obtained. This observation is confirmed by such a simple (although not definitive) measure as depth of shaft. Depth of shaft averages a few hundred feet in the bituminous coal fields, as contrasted with a few thousand feet in the metal mining camps.[11] We should note also that not all underground bituminous mines are shaft mines, but that many bituminous deposits are still reached by slopes and drifts, some even above the ground-water level.[12] Except in bituminous coal, such a condition is rarely encountered

[8] F. G. Tryon and F. E. Berquist, "Mineral Economics—An Outline of the Field" in *Mineral Economics*, ed. by F. G. Tryon and E. C. Eckel (McGraw-Hill, 1932), p. 27.

[9] See also Willard E. Hotchkiss and others, *Bituminous-Coal Mining* (National Research Project, Philadelphia, 1939), p. 8.

[10] Glen L. Parker, *The Coal Industry* (American Council on Public Affairs, Washington, 1940), pp. 2-3.

[11] In 1926 the average depth of all underground bituminous mines was about 320 feet; averages for individual states ranged from 730 feet for Utah to 70 feet for North Dakota (Hotchkiss and others, *Bituminous-Coal Mining*, pp. 58-60). See also F. G. Tryon, "The Changing Distribution of Resources" in *Migration and Economic Opportunity* by Carter Goodrich and others (University of Pennsylvania Press, 1936), p. 264.

[12] F. G. Tryon and Margaret H. Schoenfeld, "Comparison of Physical Conditions in British and American Coal Mines," reprint from *Coal and Coal Trade Journal*, Sept. 1, Sept. 8, Oct. 7, and Nov. 4, 1926, p. 4.

in any but the very early stages of mineral exploitation, and is a far cry from the elaborate measures used to gain access to the typical underground metal deposit. It seems reasonable to conclude, therefore, that bituminous coal mining has been more fortunate than most other mineral industries with regard to the mining conditions encountered. If we wish to explain the comparatively slow rise of output per worker in bituminous coal mining we must, evidently, look for other causes.

## TECHNOLOGY

Besides the character of resource occurrence, the chief determinant of productivity in an industry is its level of technological attainment. Since we are interested in relative behavior, we must ask how technological advance in bituminous coal mining compares with that in other mining industries. What are the other industries most relevant to such a comparison? The productivity of anthracite mines has increased even less rapidly than that of bituminous coal mines; and the technology of oil and gas production is so dissimilar that useful comparisons cannot be drawn. Consequently the discussion resolves itself, at this point, into a comparison of technological conditions in bituminous coal mining and in the metal mining industries. Certainly in each of the three main divisions of metal mining, productivity has increased more rapidly than in the soft coal industry.[13] How far, if at all, can these differences be explained in terms of divergence in technological background?

First, we should notice a significant difference between the coal industry and metal mining. As we shall see, iron ore and copper, which among the metals have made the greatest strides, depend heavily upon open pit mining. Power-shovel strip mining of soft coal, this industry's version of the open cut mining technique, is a response to special resource conditions and is rather unimportant.[14] Despite the increasing share of strip methods in the mining of coal since the first World War, these operations accounted for less than 10 percent of bituminous output in 1939. The typical coal mine is therefore an underground mine. Compared with stripping, underground mining has two disadvantages. Mechaniza-

[13] Table 11 and Chart 30, above.
[14] It is not at present practiced where the coal lies at greater depths than 60 to 80 feet.

tion is more difficult to achieve in cramped spaces below ground; and the benefits of scale are less easily obtained, since maximum practicable daily tonnages are limited by the capacity of underground transportation systems and of hoisting equipment. Yet its greater dependence upon underground production does not account for the apparent backwardness of bituminous coal mining in comparison with other forms of extraction. For between 1914 and 1936, at least, underground copper mines increased their productivity almost as fast as open pit mines, and very much faster than underground coal mines (Chart 38). It is to the backwardness of the underground coal mine, therefore, and not to the back-

Chart 38
UNDERGROUND AND OPEN PIT MINES
Output per Manday, 1914 – 36
(1914 . 100)

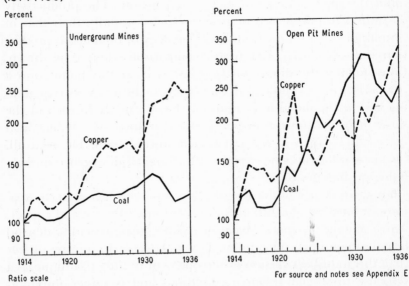

Ratio scale                                        For source and notes see Appendix E

wardness of underground mining in general, that we must look if we wish to explain the laggard behavior of productivity measures in bituminous coal.

In making comparisons between coal and copper, or some other type of mining, we must remember that the mechanization of certain functions in a given industry may be delayed through physical conditions peculiar to that industry. Thus, even after a machine has been successfully utilized by a mine producing one mineral, another mine producing some other mineral, or even the same mineral, may be balked in its attempt to use the machine by a set of geological circumstances entirely different from those encountered in the first mine. Often it can adapt the machine to its own needs, but sometimes it cannot do so. Another difficulty we face in making comparisons between the technology of different industries is the fact that certain functions are of more importance in one type of mine than in another. For example, drilling is a much more vital operation for the hard materials encountered in metal mines than it is for bituminous coal mines, where softer materials occur. On the other hand, the many miles of haulageways to be found in bituminous mines, partly because of their age, make transportation a far more serious problem in these mines. It has been said that there are more miles of railroad track below the surface in the coal mines of Pennsylvania than above ground in the entire state.[15]

It is clearly inadvisable to attempt to compare the degree of mechanization of each mining function considered separately. Yet a meaningful comparison can be made between the general level of technology in bituminous coal and in other types of mines. At this point we may note merely that many of the production techniques that have come into prominence in these other industries (especially metal mining) during the past four decades depend on a careful organization of production with an integration of functions within the mine, as well as upon an articulation of mine and beneficiating plant.[16] This is eminently true both of open cut metal mining and of certain techniques (especially caving and other gravity loading methods) for the mass production of ores underground. How does the bituminous coal industry compare in this respect?

In 1921, several years before the emergence of mechanized loading, the managing editor of *Coal Age*—the industry's principal trade journal—wrote: "Mining [of coal] is still in a way a 'cottage' industry, only the cottage is a room in the mines." [17] This state-

[15] Thomas T. Read, *Our Mineral Civilization* (Williams and Wilkins, Baltimore, 1932), p. 8.

[16] See Chapters 11 and 12 on iron ore and copper, respectively, and the discussion of technological change in Chapter 5 above.

[17] R. Dawson Hall, "Have Mining Engineers Accepted All That Developments in Machinery for Handling Coal Imply?", *Coal Age*, July 7, 1921; quoted in Carter Goodrich, *The Miner's Freedom* (Marshall Jones, Boston, 1925), p. 19.

ment answers the question posed at the end of the preceding paragraph, but it does more than that. It takes us to the crux of the problem by leading us to the heart of the coal mine. For it is in the room where the miner works that the problems of coal production have to be solved.

The prevailing system of mining in the bituminous coal mines of this country is the room-and-pillar method (Chart 39). This title aptly describes the technique, for the actual breaking and

Chart 39

ROOM-AND-PILLAR MINING OF BITUMINOUS COAL

Diagrammatic Plan of Workings

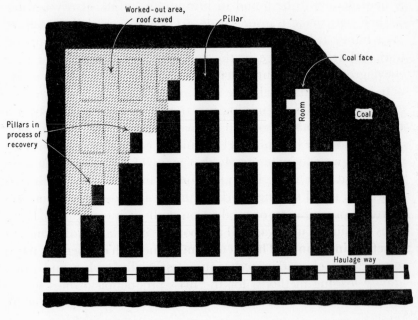

For source and notes see Appendix E

loading of the coal is done by miners working in rooms separated by pillars left in place to support the mine roof. Work goes on at one end of the room—known as the working face—and the room is constantly being pushed toward the boundary of the coal seam. The mine is broken up into many of these rooms, each with a working face large enough only for one or two working miners.

When the mines were small, as they must have been when the method was first utilized, the working faces were probably fairly close to each other. But with the growth of the mines the number of rooms and working faces has increased, and the area over which they have been scattered has grown constantly larger. An expansion in the volume of output from any mine was usually met in only one way—by the development of more working rooms. Since resources were usually abundant, this sort of expansion was quite feasible.

As the mines grew, and operations became less concentrated, the problem of supervision became increasingly difficult. So long as mining remained a craft industry the miners who worked a room were completely responsible for mining the coal it contained. They performed all the functions, from making the undercut and drilling blast holes to cleaning and loading the coal. As a result there was little need for supervisory control (especially since the miners were piece workers) or for coordination, and the system no doubt worked tolerably well.

Then came the mechanical cutter. In the mines in which it was adopted, undercutting of the coal seam ceased to be part of the hand miner's craft. As the device caught on and its use became more general (see Table 15), a new group of mine workers came into being—the machine runners. Because each room could not be provided with cutting machines it was necessary to have a group of men whose job it was to go from room to room and cut the coal for the miners. Since the miners were now obliged to wait for the machine runner before they could break down the coal, there arose an obvious need for coordination of activities. The lack of supervision associated with the room-and-pillar system of mining should have become a source of concern. Perhaps it did, but apparently the condition was not remedied. Machine cutting was somehow worked into the prevailing mine routine, and it was probably less effective than it would have been if there had been more intensive efforts to coordinate the new development with the customary layout of the work.[18]

Machine cutting did not force any important modification in the room-and-pillar system of mining. Loading was still a hand operation, and as long as mechanization was confined to cutting it could readily be absorbed into existing mining practice. The center of activity was still the room in which the miner worked;

[18] See Hugh Archbald, *The Four Hour Day in Coal* (H. W. Wilson Co., 1922), p. 48; also U. S. Coal Commission, *Report*, Part III (1925), especially pp. 1944-51.

TABLE 15

BITUMINOUS COAL: MECHANICAL CUTTING AND LOADING IN UNDERGROUND MINES[a]

| Year | Mechanically Cut | | Mechanically Loaded[c] | |
|---|---|---|---|---|
| | Quantity (Mil. s.t.) | Percent of Total Underground Output[b] | Quantity (Mil. s.t.) | Percent of Total Underground Output |
| 1899 | 44.0 | 22.7 | .. | .. |
| 1900 | 52.8 | 24.9 | .. | .. |
| 1901 | 57.8 | 25.6 | .. | .. |
| 1902 | 69.6 | 26.8 | .. | .. |
| 1903 | 78.0 | 27.6 | .. | .. |
| 1904 | 78.6 | 28.2 | .. | .. |
| 1905 | 103.4 | 32.8 | .. | .. |
| 1906 | 118.8 | 34.7 | .. | .. |
| 1907 | 138.5 | 35.1 | .. | .. |
| 1908 | 123.2 | 37.0 | .. | .. |
| 1909 | 142.5 | 37.5 | .. | .. |
| 1910 | 174.0 | 41.7 | .. | .. |
| 1911 | 178.2 | 43.9 | .. | .. |
| 1912 | 210.5 | 46.8 | .. | .. |
| 1913 | 242.4 | 50.7 | .. | .. |
| 1914 | 218.4 | 51.8 | .. | .. |
| 1915 | 243.2 | 55.3 | .. | .. |
| 1916 | 283.7 | 56.9 | .. | .. |
| 1917 | 306.4 | 56.1 | .. | .. |
| 1918 | 323.9 | 56.7 | .. | .. |
| 1919 | 276.0 | 60.0 | .. | .. |
| 1920 | 339.8 | 60.7 | .. | .. |
| 1921 | 272.7 | 66.4 | .. | .. |
| 1922 | 267.0 | 64.8 | .. | .. |
| 1923 | 377.4 | 68.3 | .. | .. |
| 1924 | 336.3 | 71.5 | .. | .. |
| 1925 | 366.7 | 72.9 | .. | .. |
| 1926 | 410.9 | 73.8 | .. | .. |
| 1927 | 374.0 | 74.9 | .. | .. |
| 1928 | 369.7 | 76.9 | 21.6 | 4.5 |
| 1929 | 403.6 | 78.4 | 37.9 | 7.4 |
| 1930 | 362.4 | 81.0 | 47.0 | 10.5 |
| 1931 | 302.3 | 83.2 | 47.6 | 13.1 |
| 1932 | 244.0 | 84.1 | 35.8 | 12.3 |
| 1933 | 267.0 | 84.7 | 37.8 | 12.0 |
| 1934 | 284.7 | 84.1 | 41.4 | 12.2 |
| 1935 | 293.7 | 84.2 | 47.2 | 13.5 |
| 1936 | 348.3 | 84.8 | 67.0 | 16.3 |
| 1937 | d | d | 83.5 | 20.2 |
| 1938 | 278.3 | 87.5 | 85.1 | 26.7 |
| 1939 | 314.0 | 87.9 | 110.7 | 31.0 |

*For footnotes see opposite page.*

and miners continued to perform the several mining operations as they had in the past—largely unaffected by any fixed routine of underground operation. In brief, even after cutting machines were used widely, the industry as a whole could be characterized as unaffected by "modern methods of quantity production, modern labor saving machinery, modern methods of management."[19] With the exception of the machine runners, and to a much smaller extent, of power drilling crews, there was no division of labor of the sort found in other types of mining. Division of labor implied coordination of functions, and the coal industry had not yet solved the problem of over-all supervision.[20] Indeed, the failure of mine operators to work out a system that could cope with problems of supervision and coordination acted to a large extent as a positive deterrent to greater mechanization of the coal mines.

This, then, was the situation in the early 1920's—about half way through the period covered by our indexes—as established by the many studies of the industry made at that time.[21] These studies were, however, carried through when the industry was presumably on the threshold of a technological rebirth, and when observers were looking forward to seeing bituminous coal engulfed in the "onward sweep of the machine process." What bulked large on the technological horizon was the loading machine, which was destined to revolutionize the tasks of the mine worker. Since the early 1920's machine loading has grown considerably (see Table 15), and today about 30 percent of the underground output is

[19] Walton H. Hamilton and Helen R. Wright, *The Case of Bituminous Coal* (Macmillan, 1925), p. 61.

[20] See Carter Goodrich, *The Miner's Freedom* and Hugh Archbald, *op. cit., passim*.

[21] In addition to the works by Goodrich, Archbald, and Hamilton and Wright already cited, mention should be made of a study of "Underground Management in Bituminous Coal Mines" prepared by Sanford E. Thompson for the U. S. Coal Commission, and included in Part III (1925), pp. 1893–1969, of the Commission's *Report*. The industry also was the subject of discussion at the annual meeting of the American Economic Association in 1920 (see *American Economic Review*, March 1921, Supplement).

*Footnotes to Table 15.*

[a] All data are from *Minerals Yearbook* and its predecessor, *Mineral Resources*.

[b] For 1913 and earlier years the figures in this column are percentages of total output. Since strip mining of bituminous coal was zero or almost zero in these years, no error is involved in this procedure.

[c] Mechanized loading began to be adopted widely in 1923. The Bureau of Mines collected figures for the first time in that year, but before 1928 it excluded certain types of loaders which it included in later years. Figures for 1923–27 are not, therefore, strictly comparable with those for later years, and have not been reproduced.

[d] Not available.

loaded by machine. This development has recently been covered in a report of the National Research Project, which analyzes performance records of mines employing hand and machine loaders and indicates the many factors that influence the adoption and efficiency of the various loading devices.[22] For a discussion of these factors the reader is referred to Chapter 6 above. Here we shall merely deal very broadly with the development of technology in the bituminous coal industry since the early 1920's.

There can be little doubt that mechanized loading, in the mines that have passed beyond experimental use of this technique, has changed mining methods very radically. To the extent that loading machines have replaced hand loading, bituminous coal mining must have become an industry in which many of the old craft traditions have had to be discarded. Each working face does not have its own loading machine; rather loading-machine crews have taken their place with drill crews and cutting-machine crews as workers performing a specialized function in the larger process of mining. Ideally, a single working face is attacked in sequence by cutters, drillers and blasters, and loaders, each group working in close coordination with the others. The coal face is subjected to a kind of assembly-line technique, in which a series of specialized tools is brought to the material to be treated, instead of vice versa. The old routine (or lack of routine) has given way, apparently, to a systematic planning of production with a closely supervised execution of the production process.

The traditional room-and-pillar system of mining—with the isolated mine worker in his room somewhere off in a corner of the mine—exists no more in the mechanized mine. It may still be a room-and-pillar mine in the strictly engineering sense, but even so the design of individual mines undoubtedly has had to be modified to accommodate the cycle of mechanized operations. It is probable, too, that supervision has been made simpler by the fact that production in the mechanized mine can be concentrated in a smaller area without any loss in volume of output.[23]

Basically, however, the mechanization of the mining of soft coal has been superimposed upon a traditional, one might almost say an ancient, method of mining and mine layout. The completely mechanized coal mine is still an exception, despite the general

22 Hotchkiss and others, *op. cit.*
23 U. S. Coal Commission, *Report*, Part III, pp. 1914-15.

spread of mechanization in recent years. Hand loading accounted
for about 70 percent of underground production in 1939, and it
seems evident that even today many mines are correctly characterized by our description of nonmechanized room-and-pillar
mining.[24] No such radical innovations as the block caving and
gravity loading methods of underground copper mining, for instance, have been found applicable in the winning of coal. The
simultaneous removal of valuable mineral and of quantities of
waste material, all to be separated at a later stage of the mining
process, distinguishes contemporary metal mining from the mining of coal.

It remains for us to consider whether depletion has stimulated
technological advance. We have seen that the direct effects of depletion, i.e., reduction of productivity through increased difficulty
of extraction, have probably not been important in coal mining.
Indirectly, however, the exhaustion of easily worked sources may
have influenced productivity either by inducing or by retarding
technological change. Depletion of minerals reacts upon the technological state of the producing industry in two principal ways:
(1) the individual establishment may find that a decline in the
grade of its own resources makes it unable to compete with other
establishments in the field unless it can manage somehow to reduce its costs of production; and (2) depletion throughout the entire industry may increase interest in new techniques and in deposits formerly regarded as unprofitable fields for exploitation.
The latter situation is probably not serious in bituminous coal
mining: from what we have already learned concerning this country's soft coal resources [25] we may conclude that major changes in
technology have not so far been required to offset the pressure of
demand upon dwindling sources of raw material. As for the first
situation—in which the individual mine is forced to revise its techniques of exploitation and recovery because of a decline in the
grade of its own resources—such conditions must have developed
at times, though not too frequently, for high grade material has

[24] It has been observed that old mines have lower manday output than new
ones. This is due partly to the longer underground hauls necessary in old mines,
and partly to their less frequent mechanization (either because mechanical methods
are impossible without a change in mine layout, or because the approach of exhaustion discourages expenditure for mechanization): see Hotchkiss and others,
*Bituminous-Coal Mining*, pp. 79-80.

[25] See pp. 167-69 above.

also been a characteristic of most individual mines. It appears, then, that depletion, which has clearly been a stimulus to technological advance in certain other extractive industries—notably copper mining—cannot have affected the techniques employed in the winning of bituminous coal in any significant degree.

Evidently technological advance can scarcely have been stimulated by the necessity of counteracting the effects of depletion. Some other features of the industry's history may actually have retarded progress in this direction. For example, coal miners are, and always have been, predominantly piece workers. They are paid by the ton.[26] Thus the cost of inefficiency is in large measure transferred from the business enterprise to the individual miner, for the operator has little incentive to seek an increase in output when much of the increment in his revenue is mortgaged in advance. Any innovation that is not sufficiently important to justify a reduction in piece rates therefore has small chance of adoption. It is true, of course, that a change as far-reaching as the introduction of cutting machines did lead to a reduction in piece rates: miner and operator shared the benefits of greater efficiency. The question was naturally whether the benefit received by the latter was great enough to justify mechanization. In Illinois, in particular, it was claimed that the "machine differential," i.e., the reduction in piece rates on the advent of machinery, was so small as to retard mechanization, but this does not seem to have been its effect. On the other hand, the object of the United Mine Workers in limiting the differential was apparently to prevent machine-cut coal from underselling pick-mined coal, and so to avoid the elimination of pick mines where the use of machinery is impracticable.[27] To this extent methods of wage payment may have preserved inefficient forms of production. [28]

Furthermore, the bituminous coal industry has been plagued by intermittency of operation during the entire period covered

[26] The impression, derived from recent wage controversies, that miners are paid . by the day is quite erroneous, so far as concerns workers who actually extract the coal. Of course when the daily rates of those who work for time wages are changed, a corresponding adjustment to piece rates is made.

[27] Isador Lubin, *Miners' Wages and the Cost of Coal* (McGraw-Hill, 1924), Chs. VI and XIII.

[28] In reviewing the manuscript of this report, Mr. F. E. Berquist suggested that (at least until recently) the responsiveness of the wage structure to the pressure of low prices eliminated a tendency toward mechanization which might have arisen with a more rigid wage level. He added that in many mines loading could be mechanized only with specially designed equipment.

here. Out of a possible 308 working days,[29] the number of days
actually worked per mine in the years since 1899 has ranged from
142 to 249, with an average working year of 200 days for the entire period.[30] Where production is so irregular the willingness of
the operator to take on additional fixed costs is reduced considerably.[31] And technological advance means that the operator must
assume a burden of fixed costs not only because of carrying
charges, etc., on machine installations, but also because the relatively high priced technical and supervisory personnel required
for mechanized mines are usually paid whether the mines work
or not. An operator who can keep his mine in operation only 200
days a year should not be judged too harshly if he prefers the easy
adjustments possible with the nonmechanized mine to the relative
rigidity of the modern mine. His choice would be a difficult one
even if workers were paid regular wages. The prevalence of piece
rates makes it doubly hazardous.

The emphasis of the foregoing discussion has been placed deliberately upon changes in productivity. We have tried to suggest
some of the factors that help to explain the comparative backwardness of the soft coal industry in improving its productive
efficiency. For there is no doubt that, according to the criterion
we have chosen to set up, many other branches of extraction have
made much more rapid progress during the past forty years than
has bituminous coal. Yet we might well apply other standards that
would provide a much more flattering picture. In tonnage terms,
output per manday in the bituminous industry is nearly twice as
high as in anthracite.[32] Again, in the United States the soft coal
industry is apparently far more efficient than it is abroad. In a
comparison undertaken during the 1920's, it was found that manday output was about four times as great as in Britain.[33] Moreover,

[29] U. S. Coal Commission, *Report*, Part III, p. 1111.

[30] The average-days-active figure is found together with the data on employment
in *Minerals Yearbook* and its predecessor *Mineral Resources of the United States*.
It is not possible here to enter into a discussion of the reasons for the short work
year prevailing in the bituminous coal mine. We should note, however, that irregular production is something the individual enterprise can do little to correct.

[31] See Harry Jerome, *Mechanization in Industry* (National Bureau of Economic
Research, 1934), pp. 336-37.

[32] The figures are 4.8 and 2.9 tons respectively per manday for 1937-39; see
Appendix Tables A-1 and A-3.

[33] About 4.1 and 1.0 long tons for an eight hour shift, respectively; see Harold
M. Watkins, *Coal and Men* (Allen and Unwin, London, 1934), pp. 109-25, for a
most interesting comparison of physical conditions of mining in the two countries.
Mr. Watkins explains the difference in terms of the greater age of British workings

it would appear that productivity is actually declining in British coal mines.[34] Standards of comparison are entirely relative. If we have spoken of the backwardness of soft coal mining in this country, we have done so only because of the much more rapid progress made in other mining industries, which frequently are subject to quite different physical conditions.

---

(average depth 1,020 feet compared with 260 feet in U. S.), longer haulage underground, less frequent mechanization, due partly to greater roof pressures, tilted beds, and more numerous faults. However, in this country the accident rate is apparently higher than in Britain.

[34] From about 450 tons per manyear in the 1880's to 350 immediately before the first World War, and perhaps less than 300 in recent years (F. G. Tryon and F. E. Berquist, "Mineral Economics," in *Mineral Economics,* ed. by F. G. Tryon and E. C. Eckel, McGraw-Hill, 1932, p. 28). Since days worked per year have probably declined, the fall in manday output may be less severe.

# Chapter 9

# Pennsylvania Anthracite [1]

ANTHRACITE HAS been mined regularly in Pennsylvania since about 1820. It was one of the earliest branches of mineral production to resort to underground mining, and to face such basic problems as pumping, ventilation and roof support.[2] Yet some of the anthracite beds lie quite near the surface, and these have been worked by stripping within recent decades, thanks to the development of the power shovel. About 11 or 12 percent of total output is now obtained from open pit mines. Not all anthracite currently produced is freshly mined. In an earlier day substantial amounts were wasted through difficulties in washing or breaking. The waste was deposited in heaps called "culm banks," or in streams. As in the case of copper and several other branches of mining, improved technology has made it worth while to recover increasing amounts of material from these waste heaps. In 1939 some 5 percent of the total output of anthracite came from culm banks; nearly 2 percent was river coal, obtained chiefly by dredging.

In some areas, particularly in Southern Pennsylvania, coal lies near the surface. Here, because of the accessibility of the mineral, numerous small workings have been opened in the past two decades without the consent of the owners of the mineral rights. The practice has been facilitated by the use of motor trucks to ship the product to nearby towns. According to the Bureau of Mines such bootleg operations added in 1939 some $3\frac{1}{2}$ to 4 million tons, or perhaps 8 percent, to legal output.[3] The figures given

[1] The production of anthracite coal in this country is not confined entirely to Pennsylvania, but because of the organization of the industry and the character of the available statistics this chapter will be limited to a discussion of anthracite production in that state.

[2] See above, Chapters 5 and 6.

[3] Estimates of the importance of bootlegging are necessarily rough. Apparently in 1939 some 2,500 bootleg holes employed 9,000 men to produce, say, $3\frac{3}{4}$ million tons, or some 420 tons per man (*Minerals Yearbook, 1940*, p. 849). The 51 million tons produced by the legal industry employed about 93,000 men, and the output was therefore about 550 tons per man. However, only 183 days were worked on the average in the legal mines in 1939. Since days worked per year and hours worked per day are probably greater in the illicit than in the regular mines, the difference in productivity, if measured in terms of mandays or manhours, would probably be considerably larger than is suggested by the figures quoted.

for anthracite in this chapter and elsewhere in the volume relate exclusively to legal production.[4]

The output of anthracite is more homogeneous than that of bituminous coal, although it is marketed in many different forms and a trend toward smaller sizes has been encouraged through the use of automatic stoking equipment. Breaking is carried on near the mine and is an integral part of the industry.[5] Insofar as preparation has become more elaborate, changes in quality may have occurred, but we have no means of taking account of this development in our indexes. Output is measured by a single series on tonnage.

Chart 40

PENNSYLVANIA ANTHRACITE

Output, Employment and Productivity, 1880 – 1939

(1899 : 100)

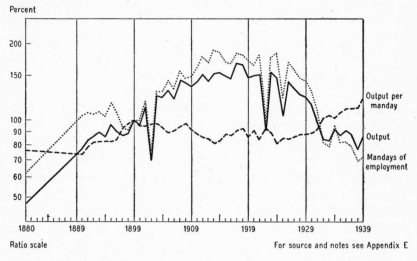

Ratio scale                                        For source and notes see Appendix E

## THE RELATION BETWEEN OUTPUT
## AND EMPLOYMENT

The various series for the industry are shown in Charts 40 and 41. At the opening of the century output was rising fairly steadily—

[4] Scattered data on the bootleg industry will be found in various annual issues of *Minerals Yearbook*. For further information the reader is referred to the investigation by the Commonwealth of Pennsylvania, *Report of the Anthracite Coal Industry Commission* (Harrisburg, 1938).

[5] See Chapter 7 above.

except for the strike year 1902. After about 1907 a slackening in the rate of growth set in, and production reached a peak during the first World War. Since that time output has tended to decline, with several strikes again interrupting the trend. The demand for anthracite has been reduced by economy in its use and still more by the competition of other fuels. These factors in the situation were treated in Chapter 2 and will not be considered further here.

We saw in Chapter 4 that the rise in output per manday between 1902 and 1939 was smaller for anthracite than for any other mining industry for which we have collected data. From

Chart 41

PENNSYLVANIA ANTHRACITE

Productivity, 1902 – 39

(1902 : 100)

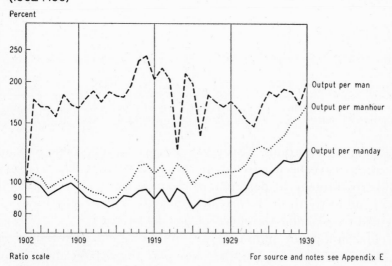

Percent

Output per man

Output per manhour

Output per manday

Ratio scale                                    For source and notes see Appendix E

Chart 40 it is clear that for much of our period the trend in productivity was horizontal or even downward, and that any rise that has occurred in output per manday is confined entirely to the most recent decade. Because of curtailment of the work day, output per manhour makes a somewhat more favorable showing (Chart 41). On the other hand, output per man exhibits practically no upward trend at all, for increases in manday or manhour productivity are absorbed by a reduction in the average number of days or hours worked per year. Intermittent operation was responsible for fluctuations in output per man, and these in turn were aggravated by several major labor disputes.

As in other branches of mining, the change—or absence of change—in productivity must be ascribed to technology, to resource conditions, and to reactions between them. Anthracite contrasts sharply with bituminous mining, where, as we have seen, depletion has had slight effect upon productivity. In the anthracite industry adverse resource conditions clearly have played an important role in keeping the rise in output per manday within

TABLE 16

PENNSYLVANIA ANTHRACITE: THICKNESS OF BEDS MINED AND DEPTH OF WORKINGS, 1872–1922

| Year | Average Thickness (inches) | Average Depth (feet) |
|------|---------------------------|----------------------|
| 1872 | 158 | 235 |
| 1882 | 130 | 310 |
| 1892 | 108 | 360 |
| 1902 | 93 | 390 |
| 1912 | 84 | 400 |
| 1922 | 80 | 415 |

Source: R. A. Walter and C. E. Lesher, "Capacity for Production of Domestic Anthracite," Report of the United States Coal Commission (1925), Part II, p. 661.

moderate proportions. This restraint upon rising productivity appears to have been effected in two more or less distinct ways: directly through the depletion of the most easily worked mineral, and indirectly through increased difficulty of mechanization, designed to overcome the effects of this depletion.

The mining of anthracite is a relatively old industry, as we noted in Chapter 1. For the most part the deposits now being worked were discovered long ago, and mining is carried on in much the same localities. Depletion has not been counteracted as it has in so many other mineral industries, by discovery of newer, richer or more accessible deposits. The results of this situation are illustrated in Table 16. It will be seen that over the half century for which we have data the average width of seam worked declined steadily, and the average depth to which it was necessary to carry the workings increased equally steadily. Both these factors operated to reduce the effectiveness of labor in the industry.

Meanwhile numerous reports indicate that the anthracite industry has been peculiarly difficult to mechanize. We learn, for example, that in 1901 machinery, except for drilling, had not been adopted in the industry (although it was already in use in many bituminous coal mines) because of the pitch or slope of

TABLE 17

PENNSYLVANIA ANTHRACITE: PRODUCTION, BY MINING METHOD, 1927–40[a]

*Million short tons*

| | From Mines | | | | | | Percent of |
| | UNDERGROUND | | | From | From | | Underground |
| Year | | | STRIP | Culm | River | Total[b] | Production |
| | Mechanically | Hand | PITS | Banks | Dredging | | Mechanically |
| | Loaded | Loaded | | | | | Loaded |
|------|------|------|------|------|------|------|------|
| 1927 | 2.2 | 71.4 | 2.2 | 3.3 | 1.0 | 80.1 | 3.0 |
| 1928 | 2.4 | 67.4 | 2.4 | 2.3 | .9 | 75.3 | 3.4 |
| 1929 | 3.5 | 66.5 | 1.9 | 1.2 | .7 | 73.8 | 5.0 |
| 1930 | 4.5 | 60.5 | 2.5 | 1.3 | .6 | 69.4 | 6.9 |
| 1931 | 4.4 | 49.1 | 3.8 | 1.9 | .5 | 59.6 | 8.2 |
| 1932 | 5.4 | 38.4 | 4.0 | 1.6 | .5 | 49.9 | 12.4 |
| 1933 | 6.6 | 34.5 | 4.9 | 3.0 | .5 | 49.5 | 16.0 |
| 1934 | 9.3 | 39.3 | 5.8 | 2.1 | .7 | 57.2 | 19.1 |
| 1935 | 9.3 | 34.4 | 5.2 | 2.7 | .6 | 52.2 | 21.2 |
| 1936 | 10.8 | 33.9 | 6.2 | 3.2 | .5 | 54.6 | 24.2 |
| 1937 | 10.7 | 31.9 | 5.7 | 2.7 | .8 | 51.9 | 25.1 |
| 1938 | 10.2 | 28.0 | 5.1 | 2.3 | .6 | 46.1 | 26.6 |
| 1939 | 11.8 | 30.8 | 5.5 | 2.6 | .7 | 51.5 | 27.7 |
| 1940 | 12.3 | 29.2 | 6.4 | 2.8 | .9 | 51.5 | 29.7 |

[a] *Minerals Yearbook.*
[b] Total coal produced, including that used for colliery fuel. In some years there is difficulty in segregating from culm bank coal the coal coming from underground mines. On this account the sum of the items in the breakdown does not always agree exactly with total reported production. The latter is the series we use in constructing output indexes: see Appendix Table A-1.

the beds, which often attained an angle of 60 degrees to the horizontal.[6] In addition, faults and other geological irregularities are encountered. These circumstances probably explain why, even today, less than 5 percent of the output from underground mines is cut by machine.[7] Even mechanical loading is a relatively recent development (Table 17).

These facts—deterioration of resource conditions and inability to mechanize—explain why output per manday was lower at the

[6] *Report of the Industrial Commission,* Vol. XII (1901), pp. 150, 651.

[7] In 1939, 4.4 percent of anthracite from underground mines was cut by machine; the comparable figure for bituminous coal was 87.9 percent.

end of the 1920's than it had been at the opening of the century.[8] There remains the question why, after many decades of stagnation, productivity rose during the 1930's, with the result that manday output was 40 percent higher in 1939 than it had been in 1929.[9]

The most notable change of the past ten or fifteen years is the introduction of mechanical loading. For this purpose the commonest type of equipment used is the conveyor. Even where conveyors must be loaded by hand, they are considered a form of mechanical loading equipment and yield a notable increase in efficiency. There are, moreover, some fully automatic loading devices. Mechanically loaded anthracite accounted for but 3 percent of the product of all underground mines in 1927 (the first year for which we have data) and for as much as 28 percent in 1939 and 30 percent in 1940 (Table 17). While it may have prevented, and may still prevent, other forms of mechanization, irregularity of geological formation has certainly not hindered the introduction of mechanical loading devices into a substantial number of the anthracite mines of Pennsylvania. The question therefore arises, why were such devices not introduced earlier? We have been unable to collect any real evidence on this point. Perhaps peculiar problems of adaptation had to be solved to meet the irregularity of anthracite workings. It is possible, too, that competition of other fuels and the shrinking market for the product provided a spur to modernization that previously had been lacking.[10]

The introduction of mechanical loading into an important

[8] It should be remembered that the length of the work day was about 9½ hours in 1902, 8 hours in 1929 (Table 10 above). Output per manhour increased slightly between the two dates (Chart 41).

[9] Output per manhour rose 59 percent between the two dates, the length of the work day having been reduced during the decade from 8 to 7 hours.

[10] Adverse economic conditions have been cited as the prime reason for mechanization in many British coal mines, as the following quotation shows: "The argument that natural conditions make impossible the employment of machine mining on a large scale is not a new one in the British coal industry. . . . But when in the thinner seams of Scotland it became a question of survival, means were soon found which made the machine practicable. . . . Likewise in the older districts, Durham for example, natural difficulties were quickly overcome under the spur of economic necessity" (Isador Lubin and Helen Everett, *The British Coal Dilemma*, Macmillan, 1927, pp. 149-50). Equally, the profitability of anthracite mining during the 1920's has been cited as a factor that postponed mechanization and reinforced conservatism in industrial practice: see U. S. Coal Commission, *Report*, Part III (1925), p. 1884.

segment of the anthracite industry must certainly have contributed to the sharp rise in productivity in recent years. Several other factors may have been operating as well. One is the installation of larger and more efficient washing and breaking equipment. Another is the increasing relative importance of open cut mining: 2.6 percent of total output came from stripping operations in 1929, 10.7 percent in 1939 (Table 17). Productivity at such operations is higher than at underground mines.[11] Finally, the output of the industry has fallen sharply in recent years (Chart 40). It is likely that production has been concentrated, to some extent at least, in the more efficient mines or workings. Yet, in terms of tons per manday, the level of productivity in anthracite is still much below that which obtains in the bituminous coal industry. The burden which adverse resource conditions have imposed upon the industry can be overcome only through wider use of mechanized loading, or perhaps through the eventual development of a satisfactory method of cutting by machine.

[11] If surface employees are excluded, output per manday in 1939 was 3.3 tons at underground mines; at stripping operations the corresponding figure was 7.4 tons. (*Minerals Yearbook, Review of 1940,* p. 846; "Coal-Mine Accidents in the United States, 1939," U. S. Bureau of Mines, p. 69.)

# Chapter 10

# Petroleum and Natural Gas

IN TERMS of value, the production of petroleum, natural gas and byproduct natural gasoline is the most important mining activity in the United States. Our over-all indexes of production, employment and productivity are strongly influenced by the movement of this component of the total, and certain outstanding characteristics of the indexes of output and productivity are directly traceable to the role played by petroleum and natural gas in mineral enterprise as a whole. Unfortunately this industry, which is so important, is not representative of mining in general. Indeed it is in many respects unique, a fact which underlies many of the problems associated with the derivation and interpretation of the statistical measures for the industry.

To begin with, the production process differs markedly from that prevailing in most other mining industries.[1] Except in rare instances petroleum and natural gas have not really been "mined" in this country. Shafts are not sunk into the underground formations so that the petroliferous sands may be dug out.[2] Instead the underground oil-bearing formations are penetrated by means of wells, and often the actual production process consists of little more than harvesting the free flowing oil and gas and controlling the rate of flow. If the oil does not flow freely—as is usually the case after the early period of production—it may become necessary to lift the oil by artificial means.

These steps make up the actual "extraction" process. However, "mining" of most minerals is commonly defined to include not only the operations of extraction proper, but also certain associated tasks of cleaning the mineral (beneficiating), as well as operations designed to prepare the mineral body for future ex-

[1] At least two industries have utilized production techniques which bear some resemblance to those in petroleum and natural gas: they are salt and sulfur. We do not include salt in our indexes, and sulfur is nowhere treated separately in the discussion.

[2] Such methods of petroleum extraction have been used in some foreign countries. In the United States "mining" of petroleum has been tried, but with no commercial success. See G. S. Rice, "Mining Petroleum by Underground Methods," U. S. Bureau of Mines, *Bulletin 351* (Washington, 1932).

ploitation. In the petroleum and natural gas industry the last activity—usually called development work—is of very great importance. Oil and gas wells are typically short lived and production has, in the past, been maintained or increased only through the continual drilling of new wells. This work of new construction normally occupies a very much larger part of the industry's labor force than does similar work in other industries. In 1939, for example, about one fourth of the manhours of employment at petroleum and natural gas operations were apparently absorbed in the construction of new wells.[3]

In addition to development work and the purely extractive operations of the industry there is also the production of natural gasoline, which is quite distinct from the production of either petroleum or natural gas. The latter two are direct products of the well, and are, in fact, very often produced from the same wells.[4] Natural gasoline, on the other hand, represents a secondary stage of production, for it is derived from natural gas, one of the primary products. To be sure, the production process utilized is by no means as elaborate as actual petroleum refinery operations, but nonetheless it is clearly a stage or so removed from the simple process of taking mineral from the earth. It may be considered as comparable with certain of the more elaborate beneficiating techniques used in the treatment of copper, lead and zinc ores,[5] for example, although it is functionally different from them.

The industry is further set apart from other mining industries by the fact that much of the work of production and development is handled by contractors. Drilling of wells and associated tasks of derrick and rig building have long been performed in many fields by contract specialists. In recent years, moreover, other and more routine tasks of oil and gas field maintenance have been contracted out. All told, contract work accounted for about 25 percent of all manhours of employment in this industry in 1939.[6] The

[3] Census of Mineral Industries, 1939, "Crude Petroleum and Natural Gas," released May 1942, and "Oil and Gas Field Services Performed by Contractors," released December 1941.

[4] Of the total output of natural gas in 1939, 45 percent came from oil wells and the remainder from wells which produced only natural gas (Minerals Yearbook, Review of 1940, p. 1032; ratio derived from gross production figures).

[5] See Chapter 7 above.

[6] Figures derived from preliminary releases of the Census of Mineral Industries, 1939, on "Petroleum and Natural Gas," "Natural Gasoline" and "Oil and Gas Field Services Performed by Contractors."

extent of contract employment here may be compared with that in other major mining industries, where such employment is of minor consequence.[7] Pennsylvania anthracite is an outstanding exception, but even in this field, where much of the strip mining is done by contractors, contract manhours accounted for less than 4 percent of total manhours in 1939.[8]

It is not because there is any real difference between the product of contractors on the one hand, and regular operators on the other, that we point to contract employment as a distinctive feature of the petroleum and natural gas industry. The significance of contract work lies in the fact that because of the peregrinating nature of contract activities (and perhaps also because of the impermanent character of some contract enterprises), they are usually not adequately covered in official canvasses. In the petroleum and natural gas industry we find that with the exception of the 1902 and 1939 Censuses, no appreciable attempt to cover contractors has ever been made. For this reason it is necessary to rely on estimates of contract employment, and these are, in the nature of things, unsatisfactory.[9] To exclude contract employment entirely would be even less satisfactory than to attempt to estimate its magnitude, for the data on physical output do not permit any distinction between contract and noncontract goods. Since contract employment has been of shifting importance, its exclusion would necessarily upset historical comparisons of productivity.

## THE RELATION BETWEEN OUTPUT
## AND EMPLOYMENT

Before we consider the behavior of the index of productivity it is advisable to comment briefly on the nature of the index of physical output of the petroleum and natural gas industry. This index is derived from series relating to the output of the industry's three products: petroleum, natural gas and natural gasoline.[10] The basic output and price data are given in Appendix Table A-1. It will

[7] In bituminous coal, copper and iron, for example, contract manhours were less than 1 percent of regular manhours in 1939. For data on contract employment see 1939 Census of Mineral Industries, "General Contract Services for Mineral Industries" released December 1941.

[8] See the 1939 Census release cited in the preceding footnote, and also the release on Pennsylvania anthracite.

[9] See notes to Appendix Table A-3.

[10] Oil and gas wasted is not included.

be noted that for years before 1919 we have separated Pennsylvania grade from all other petroleum. Actually one may distinguish three main types of petroleum—paraffin-base, asphalt-base,
and mixed-base—which exhibit significant price differentials.
Paraffin-base, or Pennsylvania grade oil, commands the highest
price because it is lightest in weight, most fluid, and particularly
rich in gasoline, wax and lubricants. The production of this grade
of oil has been slight in recent years, but in the earlier years covered by our analysis paraffin-base petroleum was of much greater
importance than it is today. From 1899 until 1919 its representa-
tion in the industry's output shrank continually; since 1919 it has
failed to recover its earlier importance. Because of the higher
price which Pennsylvania grade commands, failure to take account of this shift in the composition of the industry's output
would have resulted in an upward bias. Therefore we estimated
Pennsylvania grade production for the period 1899–1919 by combining the output of New York, Pennsylvania, West Virginia, and
southeastern and central Ohio. Since we were unable to divide
the remainder into the two general grades of oil included, we
used a single series for all other grades.

Our indexes of output and employment for the petroleum and
natural gas industry, along with our index of productivity, are
plotted in Chart 42. Although the lines extend over the period
1902–39 they are formed by connecting points representing very
few years: 1902, 1929, and 1935–39. Our index of physical output
for the industry covers all years during this period; but employment data, unfortunately, are available only for those years which
have been plotted and in terms of manhours alone.[11] All we can
obtain, then, is a picture of the long run changes in the relationship between output and employment in the industry. This picture shows that both output and employment increased greatly
over the period. Between 1902 and 1939 output multiplied eleven
times, a larger gain than that achieved by any other mining industry. Over the same period manhours of employment more than
doubled, but this is a much smaller rate of growth than that
recorded for output.

Despite the apparent decline in employment between 1929 and
1939, the net increase in manhours of employment over the entire

[11] The industry's employment data are discussed in notes to Appendix Table
A-3.

Chart 42

OIL AND GAS WELLS

Output, Employment and Productivity, 1902 – 39

(1902 : 100)

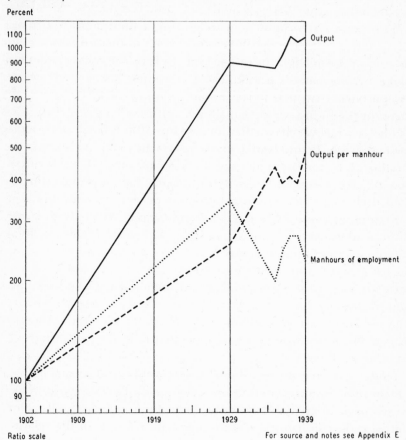

Percent

1100
1000
900
800
700
600
500
400
300
200
100
90

Output

Output per manhour

Manhours of employment

1902        1909        1919        1929        1939

Ratio scale                                    For source and notes see Appendix E

period covered by our study puts the industry in a class by itself
(see Table 11 above). In all other mining industries for which we
have data on manhours over the same period (with the sole exception of gypsum) the net change was negative. This result is especially noteworthy in view of the fact that oil and gas wells also
rank near the top when the various mining industries are arranged
in order of increase in manhour productivity during the period.
Over the four decades the rise in output was more than sufficient
to offset the rise in the industry's productivity—so great, indeed,
that employment rose more than in any other major branch of

mining. The birth of the petroleum industry antedates the Civil War; but the expansion in its market and the advances in its technology alike suggest a new rather than an old industry.

As in the case of other mining industries, our measure of the productivity of oil and gas wells is a simple ratio of output to employment. In addition to the usual ambiguities surrounding such a measure of productivity, this industry is affected by some of its own. A few of the reasons for the ambiguities in the productivity measure for the industry have been touched on in the first section of this chapter. Let us explore them somewhat further at this point.

The concept of output per manday or manhour is a fairly simple one when the efforts of a man—or a man and a machine—materialize in a product. The product may be a good or a service, it may be tangible or intangible, but, in any case, it can be attributed directly to labor expenditure and machine utilization.

Picture now a free-flowing oil well with an attendant on hand to control the flow. The attendant opens a valve so much and a certain volume of oil is released during a given time period: he opens the valve somewhat more and a larger volume of oil is released during a time period of equal length. In the second case output per manhour is greater than in the first case, but is this due to more efficient expenditure of labor or to more intensive utilization of machinery—or is it just a windfall gain, a kind of unearned increment?

Once more, picture two oil wells just coming into production. Large volumes of natural gas are being released in the process. At one well, whatever the reason, the gas is allowed to blow into the air and is wasted; at the other, the flow of gas is controlled and the gas is marketed. In the first case the well produces only oil, in the second case it produces both oil and gas. To what may we attribute the larger production of the second well? The closest we can come to duplicating this situation is the production of some of the nonferrous metals, where byproduct metal can be recovered with improved beneficiating techniques. Sometimes the byproduct metals are recovered, sometimes they are not. But if they are recovered it is at the expense of some labor and machine effort. In the case of natural gas the increased production may be attributable also to increased expenditure of effort. More likely, however, it can be credited to the design of the well, or to increased knowledge of the geology of oil and gas fields and of the behavior of oil and gas when underground reservoirs are tapped.

These are not hypothetical situations. A deliberate restriction of the flow of oil marked many flush production fields in which control schemes were instituted between 1926 and the end of our period of study. The conservation and use of natural gas that was formerly wasted represents a long-time change in technology which has been typical of the industry. Each of these phenomena renders the interpretation of productivity measures more difficult than would otherwise be the case.

Again, the output of the industry, as measured by our index, consists of petroleum, natural gas and natural gasoline. Yet it is conceptually possible that in a single year there could be a high volume of industrial employment without the production of any of these three products. This could occur if all of the labor during the year were expended in exploration for wells and in drilling, and if there were no production by old wells while the new wells remained uncompleted at the year's end. Would the industry have produced nothing in that year? Obviously not. It clearly produced wells which would go into production, say, in the following year. But the construction of new wells is not included in our index of physical output; in such a case, then, we should obtain a productivity ratio of zero.

From this admittedly extreme and unlikely case it becomes apparent that our definition of output is perhaps too narrow, or our definition of employment too broad. Although both definitions may be defended on grounds of statistical expediency, it is nonetheless clear that an incomparability between output and employment exists. The importance of the incomparability when year-to-year comparisons are made is determined by two factors: (1) the absolute magnitude of well-development work, and (2) the relative importance of such development work from year to year. If the absolute magnitude is slight (as is true in most other mining industries[12]) or relatively constant, we may disregard the influence of development activities on the index. As we have seen, however, work of this sort is particularly important in the petroleum industry, and, as Table 18 suggests, it is more likely to shift from

[12] The only other industry here discussed in which development work is sufficiently important to create a similar difficulty is open cut iron mining: see below, Chapter 11.

TABLE 18

OIL AND GAS WELLS, 1899–1940

*Thousands, except where percentages are shown*

| Year | Wells Drilled during Year[a] | | | | | Oil Wells | |
| | Oil | Gas | Dry | Total | Dry as Percent of Total | Producing, December 31[b] | Drilled as Percent of Producing |
|---|---|---|---|---|---|---|---|
| 1899 | 11.6 | c | 2.7 | 14.4 | 19 | .. | .. |
| 1900 | 13.7 | c | 3.4 | 17.1 | 20 | .. | .. |
| 1901 | 11.8 | c | 3.3 | 15.1 | 22 | .. | .. |
| 1902 | 13.0 | c | 3.4 | 16.5 | 21 | .. | .. |
| 1903 | 15.2 | .3 | 3.7 | 19.2 | 19 | .. | .. |
| 1904 | 16.0 | .4 | 4.1 | 20.5 | 20 | .. | .. |
| 1905 | 12.6 | .4 | 3.6 | 16.6 | 22 | .. | .. |
| 1906 | 14.6 | .5 | 3.8 | 18.8 | 20 | .. | .. |
| 1907 | 15.5 | .6 | 3.6 | 19.7 | 18 | .. | .. |
| 1908 | 13.2 | .6 | 3.1 | 17.0 | 18 | .. | .. |
| 1909 | 13.9 | 1.1 | 3.5 | 18.5 | 19 | .. | .. |
| 1910 | 11.0 | 1.5 | 2.5 | 15.0 | 16 | .. | .. |
| 1911 | 9.8 | 1.6 | 2.4 | 13.8 | 17 | .. | .. |
| 1912 | 12.5 | 1.8 | 2.9 | 17.2 | 17 | .. | .. |
| 1913 | 19.1 | 2.5 | 4.0 | 25.6 | 16 | .. | .. |
| 1914 | 16.7 | 2.4 | 4.2 | 23.2 | 18 | .. | .. |
| 1915 | 9.2 | 2.0 | 3.0 | 14.2 | 21 | .. | .. |
| 1916 | 18.8 | 1.8 | 4.0 | 24.7 | 16 | .. | .. |
| 1917 | 16.6 | 2.0 | 4.9 | 23.5 | 21 | .. | .. |
| 1918 | 17.9 | 2.3 | 5.6 | 25.8 | 22 | .. | .. |
| 1919 | 21.0 | 2.2 | 6.1 | 29.3 | 21 | .. | .. |
| 1920 | 24.3 | 2.3 | 7.5 | 34.0 | 22 | .. | .. |
| 1921 | 14.7 | 2.1 | 5.2 | 22.0 | 24 | 274 | 5.3 |
| 1922 | 17.3 | 2.0 | 5.5 | 24.8 | 22 | 285 | 6.1 |
| 1923 | 16.2 | 2.3 | 6.2 | 24.8 | 25 | 290 | 5.6 |
| 1924 | 14.8 | 2.2 | 5.0 | 21.9 | 23 | 299 | 4.9 |
| 1925 | 16.6 | 2.3 | 6.7 | 25.6 | 26 | 306 | 5.4 |
| 1926 | 19.0 | 2.3 | 8.0 | 29.3 | 27 | 319 | 6.0 |
| 1927 | 14.4 | 2.5 | 7.2 | 24.1 | 30 | 323 | 4.5 |
| 1928 | 12.5 | 2.7 | 7.1 | 23.3 | 30 | 328 | 3.8 |
| 1929 | 15.6 | 2.9 | 7.9 | 26.4 | 30 | 328 | 4.7 |
| 1930 | 11.6 | 2.9 | 6.7 | 21.2 | 32 | 331 | 3.5 |
| 1931 | 6.8 | 2.0 | 3.7 | 12.4 | 29 | 316 | 2.1 |
| 1932 | 10.4 | 1.0 | 3.6 | 15.0 | 24 | 322 | 3.2 |
| 1933 | 8.1 | .9 | 3.3 | 12.3 | 27 | 327 | 2.5 |
| 1934 | 12.5 | 1.4 | 4.3 | 18.2 | 24 | 333 | 3.8 |
| 1935 | 15.1 | 1.4 | 4.9 | 21.4 | 23 | 341 | 4.4 |
| 1936 | 17.8 | 2.1 | 5.3 | 25.2 | 21 | 349 | 5.1 |
| 1937 | 22.1 | 2.8 | 6.4 | 31.4 | 20 | 363 | 6.1 |
| 1938 | 18.4 | 2.2 | 6.0 | 26.7 | 23 | 370 | 5.0 |
| 1939 | 17.5 | 2.1 | 6.4 | 26.0 | 24 | 380 | 4.6 |
| 1940 | 19.1 | 2.4 | 6.6 | 28.1 | 24 | 389 | 4.9 |

*For footnotes see next page.*

195

year to year than to remain constant.[13] The absence of a clear and well defined correspondence in time between employment and the production associated with it makes the interpretation of our statistical measures more difficult. It must not be concluded, however, that the measures are therefore of little value. For it is possible to form an opinion of the relative importance of development work in different years, and thus to clarify our comparisons.

We may turn, after this brief introduction, to a consideration of the behavior of the industry's productivity index. Between 1902 and 1939 output per manhour at oil and gas wells increased nearly fivefold.[14] No other major mining industry bettered this record: only the phosphate rock and gypsum industries show larger gains in productivity. In view of the small number of intervening years for which we have data, there is little we can say about other aspects of the case. We know nothing of what took place between 1902 and 1929 and are therefore not in a position to comment on changes in the rate of growth of productivity between these two years. Over the period as a whole there seems to be no evidence of a slackening in the growth of manhour output in the industry. Indeed, it appears from Chart 42 that the rate of increase after 1929 was more rapid than it had been dur-

---

[13] We have endeavored to include both exploration and drilling activity in the industry's labor input, but the extent to which the employment figures do actually include development work is open to doubt. Employment in rig building and drilling, operations performed mainly by contractors, appears to be adequately covered. As for exploratory work, it is usually done by the larger producers on their own account, and they presumably report the employment to which it gives rise; but some of the smaller concerns may not adequately report their activities. The 1939 Census release on oil and gas field contract services is the only source to list exploration as a separate activity, and the amount of employment there reported is not large. For a description of the manner in which we derived our employment estimates, see the notes to Appendix Table A-3.

[14] The available evidence suggests that there was no marked difference in the level of importance of development work in the industry between the years 1902 and 1939. In 1939 about one fourth of total manhours were devoted to well drilling; in 1902 the corresponding proportion was approximately the same, if we may judge from the ratio of contract to regular employment. For a discussion of the nature of contract activities, see U. S. Bureau of the Census, *Special Reports,* "Mines and Quarries, 1902," p. 724. According to our estimates contract manhours accounted for about 30 percent of total manhours in 1902, but this includes some work which was not strictly developmental in character.

---

*Footnotes to Table 18.*

[a] For 1899–1934, *Oil and Gas Journal* (Dec. 19, 1935), p. 12. These series are available back to 1859 when drilling started. For 1935–40, *Minerals Yearbook.*

[b] *Minerals Yearbook* and its predecessor *Mineral Resources.* Data are not available for years prior to 1921.

[c] Fewer than 50.

ing the period 1902–29.[15] If the data we can assemble offer only tenuous evidence of changes in the rate at which productivity has grown, there is no question of the net rise over the long run. We shall attempt, therefore, to cast some light on the background of long period changes. As in other mineral industries we may consider the factors that have influenced productivity under two broad headings: resource conditions and technology.

## RESOURCE CONDITIONS

When we speak of resource conditions as a factor influencing industrial productivity we mean the grade and accessibility of those resources which the industry is currently exploiting. That is to say, we are not concerned with the fact that depletion of oil and gas wells has normally proceeded at a very rapid rate. Such a condition will affect the behavior of an individual well's productivity over time, but will have little influence on an index of productivity for the industry if other wells or other pools come into production and replace the declining well or pool.

Viewed in this light, the grade of petroleum and natural gas resources has not declined during the period with which we deal. For the industry has been blessed with a seeming abundance of new fields to which production could constantly shift when older fields began to suffer from depletion. One of the outstanding characteristics of the history of oil and gas exploitation in this country has been the continual migration to new flush production areas. The National Research Project collected evidence on this point. Geographical centers of production were calculated and these indicate that since the early days of the industry in Pennsylvania, production first moved westward and then in a southwesterly direction.[16] Such shifts in the areas of production were of course occasioned by the new discoveries which have played such an extraordinary part in the maintenance and expan-

[15] This is the case despite the fact that schemes of production control introduced in the 1930's kept production of flush wells to a fraction of their potential. In addition, such schemes often operated to encourage excess well drilling which might be expected to affect the productivity ratio adversely on still another count. See U. S. Bureau of Mines release, "Recent Trends in Employment and Productivity in the Oil and Gas Fields" (April 24, 1939), p. 3. See also O. E. Kiessling and others, *Petroleum and Natural-Gas Production* (National Research Project, Philadelphia, 1939), pp. 44, 161-62; National Resources Committee, *Energy Resources and National Policy* (1939), pp. 198, 203.

[16] Kiessling and others, *op. cit.*, pp. 35 *et seq.*

sion of petroleum output (Chart 43). The data indicate not only
that these new fields have replaced fields of declining productivity,
but that successive shifts in production have also been accom-

Chart 43

PETROLEUM

Discoveries and Reserves, January 1, 1900 – 42

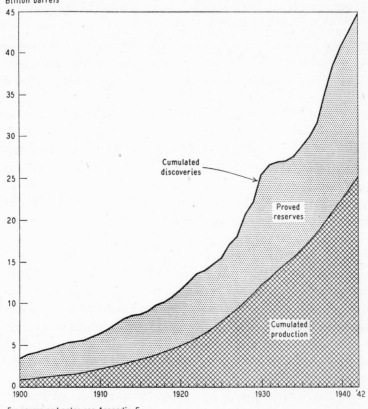

Billion barrels

For source and notes see Appendix E

panied by higher levels of productivity per well than obtained in
older fields even in their heyday.[17]

Although migration to new fields is thus seen to have favorably
affected resource conditions in the industry, we must also note

[17] *Ibid.,* p. 44. This observation should be qualified, for it is evident that new
fields have also utilized new production techniques. Hence any comparison made
with peak production days of older fields suffers from the fact that those fields
employed production techniques then current. Basically, however, this observation
is well founded in view of the fact that the deeper formations struck in new fields
have meant production with greater natural pressure.

one *negative* factor in the situation. The oil and gas formations exploited in the newer fields of the West and South generally lie at a greater depth than the producing formations of an earlier day. Striking evidence on this point also is to be found in the National Research Project report on the industry.[18] Greater depth usually has brought with it increased drilling difficulties, both because of the greater distances involved and because of the more troublesome formations encountered. In addition, until improved exploration techniques partially overcame this difficulty, increasing depth seems also to have resulted in a greater proportion of dry holes drilled.[19] Dry holes, it should be explained, are drillings which produce no oil or gas, and so turn out a disappointment to those who drill them.

In general it may be said that technology has been able to cope with increasing difficulties of this nature. In any case, the obstacles shrink into insignificance beside the outstanding fact of resource plenty in the industry.[20] It is clear, therefore, that a large measure of importance must be assigned to the pattern of resource occurrence in the industry when reasons for the rapid rise in productivity are sought.

## TECHNOLOGY [21]

Bountiful resources have had a powerful ally in technology, which has operated on three fronts in the crude petroleum and natural gas industry: exploration, drilling and production. In other mining industries it is sufficient to consider only those advances that have been made in the operations included under the last of

[18] *Ibid.*, Figure 20, p. 192.

[19] See Table 18. Note particularly the jump in the ratio of dry holes to total wells drilled in the 1920's. This is perhaps partially the result of the high level of production in these years, which stimulated exploration activity of all sorts.

[20] It should be clear that we speak of resource plenty in a historical sense. We do not mean to imply that petroleum and natural gas resources are endless in this country, but rather that over the period considered by us the average grade of resources in current exploitation has not declined. The very prodigality with which new resources have been exploited—although it has resulted in a high level of manhour productivity—may have weakened the industry's future position with regard to resource abundance.

[21] In writing the remainder of this chapter we have drawn heavily upon the following sources: O. E. Kiessling and others, *Petroleum and Natural-Gas Production* (National Research Project, Philadelphia, 1939); Max W. Ball, *This Fascinating Oil Business* (Bobbs-Merrill, 1940); and David D. Leven, *Done in Oil* (Ranger Press, 1941).

these headings. However, as we have already had occasion to point out, development work is of unusual importance in this industry.

*Exploration*

Improvements in exploration techniques do not affect industrial productivity directly. We are interested in advances in this portion of oil industry technology, not because of their effect on labor requirements in exploratory operations, but because through them the location of new sources of oil and gas is made possible. As we have seen, the appearance of new fields has been a factor of strong significance in the history of the industry. In this respect the extraction of petroleum and natural gas differs from most other forms of mining in which the "finding of new ore bodies has been subordinated to economic extraction";[22] while other forms of mining have been characterized by the intensive exploitation of known resources, the petroleum and natural gas industry has been extending its resource frontiers.

This fact is plainly revealed in Table 19 in which the discoveries of new oil fields are compared with the discoveries of new metal mining districts. Whereas all of the 35 leading metal mining districts were discovered before the first decade of the present century, 36 out of the 50 leading oil fields discovered before 1933 were found after 1910. Moreover, when rates of discovery in the search for oil are calculated, it appears that the *rate* of discovery was increasing, at least until the period after 1930. It declined from 1931 to 1935, having reached its long time peak between 1926 and 1930.[23]

The constant replenishment of our oil and gas resources through new discoveries has been made possible, in good part, by the evolution of improved exploration techniques. In the early days of the industry and, indeed, well into the twentieth century,

---

[22] See Chapter 5 above.

[23] Wallace E. Pratt, "Discovery Rates in Oil Finding," *Bulletin* of the American Association of Petroleum Geologists, Vol. 21, No. 6 (June 1937), pp. 698-99. Pratt's method of calculating discovery rates over the period 1900-35 is as follows: The discovery of reserves is fixed as of the year during which the first commercial well was completed. These discoveries are summed for 5-year periods, and for the whole period. Then the percentage of the total discovered in each 5-year period is computed. This percentage represents the "rate" of oil discovery in that period.

Data cited in *Energy Resources and National Policy* suggest that the rate may once again have jumped in the period 1936-40, although we cannot yet say whether it exceeded the 1926-30 peak. (See Table 6, page 134 of the report.)

exploration was essentially unscientific. Prospectors tended to rely almost exclusively on various surface indications which were supposed to betray the presence of oil underground. The indicators were generally such things as oil seepages, deposits of asphalt and other bitumens, etc., and topographic features which empirical evidence had associated with oil. Such methods were far from foolproof, but the record suggests that they served nevertheless to uncover large reserves of oil and gas.

TABLE 19

METAL MINING DISTRICTS AND OIL FIELDS

Number Discovered, or First Developed, in the United States, 1840–1933[a]

| Period | Metal Mining Leading 35 Districts[b] | Oil Fields Leading 50 Fields[c] |
|---|---|---|
| Before 1840 | 3 | .. |
| 1840–49 | 2 | .. |
| 1850–59 | 5 | .. |
| 1860–69 | 4 | .. |
| 1870–79 | 7 | 1 |
| 1880–89 | 7 | 1 |
| 1890–99 | 2 | 3 |
| 1900–09 | 5 | 9 |
| 1910–19 | .. | 15 |
| 1920–29 | .. | 20 |
| 1930–33 | .. | 1 |
| TOTALS | 35 | 50 |

[a] Table and notes reproduced from Carter Goodrich and others, *Migration and Economic Opportunity* (University of Pennsylvania Press, 1936), p. 258.

[b] Districts producing gold, silver, copper, lead, zinc and iron that have yielded the largest value of product since earliest development. There are, of course, a great many lesser districts. Classification by decade usually relates to year of first significant production, and a number of these districts were first discovered much earlier. In several of these major districts there have of course been notable extensions, such as the Picher field in the Tri-State zinc and lead district. Alaska is not included.

[c] Compiled from tabulation in *Oil and Gas Journal*, issue of Oct. 31, 1935, with the addition of two Texas fields (Breckenridge and Electra) to the 48 there listed. The 50 fields have yielded 58 percent of the country's all-time production.

More recently such "practical" methods have been reinforced or replaced by a more scientific approach to the problem. The geologist with his expert knowledge of structural formations has been recruited by the industry in its effort to locate oil where surface indications are no longer of value. By the beginning of the post-World War period most areas in which there were surface indications of oil had been thoroughly prospected, so that judgments based on geological theories of oil formations now became more acceptable.

Since the early 1920's the geologist has been of invaluable assistance in exploration activities. In addition, the technological staff of the industry has come to include also the geophysicist, who devises methods of detecting oil through the utilization of precision instruments which can determine the physical properties of underground formations. One such method uses a magnetometer to determine the distance of iron-bearing, and particularly of metamorphic, rocks below the surface: where they come nearest to the surface the overlying sedimentary rocks are apt to be folded in an "anticline" which may contain oil. Another method employed by the geophysicist consists in placing electrodes in the surface of the earth at distances of a few hundred or a few thousand feet and passing a current through the intervening rocks: the drop in potential between different points gives a clue to the character of underlying strata. Still another method uses the sensitive torsion balance to measure minute variations in the force and direction of the earth's gravitational pull: by this means the density, and hence the character, of underlying formations may be ascertained. Finally, the geophysicist may explode a charge of dynamite, and use a seismograph to measure the timing and intensity of the tremors reflected by that which lies below. These various methods may be used individually or in combination: perfected by the geophysicist, their results are employed by the geologist.

Geology and geophysics have been aided by allied sciences in the discovery of new sources of oil and gas. Basically, however, they remain the two outstanding scientific techniques utilized, and together they have accounted for an ever-increasing portion of recent discoveries. They have not replaced random drilling entirely, but very few discoveries in recent years have been made by haphazard techniques.[24]

## Drilling

The first oil deposits were discovered accidentally by persons drilling for salt brine, and the early methods of well drilling were taken over from the brine industry. The technique in almost universal use at that time (1860) employed the churn or cable drill, essentially a percussion instrument relying on gravity for its effec-

24 Kiessling and others, *op. cit.*, pp. 60-63.

tiveness. The original well which Drake drilled at Titusville, Pennsylvania, was less than 100 feet deep. He used a wooden derrick 30 feet high. The raising and lowering of the drill was achieved with a steam engine of the kind used in river steamboats. Most of the early drill tools were forged by local blacksmiths.

At the opening of our period, in 1899, the cable-tool system of drilling, operated by steam power, was still in the ascendant. Naturally it had been improved during the forty years of the industry's history prior to 1899, but the principle had survived unchanged. The steam engine actuated a long seesaw, known as a walking-beam, in a vertical plane. The end remote from the engine was immediately over the well and the heavy drill tool was attached to it by cable. The drill tool was removed from the hole by a winding apparatus in the derrick. The cable drill is particularly effective in boring through hard rock, such as limestone, where great depths do not have to be attained. It has also the advantage that it can readily be used with a portable outfit, and thus moved from site to site. It is still employed extensively where these advantages are important.

The rotary drill, originally developed for boring artesian water wells, was first used by the oil industry in 1901. In this device the shaft is hollow and a stream of water is forced down inside the drill, returning in the space between shaft and rock. Thus the material removed by the drill is extruded automatically. It is no longer necessary, as with the cable drill, to interrupt operations periodically to remove cuttings from the drill hole. Further, the column of returning water or mud reduces the hazard of a cave-in of the well. On the other hand, unless a special form of rotary equipment which yields a solid core is employed (usually known as a diamond drill), rotary drilling yields less information about the strata penetrated than does the cable-tool: in a new field such information is important; in an old field it may not be of interest.

The rotary drill was originally used exclusively for drilling soft formations such as those found on the Gulf coast and in California, but with the development of roller and cone bits of alloy steel its application soon spread to other areas where harder materials had to be penetrated. The rotary drill proved particularly valuable in boring very deep wells, for it was necessary with the cable drill to reduce the diameter of the hole as drilling advanced.

A rotary driven hole is the same diameter at the lower end as at the upper: on occasion rotary drills have pushed nearly three miles deep.

Another improvement in drilling technique relates to the operation of cementing the casing of the well. Special oil well cements, susceptible of continuous mixing, have been developed. Since several thousand sacks of cement may be needed to complete a single well, it is easy to perceive the importance of this innovation.

Since the opening of our period the technology of pressure control has advanced significantly, and it has become crucial in contemporary oil well operation. In earlier times, especially when the cable or churn drill was used, the completion of drilling was frequently heralded by the dramatic eruption of a fountain of oil. Besides wasting valuable oil, the early gushers often caught fire and caused much property damage. Nowadays even wells with very high pressures are brought into operation quite smoothly without the loss of any oil at all. This saving has been achieved by the use of the heavy column of mud-laden water, available with the rotary drill, to repress the oil and prevent its blowing out. In addition blow-out preventers, which can be closed around the drill pipe, are available in case of emergency. Testing and recording devices which reveal conditions at the foot of the well may also play a part in warning the operator of the approach of danger.

*Oil Well Operation*

Technological advances in oil well operation have been equally striking. The efficiency of recovery and the length of life of the well raise technological questions of the first importance. Thus in many of the early wells, which were allowed to gush or flow freely or were pumped by some simple device and subsequently abandoned, recovery reached only 10 to 20 percent of the total amount of oil in the sands or other strata. With modern techniques 70 or 80 percent of the oil may be obtained, leaving but a small fraction of the original deposit to be reached in some other way, perhaps eventually through mining.

Probably the earliest means adopted to increase the yield or prolong the life of the oil well was "shooting" or blasting with explosive. In this method the charge is lowered to the foot of the well and there detonated, so that the surrounding strata may be shattered and the oil released. Where the oil is associated with limestone the injection of hydrochloric acid performs a similar function.

The principal agent which forces oil to the surface is, of course, the natural gas occluded in subsurface reservoirs. When a well no longer flows freely it may be abandoned, as indeed was often done before the knowledge that large amounts of oil remained in the ground stimulated the development of artificial measures for forcing it to the surface. One of the most interesting of these techniques is the restoration of the gas pressure by pumping air, or more usually gas itself, into the oil-bearing strata through an existing well or through a hole bored for the purpose. Apparently repressuring was first successfully undertaken in 1911; since then it has been widely used, especially in shallow fields where the natural pressure is insufficient to eject more than a small fraction of the total amount of available oil.[25]

If repressuring is uneconomical or difficult, perhaps because of the geological formation, other methods are available. Where the problem is not so serious as to require mechanical pumping, gas lifting methods may be used. Gas under pressure is forced through a pipe to the foot of the well, whence it returns with the oil to the surface. The gas is then collected, compressed, and used over again for the same purpose.

Where the well is too deep, or gas lifting methods alone are inadequate, resort must be had to pumping. Since oil can be sucked only from depths of 20 or 30 feet, the pumping mechanism must be placed within this distance of the bottom of the well and the oil forced from there to the surface. The operation is commonly accomplished by means of a rod inserted in the well and connected to the pump: the power used at the surface to actuate the rod is sometimes centralized for a number of wells by cables. Special difficulties are encountered in the case of very deep wells —say, more than 5,000 feet. Here special types of pump may be used—for example, hydraulically operated rodless pumps, or elec-

[25] Experiments in repressuring were originally undertaken as a means of utilizing surplus gas: they had already been begun some years before 1911 (A. Beeby Thompson, *Petroleum Mining and Oil-Field Development*, Van Nostrand, 1910, p. 92).

tric pumps in which the motor is lowered into the well and fed by armored cable.

Because of the labor involved in drilling, the most important single influence upon the productivity of oil and gas wells in the long run is probably the proportion of available oil that is ultimately recoverable by the methods in vogue. The cost of drilling a well of a given depth is much the same whether only 40 percent, or as much as 80 or 90 percent, of the oil in the formation is actually recovered during the lifetime of the well. Hence it is to the interest of the individual operator to secure maximum recovery.[26] The question is also an important one from the conservation standpoint, and it is likewise to the interest of the community that as little oil as possible be left in the ground. Once oil has ceased to flow, and can no longer be pumped, its recovery becomes hazardous and expensive, and there may in fact be no way in which such oil can ever be recovered.

The principal method by which the percentage of oil eventually recoverable may be increased is through the preservation of underground gas pressures, the artificial restriction of the flow of oil, and the consequent lengthening of the life of the well. This may be achieved by the use of valves at the surface; or by the insertion of tubing only 2 or 3 inches in diameter inside the casing of the well. It is obvious such methods reduce the rate of flow: it is not so obvious that they will improve eventual recovery. Regulation of flow contributes to the latter object in two principal ways. If a well is allowed to flow freely it may happen that the pressure at the foot of the well is insufficient to keep the natural gas in solution, in which case free gas will be obtained—gas that has made no contribution to the task of raising oil to the surface. With artificial reduction of the flow of oil the pressure at the foot of the well is maintained more nearly equal to the pressure in distant parts of the reservoir, and the expansion of a given amount of natural gas is made to raise a larger quantity of oil to the surface. The second way in which the regulation of the flow of oil contributes to its eventual recovery is by reducing the migration of subsurface water. It has been found that water moves more readily than oil in response to a given pressure gradient, and

[26] However, if neighboring wells are rapidly draining the field, the attempt to maximize recovery for each individual well may merely encourage waste, and eventually leave much oil in the ground. It is nonetheless to the operators' common interest that the entire field shall be so exploited that maximum recovery results.

moves through strata which are impermeable to oil. Where flow rates are excessive, underground pressure differences between various parts of the field are increased, and water is apt to work through coarse textured strata, thus cutting off oil in fine textured sands and rendering it irrecoverable by existing methods.

Where neighboring wells are operated by many different producers, these considerations do not diminish the immediate advantage which may accrue, or appear to accrue, to any individual producer through a policy of unrestricted production on his part. Such a policy may indeed diminish the eventual output of the field, but it may still yield the individual who pursues it a larger fraction of this smaller total. This is why more and more attention has been devoted to the desirability of framing state proration laws and other conservation measures, in order not only to prevent wells from being spaced too closely, but also to reduce the rate of flow of existing wells.[27]

We should note, finally, that measures such as those described, which diminish output now in order to increase eventual recovery, make the interpretation of productivity measures in the petroleum industry especially difficult. For a deliberate reduction in the rate of flow does not reduce the input of labor correspondingly, or indeed at all. Over the entire life history of the well, output per man may be the same as it would have been had no conservation measures been undertaken. Yet it is true, too, that in the early years of its life output per man is reduced by the practices adopted. The effect on our productivity index depends upon the age distribution of producing wells and their eventual life. Although the new conservation practices have probably depressed the level of productivity in recent years, in the long run they may lead to even greater output per man than would otherwise have been achieved.[28] To have maximum significance, and to

[27] "It is obvious that by lessening the waste of gas or reservoir energy proration increases the total amount of oil that will be recovered. The amount of this increased recovery will not be known for many years, until a large number of prorated fields have approached exhaustion and their recoveries can be compared with those of fields produced by former methods. All that can now be said is that the increase in recovery—the saving of oil that unrestricted production would have left in the ground—will be large" (Max W. Ball, *This Fascinating Oil Business*, p. 148).

[28] Where conservation measures reduce current production per well, current productivity is depressed, but eventual recovery may be increased. If output and man-hours are each summed over the entire life of the well, output per manhour may be increased, too. Productivity in recent years may also have been depressed by the tendency of proration, where carelessly administered, to encourage unnecessary drilling (see footnote 15 above). Here no long run benefit to productivity accrues.

report the full benefits of technological change, productivity comparisons in the petroleum industry should probably be made over rather long periods, and between groups of years instead of between isolated years. It is all the more remarkable that the measures we are able to present, which are primarily a comparison between the two years 1902 and 1939, should reveal the substantial increase in output per manhour which they do in fact show.

# Chapter 11

# Iron Mining and Beneficiating

FROM COAL MINES and oil wells—the source of the nation's fuel—we turn, in this chapter and the next, to a review of two important metal mining industries—iron and copper. The first of these, like bituminous coal mining, is geographically scattered. Most iron ore comes from the Lake Superior district (Minnesota, Michigan and Wisconsin), from Alabama, or from the northeastern district (New York, New Jersey and Pennsylvania); but iron is also mined in many other states. The ore is obtained both from underground and from open pit mines, but principally from the latter (Table 21 below). Of all ore mined, about one ton in five is beneficiated (Table 20 below),[1] and the remainder is shipped to smelters as crude ore. Even the ores that are beneficiated undergo only a very simple treatment which serves to raise the grade of ore to such a level that they can be used directly in the blast furnace. The additional treatment results, therefore, in a fairly homogeneous total product, and for this reason it is possible to utilize ore tonnage as a measure of physical output in the industry for a given year. It must be specified, however, that such a figure would relate to merchantable ore, which means that where beneficiation has been employed the data refer to the beneficiated product.

It is possible, of course, for average grade of ore to change considerably over the long run even though output for any single year is homogeneous. It happens this, too, is not the case in iron mining.[2] Any tendency for increased mining of lean ore to dilute grade has been overcome by the wider use of beneficiating. Hence, a ton of (beneficiated) ore at the end of the period was pretty much the same as a ton at the beginning, a fact which obviates a

---

[1] The process was described in Chapter 7.

[2] Data in N. Yaworski and others, *Iron Mining* (National Research Project, Philadelphia, 1940), Table A-4, p. 206, indicate a barely perceptible diminution in the average grade of merchantable ore from 1880 to date.

host of statistical problems that arise when such a happy situation does not obtain.[3]

Actually, the quantity data available for iron mining and beneficiating permit the derivation of an index of physical output which approaches quite closely the ideal index[4] for a metal mining industry. This is noteworthy because in the case of most nonferrous metals we have to be satisfied with data which result only in rough approximations to such an index. Any variations that do arise within total iron ore production in any year are accounted for in the fourfold classification of ores we have utilized. Even here, however, one variety of ore—hematite—is of such preponderant importance that the utilization of the breakdown results in an index which deviates but slightly from one based on a single series embracing all varieties of ore.[5]

## THE RELATION BETWEEN OUTPUT
## AND EMPLOYMENT

The World War period provides a convenient dividing point in the history of output and employment in the iron ore industry. In 1917 both employment and output reached their peak after a general upward movement over the entire period preceding the war. After that conflict both output and employment tended downward. In both periods, as is evident from Chart 44, there were short run reversals in the direction of movement (largely cyclical in nature), but the general impression of growth in one period, and decline, or at least absence of growth, in the other, is unmistakable.

Although the entire period preceding the World War witnessed a similarity of general movement in both output and employment, there was a difference in their respective rates of growth. This is clear from the fact that from 1902 until 1917 production increased by 114 percent while mandays of employment rose only

---

[3] Compare, for instance, the difficulties encountered in measuring the output of copper (discussed in Chapter 12 below and in Appendix D) where the opposite conditions prevail.

[4] I.e., a measure which, in the absence of price changes, would be proportional to value of products.

[5] See Appendix Table A-1.

Chart 44

IRON MINING AND BENEFICIATING
Output, Employment and Productivity, 1880 – 1939
(1902:100)

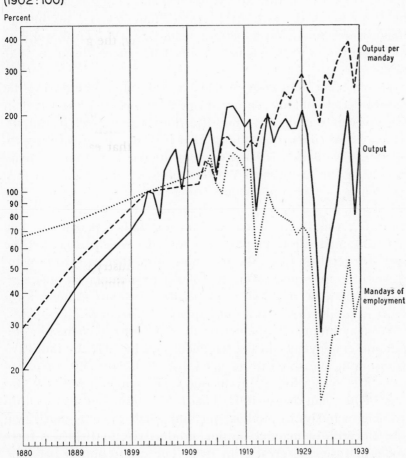

Percent

Ratio scale                                    For source and notes see Appendix E

41 percent.[6] Similarly in the post-war period the decline in employment is much more marked than that in production: output
in the post-war period almost regained its wartime peak on sev-

[6] By using data in Yaworski and others, *Iron Mining*, we may extend our series
back to 1880. In the period from 1880 to 1902 the same tendency manifests itself
although in a more pronounced form than in the later period of more moderate
growth. Thus, from 1880 to 1902 there was a fivefold increase in production while
employment rose by about 50 percent (Chart 44).

eral occasions, whereas employment continued to decline. This is abundantly clear from a comparison of successive peaks in output in 1920, 1923, 1929 and 1937, each of which is associated with a level of employment relatively lower than in the preceding peak. By 1937 this progressive divergence culminated in a production index which stood but 4 percent below the 1917 level; employment, on the other hand, had declined 62 percent from its 1917 peak.

Employment, it is clear, reached a peak some time during the second decade of this century. Prior to about 1917 the trend in employment was in the same direction as the trend in output, which was of course expanding. That is to say, the growth in production was sufficiently large to offset the rise in output per manday. After the first World War circumstances had changed. Production was stagnant; hence rising output per manday was translated into a decline in the volume of employment in the industry. And the post-war decline was rather persistent. The only sustained rise in employment was that which succeeded the very low level of 1932. We may note, also, that each case of increase of employment over that of the preceding year was associated, not with any decline in productivity, but rather with a spurt in production which outstripped the rise in productivity.

We may summarize the net result of 37 years of change in output and employment in the statement that by 1939 the industry's labor input, measured in mandays, had declined to 40 percent of the 1902 level, whereas production had risen to a level 50 percent higher than that of 1902. That is, the industry used two fifths as many mandays to produce one and a half times as much iron ore. In terms of manday output, productivity in 1939 was three and a half times as great as in 1902. The rise in output per manhour was even larger: according to the best estimate we can make, the later was four and a half times the earlier level. Thus manhour productivity in iron ore mining expanded about twice as rapidly as in the metal mining group as a whole, and at about the same pace as it did in the petroleum and natural gas industry. Among industries for which we have data, only phosphate rock and gypsum—both of minor importance—bettered this record.

With the exception of the first decade of the period covered by our analysis, the increase in productivity seems to have been spread quite evenly over the years included. That is to say, from about 1911 to 1939 it is not possible to point to a single period to which the bulk of the net increase between the two years may be allocated. Even so, there are marked short time fluctuations in the direction of movement of the productivity index. Between 1911 and 1939 there are almost as many years in which productivity declined from the preceding year as there are years in which a rise from the preceding year occurred. Several of these declines were of only one year's duration, but there are two cases where the decline continued over three years. Moreover, even the declines that lasted only a year were rather severe on two occasions. Thus, the net increase between 1911 and 1939 is made up of successive short spurts in productivity of sufficient magnitude to outweigh intervening short run declines.

Both the substantial long period rise and the erratic year-to-year behavior of the index are part of the same picture so far as productivity in iron mining is concerned. Both have their roots in certain basic factors operative in the industry. The most important of these factors is open cut mining—the industry's response to a unique resource condition.

## RESOURCE CONDITIONS

The striking rise in productivity disclosed by our figures suggests that little if any deterioration has occurred in the physical conditions under which the ore is mined. To be sure, the highest grades of ore are being rapidly depleted.[7] But it does not necessarily follow that the accessibility or ease of mining of iron ore currently extracted is less than it was some decades ago. We should like to know whether the difficulties of gaining access to ore have increased over time, or whether the efforts of the iron miner today yield a product significantly lower in grade than that produced at the turn of the century. In copper mining, as we shall see, the answer to both of these questions is an emphatic affirmative. Increases of productivity in that industry have been achieved in the face of a deterioration in the physical conditions of mining. The production of iron ore, by contrast, is not sharply characterized by aggravation of natural difficulties.

We may consider first the accessibility of the ore itself. Since deterioration in this respect has occurred primarily in underground mining, the pronounced shift toward open cut technique

[7] Yaworski and others, *Iron Mining*, Chapter VI.

has tended, in part, to eliminate this difficulty.[8] It still prevails in many places, however, for underground mines are even now of considerable importance in the industry; indeed, in years of low production such mines may well outproduce the open cut enterprises. In the underground mining of iron—as in the underground mining of most other minerals—the miners have been forced to go to greater depths to reach the ore,[9] so that the many problems associated with deep mining have been intensified.[10]

It is when we consider the trend in grade of ore that the good fortune of iron mining becomes most apparent. Compared with other metals, and especially copper, iron resources have undergone remarkably little deterioration. Our best indicator of the trend in the grade of iron ore is the changing percentage of total ore produced that requires beneficiation. Data presented in Table 20 indicate that this fraction increased from about 10 percent in 1914 to roughly 18 percent in most recent years.[11] Although there was almost a twofold rise in ore requiring beneficiation over this period it is significant that even at the present time no more than about a fifth of the merchantable ore produced undergoes beneficiation. A comparison with the copper industry, in which 95 percent of the ore mined in 1939 had to be concentrated (equivalent to 84 percent of recoverable copper metal),[12] indicates that the relative importance of concentration in the iron mining industry is still remarkably low.

Equally significant is the fact that among the ores that need beneficiation no marked decline in grade is apparent.[13] This sug-

[8] To a certain extent open pits also are hampered by greater depth of operation, but the disadvantages imposed by greater thickness of overburden do not seem to be of the same order as those encountered in underground mines. For a description of the difficulties of the open cut mine, see Yaworski and others, *Iron Mining*, p. 30.

[9] For instance, from 1916 to 1937 the average maximum vertical depth of underground mines in the Lake Superior district increased by about 650 feet—from 854 feet in 1916 to 1,511 in 1937 (Yaworski and others, *Iron Mining*, p. 29).

[10] The auxiliary functions of drainage and ventilation are rendered more difficult; men and materials must be hoisted over greater distances; the presence of more overlying rock strata increases the difficulties of support, etc.

[11] In Yaworski and others, *Iron Mining*, there is also a 1909 figure which indicates that beneficiation was practically negligible at that time.

[12] See below, Chapter 12, Table 22.

[13] This may be deduced from data in Yaworski and others, *Iron Mining*, Table A-8, p. 227, which indicate little change over the period 1914–37 in the ratio of crude ore consumed to concentrates produced. If anything, the ratio tends to decline. The decline may, however, merely reflect increased recoveries in beneficiating. This possibility must be considered if the ratio is to be used to indicate changes in grade.

Table 20

BENEFICIATION OF IRON ORE SHIPPED FROM MINES IN THE
UNITED STATES, 1914–40[a]

| Year | Beneficiated[b] (Th. long tons) | Total (Th. long tons) | Percentage Beneficiated of Total |
|------|------|------|------|
| 1914 | 4,130 | 39,714 | 10.4 |
| 1915 | 5,581 | 55,493 | 10.1 |
| 1916 | 8,105 | 77,871 | 10.4 |
| 1917 | 8,167 | 75,573 | 10.8 |
| 1918 | 7,882 | 72,021 | 10.9 |
| 1919 | 7,356 | 56,373 | 13.0 |
| | | | |
| 1920 | 8,515 | 69,281 | 12.3 |
| 1921 | 3,728 | 26,653 | 14.0 |
| 1922 | 6,623 | 50,613 | 13.1 |
| 1923 | 10,687 | 69,811 | 15.3 |
| 1924 | 7,093 | 52,083 | 13.6 |
| 1925 | 8,736 | 63,925 | 13.7 |
| 1926 | 8,372 | 69,293 | 12.1 |
| 1927 | 8,115 | 61,232 | 13.3 |
| 1928 | 8,621 | 63,433 | 13.6 |
| 1929 | 9,424 | 75,603 | 12.5 |
| | | | |
| 1930 | 8,974 | 55,201 | 16.3 |
| 1931 | 4,676 | 28,516 | 16.4 |
| 1932 | 407 | 5,331 | 7.6 |
| 1933 | 3,556 | 24,624 | 14.4 |
| 1934 | 4,146 | 25,793 | 16.1 |
| 1935 | 6,067 | 33,426 | 18.1 |
| 1936 | 9,659 | 51,466 | 18.8 |
| 1937 | 12,350 | 72,348 | 17.1 |
| 1938 | 4,836 | 26,431 | 18.3 |
| 1939 | 9,426 | 54,827 | 17.2 |
| | | | |
| 1940 | 12,926 | 75,198 | 17.2 |

[a] *Minerals Yearbook* and its predecessor *Mineral Resources*. Excludes ore containing 5 percent or more of manganese and ore sold for paint.
[b] Excludes ores that undergo no treatment beyond crushing and screening to improve their physical structure.

gests that in the past, once a mine changed from the production
of direct-shipping ores to ores requiring beneficiation, grade remained rather stable and, in addition, that accretions to the group
of ores requiring beneficiation were of approximately the same
grade as the ores already in the group. In the case of copper, on
the other hand, the decline in the grade of concentrating ores as
such has been a problem solved only through increased elaboration of milling techniques. Iron has still another advantage, in that
the level of grade of ore undergoing concentration (as compared with

the grade of the merchantable product produced) is much higher than in copper, as is apparent from the fact that the ratio of concentration in iron is about 2 to 1, whereas in copper it is commonly 20 or 25 to 1. About 2 tons of crude iron ore will yield one ton of iron concentrates (merchantable iron ore), but it takes 20 or more tons of copper ore to produce one ton of copper concentrates.[14] Thus, by comparison with copper—which represents an extreme example of declining grade—the relative decline in the grade of iron ore is remarkably slight and the absolute level of iron ore grade is exceedingly high.

It appears that neither in accessibility nor in grade of ore have iron ore resources seriously deteriorated. Evidently, in its efforts to raise the level of productivity, technology has had a clear field.

## TECHNOLOGY

The recent history of the industry's technology is dominated by the rise of open cut iron mining. Prior to 1892 the surface mining of iron ore played an insignificant role: in 1937 two thirds of all merchantable ore produced in the United States came from open cut mines. Thus, within the space of four or five decades, the character of iron mining in this country underwent a radical change. Unfortunately the statistical record of this change does not begin before the year 1909; we have assembled such data as are available in Table 21.

Both the shift toward open cut mining and the fluctuating contribution of open cut mines to the total help to explain the two characteristics of iron mining productivity that we noticed earlier in this chapter. To begin with, open cut mines are characterized by a higher output-labor ratio than underground mines. This is clearly evident from Table 21, which gives figures on tons per man-hour for both types of mine. Hence any tendency for open cut mines to increase their share of the total—even without a rise in the productivity of either type of iron mining operation—would cause the productivity ratio to rise. Part of the net change over the period 1902–37 is certainly to be attributed to this factor. It is more convenient, however, to postpone our consideration of the long run net change to a later point in the discussion and to deal

[14] Data for iron are taken from the source cited in the preceding footnotes; data for copper from Appendix Table D-3.

## TABLE 21

OPEN CUT AND UNDERGROUND IRON MINES, 1909–38
Percentage Contribution to Total Production and Output per Manhour[a]

| Year | Open Cut Mines | | Underground Mines | |
|------|------------------------------|----------------------------------------|------------------------------|----------------------------------------|
|      | Percent of Total Production | Output per Manhour[b] (long tons) | Percent of Total Production | Output per Manhour[b] (long tons) |
| 1909 | 46.7 | c | 53.3 | c |
| 1915 | 39.9 | 1.121 | 60.1 | .389 |
| 1916 | 46.4 | 1.104 | 53.6 | .369 |
| 1917 | 47.1 | .912 | 52.9 | .347 |
| 1918 | 51.3 | .832 | 48.7 | .321 |
| 1919 | 46.3 | 1.062 | 53.7 | .313 |
| 1920 | 48.3 | .966 | 51.7 | .351 |
| 1921 | 47.0 | .762 | 53.0 | .364 |
| 1922 | 52.4 | 1.087 | 47.6 | .395 |
| 1923 | 56.4 | 1.171 | 43.6 | .408 |
| 1924 | 47.2 | .989 | 52.8 | .438 |
| 1925 | 48.4 | 1.393 | 51.6 | .493 |
| 1926 | 51.1 | 1.784 | 48.9 | .510 |
| 1927 | 50.0 | 1.591 | 50.0 | .493 |
| 1928 | 53.1 | 1.815 | 46.9 | .548 |
| 1929 | 55.7 | 1.837 | 44.3 | .589 |
| 1930 | 49.6 | 1.496 | 50.4 | .563 |
| 1931 | 45.0 | 1.212 | 55.0 | .583 |
| 1932 | 34.9 | .931 | 65.1 | .503 |
| 1933 | 64.6 | 1.993 | 35.4 | .508 |
| 1934 | 57.1 | 1.791 | 42.9 | .598 |
| 1935 | 58.7 | 2.470 | 41.3 | .663 |
| 1936 | 63.1 | 2.655 | 36.9 | .701 |
| 1937 | 65.8 | 3.005 | 34.2 | .692 |
| 1938 | 48.9 | 1.795 | 51.1 | .642 |

[a] N. Yaworski and others, *Iron Mining* (National Research Project, Philadelphia, 1940), Table A-6, p. 218. Some mines using a combination of underground and open cut methods did not report separately for the two; the breakdown in these cases was estimated by the authors of the NRP report. The figures are based on data whose coverage of the industry, in terms of output, varies from 88.4 to 100.0 percent. Ore containing 5 percent or more of manganese is not included.
[b] Ratio derived from employment figures including beneficiating plants at the mine.
[c] Not available.

first with the erratic year-to-year behavior of the productivity index.

Shifts in the internal composition of total iron ore output from year to year must exert some influence on industrial productivity. As we have noted, the relative importance of open cut mines has tended to change from one year to another, so that this factor may afford a partial explanation of the jerky movement of produc-

tivity in iron mining. Indeed, if we compare the years in which
iron ore productivity has declined from the preceding year's level
with those in which the relative contribution of open cut mines
has decreased, we find a marked similarity of movement. Since
1915 productivity has declined from the preceding year's level on
11 occasions: in 9 of these years the relative contribution of open
cut mines also dropped; the other 2 were war years, when productivity might be expected to fall for other reasons.

There appears to be still another factor—closely associated with
the first—which helps to influence the short-run fluctuations in
productivity. It derives from the fact that in open cut mining
barren rock must be removed before the underlying ore deposits
are reached. However, the stripping of overburden is an operation which need not be evenly distributed over time (at least not
in proportion to ore production) and usually is not so distributed.
Hence we find that in some years more overburden per unit of
output is removed than in others. In those years, then, the relative
amounts of labor devoted to direct mining, and to the tasks of
preparing certain sections of the mine for future exploitation,
have been altered in favor of future operations. Relatively less
labor is allocated to mining proper, and relatively more labor is
used in preparations for the future: the result is a fall in output per unit of total employment (our sole measure). This may
happen in two ways: either stripping of overburden is purposely
carried through at the expense of the extraction of iron ore, or
else production of iron ore falls to such low levels that even a
"normal" amount of stripping will appear large in relation to
current production. It is significant, however, that both of the
ways in which this influence may operate seem to be concomitants
of a low level of activity in the industry. Not only would "normal"
stripping activities appear relatively large in a year of low production, but the possibility of keeping men and machinery active
in the face of a low level of demand by assigning them to prepare
for future operations would play a part in the mine operator's
calculations.[15] It seems likely, then, that a low level of activity in

15 Data bearing on this point are available only for the years since 1923, and for
Minnesota alone. During this period Minnesota produced, on the average, close to
90 percent of total open cut production and may therefore be considered a good
indicator of movement of the United States totals. The ratio of overburden stripped
to ore produced in Minnesota open cut mines increased on nine occasions after 1923
and in six of these nine years the increase was associated with a decline in produc-

open cut mining would be associated with a lower output-labor ratio than would a higher level of productive activity.[16]

Chart 44 reveals a clear synchronization in the fluctuations of productivity and production. Although deviations from the general pattern have occurred, there can be little doubt that in this industry there is a definite tendency for year-to-year movements in productivity to proceed in the same direction as those in production. What happens, apparently, is that a decline in the absolute level of production usually results in a greater relative decline in the output of open cut mines than of underground mines.[17] This shift in the relative importance of the two types of producers exerts a depressing influence on productivity. And, as we have noted, there is an additional tendency for open cut productivity to decline when production is at a low level because of the relative increase in stripping operations. This may be expected to intensify the depressing effect of the first influence, and the combination of the two factors probably accounts in good part for the year-to-year fluctuations of productivity in the industry.

Despite the undulations of productivity in iron mining and beneficiating, we find a decided long term increase in output per manday and per manhour. Similarly, the fluctuating importance of open cut mines in the industry has not prevented a marked long term increase in the relative share of this type of mine in the output of the entire industry. It is reasonable to conclude, moreover, that the secular rise in the relative importance of the open cut technique (aside from any change in open cut productivity) has been a factor of great importance in the net increase in output per man. For in 1937 (the year of peak productivity) out-

tion; in the remaining three years (1928, 1934 and 1937) the change in the stripping ratio was very slight. (Data from Yaworski and others, *Iron Mining*, Table A-19, p. 238.)

[16] It is true that other influences, more or less common to all industries, affect productivity during periods of low activity. Here we are concerned not with these influences but with a special factor which operates in open cut iron mining alone. For a statement of some more general cyclical influences on productivity as we are able to measure it, see Solomon Fabricant, "Productivity of Labor in Peace and War," *Occasional Paper* 7 (National Bureau of Economic Research, 1942), pp. 13-14.

[17] This phenomenon is clearly observable. It is probably explained by the greater flexibility of operation of open cut mines, which can cease production in response to curtailed demand without running up against the fixed costs for drainage and other types of maintenance that burden the underground mine operator. (See *Minerals Yearbook, 1934*, p. 323.) In addition, the open cut operator may find it simpler to curtail production because of the ease with which men and machines can be shifted to the task of preparing the mine for future operations.

put per manhour in open cut mines was 4.3 times that in underground mines. If we take the period 1915–38 as a whole in order
to even out such influences as changes in the stripping ratio, manhour productivity of open cut mines is still about three times as
great as the average for underground mines (see Table 21).[18]

The shift to open cut mining, although in the nature of a
response to a unique resource condition, represents one aspect of
technological change in iron mining. Technological change has
appeared also in other forms. Within the framework of the open
cut technique important mechanical improvements have been
achieved; these, for the most part, have centered about the development of the power shovel and the attendant increases in its
strength, capacity and flexibility.[19] In addition technology has
effected changes in underground iron, as in other underground
metal, mines. Here mechanization of functions and improvement
in tools have been a continuing influence over the entire period
covered by our analysis. New methods of mining have been developed which use gravity for breaking and loading the ore, and
greatly reduce the need for drilling and blasting.[20]

The striking rise in the productivity of iron mining is therefore to be attributed to the exceptionally favorable circumstances
of the industry. It has been able to share to the full in the many
innovations introduced into the metal mining industries during

[18] Output per manday in iron mining rose from 4.6 long tons in 1915–17 (annual
average) to 10.6 tons in 1935–37, or by 6.0 tons. Using the method of Table 13 (reading long tons of iron ore for dollars, and mandays for manhours) we may associate
4.6 tons of the increase with changes in underground and open pit productivity as
such, and 1.4 tons with the shift from the former to the latter method of mining.
(Data are from Yaworski and others, *Iron Mining*, Table A-5, p. 216.) The relative
contribution of the shift in mining method to the rise in productivity during the
last 20 or 25 years appears to have been slightly greater in iron than in copper
mining: see Chapter 12, footnote 16.

[19] For a much fuller discussion of these changes, see Chapter 6 above.

[20] See above, Chapters 5 and 6. So far as concerns underground production, the
soft ores of the Lake Superior district were mined mainly by square-set methods
until top slicing was introduced after 1885, and sublevel caving after 1890. The
substitution of these methods for square-set mining was stimulated by the development of scraper mechanisms and improved ventilation after 1900. Shrinkage began
to replace open stoping in mining the hard ores of New Jersey after 1912. These
changes greatly reduced the amount of timbering required and led to increased use
of gravity in loading the ore. Block caving has been seldom used in underground
iron mines, but it is thought possible that it may eventually play a role in winning
ores of lower grade than those at present mined. During 1929–37 about half the output of iron ore from underground mines was produced either by top slicing or by
sublevel caving, about one third by stoping methods (especially in Alabama), and the
remainder by combinations of stoping and caving. (See Yaworski and others, *Iron
Mining*, Chapter V.)

the past several decades; but, unlike most other metal mining industries, it has not felt the pressure of increasing natural difficulty. In the next chapter we turn to copper mining, a form of extraction in which technological advance has been, if anything, even more rapid than in iron mining, but in which the deterioration of resource conditions has played an important role.

# Chapter 12

# Copper Mining and Ore Dressing

FROM IRON ORE we pass to another important metal mining industry, that producing copper. Today copper comes chiefly from the mountain states (especially Arizona, Utah, Montana and Nevada), although considerable quantities of the metal are still produced from Michigan ores. Like iron mining, the extraction of copper has increasingly become an open pit enterprise. A peculiarity of the industry is that most copper mines yield small amounts of other nonferrous metals—especially gold and silver—as byproducts. The process of bringing metallic copper to market usually involves four distinct operations: (1) mining; (2) ore dressing; (3) smelting; and (4) refining. Customarily the first two of these operations are regarded as nonmanufacturing, and the last two as manufacturing, processes. In our treatment the customary definition is employed: the indexes presented in this study refer to the mining and dressing of ores by establishments whose output is valued chiefly for its copper content.

The copper industry, thus defined, has two types of final product: ores and concentrates. Ores are, of course, produced by all copper mines, but in most cases the ores as taken from the earth are not sufficiently rich in metal or simple in mineralogy to be smelted directly. Hence most ores are subjected to a preliminary treatment designed to expedite the subsequent extraction of their metallic content. This treatment, variously known as ore dressing, concentrating, milling or beneficiating, involves, essentially, reducing the amount of barren rock in which the metal is imbedded and, when the ore contains metals other than copper, separating the important metallic constituents of the ore into products in each of which one metal predominates. The products resulting from this treatment are known as concentrates because, basically, they consist of ore that has been concentrated into smaller bulk through the removal of waste.[1]

---

[1] The development and significance of ore dressing techniques were discussed above in Chapter 7.

Not all ores are concentrated; some may be smelted without any preliminary treatment. Such ores are known as direct smelting ores. They are to be distinguished from the far more important class of concentrating ores, for they appear as a final product of the copper mining industry in the form of ore, while the others appear as concentrates.[2]

Neither direct smelting ores nor concentrates constitute a homogeneous grouping. Within each category there are broad variations in type and quality. These comprise differences in grade (metal content per ton); differences in the form in which the metal occurs (ease with which it can be smelted); differences in the amount of other metals, such as gold and silver, associated with the copper (which in some ores may mean that a metal other than copper is of chief value), etc. Defined precisely, therefore, the output of the copper industry consists of direct smelting ores and concentrates of varying qualities and types which, when smelted and refined, will yield metallic copper and perhaps several other metals.[3] We measure this output (Chart 45 and Appendix Table A-5) in terms of the recoverable content of copper, gold and silver in the ores and concentrates the industry produces, with each metal weighted by its price.[4] This index of course differs from the index of output for the commodity copper (Chart 4 and Appendix Table A-7), for it includes those amounts of gold and silver which come from copper ores.

We chose not to base our measure of output upon tonnage of ore chiefly because quality of ore varies within rather wide limits. If quantity and value data for both ores and concentrates were available in sufficient detail to be classified into fairly homogeneous categories and suitably weighted, an adequate index based upon such statistics could be constructed. Unfortunately such data are not available.[5] The data we have are of two kinds: (1) tonnage

[2] For a discussion of concentrates and direct smelting ores—regarded as the two commodities produced by the copper mining industry—see Appendix D.

[3] The metals these ores contain, in addition to copper, are mainly gold, silver, lead, zinc and molybdenum. See "Copper Ore," preliminary release of the Census of Mineral Industries, 1939 (March 1941).

[4] The construction of our indexes of output for the various nonferrous metal mining industries is described in greater detail in Appendix B.

[5] It is, indeed, doubtful that such data could be collected, if only because the almost infinite variety of cupriferous ores and concentrates would hardly allow for a simple system of classification into which ores and concentrates would conveniently fall. The most convenient classification would be based on metal content, as in manganese ore, but so many factors other than content of copper determine quality

Chart 45

## COPPER MINING AND ORE DRESSING
Output, Employment and Productivity, 1880 – 1939
(1902 : 100)

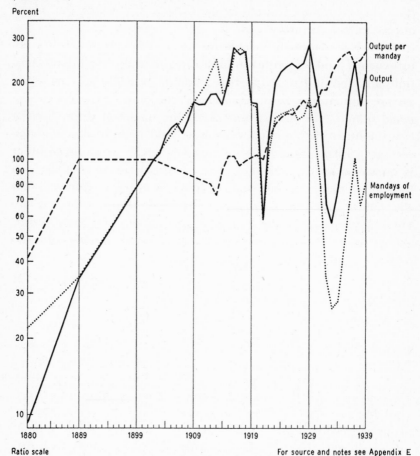

Ratio scale

For source and notes see Appendix E

---

that a very large number of classifications and subclassifications would undoubtedly
be needed in this case. In addition, the marketing of metalliferous ores and concentrates—as epitomized in the bewildering smelter contract with its system of de-
ductions, bonuses, and penalties, in which value is determined not only by the
amount of metal contained, but also by the presence or absence (above a certain
percentage) of various constituents deemed necessary to efficient smelting—is of such
a nature that the values per ton of certain ores and concentrates that might conceivably fall into the same classification would vary within rather wide limits. For
a comprehensive treatment of the marketing of ores and concentrates see A. B.
Parsons, "Metalliferous Ores and Concentrates," in *The Marketing of Metals and
Minerals,* ed. by J. E. Spurr and F. E. Wormser (McGraw-Hill, 1925), pp. 583-626.

of copper ore (in the case of milling ores, before concentration); and (2) recoverable metallic content of ores and concentrates produced. Data of the first kind take no account of the changing composition of total tonnage: because of the persistent downward trend in the copper content of ore (Table 22) an average ton of ore in 1939 is a quite different commodity from an average ton in 1899. Nor is metallic content of ore a perfect measure of physical output. Only if grade or quality of ore and concentrates were uniquely determined by metallic content or, more specifically, if an ore containing twice as much copper per ton were worth twice as much per ton, would an index based on these data be equivalent to one based on a detailed breakdown of ores and concentrates. Although this is not exactly the case, metallic content is undoubtedly the chief factor determining value per ton, and we may, therefore, assume that an index based on metallic content is a fairly close approximation to an ideal measure of output.[6] For this reason we have employed metallic content rather than ore tonnage to measure the physical output of copper mining, as of other nonferrous metal mining industries.

## THE RELATION BETWEEN OUTPUT
## AND EMPLOYMENT

Between 1902 and 1939 output more than doubled, whereas in the latter year manday employment stood slightly lower than in the former. In other words, output per manday rose by about the same amount as production over the 37-year period. Both output and employment appear to exhibit first a rising and then a falling trend, but peaks in the two series are separated by a twelve-year

[6] While superior concentrating techniques appear to have raised the grade of material leaving the mining industry (see Appendix Table D-3), high grade concentrates tend to have a disproportionately high value per ton. To this extent the use of series for recoverable content may understate the rise which would be reported by an index of ore production weighted by the prices of different grades of ore, could this be computed. Besides this weakness there is the added difficulty that the measure relates to metal recoverable at a stage in the production process one or two steps removed from mining. If an increase in the efficiency of smelting and refining were to result in the extraction of more metal than formerly, the index would suffer from an upward bias. However, it seems that the improvement in smelter recovery has been slight (see Appendix Table D-1). It is obvious that to some extent these considerations cancel each other. The adequacy of our index, based upon recoverable content, is appraised from these and other viewpoints in Appendix D.

interval. In employment the high point was reached in 1917 (or, at least, during the years 1916–18), but the peak in production did not occur until 1929. It is noticeable, however, that the 1929 peak in output is only slightly above the level reached in 1916, and that 1929 is in fact the sole year in which the 1916 level was surpassed.

The increase in manday productivity from 1902 to 1939 was 168 percent. This is only about one half of the percentage gain in iron mining, and is about equal to the increase for the entire metals group. In terms of manhours the comparison offers much the same picture. Output per manhour in copper rose by 200 percent over the entire period, a net gain similar to that in metal mining as a whole, in which output per manhour jumped 196 percent. In iron mining during the same period manhour output increased by 346 percent, or nearly twice as much as in copper (see Table 11 above). Productivity in iron mining, although subject to sharp fluctuations from year to year for reasons discussed in Chapter 11, rose rather continuously over the period: in copper mining practically no advance in productivity occurred between the turn of the century and the close of the first World War.

Both output and employment rose substantially between 1902 and 1916–18. Chart 45, in which data for 1880 and 1889 are plotted also, reveals that the rise in these two series during this period is merely a continuation of the general upward movement before the turn of the century. The rise in output per manday was more uneven. During the earliest decade (1880–89) production rose considerably faster than employment, but from 1889 to 1916 output per manday failed to rise appreciably, even though the industry was passing through its period of most rapid expansion. The relative stagnation of productivity in copper mining during these years contrasts sharply with the experience of iron mining, the other principal metal mining industry, discussed in the preceding chapter.

After the World War both output and employment fell to a low level in 1921. Once again it is noteworthy that the net change from 1916–18 in the two series was approximately the same: the productivity index did not change appreciably. Not until the period of the 1920's did the movements of the two series begin to diverge once more, and output per manday resume its rise. In the next decade the divergence widened, and by 1937 employment had fallen 42 percent from the 1929 level while production had declined by 14 percent.

Thus the year 1921 seems to mark a dividing point in the behavior of productivity in copper mining. Output per worker in that year was roughly the same as it had been in 1889. After 1921 the productivity index rose rapidly and the period of the 1920's and 1930's saw a persistent gain in the efficiency with which the industry used its labor input. The comparative stagnation of output per worker during the 32 years 1889–1921 deserves further comment. Copper mining underwent at least as great a technological change as, perhaps an even greater one than, any other metal mining industry. This suggests that other factors besides technological change were at work. In the last analysis industrial productivity is the net result of the interplay of technology and resource conditions. The role of each of these two elements will now be considered.

## RESOURCE CONDITIONS

Probably in few other mineral industries have increasing natural difficulties been as important as in copper mining, which has been beset both by increasing difficulties in gaining access to ore,[7] and by declining grade of ore. Of the two the latter has probably exerted the greater influence.

The drain upon productivity in copper mining exerted by the decline in grade of ore is not easily determined. In fact, it is doubtful that in principle a decline in grade must affect productivity adversely, for low grade ores are mined and treated according to a technique quite different from that applied to high grade ores. For the entire industry, average grade, measured by yield of copper, declined from about 60 pounds per ton in 1880 to about 25 pounds in 1939. These figures, however, give an exaggerated impression of the increased difficulty of obtaining the metal, as we shall now explain.

We have mentioned that United States copper mines produce both direct smelting ores and concentrating ores. Although the latter group is by far the more important of the two, it is evident from Table 22 that the relative importance of the two types of

[7] For instance, from 1905 to 1935 the average depth of shafts in underground copper mines in Arizona, Montana and Michigan increased by 50 to 100 percent. (Y. S. Leong and others, *Copper Mining*, National Research Project, Philadelphia, 1940, p. 84.)

TABLE 22

PRODUCTION AND YIELD OF DIRECT SMELTING AND MILLING COPPER ORES, 1902–39[a]

| Year | Total[b] | | Smelting Ores | | Milling Ores | |
|------|----------|---|---------------|---|--------------|---|
| | (Th. s.t.) | Yield of Copper (Percent) | (Th. s.t.) | Yield of Copper (Percent) | (Th. s.t.) | Yield of Copper (Percent) |
| 1902 | 11,465 | 2.73 | 4,905 | 4.19 | 6,559 | 1.68 |
| 1907 | 20,253 | 2.11 | 3,958 | 4.05 | 16,296 | 1.41 |
| 1908 | 22,291 | 2.07 | 4,387 | 4.27 | 17,761 | 1.49 |
| 1909 | 27,933 | 1.98 | 5,268 | 4.15 | 22,665 | 1.47 |
| 1910 | 28,497 | 1.88 | 5,001 | 4.14 | 23,496 | 1.40 |
| 1911 | 29,988 | 1.82 | 4,356 | 4.66 | 25,633 | 1.34 |
| 1912 | 35,656 | 1.71 | 5,014 | 4.45 | 30,642 | 1.26 |
| 1913 | 36,337 | 1.67 | 5,290 | 4.22 | 31,046 | 1.22 |
| 1914 | 35,176 | 1.60 | 4,597 | 4.23 | 30,478 | 1.20 |
| 1915 | 43,404 | 1.66 | 5,434 | 4.60 | 37,970 | 1.26 |
| 1916 | 57,863 | 1.70 | 6,928 | 4.72 | 50,935 | 1.28 |
| 1917 | 58,483 | 1.60 | 7,438 | 4.39 | 51,045 | 1.19 |
| 1918 | 62,289 | 1.51 | 6,224 | 4.51 | 53,938 | 1.18 |
| 1919 | 36,122 | 1.65 | 3,466 | 4.64 | 30,770 | 1.35 |
| 1920 | 36,765 | 1.63 | 3,201 | 4.89 | 31,348 | 1.34 |
| 1921 | 13,396 | 1.70 | 1,236 | 4.77 | 11,023 | 1.44 |
| 1922 | 26,893 | 1.74 | 2,278 | 5.36 | 23,259 | 1.43 |
| 1923 | 45,519 | 1.58 | 3,497 | 5.12 | 40,210 | 1.29 |
| 1924 | 49,178 | 1.59 | 3,555 | 5.08 | 44,427 | 1.33 |
| 1925 | 53,103 | 1.54 | 3,877 | 4.90 | 48,187 | 1.28 |
| 1926 | 57,182 | 1.46 | 3,768 | 4.75 | 52,084 | 1.24 |
| 1927 | 56,725 | 1.41 | 3,408 | 4.67 | 49,179 | 1.23 |
| 1928 | 62,097 | 1.41 | 3,766 | 4.44 | 54,214 | 1.24 |
| 1929 | 68,422 | 1.41 | 4,235 | 4.60 | 59,728 | 1.22 |
| 1930 | 47,382 | 1.43 | 2,984 | 4.57 | 41,327 | 1.23 |
| 1931 | 34,051 | 1.50 | 1,520 | 5.38 | 30,057 | 1.33 |
| 1932 | 12,320 | 1.83 | 759 | 6.98 | 10,965 | 1.51 |
| 1933 | 8,388 | 2.11 | 872 | 6.30 | 7,476 | 1.63 |
| 1934 | 11,724 | 1.92 | 977 | 6.21 | 10,682 | 1.53 |
| 1935 | 19,112 | 1.89 | 1,612 | 5.42 | 17,065 | 1.57 |
| 1936 | 38,514 | 1.54 | 2,389 | 5.05 | 36,117 | 1.31 |
| 1937 | 61,513 | 1.29 | 2,763 | 4.30 | 58,738 | 1.15 |
| 1938 | 37,795 | 1.34 | 2,028 | 4.49 | 34,374 | 1.17 |
| 1939 | 55,239 | 1.25 | 2,396 | 4.61 | 50,710 | 1.09 |

[a] For 1902–36 data are from Y. S. Leong and others, *Copper Mining* (National Research Project, Philadelphia, 1940), Table A-4, p. 220; for 1937–39 from *Minerals Yearbook*. In some years small amounts of copper ore were produced in Alaska, and these are generally included.

[b] Includes ores that were leached and other ores not reported as smelted or milled. Figures for earlier years read: 1889—3,323 th. s.t. yielding 3.32 percent copper; and 1880—1,007 th. s.t. yielding 3.00 percent copper. Data for 1889 cover Michigan, Montana, Arizona and New Mexico only, but production from other states was negligible.

ores has undergone a considerable change since 1902. Whereas 95 percent of the ore mined in 1939 was concentrated, only 57 percent of the ore produced in 1902 required (or at least received) such treatment. (In terms of metallic copper produced the percentages are 84 in 1939 and 35 in 1902.) Since the average smelting ore ordinarily contains between 3 and 4 times as much copper as does concentrating ore, it is evident that the increase in the relative importance of concentrating ores must have exerted a depressing influence on average grade. For the industry as a whole a large part of the decline in average grade since 1902 can be traced to this shift.

The fact that decline in average grade has resulted partly from a shift from one type of ore to another has mitigated its adverse effect upon productivity. For the concentrating ores, as a class, or at least the porphyry ores within the group, are produced—especially in the open pit mines of the West—under conditions strikingly different from those obtaining in mines turning out direct smelting ores. And because of wide differences in method of production, output per worker in mines producing the former type of ore is generally higher than in mines that provide the much higher grade, direct smelting ores (in this context output is measured, of course, in terms of metal content). This situation arises, however, not so much because the low grade ore mines are more advanced in the application of technological innovations, as because the ores of low grade often lend themselves to certain highly productive methods of exploitation which cannot be utilized with ores of superior grade. [8] The important consideration, then, is that the utilization of such ores does not necessarily mean that productivity has risen less rapidly than it would have if the same technological advances had been applied to ore bodies of a considerably higher grade, because the technological advances are often of such a nature that they cannot be utilized except with relatively low grade ores.

How, then, does the decline in grade of ore operate to lessen

[8] In particular, large scale open pit mining and caving methods of underground mining, used in conjunction with rather elaborate concentration techniques: see Chapters 5 and 7 above. It can, of course, be argued that, because of differences in mining methods, grade of ore should not be interpreted to mean merely metallic content. Certainly, in the valuation of an ore body, possible methods of exploitation are as important a factor as metallic content per ton of ore. However, such factors as method of exploitation cannot be consolidated into a single simple measure to indicate the grade of the resources.

the increase in productivity which might otherwise have followed the technological changes in copper mining and ore dressing? Obviously this question must be answered cautiously, yet it seems certain that major importance must be attached to the decline in grade within the categories of direct smelting and concentrating ores, rather than to the shift in their relative importance. If, for instance, the grade of porphyry ores had not declined, the mines producing such ores must almost certainly have experienced a greater increase in output per worker, in view of progressing technology, than was actually the case. In other words, it is not in the large decline in the average grade of copper ore as a whole between 1902 and 1939 that we can find an explanation of the relative moderation of the rise in the copper productivity index, but rather in the (much smaller) changes in grade within the two categories of ore produced in the industry. The concentrating ores, in particular, have grown leaner during the period under review, and we may surmise that the benefits derived from technological advances in producing them have to some extent been swallowed up by the decline in their grade.

Unfortunately we can do little more than indicate the manner in which declining grade of ore operates to affect industrial productivity. To go beyond this point and attempt to measure the downward pressure exercised upon productivity by declining grade would require data we do not possess. There are, however, certain figures which have at least suggestive value.

In the concentrating ores, which since 1902 have become an ever more important segment of the industry's output, copper yield (in pounds per ton) has declined about 35 percent (see Table 22). If yield has dropped by this much, the original content of the ore (before milling) must have fallen off by a still higher percentage, for mill recovery has increased substantially during this period.[9] According to some authorities mill recovery rose from about 60 to 75 percent of content in the early 1900's to about 90 percent in the 1930's.[10] If these figures are correct the 35 per-

[9] This is well illustrated by the data in Appendix D. Among several important porphyry operations the yield of copper (in the form of concentrates) in pounds per ton of ore declined by 11 percent from 1913 to 1929. Yet between the same two years the original content of copper (before milling) per ton of ore declined by 30 percent, almost 3 times as much as yield.

[10] Andrew V. Corry and O. E. Kiessling, *Grade of Ore* (National Research Project, Philadelphia, 1939), p. 50; see also Appendix Table D-3.

cent drop in yield is actually equivalent to a decline in content of between 45 percent and 60 percent.[11] This means that if all other factors (including technology) had remained constant, output per worker engaged in producing concentrating ores (and concentrates therefrom) could be expected to fall between 45 percent and 60 percent from 1902 to 1939—a rough measure of the handicap with which technology in the predominating sector of this industry has been burdened over the long run.

The inclusion of direct smelting ores in the output index for the industry probably tends to mitigate this disadvantage somewhat. For in the case of these ores there is no evidence of a secular decline in grade. Indeed, over the entire period yield of copper per ton of direct smelting ore rose by about 10 percent. Of course, this may merely be a reflection of the increasing effectiveness with which the smelters recover metal from these ores, and their content may actually have declined. But even if this is so, the additional effort which was required to maintain and even increase yield was not exerted within the mining end of the industry, and hence productivity could not have been adversely affected.[12] It seems likely, however, that increasing difficulties of access played a more important role with this group of ores than with the milling ores, since milling ores occur largely in deposits near the surface, whereas direct smelting ores come from deep mines. Unfortunately, we are not able to evaluate the importance of this factor.

[11] Provided, of course, that there has been no important secular change in the percentage of copper recovered from concentrates by smelters and refiners. If improved recoveries have also characterized this branch of the industry, the actual decline in content would be even greater. However, the evidence at hand suggests that smelter recovery has not changed greatly (see Appendix Table D-1).

[12] The case of direct smelting ores illustrates the ambiguity inherent in an index of production not based on the original metallic content of mine output. For if our index were based on the latter rather than recoverable content, any decline that occurred in the grade of mine output would have affected physical output directly, and have affected productivity through the index of physical output. The same is true also of milling ores, so far as the index of physical output is concerned. However, in the case of milling ores the additional effort required to maintain yield in the face of a decline in content is to be traced (for the most part) to the nonmanufacturing end of the industry, whereas with direct smelting ores it is, as we have noted, expended in the manufacturing end, i.e., in smelting. It should be noted that our estimate of the decline in the content of concentrating ores does not (as noted in the preceding footnote) take into account possible improvements in smelter and refinery recovery of metal from concentrates. It may thus be an incorrect measure of the decline in grade. Yet even if it is incorrect, it is the best way to estimate the handicap with which mining technology has been burdened, for the "correct" measure of decline in grade would have included that part of the handicap (if any) which manufacturing has overcome.

## TECHNOLOGY

It should be sufficiently clear from references in the preceding section that technological advance has been instrumental in facilitating the utilization of ores of a considerably lower grade than those commonly exploited at the end of the last century. This influence has been exerted in two ways: (1) new mining methods, based on the large scale extraction of very low grade ore, have been devised; and (2) existing techniques have been improved so that productivity has increased even in the face of the growing natural difficulties associated with each method of mining. The first category comprises open cut mining, together with caving methods of underground mining, both essentially nonselective in character, and inapplicable to the winning of rich deposits.[13] In the second category we count such factors as the mechanization of the mining process and the elaboration of milling techniques.[14] Most of these innovations are common to other metal mining industries, but they have played a particularly important role in copper. Nor, within the copper mining industry, do they represent independent lines of development. Improved milling, for instance, was of great value in the working out of new mining techniques and, even within new mining methods, mechanization has been of considerable importance. However, it is best to treat these two types of technological change separately, if only for convenience in presentation. In Part Two the nature of these changes was examined in some detail. Here we are concerned primarily with the contribution of such technological innovations to increasing productivity in the industry.

The trend of output per manday at underground and open pit mines and in all copper mining (excluding employment in milling) is shown in Chart 46. A comparison of output per manhour in open pit and in various underground methods of mining is offered in Table 23. Among the several methods utilized in mining copper ore, the open cut ranks highest in output per manhour. This is demonstrated by data from the National Research Project's report on copper (reproduced in Table 23) which indicate that in 1929 output per manhour in open cut mining was more than twice the average for all methods of underground

13 For a description of these and other mining methods, see Chapter 5 above.
14 Current practice in the milling of nonferrous ores was described in Chapter 7.

TABLE 23

COPPER MINING, 1917–36

Output per Manhour According to Mining Method[a]

*Copper plus copper equivalent of accessory metals in pounds*[b]

| Year | Open Cut | All Methods | Block Caving | Open Stope | Square Set | Cut and Fill | Shrinkage |
|------|------|------|------|------|------|------|------|
| | | | *Underground Methods* | | | | |
| 1917 | 34.1 | 13.8 | 18.3 | 8.2 | 13.6 | 16.0 | 21.6 |
| 1918 | 34.1 | 13.2 | 19.9 | 6.9 | 13.3 | 14.6 | 18.8 |
| 1919 | 31.2 | 13.9 | 22.3 | 8.6 | 13.5 | 14.9 | 18.0 |
| | | | | | | | |
| 1920 | 32.9 | 15.7 | 20.6 | 10.3 | 15.0 | 16.0 | 24.7 |
| 1921 | 45.0 | 15.8 | 30.5 | 11.1 | 14.5 | 9.9 | 34.0 |
| 1922 | 57.8 | 16.4 | 22.8 | 9.4 | 15.8 | 14.4 | 30.8 |
| 1923 | 38.8 | 17.6 | 20.3 | 12.0 | 16.1 | 19.3 | 28.1 |
| 1924 | 39.1 | 18.8 | 21.6 | 12.1 | 18.3 | 19.1 | 28.5 |
| 1925 | 35.0 | 19.6 | 23.8 | 13.1 | 18.1 | 21.7 | 27.6 |
| 1926 | 39.2 | 18.9 | 22.9 | 11.8 | 17.8 | 23.3 | 25.1 |
| 1927 | 45.5 | 18.7 | 24.1 | 12.2 | 16.4 | 25.1 | 24.3 |
| 1928 | 48.9 | 19.6 | 24.9 | 13.0 | 18.2 | 24.3 | 21.9 |
| 1929 | 43.8 | 18.8 | 23.6 | 12.2 | 17.8 | 24.7 | 18.3 |
| | | | | | | | |
| 1930 | 42.4 | 20.0 | 29.1 | 12.1 | 21.0 | 22.7 | 19.0 |
| 1931 | 53.0 | 23.1 | 40.2 | 13.6 | 23.6 | 21.6 | 24.8 |
| 1932 | 47.5 | 25.2 | 48.4 | 10.7 | 29.7 | 30.4 | 34.3 |
| 1933 | 56.9 | 29.1 | 24.1 | 20.8 | 30.1 | 34.9 | 10.6 |
| 1934 | 60.7 | 29.8 | 106.4 | 21.3 | 25.8 | 36.8 | 13.6 |
| 1935 | 74.8 | 33.3 | 60.3 | 25.5 | 28.8 | 38.8 | 47.9 |
| 1936 | 82.7 | 31.3 | 58.0 | 26.8 | 23.3 | 37.6 | 43.5 |

[a] Y. S. Leong and others, *Copper Mining* (National Research Project, Philadelphia, 1940), Table A-7, pp. 224–37. In line with the procedure adopted in that report, the ratios here are based on employment figures which exclude employment in ore dressing. The data relate only to those mines whose output of copper in 1929 was more than 2,000,000 lbs. Mines were classified according to the mining method predominating over the entire period 1917–36. Thus, to the extent that mines used more than one method, the categories are not definitive. The various methods named were described in Chapter 5: see also Glossary at end of volume.

[b] Accessory metals have been converted to copper equivalent as follows: the quantity of each metal is multiplied by a constant price for that metal, the values are aggregated, and the sum is divided by a constant price for copper to yield the number of pounds of copper equivalent.

mining.[15] The high productivity associated with the open cut technique assumes significance in the light of the pronounced shift toward this method of mining following its introduction in

[15] We use 1929 rather than later years since the 1930's witnessed a revival of "selective" mining (because of the slump in the copper market) which made for higher levels of productivity in some methods than would have been the case under more normal conditions. In its present context the term "selective" mining refers to the deliberate exploitation of the richer portions of an ore deposit (see discussion in Chapter 5 above). This may occur even in a mine in which nonselective methods are normally employed. Data on output per manday for open cut and underground methods from 1914 to 1936 will be found in Appendix Table A-10; these are reproduced in Chart 46.

1906. In 1907, the first year for which data covering output by the several methods are available, open cut mines accounted for only 2 percent of the recoverable copper content of ores produced, whereas in 1936, the last year covered by the NRP report, open cut mines produced 44 percent of the recoverable copper content

Chart 46

COPPER MINING

Output per Manday at Underground and
Open Pit Mines, 1914 – 36

(1914 : 100)

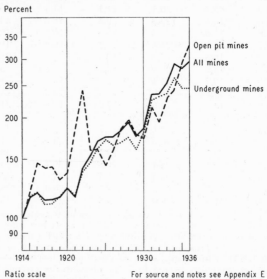

of ores,[16] or 39 percent of the copper industry's output if allowance is made for other metals (Table 24).

In underground mining, caving methods increased their relative importance, accounting for 5.8 percent of recoverable copper in 1907 and for 10 percent in 1936.[17] According to the breakdown reproduced in Table 24, however, it appears that block caving and

[16] Leong and others, *Copper Mining*, Table A-2, p. 216. According to Appendix Table A-10, output per manday in copper mining rose from 88 lb. (recoverable content) in 1914 to 259 lb. in 1936, or by 171 lb. Using the method of Table 13 (reading pounds of copper for dollars, and mandays for manhours), we may associate 139 lb. of the increase with changes in underground and open pit productivity as such, and 32 lb. with the shift from the former to the latter method of mining. The relative contribution of this shift in mining method to the rise in productivity during the last 20 or 25 years appears to have been slightly less in copper than in iron mining: see Chapter 11, footnote 18.

[17] *Ibid.*

shrinkage—the two underground methods which we may broadly class as large scale and nonselective in character, and which employ gravity loading—had attained their greatest extension by the early 1920's, and during the thirties suffered a temporary eclipse. (Data for years since 1936 are not available; but the importance of the methods in question has probably revived since then with the current expansion in copper output.) The decline in the relative importance of caving and shrinkage during the 1930's coincided with a low level of copper mining activity, and with a return, in the case of underground mining, to more selective methods of exploitation. Thus in underground copper mining large scale methods appear to be marginal, in the sense that, when the market for copper deteriorates, mines using them will close down before mines using traditional cut-and-fill or stoping methods. In view of the apparent high efficiency of caving and shrinkage among underground methods of copper mining (Table 23), this finding presents something of a paradox. The matter seems worth pursuing. Let us assume, which is not strictly accurate, that unit cost of production varies inversely with output per manhour. It may be that the greater efficiency shown by the newer methods in Table 23, where data are calculated from figures which exclude mill employment, is absorbed by relatively higher milling costs; [18] in this case, mines using caving and shrinkage are not really more efficient than mines using the traditional methods. That is to say, we should have to conclude that the advantages of scale and the use made of gravity in these mines are offset, or more than offset, by poverty of the ore: otherwise the lack of competitive power shown by large scale methods in a period of depression such as the early 1930's is hard to explain.[19]

[18] Both block caving and shrinkage are nonselective in character, and produce chiefly milling ores. The grade of ore from shrinkage mines does not differ greatly from the average for all underground mines; ores produced by block caving are below average in grade (Leong and others, *Copper Mining*, Table A-11, p. 254).

[19] It may be argued that the proposition, that nonselective methods of underground copper mining are marginal in the sense indicated, is negated by the relatively large contributions which block caving and shrinkage methods made to copper output in 1921. But the depression of that year, though intense, was of short duration. A feature of nonselective methods of underground metal mining is the elaborate planning, and substantial maintenance activities, which are necessary: for this reason their exploitation is probably not very sensitive to short run changes in the demand for the product, and the depression of the 1930's, which lasted longer, is a better test of competitive power.

As an alternative explanation of the lack of competitive power shown by large scale methods of underground mining, at least in the depression of the 1930's, we

If the hypothesis advanced in relation to block caving and shrink-age is plausible, it may be worth while to apply it to the inter-pretation of the figures for open cut mining in Tables 23 and 24. Typically this method produces ores of very low grade. Although by 1921 open cut mining had already become more efficient than any other method shown in Table 23, its contribution to output suffered a sharp decline in that year (Table 24). We may suppose that greater costs of concentration outweighed the higher man-hour output in mining; moreover, the method is very flexible and shutdown costs are low. But during the depression of the 1930's, by contrast, the share of open cut mining increased rather steadily to an all-time high (for the period shown) in 1936: during these years its behavior is quite dissimilar to that exhibited by the two nonselective underground methods for which we have data. We may suppose that advances in milling, especially of porphyry ores, were sufficient, despite the slump in the copper market, to offset the low grade of the open cut product; just as we must infer that the need to handle and process low grade ores offered disadvantages which many underground mines using block caving and shrinkage methods were unable, during these years, to overcome.[20]

The light cast by the figures in Tables 23 and 24 upon the rela-

---

may hazard the guess that caving and shrinkage methods are more efficient than other methods of underground mining only when the mine using them is working at or near capacity. (If true, this might also explain the low level of manhour out-put for block caving and shrinkage reported for 1933: see Table 23.) If this is the case, it is conceivable that imperfections in the market for copper concentrates might prevent mines which use the methods discussed from pressing home the advantage which would otherwise accrue to them in periods of depression. To most readers this explanation will probably appear less plausible than that advanced in the text.

It is sometimes said that mines which do not employ large scale methods derive a competitive advantage in periods of depression from their ability to return to more selective methods of mining, and that during such periods their costs are lowered by the rise in the grade of ore which results. We think it will be found that this suggestion leads, according to the assumptions chosen, either to the explana-tion advanced in the text (i.e., that the costs of large scale nonselective underground mines are not really lower than those of mines using traditional methods); or (2) to the explanation of the preceding paragraph of this note (i.e., that large scale mining is more efficient than the traditional methods, but that the market is imperfect); or (3) to the conclusion that the richer ores obtained from selective mining are not adequately assessed with depletion costs, and that the advantage apparently enjoyed by the older methods during depression periods is illusory.

[20] Advances in the milling of low grade ores are discussed in Chapter 7, above, and in Appendix D. Since the data in Table 23 are based upon recovered metal, they reflect improvements in mill recovery; but they take no account of changes in the amount of metal processed per mill employee.

tive advantages of different mining methods, from one period to another, is at best uncertain. The categories are not definitive, for some mines use more than one method or a combination of several; and year to year changes in manhour output are of doubtful significance. But the rise in productivity in the copper mining industry as a whole (Charts 45 and 46) is well established. In part it has been caused by the substitution of open cut for underground methods, but mainly by the rise in manhour output recorded for each of the methods shown in Table 23.

Let us recall the peculiar behavior of productivity in copper

TABLE 24

COPPER MINING, 1917–36
Percentage Contributions of Different Mining Methods to Total Output[a]

| Year | Open Cut | Total | Underground Methods | | | | |
| | | | Block Caving | Open Stope | Square Set | Cut and Fill | Shrinkage |
|---|---|---|---|---|---|---|---|
| 1917 | 23.6 | 76.4 | 14.5 | 11.1 | 30.3 | 12.9 | 7.6 |
| 1918 | 23.7 | 76.3 | 16.4 | 9.9 | 31.8 | 11.7 | 6.5 |
| 1919 | 20.9 | 79.1 | 17.4 | 13.1 | 28.5 | 13.1 | 7.0 |
| 1920 | 20.9 | 79.1 | 15.8 | 11.4 | 30.4 | 13.1 | 8.5 |
| 1921 | 14.2 | 85.8 | 17.1 | 13.7 | 23.2 | 15.5 | 16.3 |
| 1922 | 17.1 | 82.9 | 18.5 | 10.0 | 31.9 | 11.7 | 10.8 |
| 1923 | 24.7 | 75.3 | 16.9 | 8.2 | 28.9 | 12.9 | 8.3 |
| 1924 | 26.8 | 73.2 | 16.9 | 7.4 | 28.5 | 13.1 | 7.3 |
| 1925 | 26.1 | 73.9 | 16.4 | 8.3 | 28.6 | 13.4 | 7.2 |
| 1926 | 28.4 | 71.6 | 16.1 | 9.2 | 26.5 | 13.2 | 6.6 |
| 1927 | 28.7 | 71.3 | 17.1 | 9.8 | 24.9 | 13.1 | 6.4 |
| 1928 | 31.6 | 68.4 | 15.6 | 9.1 | 24.7 | 13.8 | 5.3 |
| 1929 | 29.2 | 70.8 | 15.5 | 9.1 | 27.0 | 14.4 | 4.8 |
| 1930 | 25.2 | 74.8 | 17.5 | 12.4 | 25.9 | 13.5 | 5.6 |
| 1931 | 28.3 | 71.7 | 17.8 | 11.2 | 28.4 | 9.9 | 4.4 |
| 1932 | 26.7 | 73.3 | 14.1 | 10.8 | 26.9 | 19.0 | 2.6 |
| 1933 | 32.7 | 67.3 | .8 | 12.2 | 27.8 | 26.3 | .1 |
| 1934 | 37.6 | 62.4 | 3.0 | 10.8 | 20.3 | 28.2 | .1 |
| 1935 | 34.5 | 65.5 | 4.9 | 8.3 | 25.0 | 24.9 | 2.3 |
| 1936 | 38.7 | 61.3 | 8.9 | 7.8 | 20.8 | 19.9 | 4.1 |

[a] Y. S. Leong and others, *Copper Mining* (National Research Project, Philadelphia, 1940), Table A-7, pp. 224-37. The data relate only to those mines whose output of copper in 1929 was more than 2,000,000 lbs. Mines were classified according to the mining method predominating over the entire period 1917–36. Thus, to the extent that mines used more than one method, the categories are not definitive. The various methods named were described in Chapter 5; see also Glossary, at the end of this volume.

Total output is measured as copper plus copper equivalent of accessory metals. The latter have been converted to copper equivalent as follows: the quantity of each metal is multiplied by a constant price for that metal, the values are aggregated, and the sum is divided by a constant price for copper to yield their amount as copper equivalent.

mining over the long run—several decades of stability, apparently preceded and certainly followed by periods of sharp increase in output per manday. It is evident that these movements can be explained only in terms of the reaction between technological change and resource conditions. On the one hand, depletion has led to a decline in grade of ore, and in some underground mines to greater inaccessibility of the deposits; on the other, there have occurred important technological developments. A conflict of this kind may lead to decisive results, or it may end in a draw. Evidently a draw would mean unchanging productivity, whereas a victory for technology would mean rising productivity—just as we may interpret declining productivity as a triumph of nature. Between, say, 1890 and 1920 the contest between these forces seems, in the copper industry, to have been indecisive. After 1920 technological developments apparently outweighed the effects of depletion.

Nevertheless, we should beware of assuming that these conflicting tendencies are independent of one another in their operation. Few industries have encountered such natural handicaps, or have been forced to revise so drastically their conceptions of what was, and what was not, workable mineral. And yet the rise in productivity over the period as a whole has been substantial, as we have seen. It is not unreasonable to suppose that the deterioration of resources acted as a stimulus to technological development. We may notice, especially, that the lean ores of the western states, developed during the last three decades, required an entirely new technique for their exploitation—a technique whose efficiency no doubt astonished those who were prone to judge commercial possibilities mainly in terms of grade of ore mined. What seems to have happened, in part at least, is that the very process of continuing combat against natural difficulties led to such important changes that the level of productivity was, in the end, higher than before the deterioration of resources had begun.[21]

[21] This suggestion is not new. Simon Kuznets (*Secular Movements in Production and Prices,* Houghton Mifflin, 1930, Ch. 1) offers the hypothesis that impoverishment of raw materials in the extractive industries provides a constant stimulus to technical progress. Hence the slackening in the introduction of innovations, which he observes in manufacturing, is not found in mining. Kuznets argues, however, that output per worker tends to react less and less to such innovations because of the very factor of increasing natural difficulties. He offers some statistical evidence of this tendency, but is fearful lest the presentation of such proof appear in the

Why the increase in productivity did not begin until after 1920 it is difficult to say. A more thorough investigation of the dates at which technological changes were generally adopted, and at which shifts from one type of mining to another occurred, would doubtless be necessary.[22] At any rate it is clear that the renewed growth in productivity cannot have been due to a reversal of the trend toward increasing natural difficulty; for we know that the grade of ore continued to decline, and it is obvious that the large output of the 1920's must have continued the pressure on available resources. To be sure, a return to more selective methods produced a recovery in grade of ore mined during the early 1930's, but this proved to be a temporary phenomenon. Unless new deposits of copper should be discovered in this country, or invention have surcease, the struggle will continue, and upon its outcome the future level of productivity in copper mining will depend.

We have examined the history of two important metal mining industries—iron and copper—in each of which the development of techniques of open pit exploitation played an important role in the rise of productivity levels. We turn briefly in the next and final chapter of Part Three to the prototype of all open pit operations—the quarrying of stone.

---

nature of supererogation, since increasing difficulties of production must obviously produce effects of this sort sooner or later.

Yet, as the copper industry illustrates, it is difficult to say at what point the slackening in productivity growth, or its actual decline, becomes inevitable. Certainly an investigation of copper productivity that ended in the early 1920's would have led to the conclusion that in copper that stage had already been reached. But copper productivity began to rise thereafter, and the investigator would find that he had failed (perhaps inevitably) to take full cognizance of the magnitude of certain innovations which had already evolved (or might in the future appear) in the course of adjustment to an unfavorable environment. Eventually, of course, a resource may be entirely exhausted, but with most minerals depletion still occurs only in a relative sense, in that grade declines and natural conditions become more difficult, but absolute exhaustion rarely takes place. And as long as this remains true, the possibility of a rise in productivity following even a prolonged decline exists, provided, of course, that technological advance does not come to a standstill.

[22] A possible explanation lies in the fact that the flotation process of ore concentration (see Chapter 7), which had been developed around 1912, was the subject of litigation for most of the succeeding decade. Hence the improved recoveries associated with this technique were not realized until it came into general use about 1922 (see A. B. Parsons, *The Porphyry Coppers,* American Institute of Mining and Metallurgical Engineers, 1933, p. 452).

Chapter 13

# Stone Quarrying

THE STONE industries include the quarrying, and to some extent also the dressing or milling, of all except precious and semi-precious stones. The principal kinds of stone produced in quantity are marble, granite, limestone, sandstone, basalt (or trap rock) and slate; some other varieties of less importance are reported by the Bureau of Mines under the heading "miscellaneous." The output of each of these varieties comes partly as dimension stone (i.e. shaped for building, paving or monumental work); and partly as crushed or nondimension stone. Quarries can mostly be classified either as dimension or as nondimension, according to the nature of their product. However, dimension basalt is practically a byproduct of crushed basalt, and we have therefore included it in the indexes for crushed stone; similarly, crushed marble and crushed slate (granules) are byproducts of the respective dimension stones, and have been included with the latter. The segregation of enterprises according to whether they produce dimension or crushed stone is admittedly far from perfect. A certain amount of crushed granite, limestone and sandstone comes from dimension quarries as well as from those we have classed as nondimension enterprises.

Much of the employment reported for the stone industries relates to dressing or milling, operations frequently carried on by the enterprises which perform the quarrying. Stone dressing, however, is an activity covered in some degree by the Census of Manufactures, and is therefore properly considered as manufacturing —a topic treated in other volumes published by the National Bureau.[1] Yet to isolate quarrying, and to exclude all manufacturing operations from our data, would be impracticable. For reasons given in Appendix C, where this question is discussed, we regard the milling of crushed stone as part of mining activity, but exclude dressing or other finishing operations applied to dimen-

[1] Solomon Fabricant, *The Output of Manufacturing Industries, 1899–1937* (1940) and *Employment in Manufacturing, 1899–1939: An Analysis of Its Relation to the Volume of Production* (1942).

sion stone. This practice has accordingly been followed. Further, the output of noncommercial crushed stone has been excluded from our indexes in this chapter, owing to the absence of data for employment in the enterprises which produce it.

Output data for dimension and crushed stone are available for all years since 1906; these were discussed in Chapter 2. We have figures for employment in the stone industries as a whole for the period since 1911; we can construct indexes of productivity only for years since that date. A segregation of employment between dimension and crushed stone enterprises can be made only for 1922 and later years. The material on output, employment and productivity is summarized in Charts 47, 48 and 49.

Chart 47
STONE QUARRYING
Output, Employment and Productivity, 1911–39
(1911 · 100)

Percent

Ratio scale                              For source and notes see Appendix E

For the stone industries as a whole, if the years 1911 and 1939 are compared, output fell from 100 to 93, and employment from 100 to 38; during this period output per manday rose from 100 to 245. If dimension stone and crushed stone are considered sep-

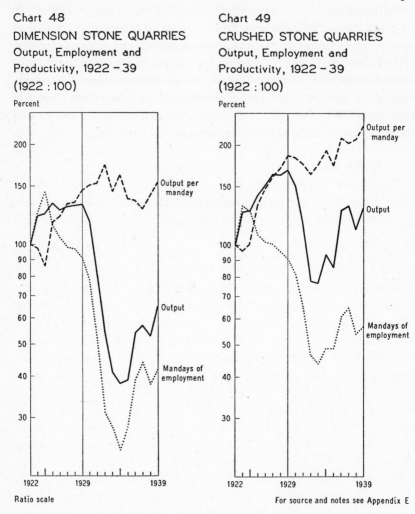

Chart 48
DIMENSION STONE QUARRIES
Output, Employment and
Productivity, 1922 – 39
(1922 : 100)

Chart 49
CRUSHED STONE QUARRIES
Output, Employment and
Productivity, 1922 – 39
(1922 : 100)

Ratio scale

For source and notes see Appendix E

arately for the period 1922 to 1939, the results are naturally less striking. When 1922 is regarded as the base year, figures for 1939 are as follows (1922:100):

|  | Output | Employment | Output per Manday |
|---|---|---|---|
| Dimension | 65 | 42 | 154 |
| Crushed | 130 | 57 | 229 |
| Total | 105 | 54 | 195 |

Evidently the two branches of the stone industry exhibit very different tendencies. For reasons analyzed in Chapter 2, dimension stone output has declined, and crushed stone output has risen. It is not surprising, therefore, that since 1922 employment in dimension stone has fallen in relation to employment in crushed stone. Productivity rose rapidly, however, and an absolute decline in employment occurred in both branches of the industry. Neither in dimension nor in crushed stone was quarrying hindered appreciably by depletion of resources, but rates of technological change were quite dissimilar. As often happens, the form of enterprise whose output was expanding improved its techniques more rapidly than did the one whose output was contracting. The greater increase in productivity in crushed, as compared with dimension, stone is not difficult to explain.

As already noted in Chapter 6, numerous technological changes have occurred in the dimension stone industry. But the scale, and to a large extent the methods, upon which the industry is conducted, are determined by the peculiar character of the product. Building stone is relatively valuable in proportion to its weight, and much depends upon the quality of the output: color, size, grain and uniformity are all important. Excessive use of explosives in breaking the rock or carelessness in handling may easily damage the product. Moreover, orders are frequently filled on a custom basis. All these factors combine to limit the scale of operations and the degree of mechanization possible in the dimension stone industry. In crushed stone production, on the other hand, explosives may be used freely, and the scale of operations may be expanded with every increase in the capacity of loading and transportation equipment. Here, too, uniformity of product is important, but it can be secured conveniently and expeditiously through the use of suitable milling and screening equipment, even though large scale methods of quarrying have been adopted. Unlike dimension stone, the crushed stone industry has been able to take full advantage of the developments in the technique of open pit mining discussed at numerous points in this report.

The six industries to which we have devoted these chapters in Part Three do not exhaust the field of mining activity. But in

selecting them for discussion, we have been able to chart movements and observe tendencies with greater care than would have
been possible had we attempted to give equal treatment to every
industry listed in the Census of Mining. Instead, we have considered successively the coal industries, the petroleum industry,
two important metal mining industries—iron and copper—and,
finally, stone quarrying. This plan has enabled us on the one hand
to notice many characteristics which are common in greater or less
degree to all forms of mining, and on the other to isolate certain
striking differences between different branches of extraction. First
among the characteristics common to more than one type of
mining enterprise may be listed the enormous superiority of open
cut to underground methods of exploitation, wherever it has been
found possible to introduce them. Another noteworthy feature is
the growth in the scale of mineral enterprise, and its progressively
greater mechanization. These changes have led to increasing specialization of function, both of workers and of equipment. Sometimes this specialization has occurred chiefly within the mine—as
with the mechanized cutting, loading and transportation of soft
coal. In other cases functions previously performed by miners have
been transferred to surface preparation plants—as with the cleaning of coal and the concentration of metallic ores.

But the six industries to which we have given detailed consideration also exhibit significant differences, not least in regard to the
role played by depletion of resources. Although all minerals are
exhaustible, the degree to which depletion has added to the burdens of extraction, and so tended to depress the level of productivity, varies greatly from one industry to another. In relation to
known reserves, rates of extraction are higher in the petroleum
and natural gas industry than in any of the other five. Yet, owing
to the peculiar resource conditions of this industry, depletion has
so far had little if any effect in making oil and gas less accessible.
In the other industries considered, the additional burdens which
depletion has placed upon mining enterprise have corresponded in
a rough way with the inroads so far made upon resources. We have
seen that the mining of bituminous coal and of iron ore, and the
quarrying of stone, have not—within the period considered—been
seriously beset by greater difficulties of extraction. The production of anthracite coal and of copper ores, by contrast, has suffered
from the effects of depletion, in the first case through greater in-

accessibility of deposits and in the second through declining grade of ore. Where, as in anthracite mining, the difficulty could not readily be overcome by changes in technology, productivity has risen but slowly; where, as in copper mining, the deterioration of resources was accompanied by a technological revolution, striking advances in productivity occurred.

In Chapter 14, which constitutes Part Four, it will be our task to tie some of these results together, and to place them in a somewhat wider setting. What evidence is there of the advent of diminishing returns in the American mineral industry? How are our results related to such problems of public policy as conservation and the tariff? What does the future hold for productivity levels, and for the volume of employment? It is with questions of this order that we shall occupy ourselves in the next and final chapter.

# Part Four

# Summary and Conclusions

". . . a capital which yields no annual interest, but once turned to light and heat and force, is gone forever into space." JEVONS

"Sisyphus in vita quoque nobis ante oculos est, . . . et semper victus tristisque recedit." LUCRETIUS

# Chapter 14

# Mining in the Nation's Economy

FOR THE mining industries as a whole the growth in output and in output per worker between 1902 and 1939 was greater even than in manufacturing, and very much larger than in agriculture (Table 12). This rapid growth in production and productivity is attributable in large measure to the contribution of oil and gas wells to the total; if the petroleum industry is excluded from the computations, the results are much less impressive. For mining other than oil and gas, the rather moderate changes in output and productivity resemble the history of agriculture—also an extractive industry and a purveyor of raw materials—more closely than the history of manufacturing. There was little if any change in manday employment between 1902 and 1939 for mining as a whole; if petroleum is excluded, employment was actually about 18 percent lower in the latter year than in the former (Table 8). In this respect, whether or not we include petroleum, mining is less like manufacturing, in which there was a substantial increase in employment,[1] than it is like agriculture, where employment was less at the end of the period than at the beginning (Table 12).

Considered as a form of economic activity, the mining industries are unique, for they are concerned entirely with the exploitation of exhaustible resources. The amount of a particular mineral in the earth's crust may be large, but it is limited. The amount accessible to the miner, and available in sufficient concentration to obviate an excessive expenditure of effort, is still more limited. Known reserves depend upon the progress of discovery and the rate of depletion in the past. They are conditioned also in some degree by the state of the arts and the price of the product, for deposits not regarded as workable, and therefore not counted as reserves, at one time, may come to be so regarded at a later date. Reserves

---

[1] The increase, however, took place entirely during the first two decades of the century. Between the close of the first and the opening of the second World War employment in manufacturing underwent no further expansion. See Solomon Fabricant, *Employment in Manufacturing, 1899–1939: An Analysis of Its Relation to the Volume of Production* (National Bureau of Economic Research, 1942), p. 331.

may be replenished by fresh discoveries, and their accessibility may be improved by technological advances, in mining or elsewhere. Meanwhile depletion is a gradual process. Rarely does it appear, even in the case of a single ore body, in the form of sudden and complete exhaustion. Its effects are much more often reflected in a slow decline in the grade of ore mined, or of gradually increasing difficulties of extraction because of the need to work narrower or poorer seams at greater depths.

Depletion has greatly influenced productivity in the mining industries, but this is not the whole story. As in other branches of economic activity, notable advances have been made in the technology of mining. In addition, the amount of effort required to obtain a ton of mineral has been sharply cut from time to time in this country's history through the discovery of fresh bodies of ore superior to those currently exploited. These are the favorable factors. They have had to contend, in most branches of mining, with slowly but steadily increasing difficulties of extraction. The history of output per worker in any given mining industry is a reflection of the current phase of the long drawn out struggle between these conflicting tendencies. Where new discoveries and technological advances counteracted successfully the depletion of existing deposits, output per worker tended to rise; where they failed to offer sufficient counterpoise, productivity declined.

In some industries—iron ore mining and phosphate rock, for instance—depletion has not so far led to increased difficulties of mining. Here output per worker has increased sharply, because the effects of technological change have not as yet been dissipated to any important extent through the exhaustion of favorably situated reserves. In the case of oil and gas wells the exhaustion of individual deposits has frequently occurred, but up to this time depletion has been fully offset by new discoveries (Chart 43). In certain other industries—for example, anthracite mining and the production of mercury—technology has been fighting a rather unequal battle with resource depletion, and technological benefits have been largely absorbed by increased difficulties of extraction.

## DIMINISHING RETURNS AND THE MINING INDUSTRIES

Except in the mining of anthracite, which is still produced in much the same localities, and sometimes by almost the same methods, as it was a century ago, the depletion of mineral resources and the increased difficulty of working them have become important factors in this country only within very recent times. This statement is not true of individual deposits: the cream has long since been skimmed from many a rich pocket of the early days. But during most of the nineteenth century the discoveries of the prospector and the spread of rail and water transportation opened up new sources of mineral wealth which more than offset the effects of depletion in the older deposits. Not only did the total amount of known ore reserves increase; in many instances the same minerals could be won more easily in the new locations than in the old. Compared to the working of minerals in Europe, mining in the United States is still young. It is not surprising, therefore, that output per worker appears to have increased faster in this country than in the Old World.[2]

Despite these indications of good fortune, we should still inquire what evidence there is, among the industries for which we have data, of the onset of diminishing returns. But the concept of diminishing returns is an elusive one. We should apply it, in the classical sense, to a situation where output per worker declines as current output rises. This may indeed describe the mining industry, as it has been held to apply to agriculture. But we are prevented from making short run comparisons of output and productivity, of a kind that would bear on this point, by the evident unreliability of reported short term movements in the latter. In any case the concept of diminishing returns in which we are interested primarily is a different one. For the distinguishing feature of the mining industries is the fact of depletion, and the increased difficulty of extraction which results therefrom. We are concerned, that is, with the question how far productivity is a diminishing function, not of current output, but of output cumulated to a given date. This is a legitimate use of the phrase diminishing returns, but it is not the use in which classical theory made these words famous.[3]

Let us, then, attempt to interpret the principle of diminishing returns as it applies to the depletion of minerals. We should expect in actual practice to observe, as time went on, a decline in

[2] *Mineral Economics*, ed. by F. G. Tryon and E. C. Eckel (McGraw-Hill, 1932), pp. 24-35.

[3] See Alfred Marshall, *Principles of Economics*, 8th ed. (Macmillan, London, 1920), pp. 166-67.

output per worker chargeable to increased difficulties of extraction. But we should also expect this decline to be interrupted by
improvements in technology. And we should be forced to regard
such improvements as more or less spontaneous in character and
not themselves the result of resource depletion. In discussing
diminishing returns classical literature clearly regards innovations as exogenous—when it mentions them at all. Indeed it seems
obvious that, if sense is to be made of the concept, the technological state of the industry must be regarded as a parameter. Returns
can be relied on to diminish, as a result of depletion or of a
scarcity of high grade resources, only under the umbrella of a
strict ceteris paribus clause.

According to this interpretation diminishing returns would
show their effect as a consequence either of a failure in the supply
of innovations, or of difficulties of extraction which increased so
rapidly that rates of technological advance of the sort we have
experienced in the past would prove inadequate to prevent a fall
in productivity. Moreover, we might reasonably expect difficulties of extraction to increase more rapidly, and opportunities
for technological improvement to be more restricted, in an old
industry than in a young one. On this score we might feel inclined to say that the decline in output per worker in the mining
of anthracite and mercury—both old industries—observed during
the first quarter of the present century (Charts 30 and 31) showed
that diminishing returns had set in. The sharp recovery in productivity in these industries during the past 10 or 15 years we
should have to attribute to adventitious circumstances such as a
sudden and unexpected revival of technological advance.

But this, which might be called the textbook version of the doc-
trine, appears too simple to fit the facts. There are numerous cases
in which innovations appeared on the scene, and changes were
made in mining methods, as the direct result of alterations in the
conditions of resource occurrence. The invention of elaborate and
extremely efficient techniques for concentrating copper and other
nonferrous ores is clearly the result of the necessity to mine low
grade minerals, and would never have been developed but for that
need. It seems equally clear that the advent of modern drilling
techniques in the petroleum industry was no accident, but arose
because deeper wells had to be bored. Most of the mining methods
of today represent the solution of a problem raised in the exploi-

tation of some particular ore body or class of mineral deposit. The interaction of resource conditions and technological advance has been continuous. So has the spread of technological improvement from one branch of mining to another: we may mention the migration of the power shovel from the Mesabi Range to the copper deposits of the West and to the modern crushed stone quarry.

If increasing difficulty of extraction has so frequently produced its own antidote, how can we speak of diminishing returns in any orthodox sense? Instead of a persistent downward tendency in productivity, interrupted only by discontinuous and autonomous changes in technique, we have a tendency that seems, in some degree at least, to be self-reversing. Nor is it safe to predict that productivity will decline when a given stage of an industry's development is reached, or when specified deposits are exhausted, even if such a trend appears certain on the basis of technical methods so far developed. The experience of copper mining is sufficient warning against any such rash generalization.

If necessity is the mother of invention, she has been prolific in the past and may perhaps be equally prolific in the future. Clearly the story hinges on the type of response that technology is able to give when difficulties of extraction are encountered. The responses that are possible in a given case are limited by geological circumstances. For instance, if deposits lie deep below the surface it is impossible to improve their accessibility by adapting open cut techniques, so efficient elsewhere, to the problem at hand. Again, the introduction of mechanical coal cutting, which has staved off any tendency for the productivity of bituminous coal mining to decline, was found of no assistance in meeting the problem created by depletion in anthracite. One could cite other instances in which lines of technological advance, successful in some places, have been prevented by geological circumstance from being useful in others. Whether—within these geological limitations—new and more efficient methods of mining are developed, perfected and adopted seems to depend upon a wide range of circumstances, mainly economic in character, at whose nature and importance we can only guess. Certainly the existence of piece rates, and the reluctance to incur fixed costs that one finds under conditions of intermittent operation, seem to have retarded mechanization in coal mining. We may guess, too, that the competition of foreign mines in the case of copper, and of other fuels in the case of anthracite, have stimulated the mechanization of production in these industries.

The response of technology to increased difficulties of extraction may not always be as favorable as it has been in the past. To some extent the age of the industry may be a factor in limiting this response, although the recent introduction of mechanical loading devices in many anthracite mines should warn us against hasty generalization in this regard. Nevertheless, however favorable the technological situation is today, it would seem that, if one takes a long enough view, the effects of depletion must eventually be of a kind which cannot be fully offset, as they have been so frequently offset in the past, by changes in mining methods. In the petroleum industry, for instance, when oil can no longer be obtained from wells it may still be mined from shale or oil-bearing sand. It seems inevitable that such a drastic change in resource conditions should be accompanied by a fall in productivity. Even if the technological response were sufficient to prevent this, eventually exhaustion of deposits must occur, and productivity become zero as the industry closes down. A more reasonable expectation is a gradual failure of technology adequately to offset the effects of depletion. But this may happen only in the very long run. Despite declines in output per worker—declines extending from a few years to decades—the data we have assembled provide no real evidence that diminishing returns have already set in, in the sense that increased difficulties of extraction have failed to elicit corresponding changes of technique. On the contrary, output per worker, at the end of the period studied here, was close to its all-time high in every industry considered. If a stage of falling productivity must eventually be reached, the American mineral industry is too young, or our period of study is too short, for us to observe it.

## THE OUTLOOK FOR THE MINING INDUSTRIES

What, then, is the prospect for the future of mining operations in this country? Shall we use more, or fewer, domestically produced minerals in the future than we have in the past? Will the rise in output per worker slow down, or even be reversed in direction? Should we expect more, or fewer, persons to find their livelihood in mining? Questions of this order cannot, of course, be answered outside the context of the particular branch of mining under consideration. In the discussion to follow we shall distinguish three broad groups of industries: metal mining, coal and petroleum.

We saw in Chapter 2 that metals are used primarily for the manufacture of durable goods and for purposes of construction. Taking the long view, we find little to suggest that the demand for durable goods is approaching saturation. Whenever the demand for particular types of equipment has been reduced to a replacement basis (e.g., railroad equipment) technological advances have created a demand for new types of durable good (e.g., highway vehicles). There is no reason to suppose that the last chapter of this story has been written. In other fields, too, large unsatisfied demands remain: for example, the continued growth of the electric power industry suggests that large amounts of metal will still be needed in this field in the future. On the other hand, it is plain from the evidence of Chapter 2 that we ought not to conclude that correspondingly large amounts of metallic ores will be required, for increasing quantities of scrap metal have become available in recent decades. For the most part metals embodied in durable goods or structures disintegrate rather slowly, and the stock of metal in all forms which civilization possesses above ground is large, and continually increasing. Clearly, much of the replacement demand for metallic objects can be satisfied from the junk pile. The future demand for metallic ores evidently depends upon the rate of wastage in our stock of metals and the rate at which we wish to increase this stock. Both will be much influenced by technological changes outside the mining industry— developments at whose nature and scope we can scarcely even guess.

The prospects for coal and petroleum are closely related, and turn upon the course of our need for power. In a civilization which depends as heavily upon elaborate manufacturing and extensive transportation facilities as does our own, continued and increasing consumption of vast amounts of power seems to be a certainty. For power is fundamental to our technological circumstances: innovations which have led to an increase of power consumption vastly outnumber the few that have reduced it. So far as concerns the mining industries, the question turns upon the probable future importance of different sources of power in relation to one another. At the present time these sources are confined almost entirely to coal, petroleum and natural gas, and water power. If we include heating and lighting, we may say that forty years ago about nine tenths of the power supply came from coal. Today about one half our power comes from coal, two fifths from petroleum and natural gas, and a tenth from water power.

Petroleum has displaced coal both through the development of the internal combustion engine and through the growing popularity of fuel oil for heating and steam raising. Natural gas has largely displaced gas manufactured from coal, both for industrial uses and in the home. In the picture as a whole the place of water power is still relatively unimportant, for in modern practice it is used only for generating electricity. The transmission of electric power over long distances and its application in the propulsion of vehicles both present obstacles which have been very incompletely surmounted. In the future, as in the past, the relative importance of different sources of power will depend upon their relative cheapness and convenience for different purposes. On these grounds alone a substantial expansion of water power seems certain to occur, even if the technology of its use progresses no farther. Should there be developments which broaden the scope of centrally generated electric power—for example, in the propulsion of vehicles and ships—it may continue to displace mineral fuels. From the viewpoint of resource conservation, water power has the supreme advantage that the problem of depletion does not have to be faced.

Insofar as hydraulic power is unsuitable or unavailable, and so long as vegetable materials (e.g., alcohol from wood) remain an unimportant source, it would seem that the power supply must continue to be furnished either by coal mines or by oil and gas wells (possibly including the mining of shale). To be sure, the situation may one day be radically changed through the development of a cheap and efficient electrical storage battery, through the harnessing of solar radiation, or through extensive utilization of tidal energy. The eventual release of atomic power for industrial purposes would doubtless alter the picture still more drastically. But in the absence of such striking events the choice remains, at least for the immediate future, between coal and oil. Despite marked economies achieved in the use of coal, it seems likely that greater convenience and adaptability will maintain or expand the place occupied by oil and gas. This situation may presently be reversed, conceivably through striking advances in the utilization of coal, but more probably through depletion of oil reserves. In terms of known deposits, the coal supply is to be measured in centuries of potential use, the petroleum supply in decades only.[4] If and when our oil reserves are used up, our coal deposits will have to supply, apart from imports of foreign oil, not only the need for heating and steam raising (which they do only in part today), but also for gasoline and lubricants (which in this country they do not do at all at present). Moreover, if petroleum should vanish from the picture, or even if it should become much more expensive, the production of alcohol and other fuels from vegetable matter would doubtless have to be given serious consideration.

It may be that we, and possibly the entire world, will eventually be forced to return to greater dependence on coal, rather than on oil, as a source of power. Nevertheless, the situation may not be as serious as the relative size of the known reserves of the two minerals might imply. The nation's coal deposits are extensive, and we have fairly accurate estimates of their size. Experts do not expect really important new discoveries in this country. In the case of petroleum, on the other hand, pessimistic predictions of early exhaustion have been repeatedly falsified through fresh discoveries, which in turn have been the consequence, at least in part, of improved prospecting techniques. Of course the more oil that has been found, the less remains to be discovered: we may not be so fortunate in the future. But the life of oil fields can be prolonged through conservation; and oil may be obtained by other means than the drilling of wells, e.g., by mining shale, though by present methods only at a considerably enhanced cost. There is the possibility, too, that if oil becomes scarce we may prefer to import it rather than to manufacture it extensively from coal. There is at least as much known oil outside the United States as at home, and many fresh deposits may still remain to be discovered in distant parts of the earth.

Evidently the future output of different minerals is conditioned largely by the extent of reserves and by the rapidity of their de-

[4] Of original reserves discovered to date we have used perhaps one hundredth part in the case of coal; one half in the case of oil (see Willard E. Hotchkiss and others, *Bituminous-Coal Mining*, National Research Project, Philadelphia, 1939, p. 53; Table A-18 below).

pletion. If the cost of mining a given metal increases, its users may obtain it from abroad, or may substitute other materials. When oil becomes more difficult or expensive to obtain, coal may be used in its place.

If patterns of consumption will ultimately be determined by what is left to consume, the future level of output per worker depends even more directly upon the effects of depletion. Except to the extent that it is delayed by technological advance or by the discovery of fresh deposits, the operation of diminishing returns must eventually set in. For a long time successive advances in technology may maintain output per worker at present levels or above; but the opposite possibility must also be considered. Reserves of natural gas, for example, may one day be more or less completely exhausted; or the decline in the grade of metallic ores may eventually be such that not even the most striking advances in technology can prevent a drop in output per worker.

The cost-raising effects of known amounts of depletion in the past, or of prospective rates of depletion in the future, cannot be accurately assessed. This is true partly because the results of technological change cannot be distinguished quantitatively or separated from the increased difficulties of mining which frequently gave rise to them, and partly because there is not enough exact knowledge concerning the character and extent of ore reserves and oil deposits. To be sure, we know that the grade of copper ore mined has declined sharply since the opening of the present century, and that this has not prevented an increase in output per worker. We know, too, that depletion had seriously reduced productivity in anthracite and in mercury mining until the recent recovery in output per worker in these industries set in. We do not know, however, just how output per worker would have behaved if there had been no changes in the technological state of these industries. Nor can we say to what extent the innovations which actually appeared were induced by greater difficulties of extraction, and to what extent they occurred independently. But, even if we cannot make exact statements about the effects of depletion, those effects are nonetheless real.

## CONSERVATION AND THE TARIFF

The rapidity with which mineral deposits are exhausted is primarily a function of current rates of output. It is determined in large part, therefore, by the level of industrial activity, and by the roles assigned to different minerals as industrial raw materials. But it is affected also in an important and increasing degree by two different but closely related aspects of public policy. The first of these comprises direct measures of conservation; the second is the manner in which fiscal policies, and especially tariff measures, affect mineral extraction.

Conservation policies designed to retard the rate of depletion of minerals were first applied in the case of petroleum and natural gas. Laws against the waste of gas date from the 1890's, and production control began to be applied to petroleum during the 1920's. At first resisted by the industry, the principle of control was accepted only after overproduction had forced down the price of oil to levels which many producers considered unprofitable.[5] Texas, Oklahoma, Kansas, New Mexico, Louisiana, Mississippi, Arkansas, and Michigan now have proration laws. Recently the National Resources Committee has suggested that conservation would be more effective if undertaken by the federal government,[6] and the Cole bill was introduced in the House in 1940 with this end in view. It should be added that the United States is itself the owner of lands containing about 15 percent of the nation's oil resources.[7] A move toward the conservation of bituminous coal was made by Congress in the Coal Act of 1937; while this act does not directly restrict production, it may do so indirectly through the establishment of minimum selling prices. The need for the conservation of coal is of course much less urgent than in the case of oil and gas, and applies chiefly to the higher grades of coking coal.[8]

The principal effect of fiscal policy upon mineral extraction is through the tariff.[9] The United States is on an export basis with respect to coal and petroleum, but it imports significant quantities of zinc, lead and copper ores (mainly in the form of concentrates),

[5] Leonard Logan, "Production Control in the Petroleum Industry" in *Mineral Economics.*

[6] National Resources Committee, *Energy Resources and National Policy* (Washington, 1939), pp. 2-3, 214-36.

[7] *Ibid.,* p. 24.

[8] *Ibid.,* pp. 15-19.

[9] There is some evidence that other types of fiscal measure have retarded conservation. For example, the taxation of mineral lands by Minnesota on an ad valorem basis has apparently had the effect of penalizing the development of low grade in comparison with high grade iron ores (see Nicholas Yaworski and others, *Iron Mining,* National Research Project, Philadelphia, 1940, p. 171).

which are in large measure subsequently exported in metallic form. A major portion of the domestic consumption of manganese, tungsten and mercury is supplied by imports. Practically all our tin, nickel and chromium comes from abroad. In spite of opposition by smelters or other users of their product, most domestic mining enterprises subject to foreign competition have sought and obtained tariff protection. Probably the first to do so was the infant lead mining industry, which has been sheltered from foreign competition ever since 1790. Copper and mercury received protection in 1883, zinc and tungsten in 1909, and manganese in the Tariff Act of 1922. The original tariff on copper was repealed in 1894, but was reimposed in 1932. Little iron ore has been imported since the Mesabi Range came into operation, and the duty imposed in 1883 was abolished in 1913.

From this brief description of the relevant tariff provisions, we turn to the principles involved. The impact of tariff policy upon the rapidity of depletion of mineral resources is clearly the obverse of the effect of the conservation measures mentioned above. Whenever the enactment of an import duty leads us to satisfy a larger fraction of our needs from domestic, and a smaller fraction from foreign sources, the output of domestic mines and the rate at which they are depleted will tend to increase.[10] For example, in copper mining the grade of ore in the United States is much below that produced in other parts of the world. This disadvantage is compensated, at least in part, by specially developed techniques of extraction and concentration, although there is evidence that foreign costs, especially in the newer African mines, are lower than in this country, mainly because the ores are richer.[11] However, in the case of copper, as in the case of lead and zinc, reserves of ore in the United States are still substantial, and the danger that a policy designed to stimulate domestic production may greatly hasten exhaustion seems remote. It is rather in the mining of manganese, tungsten and mercury that tariff protection has been criticized on the ground that early exhaustion is in prospect.[12] In none of these cases, despite some degree of tariff protection, do

[10] The effect upon world (including United States) mineral reserves is of course an opposite one: they will be depleted more slowly than would otherwise be the case.

[11] See U. S. Tariff Commission, *Copper*, Report No. 29, Second Series (1932); also a release by E. W. Axe and R. E. Houghton, "Copper" (E. W. Axe and Co., 1934).

[12] J. W. Furness, "Tariffs and Exhaustible Resources" in *Mineral Economics*.

domestic mines satisfy anything like the whole of our needs. A tariff high enough to secure self-sufficiency, which has been urged at different times by the producers of each of these three metals, would therefore involve sharp increases in rates of domestic production and of the depletion of these particular resources. Known reserves of the three minerals mentioned appear to be quite small. In one case at least, that of mercury, the United States Tariff Commission refused to recommend an increase in the duty, giving as one of its reasons the importance of avoiding rapid depletion of domestic deposits.[13]

## CONCLUSION

To what extent can technological advance be expected to overcome the effects of resource depletion? We can judge only in very rough fashion, from what has happened in the past and from what is known concerning the characteristics of different types of deposits. Where the mineral is rigidly limited in amount, and depletion shows itself not so much in greater difficulty of extraction or declining quality of mineral as in approaching exhaustion, technology can obviously accomplish little—except indeed by producing substitutes for the missing mineral. Few minerals are so situated that exhaustion can occur suddenly without any prior rise in the cost of mining: perhaps natural gas reserves are as near to this situation as any of our mineral deposits. Oil wells can be exhausted too; but even after resort has been had to pumping, much oil remains in sands and other oil-bearing strata. This oil can of course be recovered—at a price; here there is a possibility of further technological advances to which little thought has so far been given.

The exhaustion of most other minerals is likely to be a much more gradual process, and efforts at its postponement would appear to provide far greater scope for technological progress. In anthracite mining depletion has led to the working of narrower seams at increased depths: but that fact has not prevented the adoption of power loading, even if the mechanical cutting of anthracite still lies largely in the future or perhaps will never be achieved. The potential exhaustion of bituminous deposits is important mainly with respect to the better grades of coking coal.

[13] U. S. Tariff Commission, *Quicksilver*, Report No. 92, Second Series (1935), p. 2.

Immense resources of low grade bituminous coal and lignite remain to be exploited; but here the need for innovation may lie rather in the methods by which fuel is utilized than in the actual operation of winning it.

As we have seen, it would be a mistake to regard technological innovation as proceeding independently of resource depletion, at a given speed, and without reference to the rate of exhaustion. It was in fact only because conditions of resource occurrence became less favorable that many technological improvements were devised. Much of the innovation of recent decades would have been entirely inappropriate to the (often small scale) exploitation of the richer ores of the past. This has been notably true in copper mining, and doubtless in other industries as well. Most of our copper now comes from ores that are much leaner than any worked forty years ago. The decline in the grade of ore stimulated the development of large scale mining and concentrating methods which have in good measure overcome the disadvantage that gave rise to them.

Indeed it is virtually impossible for our copper reserves to become completely exhausted. There are available indefinitely large supplies of ores still leaner than those now being worked—ores containing perhaps but a few tenths of one percent of the metal. It remains to be seen whether advances in technique will make possible the working of such ores without a sharp rise in costs.

Few, if any, American mining industries are confronted by total exhaustion of their deposits within the foreseeable future. The primary problem has been, and will remain in times to come, to counteract a deterioration in the quality of resources—a deterioration which would otherwise lead to a decline in output per worker, and to correspondingly augmented mining costs. This is the task of technology. That the task has so far been discharged with notable efficiency in the majority of mining industries may be attributed in part to the comparative youth of mineral workings in this country. It is obviously unwise to assume that the effects of depletion in raising mining costs will be overcome as easily in the future as they have been in the past.

If it be true that output and productivity in the mining industries reflect the result of a struggle between advancing technology and gradually increasing difficulties of extraction, what can be said of employment? In a purely formal sense, the same factors determine the number of persons engaged in the industry. If we know how large output will be, and also the level of output per worker, we can specify the draft the industry will impose upon the labor force. Unfortunately, however, the future level of employment in the mining industries is peculiarly difficult to forecast. It, too, represents the outcome of conflicting tendencies. We have seen employment reach a peak during the first World War, and decline rather steadily since that time. If the mechanization of mining operations and the improvement of concentrating methods proceeds as rapidly in the future as in the recent past, if further advances in fuel economy and in the use of secondary metals occur, and if the effects of depletion are not seriously felt for some time to come, it is possible that the decline in employment will be resumed shortly after the conclusion of the present war. But sooner or later this downward trend may be reversed. In the first place, exhaustion of oil reserves, or vigorous measures of public policy designed to conserve these reserves, may lead to a substitution of coal for oil as a source of power. Since the amount of mining labor needed to produce a unit of energy in the form of coal is several times that required in the case of oil, the result would be an immediate upturn in total employment in mining. In the second place, productivity in anthracite and in many kinds of metal mining may presently decline through greater difficulty of extraction, insofar as technological advance is unable to counteract it. The same may be said of petroleum, if it should be found necessary (or desirable as a measure of conservation) to obtain oil by mining oil-bearing strata, instead of allowing it to flow freely from wells, or pumping it, as is done today. In that case the fraction of the labor force engaged in mining may increase.

The conclusion that, whatever the immediate outlook, the effects of depletion must eventually lead to greater employment in mining in this country is rendered hazardous, not only by further possibilities of technological innovation of which we know nothing, but by two other factors already noted. Domestic deposits are not the only source of mineral raw materials. Should innovation eventually fight a losing battle with depletion in the United States, it is possible that a rise in the price of domestically produced minerals may lead us to satisfy a larger proportion of our needs from abroad. Declining productivity and higher costs of mining, if they should occur, will be a symptom of an aging industry. The mining industries of Europe are even older than our own, and many of them have suffered severely from the effects of depletion. But there are also younger industries: the copper mines of Africa and South America, the oil wells of South America and Asia. It may be that these, or other undiscovered deposits in distant parts of the earth's surface, will eventually supply a much larger fraction of the world's needs—and of our own—than they do today. Increased dependence upon foreign supplies may indeed be accompanied by a simultaneous need for more miners at home, but the expansion of mineral imports (should it occur) would mitigate the increase in domestic employment occasioned by greater difficulties of extraction.

And in the second place we may come to depend in larger measure upon water power, or other nonmineral sources, for our supply of energy. Moreover, our need for metals may be satisfied in increasing, perhaps eventually in overwhelming, degree from the junk pile. The realization of these possibilities would, like the increased importation of minerals, counteract the tendency of depletion to force an increase in mining employment.

These conflicting characteristics render predictions about the future of the industries treated in this volume—whether considered separately or as a group—peculiarly difficult. So much is obvious. It is not perhaps so obvious that they are also, in large measure, the characteristics which distinguish mining most sharply from other forms of economic activity. To take one example: manufactured goods are produced and, once consumed, must be produced all over again, whatever may happen to the materials of which they are made. But the metal mining industries, which contribute to these materials, are distinguished by the fact that much of what they produce is wrung from the ground once and for all and can be used over and over again. In the case of metals, it has become the function of the junk pile to provide, in the accounting of society if not of the extractive industry concerned, a partial offset to depletion. However, comparative indestructibility of product, shared perhaps by certain forms of construction activity, is a peculiarity, in mining, of the metal mining industries.

Two other characteristics—localization and depletion—are common to all forms of mineral extraction and serve to distinguish mining even more sharply from other forms of production. Mining operations can be carried on only in certain definite localities where minerals are to be found, and are best concentrated (in the absence of deliberate conservation) on those parts of the earth's surface where minerals of highest grade may most easily be extracted. No other industry is subject to geographical limitations of a like nature; the resources of no other industry show a like contempt for political boundaries. Mining, moreover, alone among types of economic endeavor, must reckon with depletion of its resources. In manufacturing or transportation there is nothing to prevent the attainment of a given technological level from yielding a permanent increment in the productivity of human effort. Not so in mining, for it is an enterprise which must constantly repair its fences. No level of productivity can be considered secure, for, once attained, it must be buttressed continually with fresh innovation. The inevitable deterioration in the conditions of mining offers a challenge which has been met in the United States in recent decades, as we have seen in this volume, with significant and sometimes spectacular success. We can hope that the efforts of the mining engineer will be equally effective in the future, but of this, of course, we can have no positive assurance.

# Appendices

# Appendix A

# Basic Data and Indexes for Individual Industries

THE first four tables in this appendix bring together information on output (in physical and value terms) and employment in every mining industry for which we were able to assemble data of either kind. Tables A-5 and A-6 summarize this material, and show comparable indexes of output, employment and productivity. In Table A-7 will be found additional output indexes which are in general more comprehensive than the available employment data. Sources of data are indicated in detail in notes to the tables. It remains for us to point out some characteristics of the data and to describe the construction of the index numbers.[1]

## Definition of Mining

Mining has to be defined in order that we may know at what stage output is to be measured and what sorts of employment are to be included. The definition must perforce run in terms of processes or branches of activity, in which a certain labor input is consumed and a certain output of product results. According to many authorities, the mineral industries should be considered to include not only ore digging and hoisting proper but also the associated processes of milling, smelting and refining.[2] Trade usage frequently regards burning, calcining, smelting or refining as part of the mineral industry; even the manufacture of cement, lime, coke or steel may sometimes be included. The definition used in this study is considerably more restricted and is based upon the distinction that the Bureau of the Census now draws in presenting statistics for the mineral industries. The data for smelting and refining are included in the Census of Manufactures, and therefore excluded from this study, whereas statistics relating to all processes preliminary to smelting are presented in the Census of Mines and Quarries. "Mining" thus includes also the associated processes of ore dressing and concentration, which are necessary in the preparation

---

[1] All data are intended to relate to the continental United States; care has been taken to exclude Alaska from the statistics.

[2] See, for example, F. G. Tryon and F. E. Berquist, "Mineral Economics—An Outline of the Field" in *Mineral Economics*, ed. by F. G. Tryon and E. C. Eckel (McGraw-Hill, 1932), p. 3.

of the ore for the smelter. Again, the Census Bureau regards cement
making as a form of manufacturing, but stone crushing as a part of
the quarrying process. On page 4 of the introduction to the 1929
Census of Mines and Quarries (henceforth all references to the Census will refer to Mines and Quarries unless otherwise specified) the
following explanation appears:

> Much of the products of mines must be beneficiated, improved in
> grade, or otherwise treated at or near the mine before the material
> is suitable for smelting, manufacturing, or other purposes. Among
> the processes employed are crushing, grinding, washing, drying, air
> separation, flotation . . . etc. Although such milling processes are in
> the nature of manufacturing, they are commonly considered as be-
> longing to the mining industries, and when they are performed at
> or near the mines by mining enterprises, or by enterprises operating
> on a custom basis, the data pertaining to them are included in the
> statistics for the several mining industries. On the other hand, certain
> other processes by which the mined product is materially changed
> in nature or otherwise adapted to use, and which ordinarily repre-
> sent the major activities of the enterprises, are considered as manu-
> facturing, and data for these are not included in the statistics for
> mines and quarries. Such processes include the smelting and refin-
> ing of metals. . . .

In one sense we are forced to accept the Census definition of mining
if it is our intention to use Census data in the course of our work.
Moreover, it would seem that an argument based on more than mere
necessity can be advanced for drawing the same boundaries as those
set by the Census. For the processes of breaking, washing, concentrating, milling or otherwise beneficiating the mineral product—all of
which, following the Census, we regard as mining operations—for the
most part were formerly carried on, insofar as they were performed at
all, by the miner himself.[3] The fact that specialization of function has
transferred a portion of the miner's task to separate personnel and
equipment at the surface is not in itself a reason for defining mining
operations today in a less comprehensive fashion than was formerly
necessary. The most important function to become specialized in this
manner, the milling of metallic ores, is in essence a process whereby
ores of different minerals, and different minerals from the same ore,
are separated from waste matter and sorted. Unlike the pyrometal-

[3] "Milling is only a better and cheaper way of doing things that were at first
accomplished otherwise. It probably originated as a partial substitute for the sorting of ore by hand and this must have long remained its chief function." C. E.
Julihn, "Copper: An Example of Advancing Technology and the Utilization of Low-
Grade Ores" in *Mineral Economics,* cited above.

lurgical and other chemical processes characteristic of smelting and refining, milling involves physical rather than chemical separation materials. In this sense it is only slightly removed from the actual process of severing the ore from the earth. Milling, and other accessory functions carried on in close proximity to the mine, are therefore considered a form of mining activity. Such functions include the washing and grading of coal and the crushing of stone. On the other hand, the smelting and refining of metals, the coking of coal, the refining of crude oil, the production of cement, the calcining of gypsum and the cutting of dimension stone are considered manufacturing processes and fall outside the purview of the statistics in this appendix.

The output series provided in Table A-1 relate as far as possible to the product emerging from the last stage of the mining process as so defined, whether this product is for shipment or merely an addition to inventory. In the case of gold, silver, copper, lead, zinc and mercury, output is measured in recovered or recoverable metal content. Elsewhere the quantity data refer to amounts of actual mineral, sometimes (as with iron ore) broken down by grade. In Table A-1, the price data for gold, silver, copper, lead and zinc refer to market prices of these metals, since annual series for mine value are unobtainable. In other cases, except where noted, data in Table A-1 relate to mine value, i.e., the value of the mineral per unit at the time it leaves the mining process as we have defined that process. The same observation applies also to all data in Table A-2. Finally, the figures for employment in Tables A-3 and A-4 are intended to cover all work up to, but not beyond, the point where the product leaves the mining process.

*Method of Construction of the Output Indexes*

As in previous reports in this series, the standard basis of comparison adopted was that usually known as the Edgeworth formula:

$$\frac{\Sigma q_1 (p_0 + p_1)}{\Sigma q_0 (p_0 + p_1)}$$

where the q's refer to quantities, the p's to prices, and the suffixes identify the years to be compared. This is equivalent to the ratio of the values of the outputs in the two years, these values being computed in constant prices; for each commodity the price chosen is its mean for the two years considered. The formula has the advantage that the weighting system is revised for each new comparison, and when computed for successive pairs of years, additional commodities can be included as data become available. The index takes the form of a chain of such comparisons. However, it may readily be shown that a series of successive year-to-year comparisons between, say, 1899 and 1939, may offer a result which differs significantly from that obtained in a single direct comparison between the years in question.

At different points in this study we have been interested both in year-to-year changes and in long term trends. Some form of compromise had therefore to be adopted. Thus the construction of every index of output which rested on more than one series involved the following steps. First, comparisons were made between 1899 and 1909, 1909 and 1919, 1919 and 1929, and 1929 and 1937.[4] Second, a chain index was computed for the entire period 1899 to 1939, and this annual series was then fitted into the framework provided by the four comparisons just mentioned. That is, for the years 1899–1909 we adjusted the chain index by distributing the discrepancy between it and the direct comparison 1899–1909 in an even fashion over the decade in question. For 1938 and 1939 the chain comparisons were left undisturbed. In this way the comparison between 1899 and 1937 as reported by the index involves four links only; that between 1899 and 1939 involves six links. The comparison between, say, 1909 and 1921 is made in three links, two of which (1919–20 and 1920–21) involve a small adjustment of the type mentioned.

The output indexes will be found assembled in Tables A-5, A-6 and A-7. The indexes in Tables A-5 and A-6 have an industrial or a product coverage which makes them suitable for comparison with employment. In Table A-7 indexes of output are shown for industries or products for which we do not have comparable employment data. The index for total mining in this table is therefore more comprehensive than the corresponding index, bearing the same title, in Table A-5.

*Character of the Employment Data*

The figures for oil and gas wells in Table A-3 cover wage earners only. For other industries for which employment data are given in Tables A-3 and A-4, the figures include also those salaried employees who work in and about the mine and who are subject to accident risks. (No segregation between wage earners and these others can be carried out except for Census years.) In this respect the employment figures we have been able to assemble for the mining industries on an annual basis differ (except in the case of oil and gas wells) from corresponding series available for manufacturing and other segments of the economy,

[4] Except for 1899 and 1937 these are Census years. The year 1899 was chosen (instead of 1902) since it was the initial year covered in the study; and 1937 was selected (instead of 1939) because many calculations had to be made before data for the latter year were available.

in which the material usually relates either to wage earners or to total employment.

The employment data in Tables A-3 and A-4 are presented under the rubrics of men, mandays and manhours. The derivation of these estimates, which rest partly on Census data and partly on canvasses by the Bureau of Mines, is described in considerable detail in footnotes to the tables. The figures for manhours are obtained, in almost every case, by multiplying mandays by nominal hours per day: sometimes this multiplication was performed by the Bureau of Mines, sometimes by ourselves. In similar fashion, the figures for mandays are rarely the result of direct enumeration: in most instances they are derived, mainly by the Bureau of Mines itself, from figures for the number of persons employed. To a first degree of approximation, the figures in Tables A-3 and A-4 for men employed may be described as active period averages (as in the last column of Table 7, Chapter 3), i.e., averages reckoned in the case of each establishment over the active period of the year only. To derive manday totals these average employment figures are multiplied by the number of days during the year that the mine, or the average number of days that the industry, was active. Because of the importance of the matter, which in a quantitative sense overshadows many lesser ambiguities to be found in commonly published measures of employment, something further must be said about methods of constructing annual averages.

Undoubtedly the least ambiguous average from a statistical standpoint would be one based on daily counts. Thus, to derive the average number of men employed during a year, 365 daily counts would be summed, and the sum divided by 365. (If the establishment normally closed completely on Sundays and holidays, 300 counts might be summed, and the result divided by 300.) The sum itself is of course the number of mandays for the establishment reporting. In other words, the ideal method of averaging employment requires that the actual number of mandays worked be known.

Except occasionally in recent years, mines have not ordinarily reported their mandays of employment. Rather they report 12 monthly employment figures. To derive average employment for the year from such information, two alternative plans are possible: either the 12 monthly figures may be summed and divided by 12 (even if employment in some months is zero), or else figures for the active months only may be summed and divided by the number of such months. The Bureau of the Census uses the former, the Bureau of Mines the latter, method: the first is commonly called a full year, the second an active period average. If there are no inactive months, the two averages will agree—provided both are based upon the same set of monthly figures.

But if some mines have inactive months, average employment reported by the Bureau of Mines will run higher than average employment reported in the Census. It is important to notice that, whichever method is used, the precise character of the annual average obtained depends upon the manner in which the monthly figures themselves are derived.

If the monthly figures were themselves averages of daily counts, the Census procedure would yield a true full year average. The plan adopted by the Bureau of Mines, on the other hand, would yield neither a true full year average nor (except by accident) a true active period average, but something we may best call a hybrid. For the monthly data would themselves be full period averages, even though only active months are averaged in computing an annual figure. The Bureau of Mines average would be a true active period average only if periods of inactivity happened to coincide with calendar months. If, on the contrary, the monthly figures were active period averages, derived by summing numbers employed on active days and dividing by their number, the plan followed by the Bureau of Mines would yield a true active period average, and the Census procedure a hybrid. For the latter method averages twelve sets of monthly data, each set being an average for the active days in the month only. The Census would report a true full year average only if there were no inactive periods.

In fact the monthly counts upon which both the Census and the Bureau of Mines rely are payroll figures which relate to a representative day or week in each month. Consequently both methods in practice yield hybrid results. The best we can say is that the figure published by the Bureau of Mines is an approximation to an active period average, that reported by the Census an approximation to a full year average. This means that estimates of mandays derived from these averages are likewise only approximations. We are especially interested in the accuracy of the manday totals which the Bureau of Mines reports, for we make extensive use of these data in Tables A-3 through A-6. For the most part they are derived by multiplying active period averages (of the kind discussed) by the number of days during the year that the establishment is reported as active. Since a representative payroll count is likely to be larger than a true active period average for the corresponding month, the manday totals so obtained probably overstate mandays of employment in the various mining industries.[5]

Despite this weakness we have chosen to treat mandays as our basic

[5] If the Bureau of Mines were to use active period averages, instead of representative counts, for individual months, such a procedure would probably understate mandays of employment. The reason is that inactivity is rarely complete, and mandays worked during inactive periods by men engaged in maintenance and development work would be neglected.

measure of employment. They are clearly superior to the active period averages for men employed, for unlike the averages the manday totals pay attention to the number of days worked. The manhour figures are even further removed from the crude data than the manday figures, and involve still other assumptions (e.g., correspondence between nominal and actual hours worked). Where we had to make adjustments to the data, as described in the notes to Tables A-3 and A-4, these were performed in terms of mandays, and corresponding changes were made where necessary in the figures for men and for manhours. Where the active period averages for men employed were readily available or easily derived, we have inserted these in the tables, but have made no further use of them. Manhour figures are shown for those years for which they could be estimated.

### The Indexes of Employment and Productivity

In constructing indexes of employment (Tables A-5 and A-6) we have made no attempt to differentiate between grades of labor, or to make allowance for variations in the skill or intensity of labor in different industries or occupations. In our calculations any manday or manhour is treated as the equivalent of any other manday or manhour. Consequently the indexes of employment offered here constitute simple comparisons between manday or manhour aggregates for different years. The indexes of output per manday or per manhour were obtained by dividing the indexes of mandays or manhours into the corresponding output indexes.

The reliability of the productivity indexes hinges upon the comparability of the indexes of output and employment. Some remarks on this question will be found in the notes appended to Tables A-5 and A-6. Further information for judging the comparability of the two sets of data is presented in the footnotes to Table A-1 (output) and to Tables A-3 and A-4 (employment) respectively. Our productivity measures are probably least reliable for oil and gas wells and for stone quarrying, and most satisfactory in the case of anthracite and bituminous coal. For the metal mining industries, for gypsum and for phosphate rock mining, our measures appear to occupy an intermediate position from the standpoint of accuracy.

Finally, we should mention one obvious weakness of the data. In constructing productivity indexes for manufacturing and many other fields it is both possible and convenient to use Census data for output and for employment as well. This procedure has the great advantage that the numerator and denominator in the productivity quotient come from the same canvass, and may therefore be assumed to have the same coverage. In mining, because of the infrequency of Census inquiries and because of the wavering line which some early Censuses drew between mining and manufacturing, we cannot base our measures primarily upon the Census. We have therefore to obtain output and employment from different sources. The output figures come from trade reports to the Bureau of Mines checked against the Census by the Bureau, and are substantially complete. The employment figures, on the other hand, come for the most part from a quite separate canvass by the Bureau of Mines made for the purpose of computing accident rates. Their coverage is much less reliable than that of the output data.

Although the resulting productivity measures are less trustworthy than those which can be computed for manufacturing from the Census of Manufactures, it is true also that in another respect our data for mining are superior to those for manufacturing. Many manufactured products are not susceptible of physical measurement, and comprehensive indexes of manufacturing output have consequently to make use of such devices as the coverage adjustment, whereby changes in total value of products are invoked to supplement data available for measurable output.[6] In mining no such difficulty arises, for the products, being crude or unfabricated, can always be subjected to physical measurement.

For many lesser divisions of mining there are no employment statistics except for infrequent Census years. However, in each comparison leading to a productivity index, the industries or products included in the output index have of course been matched with those for which employment data are available. Thus the output indexes in Tables A-5 and A-6 cover only those industries for which figures on employment are given in Tables A-3 and A-4. Output indexes—no longer strictly comparable with those for employment—for other industries and products, and for all products for which we have data, will be found in Table A-7. No data for the physical output of stone quarrying are available prior to 1906, but for subsequent years the coverage of the output index for mining as a whole in Table A-7 is practically complete.[7]

*Supplementary Tables*

Statistical materials used for illustrative purposes at various points in this report are presented in the remaining tables of Appendix A. In

[6] See Solomon Fabricant, *The Output of Manufacturing Industries, 1899–1937* (National Bureau of Economic Research, 1940), especially pp. 362-72.

[7] For the period since 1919 our basic output index (Tables 1 and A-7; Charts 1 and 2) has a coverage in excess of 99 percent of all minerals for which value data are reported.

Table A-8 will be found figures for the secondary output of nonferrous metals discussed in Chapter 2. Tables A-9 and A-10 offer measures computed from sample data by the National Research Project; these permit comparisons of productivity at underground and open pit mines in the bituminous coal and copper mining industries (Chapters 8 and 12). Tables A-11 through A-15 give figures for the consumption of nonferrous metals, coal and petroleum by use, a topic discussed in Chapter 2. Tables A-16 and A-17 show the derivation of our indexes for the physical volume of construction activity, and their comparison with stone output (Chapter 2). Table A-18 gives the data on petroleum discoveries and reserves discussed in Chapter 10. Table A-19 shows the derivation of employment figures for oil and gas wells in 1939, use of which is made in Chapter 3.

## PHYSICAL OUTPUT AND MINE VALUE OF INDIVIDUAL MINERALS

*A general note appears at the end of this table,
followed by specific notes numbered in the
same manner as the columns to which they refer.*

| Year | (A) Total Quantity Mil. l.t. | Price $ per l.t. | (B) Hematite Quantity Mil. l.t. | Price $ per l.t. | (1) Iron Ore (C) Brown Ore Quantity Mil. l.t | Price $ per l.t. | (D) Magnetite Quantity Mil. l.t. | Price $ per l.t. | (E) Carbonate Quantity Th. l.t. | Price $ per l.t. |
|---|---|---|---|---|---|---|---|---|---|---|
| 1899 | 24.6 | 1.41 | .. | .. | .. | .. | .. | .. | .. | .. |
| 1900 | 27.3 | 2.40 | .. | .. | .. | .. | .. | .. | .. | .. |
| 1901 | 28.6 | 1.68 | .. | .. | .. | .. | .. | .. | .. | .. |
| 1902 | 35.3 | 1.82 | .. | .. | .. | .. | .. | .. | .. | .. |
| 1903 | 34.8 | 1.88 | .. | .. | .. | .. | .. | .. | .. | .. |
| 1904 | 27.5 | 1.55 | .. | .. | .. | .. | .. | .. | .. | .. |
| 1905 | 42.4 | 1.76 | .. | .. | .. | .. | .. | .. | .. | .. |
| 1906 | .. | .. | 42.5 | 2.13 | 2.78 | 1.78 | 2.47 | 2.05 | 18.0 | 1.75 |
| 1907 | .. | .. | 46.1 | 2.03 | 2.96 | 1.81 | 2.68 | 2.03 | 23.6 | 1.74 |
| 1908 | .. | .. | 31.8 | 2.32 | 2.62 | 1.70 | 1.55 | 2.40 | 26.6 | 1.38 |
| 1909 | .. | .. | 46.2 | 2.17 | 2.84 | 1.68 | 2.23 | 2.40 | 16.5 | 1.73 |
| 1910 | .. | .. | 51.4 | 2.52 | 2.99 | 1.76 | 2.63 | 2.36 | 22.3 | 1.61 |
| 1911 | .. | .. | 39.6 | 2.12 | 2.03 | 1.72 | 2.20 | 2.29 | 15.7 | 1.83 |
| 1912 | .. | .. | 51.3 | 1.87 | 1.61 | 1.79 | 2.18 | 2.18 | 10.3 | 1.96 |
| 1913 | .. | .. | 57.9 | 2.21 | 1.68 | 1.88 | 2.36 | 2.07 | 7.85 | 2.06 |
| 1914 | .. | .. | 38.3 | 1.79 | 1.54 | 1.72 | 1.61 | 2.39 | 5.14 | 2.44 |
| 1915 | .. | .. | 52.2 | 1.80 | 1.49 | 1.80 | 1.81 | 2.50 | 3.46 | 2.44 |
| 1916 | .. | .. | 70.7 | 2.32 | 1.90 | 2.03 | 2.53 | 3.11 | 1.80 | 3.00 |
| 1917 | .. | .. | 70.7 | 3.12 | 1.99 | 2.95 | 2.55 | 4.29 | 0 | .. |
| 1918 | .. | .. | 65.9 | 3.35 | 1.61 | 3.51 | 2.15 | 4.60 | 0 | .. |
| 1919 | .. | .. | 57.7 | 3.48 | 1.13 | 3.63 | 2.12 | 4.08 | 0 | .. |
| 1920 | .. | .. | 63.9 | 4.09 | 1.33 | 4.19 | 2.39 | 4.59 | 3.74 | .. |
| 1921 | .. | .. | 28.3 | 3.37 | .370 | 2.63 | .781 | 3.61 | 2.71 | .. |
| 1922 | .. | .. | 44.9 | 3.14 | .784 | 2.65 | 1.45 | 2.37 | 3.26 | .. |
| 1923 | .. | .. | 65.9 | 3.46 | 1.23 | 2.88 | 2.19 | 3.34 | 3.52 | .. |
| 1924 | .. | .. | 52.1 | 2.91 | .814 | 2.75 | 1.35 | 2.95 | 3.25 | .. |
| 1925 | .. | .. | 59.5 | 2.50 | .885 | 2.78 | 1.47 | 3.07 | 4.70 | .. |
| 1926 | .. | .. | 64.6 | 2.49 | .811 | 2.83 | 2.18 | 3.13 | 2.22 | .. |
| 1927 | .. | .. | 58.5 | 2.43 | .743 | 2.62 | 2.49 | 3.38 | 2.49 | .. |
| 1928 | .. | .. | 59.2 | 2.43 | .817 | 2.47 | 2.17 | 3.04 | 1.79 | .. |
| 1929 | .. | .. | 69.8 | 2.59 | .776 | 2.47 | 2.40 | 3.15 | 1.78 | .. |
| 1930 | .. | .. | 55.3 | 2.61 | .720 | 2.53 | 2.42 | 3.38 | 1.00 | .. |
| 1931 | .. | .. | 29.7 | 2.58 | .360 | 2.47 | 1.11 | 3.07 | .818 | .. |
| 1932 | .. | .. | 9.62 | 2.41 | .0617 | 2.39 | .163 | 2.87 | .477 | .. |
| 1933 | .. | .. | 16.9 | 2.59 | .235 | 2.08 | .397 | 2.83 | .499 | .. |
| 1934 | .. | .. | 23.4 | 2.57 | .286 | 2.39 | .910 | 2.87 | .640 | .. |
| 1935 | .. | .. | 28.9 | 2.48 | .267 | 2.26 | 1.35 | 2.58 | .687 | .. |
| 1936 | .. | .. | 46.1 | 2.53 | .475 | 2.32 | 2.21 | 3.20 | .533 | .. |
| 1937 | .. | .. | 68.1 | 2.89 | .666 | 2.40 | 3.35 | 2.69 | .532 | .. |
| 1938 | .. | .. | 25.6 | 2.82 | .363 | 2.31 | 2.48 | 2.79 | .448 | .. |
| 1939 | .. | .. | 47.8 | 2.89 | .597 | 2.14 | 3.38 | 2.99 | .463 | .. |

(2) Manganese Ore

| Year | (A) Over 40 Percent Manganese | | (B) Over 35 Percent Manganese | | (C) 5 to 40 Percent Manganese | | (D) 10 to 35 Percent Manganese | | (E) 5 to 10 Percent Manganese | |
|---|---|---|---|---|---|---|---|---|---|---|
| | Quantity Th. l.t. | Price $ per l.t. | Quantity Th. l.t. | Price $ per l.t. | Quantity Th. l.t. | Price $ per l.t. | Quantity Th. l.t. | Price $ per l.t. | Quantity Th. l.t. | Price $ per l.t. |
| 1899 | 9.94 | 8.28 | .. | .. | 109 | 3.23 | .. | .. | .. | .. |
| 1900 | 11.8 | 8.52 | .. | .. | 232 | 4.76 | .. | .. | .. | .. |
| 1901 | 12.0 | 9.73 | .. | .. | 291 | 3.83 | .. | .. | .. | .. |
| 1902 | 7.48 | 8.15 | .. | .. | 207 | 4.63 | .. | .. | .. | .. |
| 1903 | 2.82 | 8.97 | .. | .. | 194 | 3.64 | .. | .. | .. | .. |
| 1904 | 3.15 | 9.37 | .. | .. | 123 | 3.28 | .. | .. | .. | .. |
| 1905 | 4.12 | 8.80 | .. | .. | 131 | 2.96 | .. | .. | .. | .. |
| 1906 | 6.92 | 12.7 | .. | .. | 98.3 | 3.60 | .. | .. | .. | .. |
| 1907 | 5.60 | 11.3 | .. | .. | 104 | 2.50 | .. | .. | .. | .. |
| 1908 | 6.14 | 10.2 | .. | .. | 55.9 | 2.38 | .. | .. | .. | .. |
| 1909 | 1.54 | 12.7 | .. | .. | 68.7 | 3.14 | .. | .. | .. | .. |
| 1910 | 2.26 | 10.1 | .. | .. | 61.1 | 3.06 | .. | .. | .. | .. |
| 1911 | 2.46 | 10.0 | .. | .. | 44.4 | 2.59 | .. | .. | .. | .. |
| 1912 | 1.66 | 9.45 | .. | .. | 51.5 | .387 | .. | .. | .. | .. |
| 1913 | 4.05 | 10.0 | .. | .. | 59.4 | .423 | .. | .. | .. | .. |
| 1914 | 2.64 | 10.4 | .. | .. | 98.3 | 2.22 | .. | .. | .. | .. |
| 1915 | .. | .. | 9.61 | 11.7 | .. | .. | 181 | 4.40 | 14.8 | 1.36 |
| 1916 | .. | .. | 31.5 | 20.8 | .. | .. | 454 | 3.94 | 90.5 | 2.09 |
| 1917 | .. | .. | 129.4 | 31.8 | .. | .. | 731 | 4.16 | 130 | 2.84 |
| 1918 | .. | .. | 305.9 | 26.9 | .. | .. | 916 | 5.02 | 254 | 4.06 |
| 1919 | .. | .. | { 55.3 | 32.5 | .. | .. | 310 | 3.82 | 124 | 2.99 |
| | | | { 55.0 | 32.6 | .. | .. | 212 | 4.56 | 112 | 3.14 |
| 1920 | .. | .. | 94.4 | 25.4 | .. | .. | 357 | 4.06 | 280 | 2.30 |
| 1921 | .. | .. | 13.5 | 36.6 | .. | .. | 8.44 | 5.07 | 62.7 | 2.36 |
| 1922 | .. | .. | 13.4 | 34.0 | .. | .. | 345 | 3.11 | 252 | 2.51 |
| 1923 | .. | .. | 31.5 | 27.8 | .. | .. | 320 | 3.62 | 1,072 | 3.36 |
| 1924 | .. | .. | 56.5 | 23.1 | .. | .. | 286 | 3.24 | 587 | 2.92 |
| 1925 | .. | .. | 98.3 | 18.9 | .. | .. | 267 | 3.42 | 1,153 | 2.43 |
| 1926 | .. | .. | 46.3 | 26.6 | .. | .. | 364 | 3.24 | 835 | 2.32 |
| 1927 | .. | .. | 44.7 | 25.8 | .. | .. | 148 | 4.54 | 1,310 | 2.50 |
| 1928 | .. | .. | 46.9 | 25.9 | .. | .. | 90.6 | 4.50 | 1,085 | 2.44 |
| 1929 | .. | .. | 60.4 | 26.7 | .. | .. | 78.2 | 5.78 | 1,110 | 2.54 |
| 1930 | .. | .. | 67.0 | 21.4 | .. | .. | 77.4 | 7.31 | 708 | 2.59 |
| 1931 | .. | .. | 39.2 | 17.8 | .. | .. | 64.1 | 6.33 | 217 | 2.63 |
| 1932 | .. | .. | 17.8 | 21.2 | .. | .. | 15.6 | 4.00 | 9.80 | 3.01 |
| 1933 | .. | .. | 19.2 | 24.4 | .. | .. | 12.8 | 4.52 | 179 | 2.64 |
| 1934 | .. | .. | 26.5 | 21.6 | .. | .. | 23.2 | 4.66 | 199 | 2.58 |
| 1935 | .. | .. | 26.4 | 21.1 | .. | .. | 93.3 | 3.50 | 431 | 2.31 |
| 1936 | .. | .. | 32.1 | 21.7 | .. | .. | 99.0 | 3.40 | 842 | 2.26 |
| 1937 | .. | .. | 40.2 | 26.4 | .. | .. | 152 | 5.13 | 1,189 | 2.59 |
| 1938 | .. | .. | 25.3 | 26.9 | .. | .. | 33.6 | 4.69 | 275 | 2.55 |
| 1939 | .. | .. | 29.3 | 27.1 | .. | .. | 240 | 3.90 | 470 | 2.58 |

Table A-1—INDIVIDUAL MINERALS (continued)

| | (3) Copper, 1904–39 | | | | | | (4) Lode Gold and Silver, and Lead and Zinc outside Mississippi Valley, 1906–39 | | | |
| | (A) Copper | | (B) Gold | | (C) Silver | | (A) Gold | | (B) Silver | |
| Year | Quantity Th. s.t. | Price $ per s.t. | Quantity Th. f.oz. | Price $ per f.oz. | Quantity Mil. f.oz. | Price $ per f.oz. | Quantity Mil. f.oz. | Price $ per f.oz. | Quantity Mil. f.oz. | Price $ per f.oz. |
|---|---|---|---|---|---|---|---|---|---|---|
| 1899 | .. | .. | .. | .. | .. | .. | .. | .. | .. | .. |
| 1900 | .. | .. | .. | .. | .. | .. | .. | .. | .. | .. |
| 1901 | .. | .. | .. | .. | .. | .. | .. | .. | .. | .. |
| 1902 | .. | .. | .. | .. | .. | .. | .. | .. | .. | .. |
| 1903 | .. | .. | .. | .. | .. | .. | .. | .. | .. | .. |
| 1904 | 405 | 256 | 237 | 20.67 | 15.8 | .58 | .. | .. | .. | .. |
| 1905 | 442 | 312 | 252 | 20.67 | 15.7 | .61 | .. | .. | .. | .. |
| 1906 | 456 | 386 | 267 | 20.67 | 15.9 | .68 | 2.94 | 20.67 | 41.3 | .68 |
| 1907 | 420 | 400 | 268 | 20.67 | 13.9 | .66 | 2.63 | 20.67 | 38.4 | .66 |
| 1908 | 476 | 264 | 231 | 20.67 | 14.9 | .53 | 2.80 | 20.67 | 35.7 | .53 |
| 1909 | 561 | 260 | 270 | 20.67 | 18.3 | .52 | 3.02 | 20.67 | 38.8 | .52 |
| 1910 | 542 | 254 | 263 | 20.67 | 16.0 | .54 | 3.03 | 20.67 | 41.4 | .54 |
| 1911 | 544 | 250 | 259 | 20.67 | 16.4 | .53 | 3.08 | 20.67 | 44.1 | .53 |
| 1912 | 610 | 330 | 255 | 20.67 | 18.4 | .615 | 2.85 | 20.67 | 47.1 | .615 |
| 1913 | 607 | 310 | 269 | 20.67 | 18.0 | .604 | 2.73 | 20.67 | 52.8 | .604 |
| 1914 | 563 | 266 | 257 | 20.67 | 14.5 | .553 | 2.80 | 20.67 | 54.6 | .553 |
| 1915 | 701 | 350 | 336 | 20.67 | 17.9 | .507 | 3.04 | 20.67 | 53.3 | .507 |
| 1916 | 943 | 492 | 392 | 20.67 | 23.3 | .658 | 2.62 | 20.67 | 54.1 | .658 |
| 1917 | 903 | 546 | 328 | 20.67 | 19.3 | .824 | 2.31 | 20.67 | 50.1 | .824 |
| 1918 | 920 | 494 | 304 | 20.67 | 19.7 | .98 | 1.98 | 20.67 | 47.4 | .98 |
| 1919 | 583 | 372 | 184 | 20.67 | 12.4 | 1.12 | 1.65 | 20.67 | 38.8 | 1.12 |
| 1920 | 577 | 368 | 170 | 20.67 | 11.5 | 1.09 | 1.39 | 20.67 | 44.1 | 1.09 |
| 1921 | 205 | 258 | 51.4 | 20.67 | 4.24 | 1.00 | 1.43 | 20.67 | 41.3 | 1.00 |
| 1922 | 443 | 270 | 130 | 20.67 | 9.75 | 1.00 | 1.48 | 20.67 | 50.7 | 1.00 |
| 1923 | 696 | 294 | 270 | 20.67 | 14.0 | .82 | 1.47 | 20.67 | 55.5 | .82 |
| 1924 | 766 | 262 | 310 | 20.67 | 15.8 | .67 | 1.55 | 20.67 | 47.6 | .67 |
| 1925 | 802 | 284 | 346 | 20.67 | 17.5 | .694 | 1.37 | 20.67 | 48.5 | .694 |
| 1926 | 829 | 280 | 364 | 20.67 | 16.4 | .624 | 1.27 | 20.67 | 45.3 | .624 |
| 1927 | 797 | 262 | 368 | 20.67 | 14.0 | .567 | 1.15 | 20.67 | 44.9 | .567 |
| 1928 | 884 | 288 | 415 | 20.67 | 14.4 | .585 | 1.15 | 20.67 | 43.0 | .585 |
| 1929 | 977 | 352 | 458 | 20.67 | 17.6 | .533 | 1.02 | 20.67 | 42.8 | .533 |
| 1930 | 689 | 260 | 333 | 20.67 | 13.3 | .385 | 1.19 | 20.67 | 34.0 | .385 |
| 1931 | 518 | 182 | 215 | 20.67 | 9.38 | .290 | 1.33 | 20.67 | 20.1 | .290 |
| 1932 | 234 | 126 | 98.9 | 20.67 | 5.10 | .282 | 1.46 | 20.67 | 17.4 | .282 |
| 1933 | 191 | 128 | 106 | 25.56 | 5.84 | .350 | 1.40 | 25.56 | 17.1 | .350 |
| 1934 | 237 | 160 | 146 | 34.95 | 7.75 | .646 | 1.71 | 34.95 | 24.8 | .646 |
| 1935 | 373 | 166 | 227 | 35.00 | 12.5 | .719 | 2.06 | 35.00 | 35.6 | .719 |
| 1936 | 596 | 184 | 379 | 35.00 | 17.1 | .774 | 2.30 | 35.00 | 43.5 | .774 |
| 1937 | 825 | 242 | 496 | 35.00 | 20.1 | .774 | 2.37 | 35.00 | 50.7 | .774 |
| 1938 | 543 | 196 | 341 | 35.00 | 15.6 | .646 | 2.50 | 35.00 | 45.5 | .646 |
| 1939 | 728 | 208 | 471 | 35.00 | 18.4 | .679 | 2.66 | 35.00 | 45.7 | .679 |

| | (4) Lode Gold and Silver, and Lead and Zinc outside Mississippi Valley, 1906–39 (continued) | | | | (5) Lead and Zinc (Mississippi Valley), 1906–39 | | | | | |
|---|---|---|---|---|---|---|---|---|---|---|
| | (C) Lead | | (D) Zinc | | (A) Lead | | (B) Zinc | | (C) Fluorspar, Ill. and Ky. | |
| Year | Quantity Th. s.t. | Price $ per s.t. | Quantity Th. s.t. | Price $ per s.t. | Quantity Th. s.t. | Price $ per s.t. | Quantity Th. s.t. | Price $ per s.t. | Quantity Th. s.t. | Price $ per s.t. |
| 1899 | .. | .. | .. | .. | .. | .. | .. | .. | .. | .. |
| 1900 | .. | .. | .. | .. | .. | .. | .. | .. | .. | .. |
| 1901 | .. | .. | .. | .. | .. | .. | .. | .. | .. | .. |
| 1902 | .. | .. | .. | .. | .. | .. | .. | .. | .. | .. |
| 1903 | .. | .. | .. | .. | .. | .. | .. | .. | .. | .. |
| 1904 | .. | .. | .. | .. | .. | .. | .. | .. | .. | .. |
| 1905 | .. | .. | .. | .. | .. | .. | .. | .. | .. | .. |
| 1906 | 220 | 114 | 104 | 122 | 128 | 114 | 131 | 122 | .. | .. |
| 1907 | 222 | 106 | 96.9 | 118 | 143 | 106 | 156 | 118 | .. | .. |
| 1908 | 180 | 84 | 86.7 | 94 | 150 | 84 | 147 | 94 | .. | .. |
| 1909 | 220 | 86 | 126 | 108 | 165 | 86 | 176 | 108 | 49.7 | 5.75 |
| 1910 | 215 | 88 | 145 | 108 | 168 | 88 | 180 | 108 | 64.3 | 6.26 |
| 1911 | 242 | 90 | 158 | 114 | 185 | 90 | 174 | 114 | 81.2 | 7.12 |
| 1912 | 259 | 90 | 192 | 138 | 183 | 90 | 193 | 138 | 114 | 6.61 |
| 1913 | 299 | 88 | 228 | 112 | 184 | 88 | 185 | 112 | 105 | 6.30 |
| 1914 | 305 | 78 | 237 | 102 | 200 | 78 | 178 | 102 | 92.9 | 5.98 |
| 1915 | 324 | 94 | 356 | 248 | 218 | 94 | 232 | 248 | 136 | 5.56 |
| 1916 | 354 | 138 | 411 | 268 | 246 | 138 | 292 | 268 | 146 | 5.95 |
| 1917 | 361 | 172 | 375 | 204 | 267 | 172 | 339 | 204 | 200 | 10.3 |
| 1918 | 301 | 142 | 312 | 182 | 261 | 142 | 324 | 182 | 220 | 22.5 |
| 1919 | 197 | 106 | 220 | 146 | 232 | 106 | 329 | 146 | 125 | 26.5 |
| 1920 | 247 | 160 | 231 | 162 | 249 | 160 | 357 | 162 | 166 | 26.1 |
| 1921 | 172 | 90 | 71.7 | 100 | 242 | 90 | 185 | 100 | 27.7 | 22.0 |
| 1922 | 210 | 110 | 160 | 114 | 267 | 110 | 312 | 114 | 136 | 18.1 |
| 1923 | 289 | 140 | 218 | 136 | 258 | 140 | 392 | 136 | 110 | 21.6 |
| 1924 | 312 | 160 | 219 | 130 | 284 | 160 | 419 | 130 | 110 | 20.7 |
| 1925 | 366 | 174 | 254 | 152 | 318 | 174 | 457 | 152 | 99.3 | 18.7 |
| 1926 | 375 | 160 | 306 | 150 | 308 | 160 | 468 | 150 | 116 | 18.8 |
| 1927 | 384 | 126 | 339 | 128 | 280 | 126 | 380 | 128 | 104 | 18.4 |
| 1928 | 366 | 116 | 358 | 122 | 267 | 116 | 337 | 122 | 136 | 19.0 |
| 1929 | 379 | 126 | { 372 / 395 } | 132 | 274 | 126 | { 352 / 330 } | 132 | 138 | 19.4 |
| 1930 | 319 | 100 | 362 | 96 | 238 | 100 | 234 | 96 | 83.3 | 19.2 |
| 1931 | 221 | 74 | 280 | 76 | 182 | 74 | 130 | 76 | 51.5 | 17.6 |
| 1932 | 156 | 60 | 187 | 60 | 135 | 60 | 98.3 | 60 | 24.3 | 15.7 |
| 1933 | 161 | 74 | 239 | 84 | 110 | 74 | 145 | 84 | 70.7 | 14.3 |
| 1934 | 172 | 74 | 276 | 86 | 114 | 74 | 163 | 86 | 76.4 | 16.5 |
| 1935 | 198 | 80 | 318 | 88 | 133 | 80 | 200 | 88 | 113 | 15.1 |
| 1936 | 223 | 92 | 340 | 100 | 149 | 92 | 235 | 100 | 162 | 18.1 |
| 1937 | 259 | 118 | 382 | 130 | 205 | 118 | 244 | 130 | 166 | 20.7 |
| 1938 | 210 | 92 | 318 | 96 | 159 | 92 | 199 | 96 | 70.2 | 20.4 |
| 1939 | 215 | 94 | 352 | 104 | 198 | 94 | 232 | 104 | 165 | 20.7 |

| Year | (6) Placer Gold and Silver (A) Gold | | (B) Silver | | (7) Lode Gold and Silver, and Copper, Lead and Zinc, 1899-1906 (A) Gold | | (B) Silver | | (C) Copper | |
|---|---|---|---|---|---|---|---|---|---|---|
| | Quantity Th. f.oz. | Price $ per f.oz. | Quantity Th. f.oz. | Price $ per f.oz. | Quantity Mil. f.oz. | Price $ per f.oz. | Quantity Mil. f.oz. | Price $ per f.oz. | Quantity Th. s.t. | Price $ per s.t. |
| 1899 | 300 | 20.67 | 0 | .. | 2.94 | 20.67 | 56.5 | .60 | 284 | 342 |
| 1900 | 304 | 20.67 | 0 | .. | 3.17 | 20.67 | 60.1 | .62 | 303 | 332 |
| 1901 | 370 | 20.67 | 0 | .. | 3.15 | 20.67 | 57.8 | .60 | 301 | 334 |
| 1902 | 321 | 20.67 | 0 | .. | 3.19 | 20.67 | 57.7 | .53 | 330 | 244 |
| 1903 | 303 | 20.67 | 0 | .. | 2.93 | 20.67 | 56.2 | .54 | 348 | 274 |
| 1904 | 322 | 20.67 | 10.9 | .58 | 3.15 | 20.67 | 55.8 | .58 | 405 | 256 |
| 1905 | 348 | 20.67 | 37.7 | .61 | 3.16 | 20.67 | 56.1 | .61 | 442 | 312 |
| 1906 | 428 | 20.67 | 56.4 | .68 | 3.21 | 20.67 | 57.1 | .68 | 455 | 386 |
| 1907 | 395 | 20.67 | 51.3 | .66 | .. | .. | .. | .. | .. | .. |
| 1908 | 471 | 20.67 | 89.2 | .53 | .. | .. | .. | .. | .. | .. |
| 1909 | 522 | 20.67 | 58.0 | .52 | .. | .. | .. | .. | .. | .. |
| 1910 | 509 | 20.67 | 58.0 | .54 | .. | .. | .. | .. | .. | .. |
| 1911 | 526 | 20.67 | 59.8 | .53 | .. | .. | .. | .. | .. | .. |
| 1912 | 534 | 20.67 | 61.1 | .615 | .. | .. | .. | .. | .. | .. |
| 1913 | 559 | 20.67 | 65.3 | .604 | .. | .. | .. | .. | .. | .. |
| 1914 | 599 | 20.67 | 68.9 | .553 | .. | .. | .. | .. | .. | .. |
| 1915 | 570 | 20.67 | 72.4 | .507 | .. | .. | .. | .. | .. | .. |
| 1916 | 568 | 20.67 | 64.4 | .658 | .. | .. | .. | .. | .. | .. |
| 1917 | 552 | 20.67 | 54.2 | .824 | .. | .. | .. | .. | .. | .. |
| 1918 | 473 | 20.67 | 51.2 | .98 | .. | .. | .. | .. | .. | .. |
| 1919 | 464 | 20.67 | 45.4 | 1.12 | .. | .. | .. | .. | .. | .. |
| 1920 | 416 | 20.67 | 48.2 | 1.09 | .. | .. | .. | .. | .. | .. |
| 1921 | 473 | 20.67 | 58.8 | 1.00 | .. | .. | .. | .. | .. | .. |
| 1922 | 325 | 20.67 | 34.4 | 1.00 | .. | .. | .. | .. | .. | .. |
| 1923 | 377 | 20.67 | 35.4 | .82 | .. | .. | .. | .. | .. | .. |
| 1924 | 278 | 20.67 | 29.0 | .67 | .. | .. | .. | .. | .. | .. |
| 1925 | 280 | 20.67 | 26.2 | .694 | .. | .. | .. | .. | .. | .. |
| 1926 | 275 | 20.67 | 25.0 | .624 | .. | .. | .. | .. | .. | .. |
| 1927 | 307 | 20.67 | 26.5 | .567 | .. | .. | .. | .. | .. | .. |
| 1928 | 255 | 20.67 | 22.3 | .585 | .. | .. | .. | .. | .. | .. |
| 1929 | 209 | 20.67 | 18.3 | .533 | .. | .. | .. | .. | .. | .. |
| 1930 | 206 | 20.67 | 18.3 | .385 | .. | .. | .. | .. | .. | .. |
| 1931 | 219 | 20.67 | 18.2 | .290 | .. | .. | .. | .. | .. | .. |
| 1932 | 277 | 20.67 | 26.2 | .282 | .. | .. | .. | .. | .. | .. |
| 1933 | 331 | 25.56 | 35.7 | .350 | .. | .. | .. | .. | .. | .. |
| 1934 | 386 | 34.95 | 45.4 | .646 | .. | .. | .. | .. | .. | .. |
| 1935 | 478 | 35.00 | 52.0 | .719 | .. | .. | .. | .. | .. | .. |
| 1936 | 558 | 35.00 | 62.2 | .774 | .. | .. | .. | .. | .. | .. |
| 1937 | 619 | 35.00 | 70.5 | .774 | .. | .. | .. | .. | .. | .. |
| 1938 | 759 | 35.00 | 89.6 | .646 | .. | .. | .. | .. | .. | .. |
| 1939 | 867 | 35.00 | 109 | .679 | .. | .. | .. | .. | .. | .. |

(7) Lode Gold and Silver, and Copper, Lead and Zinc, 1899–1906 (continued)

| Year | (D) Lead Quantity Th. s.t. | (D) Lead Price $ per s.t. | (E) Zinc Quantity Th. s.t. | (E) Zinc Price $ per s.t. | (8) Bauxite Quantity Th. l.t. | (8) Bauxite Price $ per l.t. | (9) Mercury Quantity Th. flasks | (9) Mercury Price $ per flask |
|---|---|---|---|---|---|---|---|---|
| 1899 | 202 | 90 | 129 | 116 | 32.9 | 3.56 | 30.7 | 47.4 |
| 1900 | 261 | 88 | 124 | 88 | 23.4 | 3.87 | 28.5 | 44.6 |
| 1901 | 259 | 86 | 141 | 82 | 19.9 | 4.23 | 29.9 | 48.1 |
| 1902 | 267 | 82 | 157 | 96 | 27.3 | 4.41 | 34.5 | 42.9 |
| 1903 | 281 | 84 | 159 | 108 | 44.7 | 3.56 | 35.9 | 45.0 |
| 1904 | 298 | 86 | 187 | 102 | 51.0 | 4.95 | 35.2 | 43.6 |
| 1905 | 308 | 94 | 204 | 118 | 56.6 | 4.99 | 30.1 | 36.7 |
| 1906 | 336 | 114 | 200 | 122 | 70.6 | 4.89 | 25.7 | 40.0 |
| 1907 | .. | .. | .. | .. | 94.4 | 4.91 | 21.3 | 40.1 |
| 1908 | .. | .. | .. | .. | 50.1 | 5.06 | 19.5 | 44.8 |
| 1909 | .. | .. | .. | .. | 132 | 5.26 | 20.8 | 46.1 |
| 1910 | .. | .. | .. | .. | 151 | 4.81 | 20.3 | 47.1 |
| 1911 | .. | .. | .. | .. | 157 | 4.82 | 21.0 | 46.6 |
| 1912 | .. | .. | .. | .. | 161 | 4.81 | 24.7 | 42.6 |
| 1913 | .. | .. | .. | .. | 211 | 4.75 | 19.9 | 40.8 |
| 1914 | .. | .. | .. | .. | 219 | 4.88 | 16.3 | 49.7 |
| 1915 | .. | .. | .. | .. | 300 | 5.10 | 20.8 | 86.9 |
| 1916 | .. | .. | .. | .. | 425 | 5.40 | 29.5 | 127.6 |
| 1917 | .. | .. | .. | .. | 569 | 5.48 | 35.7 | 106.7 |
| 1918 | .. | .. | .. | .. | 606 | 5.69 | 32.4 | 119.1 |
| 1919 | .. | .. | .. | .. | 377 | 5.85 | 21.1 | 91.5 |
| 1920 | .. | .. | .. | .. | 521 | 6.23 | 13.2 | 80.7 |
| 1921 | .. | .. | .. | .. | 140 | 6.38 | 6.26 | 48.0 |
| 1922 | .. | .. | .. | .. | 310 | 6.50 | 6.29 | 58.6 |
| 1923 | .. | .. | .. | .. | 523 | 6.04 | 7.83 | 66.6 |
| 1924 | .. | .. | .. | .. | 348 | 6.15 | 9.95 | 69.6 |
| 1925 | .. | .. | .. | .. | 317 | 6.28 | 9.05 | 84.2 |
| 1926 | .. | .. | .. | .. | 392 | 6.16 | 7.54 | 93.1 |
| 1927 | .. | .. | .. | .. | 321 | 6.20 | 11.1 | 118.2 |
| 1928 | .. | .. | .. | .. | 375 | 6.06 | 17.9 | 123.5 |
| 1929 | .. | .. | .. | .. | 366 | 6.19 | 23.7 | 122.1 |
| 1930 | .. | .. | .. | .. | 331 | 5.83 | 21.6 | 115.0 |
| 1931 | .. | .. | .. | .. | 196 | 5.82 | 24.9 | 87.3 |
| 1932 | .. | .. | .. | .. | 96.3 | 5.69 | 12.6 | 57.9 |
| 1933 | .. | .. | .. | .. | 154 | 5.99 | 9.67 | 59.2 |
| 1934 | .. | .. | .. | .. | { 158 / 169 | { 7.15 / 6.67 | 15.4 | 73.9 |
| 1935 | .. | .. | .. | .. | 245 | 6.34 | 17.5 | 72.0 |
| 1936 | .. | .. | .. | .. | 380 | 5.78 | 16.6 | 79.9 |
| 1937 | .. | .. | .. | .. | 425 | 5.75 | 16.5 | 90.2 |
| 1938 | .. | .. | .. | .. | 311 | 5.83 | 18.0 | 75.5 |
| 1939 | .. | .. | .. | .. | 375 | 5.77 | 18.6 | 103.9 |

| Year | (10) MOLYBDENUM | | (11) TUNGSTEN | | (12) PENNSYLVANIA ANTHRACITE | | (13) BITUMINOUS COAL | |
|------|----------|---------|----------|---------|----------|---------|----------|---------|
| | Quantity Mil. lb. | Price $ per lb. | Quantity Th. s.t. | Price $ per s.t. | Quantity Mil. s.t. | Price $ per s.t. | Quantity Mil. s.t. | Price $ per s.t. |
| 1899 | .. | .. | .. | .. | 60.4 | 1.46 | 193 | .869 |
| 1900 | .. | .. | .046 | 240 | 57.4 | 1.49 | 212 | 1.04 |
| 1901 | .. | .. | .179 | 155 | 67.5 | 1.67 | 226 | 1.05 |
| 1902 | .. | .. | .184 | 185 | 41.4 | 1.84 | 260 | 1.12 |
| 1903 | .. | .. | .292 | 149 | 74.6 | 2.04 | 283 | 1.24 |
| 1904 | .. | .. | .740 | 249 | 73.2 | 1.90 | 279 | 1.10 |
| 1905 | .. | .. | .803 | 335 | 77.7 | 1.83 | 315 | 1.06 |
| 1906 | .. | .. | .928 | 376 | 71.3 | 1.85 | 343 | 1.11 |
| 1907 | .. | .. | 1.64 | 543 | 85.6 | 1.91 | 395 | 1.14 |
| 1908 | .. | .. | .671 | 343 | 83.3 | 1.90 | 333 | 1.12 |
| 1909 | .. | .. | 1.62 | 379 | 81.1 | 1.84 | 380 | 1.07 |
| 1910 | .. | .. | 1.82 | 457 | 84.5 | 1.90 | 417 | 1.13 |
| 1911 | 0 | .. | 1.14 | 358 | 90.5 | 1.94 | 406 | 1.11 |
| 1912 | 0 | .. | 1.33 | 378 | 84.4 | 2.11 | 450 | 1.15 |
| 1913 | 0 | .. | 1.54 | 437 | 91.5 | 2.13 | 478 | 1.18 |
| 1914 | .00130 | 1.00 | .990 | 439 | 90.8 | 2.07 | 423 | 1.17 |
| 1915 | .182 | .632 | 2.33 | 1,758 | 89.0 | 2.07 | 443 | 1.13 |
| 1916 | .207 | .992 | 5.92 | 2,038 | 87.6 | 2.31 | 503 | 1.32 |
| 1917 | .350 | 1.14 | 6.14 | 1,104 | 99.6 | 2.85 | 552 | 2.26 |
| 1918 | .862 | 1.46 | 5.06 | 1,393 | 98.8 | 3.40 | 579 | 2.57 |
| 1919 | .298 | 1.15 | .518 | 851 | 88.1 | 4.14 | 466 | 2.49 |
| 1920 | .0349 | .493 | .216 | 471 | 89.6 | 4.85 | 569 | 3.75 |
| 1921 | 0 | .. | 0 | .. | 90.5 | 5.00 | 416 | 2.88 |
| 1922 | 0 | .. | 0 | .. | 54.7 | 5.01 | 422 | 3.02 |
| 1923 | .0227 | .. | .241 | 600 | 93.3 | 5.43 | 564 | 2.68 |
| 1924 | .297 | .. | .374 | 535 | 87.9 | 5.43 | 484 | 2.20 |
| 1925 | 1.15 | .833 | 1.19 | 634 | 61.8 | 5.30 | 520 | 2.04 |
| 1926 | 1.43 | .833 | 1.38 | 666 | 84.4 | 5.62 | 573 | 2.06 |
| 1927 | 2.30 | .813 | 1.16 | 622 | 80.1 | 5.26 | 518 | 1.99 |
| 1928 | 3.43 | .578 | 1.21 | 624 | 75.3 | 5.22 | 501 | 1.86 |
| 1929 | 4.02 | .578 | .830 | 788 | 73.8 | 5.22 | 535 | 1.78 |
| 1930 | 3.72 | .550 | .702 | 725 | 69.4 | 5.11 | 467 | 1.70 |
| 1931 | 3.13 | .500 | 1.40 | 661 | 59.6 | 4.97 | 382 | 1.54 |
| 1932 | 2.43 | .500 | .396 | 552 | 49.9 | 4.46 | 310 | 1.31 |
| 1933 | 5.68 | .749 | .895 | 575 | 49.5 | 4.17 | 334 | 1.34 |
| 1934 | 9.36 | .693 | 2.05 | 874 | 57.2 | 4.27 | 359 | 1.75 |
| 1935 | 11.5 | .667 | 2.40 | 802 | 52.2 | 4.03 | 372 | 1.77 |
| 1936 | 17.2 | .664 | 2.61 | 890 | 54.6 | 4.16 | 439 | 1.76 |
| 1937 | 29.4 | .683 | 3.50 | 1,170 | 51.9 | 3.81 | 445 | 1.86 |
| 1938 | 33.3 | .699 | 4.00 | 1,039 | 46.1 | 3.92 | 349 | 1.87 |
| 1939 | 30.3 | .684 | 3.60 | 1,027 | 51.5 | 3.64 | 395 | 1.79 |

TABLE A-1—INDIVIDUAL MINERALS (continued)

## (14) PETROLEUM AND NATURAL GAS

| Year | (A₁) PENNSYLVANIA GRADE | | (A) PETROLEUM (A₂) ALL OTHER | | (A₁) AND (A₂) TOTAL | | (B) NATURAL GAS | | (C) NATURAL GASOLINE | |
|---|---|---|---|---|---|---|---|---|---|---|
| | Quantity Mil. bbl. | Price $ per bbl. | Quantity Mil. bbl. | Price $ per bbl. | Quantity Mil. bbl. | Price $ per bbl. | Quantity Bil. cu.ft. | Price $ per Th. cu.ft. | Quantity Mil. gal. | Price $ per gal. |
| 1899 | 33.0 | 1.30 | 24.0 | .898 | .. | .. | 223 | .090 | .. | .. |
| 1900 | 36.2 | 1.36 | 27.4 | .979 | .. | .. | 237 | .100 | .. | .. |
| 1901 | 33.5 | 1.22 | 35.9 | .717 | .. | .. | 264 | .103 | .. | .. |
| 1902 | 31.8 | 1.27 | 56.9 | .542 | .. | .. | 281 | .110 | .. | .. |
| 1903 | 31.0 | 1.59 | 69.5 | .652 | .. | .. | 298 | .120 | .. | .. |
| 1904 | 30.4 | 1.63 | 86.7 | .595 | .. | .. | 310 | .124 | .. | .. |
| 1905 | 28.2 | 1.40 | 107 | .421 | .. | .. | 351 | .118 | .. | .. |
| 1906 | 26.5 | 1.61 | 100 | .499 | .. | .. | 389 | .121 | .. | .. |
| 1907 | 24.5 | 1.75 | 142 | .545 | .. | .. | 407 | .133 | .. | .. |
| 1908 | 24.2 | 1.78 | 154 | .557 | .. | .. | 402 | .136 | .. | .. |
| 1909 | 25.9 | 1.65 | 157 | .544 | .. | .. | 481 | .131 | .. | .. |
| 1910 | 26.4 | 1.34 | 183 | .504 | .. | .. | 509 | .139 | .. | .. |
| 1911 | 23.3 | 1.31 | 197 | .525 | .. | .. | 513 | .145 | 7.43 | .0716 |
| 1912 | 25.9 | 1.64 | 197 | .618 | .. | .. | 562 | .150 | 12.1 | .0958 |
| 1913 | 25.4 | 2.48 | 223 | .780 | .. | .. | 582 | .151 | 24.1 | .102 |
| 1914 | 23.6 | 1.90 | 242 | .699 | .. | .. | 592 | .159 | 42.7 | .0728 |
| 1915 | 22.4 | 1.56 | 259 | .558 | .. | .. | 629 | .161 | 65.4 | .0788 |
| 1916 | 21.8 | 2.45 | 279 | .991 | .. | .. | 753 | .160 | 103 | .138 |
| 1917 | 21.8 | 3.24 | 313 | 1.44 | .. | .. | 795 | .179 | 218 | .184 |
| 1918 | 21.0 | 3.93 | 335 | 1.86 | .. | .. | 721 | .213 | 283 | .178 |
| 1919 | 22.5 | 3.96 | 356 | 1.89 | .. | .. | 746 | { .216 / .0826 } | 352 | .183 |
| 1920 | .. | .. | .. | .. | 443 | 3.07 | 798 | .0942 | 385 | .187 |
| 1921 | .. | .. | .. | .. | 472 | 1.73 | 662 | .101 | 450 | .137 |
| 1922 | .. | .. | .. | .. | 558 | 1.61 | 763 | .111 | 506 | .144 |
| 1923 | .. | .. | .. | .. | 732 | 1.34 | 1,007 | .100 | 816 | .0947 |
| 1924 | .. | .. | .. | .. | 714 | 1.43 | 1,142 | .0927 | 934 | .0881 |
| 1925 | .. | .. | .. | .. | 764 | 1.68 | 1,189 | .0943 | 1,127 | .107 |
| 1926 | .. | .. | .. | .. | 771 | 1.88 | 1,313 | .0950 | 1,363 | .100 |
| 1927 | .. | .. | .. | .. | 901 | 1.30 | 1,445 | .0882 | 1,641 | .0723 |
| 1928 | .. | .. | .. | .. | 901 | 1.17 | 1,568 | .0892 | 1,814 | .0766 |
| 1929 | .. | .. | .. | .. | 1,007 | 1.27 | 1,918 | .0822 | 2,234 | .0709 |
| 1930 | .. | .. | .. | .. | 898 | 1.19 | 1,943 | .0757 | 2,210 | .0580 |
| 1931 | .. | .. | .. | .. | 851 | .647 | 1,686 | .0697 | 1,832 | .0348 |
| 1932 | .. | .. | .. | .. | 785 | .867 | 1,556 | .0636 | 1,524 | .0323 |
| 1933 | .. | .. | .. | .. | 906 | .671 | 1,555 | .0624 | 1,420 | .0383 |
| 1934 | .. | .. | .. | .. | 908 | .996 | 1,771 | .0601 | 1,535 | .0394 |
| 1935 | .. | .. | .. | .. | 997 | .965 | 1,917 | .0576 | 1,652 | .0429 |
| 1936 | .. | .. | .. | .. | 1,100 | 1.09 | 2,168 | .0550 | 1,796 | .0471 |
| 1937 | .. | .. | .. | .. | 1,279 | 1.18 | 2,408 | .0513 | 2,065 | .0470 |
| 1938 | .. | .. | .. | .. | 1,214 | 1.13 | 2,296 | .0495 | 2,157 | .0405 |
| 1939 | .. | .. | .. | .. | 1,265 | 1.02 | 2,477 | .0485 | 2,169 | .0415 |

## (15) DIMENSION STONE

| Year | (A) DIMENSION GRANITE | | (B) DIMENSION LIMESTONE | | (C) DIMENSION MARBLE | | (D) NONDIMENSION MARBLE | |
|---|---|---|---|---|---|---|---|---|
| | Quantity Mil. s.t. | Price $ per s.t. | Quantity Mil. s.t. | Price $ per s.t. | Quantity Th. s.t. | Price $ per s.t. | Quantity Th. s.t. | Price $ per s.t. |
| 1899 | .. | .. | .. | .. | .. | .. | .. | .. |
| 1900 | .. | .. | .. | .. | .. | .. | .. | .. |
| 1901 | .. | .. | .. | .. | .. | .. | .. | .. |
| 1902 | .. | .. | .. | .. | .. | .. | .. | .. |
| 1903 | .. | .. | .. | .. | .. | .. | .. | .. |
| 1904 | .. | .. | .. | .. | .. | .. | .. | .. |
| 1905 | .. | .. | .. | .. | .. | .. | .. | .. |
| 1906 | 3.01 | 5.45 | 12.9 | .668 | .. | .. | .. | .. |
| 1907 | 2.73 | 5.48 | 12.8 | .699 | .. | .. | .. | .. |
| 1908 | 3.19 | 5.00 | 13.2 | .673 | .. | .. | .. | .. |
| 1909 | 3.61 | 4.58 | 14.6 | .622 | .. | .. | .. | .. |
| 1910 | 3.35 | 4.88 | 12.7 | .754 | .. | .. | .. | .. |
| 1911 | 3.43 | 4.96 | 12.5 | .751 | 405 | 17.9 | 150 | 1.95 |
| 1912 | 3.54 | 4.45 | 11.8 | .780 | 291 | 26.3 | 158 | .895 |
| 1913 | 3.60 | 4.69 | 10.6 | .810 | 314 | 24.7 | 106 | 1.19 |
| 1914 | 3.62 | 4.47 | 9.98 | .796 | 296 | 26.9 | 194 | .889 |
| 1915 | 3.05 | 4.61 | 10.6 | .798 | 263 | 25.7 | 165 | .980 |
| 1916 | { 4.55 / 1.74 | 3.06 / 7.28 | 8.59 / 1.27 | 1.12 } / 3.92 } | 274 | 24.9 | 136 | 1.54 |
| 1917 | 1.25 | 9.66 | .999 | 4.46 | 184 | 33.1 | 126 | 1.83 |
| 1918 | .961 | 11.8 | .420 | 5.75 | 136 | 38.2 | 169 | 1.75 |
| 1919 | 1.12 | 13.9 | .728 | 6.50 | 180 | 43.3 | 154 | 1.68 |
| 1920 | 1.20 | 16.3 | .843 | 10.3 | 200 | 52.6 | 232 | 2.39 |
| 1921 | 1.16 | 13.6 | .812 | 10.1 | 194 | 42.8 | 122 | 2.34 |
| 1922 | 1.12 | 13.4 | 1.24 | 10.4 | 243 | 41.5 | 185 | 2.56 |
| 1923 | 1.45 | 15.6 | 1.43 | 11.7 | 304 | 40.1 | 259 | 2.59 |
| 1924 | 1.54 | 14.4 | 1.50 | 11.0 | 324 | 39.0 | 192 | 3.36 |
| 1925 | 1.66 | 14.0 | 1.54 | 10.8 | 333 | 39.6 | 231 | 2.96 |
| 1926 | 1.59 | 14.6 | 1.66 | 12.6 | 336 | 40.1 | 227 | 3.08 |
| 1927 | 1.79 | 13.9 | 1.52 | 12.7 | 334 | 44.4 | 266 | 2.96 |
| 1928 | 1.64 | 15.1 | 1.77 | 11.9 | 343 | 46.3 | 237 | 2.30 |
| 1929 | 1.71 | 14.8 | 1.70 | 12.6 | 324 | 49.4 | 230 | 2.33 |
| 1930 | 1.33 | 16.6 | 1.94 | 9.96 | 282 | 43.8 | 196 | 2.89 |
| 1931 | 1.03 | 17.7 | 1.12 | 10.1 | 196 | 51.2 | 155 | 2.58 |
| 1932 | .648 | 18.1 | .641 | 11.1 | 179 | 40.7 | 164 | 1.44 |
| 1933 | .477 | 16.7 | .551 | 11.9 | 150 | 41.6 | 74.6 | 2.18 |
| 1934 | .543 | 16.0 | .586 | 6.18 | 81.7 | 39.1 | 95.6 | 1.84 |
| 1935 | .536 | 14.9 | .723 | 4.18 | 56.7 | 56.9 | 75.7 | 2.48 |
| 1936 | .667 | 16.6 | .805 | 6.11 | 97.8 | 56.6 | 68.0 | 3.37 |
| 1937 | .751 | 15.2 | .714 | 7.44 | 95.5 | 53.8 | 112 | 2.86 |
| 1938 | .673 | 14.5 | .704 | 7.01 | 89.0 | 55.9 | 130 | 2.11 |
| 1939 | .734 | 13.4 | 1.06 | 6.30 | 124 | 51.0 | 104 | 3.68 |

## (15) Dimension Stone (continued)

| Year | (E) Dimension Sandstone Quantity Th. s.t. | Price $ per s.t. | (F) Dimension Slate Quantity Th. s.t. | Price $ per s.t. | (G) Nondimension Slate Quantity Th. s.t. | Price $ per s.t. | (H) Miscellaneous Dimension Stone Quantity Th. s.t. | Price $ per s.t. |
|---|---|---|---|---|---|---|---|---|
| 1899 | .. | .. | 392 | 10.1 | .. | .. | .. | .. |
| 1900 | .. | .. | 429 | 9.89 | .. | .. | .. | .. |
| 1901 | .. | .. | 467 | 10.2 | .. | .. | .. | .. |
| 1902 | .. | .. | 514 | 11.1 | .. | .. | .. | .. |
| 1903 | .. | .. | 502 | 12.5 | .. | .. | .. | .. |
| 1904 | .. | .. | 455 | 12.4 | .. | .. | .. | .. |
| 1905 | .. | .. | 456 | 12.0 | .. | .. | .. | .. |
| 1906 | .. | .. | 459 | 12.3 | .. | .. | .. | .. |
| 1907 | .. | .. | 482 | 12.5 | .. | .. | .. | .. |
| 1908 | .. | .. | 498 | 12.7 | .. | .. | .. | .. |
| 1909 | .. | .. | 424 | 12.8 | .. | .. | .. | .. |
| 1910 | .. | .. | 479 | 13.0 | .. | .. | .. | .. |
| 1911 | .. | .. | 436 | 13.1 | .. | .. | .. | .. |
| 1912 | .. | .. | 461 | 13.1 | .. | .. | .. | .. |
| 1913 | .. | .. | 441 | 14.0 | .. | .. | .. | .. |
| 1914 | .. | .. | 406 | 14.1 | .. | .. | .: | .. |
| 1915 | .. | .. | 378 | 13.1 | .. | .. | .. | .. |
| 1916 | 784 | 3.60 | 354 | 14.2 | .. | .. | .. | .. |
| 1917 | 626 | 3.93 | 305 | 17.1 | .. | .. | .. | .. |
| 1918 | 312 | 4.69 | 174 | 23.4 | 280 | 2.87 | 10.0 | 3.90 |
| 1919 | 435 | 5.99 | 207 | 23.6 | 203 | 5.70 | 33.2 | 1.30 |
| 1920 | 393 | 7.79 | 200 | 33.4 | 269 | 7.62 | 14.0 | 2.67 |
| 1921 | 480 | 7.24 | 180 | 33.0 | 232 | 6.03 | 25.1 | 2.00 |
| 1922 | 607 | 6.87 | 228 | 30.7 | 380 | 5.73 | 88.5 | 1.60 |
| 1923 | 801 | 6.05 | 245 | 36.0 | 462 | 7.07 | 33.5 | 4.20 |
| 1924 | 754 | 7.61 | 215 | 40.0 | 513 | 6.20 | 22.9 | 4.33 |
| 1925 | 981 | 6.64 | 227 | 41.3 | 498 | 6.45 | 24.8 | 2.61 |
| 1926 | 544 | 10.7 | 220 | 42.5 | 498 | 6.04 | 16.6 | 2.56 |
| 1927 | 606 | 10.0 | 232 | 37.0 | 460 | 6.04 | 107.4 | 2.83 |
| 1928 | 553 | 10.0 | 232 | 38.7 | 414 | 5.96 | 37.8 | 2.41 |
| 1929 | 656 | 8.06 | 241 | 36.3 | 429 | 5.82 | 200.4 | 1.46 |
| 1930 | 644 | 8.94 | 174 | 35.7 | 290 | 5.85 | 78.0 | 2.95 |
| 1931 | 327 | 9.88 | 138 | 30.2 | 230 | 5.71 | 22.0 | 3.85 |
| 1932 | 172 | 8.85 | 74.5 | 25.6 | 210 | 5.71 | 157.3 | 3.84 |
| 1933 | 90.2 | 11.9 | 73.2 | 20.7 | 186 | 6.33 | 29.9 | 12.3 |
| 1934 | 107 | 9.16 | 66.6 | 24.7 | 166 | 6.42 | 28.4 | 9.97 |
| 1935 | 101 | 9.82 | 104 | 22.6 | 227 | 5.78 | 14.0 | 18.8 |
| 1936 | 162 | 10.2 | 165 | 23.2 | 290 | 5.69 | 39.3 | 13.2 |
| 1937 | 232 | 7.43 | 168 | 24.0 | 277 | 5.70 | 64.1 | 10.7 |
| 1938 | 166 | 8.87 | 144 | 22.0 | 349 | 7.13 | 112.4 | 5.29 |
| 1939 | 196 | 10.0 | 180 | 22.8 | 352 | 7.34 | 83.5 | 8.67 |

(16) Nondimension Stone

| Year | (A) Nondimension Basalt | | (B) Dimension Basalt | | (C) Nondimension Granite | | (D) Nondimension Limestone (incl. Limestone Used for Lime) | |
|------|-----------------|-------------|-----------------|-------------|-----------------|-------------|-----------------|-------------|
| | Quantity Mil. s.t. | Price $ per s.t. | Quantity Mil. s.t. | Price $ per s.t. | Quantity Mil. s.t. | Price $ per s.t. | Quantity Mil. s.t. | Price $ per s.t. |
| 1899 | .. | .. | .. | .. | .. | .. | .. | .. |
| 1900 | .. | .. | .. | .. | .. | •• | .. | .. |
| 1901 | .. | .. | .. | .. | .. | .. | .. | .. |
| 1902 | .. | .. | .. | .. | .. | .. | .. | .. |
| 1903 | .. | .. | .. | .. | .. | .. | .. | .. |
| 1904 | .. | .. | .. | .. | .. | .. | .. | .. |
| 1905 | 4.28 | .650 | .219 | (1.35) | 2.66 | .808 | 42.5 | .478 |
| 1906 | 5.05 | .661 | .292 | (1.35) | 2.94 | .735 | 44.7 | .488 |
| 1907 | 6.07 | .705 | .232 | (1.35) | 4.09 | .761 | 48.9 | .534 |
| 1908 | 6.06 | .661 | .207 | (1.35) | 3.10 | .789 | 40.8 | .532 |
| 1909 | 7.30 | .651 | .285 | (1.35) | 3.91 | .784 | 50.9 | .523 |
| 1910 | 9.20 | .651 | .346 | (1.35) | 5.58 | .754 | 57.0 | .500 |
| 1911 | 9.09 | .667 | .496 | (1.35) | 6.02 | .693 | 55.3 | .506 |
| 1912 | 9.20 | .689 | .902 | (1.35) | 4.61 | .752 | 62.8 | .494 |
| 1913 | 10.5 | .695 | 1.36 | (1.35) | 4.87 | .790 | 67.7 | .499 |
| 1914 | 9.03 | .690 | 1.21 | (1.35) | 5.22 | .762 | 56.5 | .521 |
| 1915 | 9.77 | .655 | 1.55 | (1.35) | 5.24 | .730 | 60.0 | .507 |
| 1916 | { 9.01 | .726 | 1.23 | .920 | 4.72 | .750 | 66.3 | .540 |
| | { 9.88 | .745 | .352 | .876 | 7.53 | .635 | 73.6 | .551 |
| 1917 | 8.68 | .824 | .425 | .989 | 4.31 | .802 | 69.7 | .669 |
| 1918 | 6.71 | 1.12 | .150 | 1.98 | 2.87 | 1.09 | 59.8 | .880 |
| 1919 | 7.30 | 1.21 | .111 | 1.10 | 3.10 | 1.22 | 55.7 | .988 |
| 1920 | 9.15 | 1.33 | .0656 | 1.23 | 3.56 | 1.52 | 65.6 | 1.15 |
| 1921 | 8.46 | 1.35 | .0690 | .988 | 3.59 | 1.35 | 49.9 | 1.11 |
| 1922 | 9.92 | 1.25 | .116 | 1.71 | 4.79 | 1.27 | 65.0 | .962 |
| 1923 | 10.6 | 1.25 | .0866 | 2.94 | 5.85 | 1.21 | 83.4 | .968 |
| 1924 | 11.6 | 1.26 | .0579 | 1.45 | 5.35 | 1.24 | 82.5 | .986 |
| 1925 | 11.7 | 1.24 | .0947 | 1.68 | 6.41 | 1.13 | 93.2 | .967 |
| 1926 | 12.8 | 1.23 | .140 | 1.45 | 7.74 | 1.14 | 99.3 | .978 |
| 1927 | 13.1 | 1.31 | .0909 | 1.74 | 8.92 | 1.16 | 107.0 | .948 |
| 1928 | 15.2 | 1.29 | .0968 | 1.05 | 7.92 | 1.17 | 104.0 | .937 |
| 1929 | 14.8 | 1.27 | .0516 | 1.36 | 9.12 | .971 | 107.5 | .934 |
| 1930 | 14.5 | 1.17 | .0394 | 1.90 | 8.72 | .962 | 93.6 | .930 |
| 1931 | 12.5 | 1.10 | .0211 | 1.02 | 7.04 | 1.10 | 71.1 | .924 |
| 1932 | 9.32 | .951 | .0133 | 1.42 | 4.47 | .947 | 50.3 | .884 |
| 1933 | 7.38 | .892 | .00989 | 1.17 | 3.95 | .856 | 49.8 | .837 |
| 1934 | 11.6 | .968 | .0113 | 1.15 | 6.25 | .993 | 61.7 | .881 |
| 1935 | 9.64 | .964 | .0306 | .648 | 5.48 | 1.01 | 62.7 | .839 |
| 1936 | 14.0 | .955 | .0374 | 1.13 | 14.8 | .798 | 94.4 | .882 |
| 1937 | 13.6 | .921 | .0251 | 1.11 | 8.51 | 1.03 | 102.1 | .912 |
| 1938 | 13.9 | .883 | .0218 | .986 | 9.76 | 1.14 | 87.7 | .955 |
| 1939 | 16.0 | .882 | .101 | .523 | 11.3 | 1.12 | 108.3 | .883 |

### (16) Nondimension Stone (continued)

| Year | (E) Limestone Used for Cement (incl. Cement Rock) | | (F) Nondimension Sandstone | | (G) Miscellaneous Non-dimension Stone | | (17) Sand and Gravel (A) Sand | | (B) Gravel | |
|------|------|------|------|------|------|------|------|------|------|------|
| | Quantity Mil. s.t. | Price $ per s.t. | Quantity Mil. s.t. | Price $ per s.t. | Quantity Mil. s.t. | Price $ per s.t. | Quantity Mil. s.t. | Price $ per s.t. | Quantity Mil. s.t. | Price $ per s.t. |
| 1899 | .. | .. | .. | .. | .. | .. | .. | .. | .. | .. |
| 1900 | .. | .. | .. | .. | .. | .. | .. | .. | .. | .. |
| 1901 | .. | .. | .. | .. | .. | .. | .. | .. | .. | .. |
| 1902 | .. | .. | .. | .. | .. | .. | .. | .. | .. | .. |
| 1903 | .. | .. | .. | .. | .. | .. | .. | .. | .. | .. |
| 1904 | .. | .. | .. | .. | .. | .. | .. | .. | .. | .. |
| 1905 | .. | .. | 1.59 | .633 | .. | .. | 18.8 | .502 | 4.42 | .407 |
| 1906 | .. | .. | 1.26 | .708 | .. | .. | 24.5 | .411 | 8.43 | .312 |
| 1907 | .. | .. | 1.34 | .739 | .. | .. | 28.6 | .385 | 13.2 | .262 |
| 1908 | .. | .. | 1.20 | .755 | .. | .. | 24.5 | .391 | 12.7 | .290 |
| 1909 | 16.8 | (.225) | 1.72 | .706 | .. | .. | 36.3 | .348 | 23.3 | .246 |
| 1910 | 19.6 | (.248) | 1.87 | .752 | .. | .. | 36.8 | .374 | 32.6 | .223 |
| 1911 | 20.1 | (.235) | 2.30 | .711 | .. | .. | 40.3 | .359 | 26.6 | .253 |
| 1912 | 21.1 | (.227) | 1.57 | .743 | .. | .. | 38.6 | .398 | 29.8 | .260 |
| 1913 | 23.5 | (.281) | 1.77 | .820 | .. | .. | 41.0 | .375 | 38.5 | .230 |
| 1914 | 22.5 | (.259) | 2.45 | .774 | .. | .. | 40.1 | .361 | 39.2 | .240 |
| 1915 | 24.2 | (.240) | 2.42 | .763 | .. | .. | 38.6 | .350 | 38.0 | .253 |
| 1916 | 23.5 | (.308) | { 2.16 / 3.90 | .771 / .715 } | .. | .. | 43.0 | .409 | 46.1 | .265 |
| 1917 | 24.7 | (.378) | 3.25 | .938 | .. | .. | 40.8 | .533 | 35.6 | .380 |
| 1918 | 17.7 | (.448) | 2.55 | 1.20 | .835 | 1.12 | 33.1 | .736 | 28.7 | .472 |
| 1919 | 19.9 | (.478) | 2.19 | 1.22 | 1.16 | 1.62 | 36.0 | .734 | 34.6 | .565 |
| 1920 | 24.9 | (.565) | 2.95 | 1.44 | 1.47 | 1.53 | 43.8 | .895 | 38.3 | .692 |
| 1921 | 24.5 | (.530) | 2.16 | 1.36 | 1.66 | 1.27 | 38.3 | .759 | 41.6 | .660 |
| 1922 | 30.2 | (.493) | 2.78 | 1.21 | 1.43 | 1.22 | 49.7 | .714 | 45.2 | .645 |
| 1923 | 34.9 | (.531) | 3.55 | 1.22 | 3.70 | 1.20 | { 67.4 / 67.1 | .720 / .720 | 72.6 / 70.7 | .585 / .583 |
| 1924 | 38.0 | (.506) | 3.14 | 1.40 | 4.30 | 1.16 | 75.2 | .646 | 77.6 | .595 |
| 1925 | 41.0 | (.496) | 3.50 | 1.26 | 5.22 | 1.16 | 86.0 | .637 | 79.0 | .623 |
| 1926 | 42.0 | (.479) | 4.43 | 1.20 | 4.74 | 1.20 | 91.4 | .604 | 83.8 | .621 |
| 1927 | 44.2 | (.453) | 4.44 | 1.09 | 7.01 | .951 | 92.8 | .580 | 96.5 | .589 |
| 1928 | 45.0 | (.439) | 4.16 | 1.19 | 6.79 | .870 | 96.8 | .576 | 103 | .563 |
| 1929 | 43.6 | (.416) | 5.13 | 1.12 | 8.18 | .948 | 97.0 | .618 | 109 | .596 |
| 1930 | 40.8 | (.403) | 3.95 | 1.15 | 8.53 | .944 | 81.8 | .598 | 95.1 | .615 |
| 1931 | 31.7 | (.311) | 4.25 | 1.02 | 5.61 | .951 | 62.4 | .570 | 66.6 | .615 |
| 1932 | 19.4 | (.285) | 2.80 | .913 | 5.81 | .684 | 40.4 | .529 | 44.8 | .582 |
| 1933 | 16.1 | (.373) | 2.71 | 1.13 | 9.43 | .807 | 31.0 | .607 | 35.1 | .586 |
| 1934 | 19.7 | (.432) | 3.50 | 1.07 | 12.3 | .866 | 34.6 | .682 | 40.7 | .609 |
| 1935 | 19.6 | (.422) | 2.91 | 1.23 | 6.82 | .892 | 37.8 | .664 | 46.8 | .558 |
| 1936 | 28.6 | (.423) | 6.09 | 1.32 | 7.76 | .990 | 54.6 | .635 | 65.3 | .575 |
| 1937 | 29.5 | (.416) | 4.84 | 1.20 | 10.4 | .863 | 57.1 | .677 | 68.2 | .593 |
| 1938 | 26.2 | (.406) | 6.15 | 1.07 | 12.2 | .810 | 48.3 | .655 | 57.4 | .581 |
| 1939 | 30.5 | (.413) | 8.66 | 1.13 | 9.30 | .841 | 57.6 | .635 | 60.8 | .569 |

(18) CLAY (INCL. FULLER'S EARTH)

| Year | (A) KAOLIN, BALL CLAY, PAPER CLAY, MISCELLANEOUS AND FIRE CLAY | | (B) KAOLIN, BALL CLAY AND PAPER CLAY | | (C) MISCELLANEOUS CLAY, INCL. FIRE CLAY | | (D) FULLER'S EARTH | | (19) GYPSUM | |
|---|---|---|---|---|---|---|---|---|---|---|
| | Quantity Mil. s.t. | Price $ per s.t. | Quantity Th. s.t. | Price $ per s.t. | Quantity Mil. s.t. | Price $ per s.t. | Quantity Th. s.t. | Price $ per s.t. | Quantity Mil. s.t. | Price $ per s.t. |
| 1899 | .843 | 1.95 | .. | .. | .. | .. | 12.4 | 6.43 | .486 | 1.55 |
| 1900 | 1.22 | 1.51 | .. | .. | .. | .. | 9.70 | 6.96 | .594 | 1.56 |
| 1901 | 1.37 | 1.88 | .. | .. | .. | .. | 14.1 | 6.86 | .634 | 1.42 |
| 1902 | { 1.72 / 1.46 | 1.49 } / 1.42 | .. | .. | .. | .. | 11.5 | 8.54 | .816 | 1.41 |
| 1903 | 1.64 | 1.58 | .. | .. | .. | .. | 20.7 | 9.20 | 1.04 | 1.63 |
| 1904 | .. | .. | 158 | 4.58 | 1.35 | 1.18 | 29.5 | 5.72 | .941 | 1.61 |
| 1905 | .. | .. | 182 | 4.39 | 1.62 | 1.21 | 25.2 | 8.52 | 1.04 | 1.68 |
| 1906 | .. | .. | 182 | 5.00 | 1.85 | 1.26 | 32.0 | 8.28 | 1.54 | 2.47 |
| 1907 | .. | .. | 166 | 4.99 | 2.02 | 1.30 | 32.9 | 8.88 | 1.75 | 1.93 |
| 1908 | .. | .. | 134 | 4.93 | 1.59 | 1.22 | 29.7 | 9.37 | 1.72 | 1.73 |
| 1909 | .. | .. | 162 | 5.20 | 2.00 | 1.31 | 33.5 | 9.01 | 2.25 | 1.62 |
| 1910 | .. | .. | 191 | 4.89 | 2.20 | 1.22 | 32.8 | 8.95 | 2.38 | 1.59 |
| 1911 | .. | .. | 192 | 4.67 | 1.99 | 1.30 | 40.7 | 9.41 | 2.32 | 1.52 |
| 1912 | .. | .. | 211 | 4.61 | 2.32 | 1.28 | 32.7 | 9.34 | 2.50 | 1.41 |
| 1913 | .. | .. | 222 | 4.68 | 2.43 | 1.29 | 38.6 | 9.58 | 2.60 | 1.51 |
| 1914 | .. | .. | 218 | 5.03 | 1.99 | 1.33 | 41.0 | 9.85 | 2.48 | 1.46 |
| 1915 | .. | .. | 216 | 5.00 | 2.15 | 1.35 | 47.9 | 10.2 | 2.45 | 1.37 |
| 1916 | .. | .. | 291 | 5.04 | 2.64 | 1.62 | 67.8 | 10.4 | 2.76 | 1.44 |
| 1917 | .. | .. | 314 | 5.84 | 2.80 | 2.22 | 72.6 | 10.6 | 2.70 | 1.80 |
| 1918 | .. | .. | 270 | 7.60 | 2.71 | 2.32 | 84.5 | 13.6 | 2.06 | 2.63 |
| 1919 | .. | .. | 218 | 9.16 | 2.06 | 2.48 | 106 | 18.8 | 2.42 | 2.98 |
| 1920 | .. | .. | 338 | 10.2 | 2.70 | 2.90 | 128 | 19.5 | 3.13 | 3.83 |
| 1921 | .. | .. | 217 | 8.92 | 1.53 | 2.69 | 106 | 18.7 | 2.89 | 3.52 |
| 1922 | .. | .. | 352 | 7.91 | 2.30 | 2.42 | 139 | 16.5 | 3.78 | 3.17 |
| 1923 | .. | .. | 434 | 8.18 | 3.00 | 2.55 | 149 | 15.1 | 4.75 | 3.04 |
| 1924 | .. | .. | 410 | 8.56 | 3.28 | 2.44 | 178 | 14.8 | 5.04 | 2.72 |
| 1925 | .. | .. | 477 | 8.22 | 3.55 | 2.48 | 207 | 14.2 | 5.68 | 2.78 |
| 1926 | .. | .. | 544 | 8.52 | 3.42 | 2.77 | 234 | 14.3 | 5.64 | 2.61 |
| 1927 | .. | .. | 574 | 8.23 | 3.28 | 2.74 | 264 | 14.2 | 5.35 | 2.47 |
| 1928 | .. | .. | 617 | 8.22 | 3.41 | 2.68 | 287 | 13.6 | 5.10 | 1.90 |
| 1929 | .. | .. | 636 | 8.28 | 3.71 | 2.58 | 316 | 13.6 | 5.02 | 1.97 |
| 1930 | .. | .. | 627 | 7.39 | 3.34 | 2.36 | 336 | 12.9 | 3.47 | 1.91 |
| 1931 | .. | .. | 526 | 6.82 | 1.99 | 2.39 | 288 | 10.6 | 2.56 | 2.02 |
| 1932 | .. | .. | 393 | 5.92 | .999 | 2.88 | 228 | 9.76 | 1.42 | 2.09 |
| 1933 | .. | .. | 476 | 5.82 | 1.36 | 2.99 | 224 | 9.28 | 1.34 | 1.92 |
| 1934 | .. | .. | 489 | 6.38 | 1.70 | 2.99 | 220 | 9.47 | 1.54 | 1.90 |
| 1935 | .. | .. | 620 | 7.09 | 2.30 | 2.79 | 228 | 9.79 | 1.90 | 2.00 |
| 1936 | .. | .. | 740 | 7.07 | 3.04 | 2.69 | 231 | 9.81 | 2.71 | 1.94 |
| 1937 | .. | .. | 854 | 7.31 | 3.38 | 2.80 | 226 | 10.2 | 3.06 | 2.23 |
| 1938 | .. | .. | 690 | 7.94 | 2.04 | 3.08 | 171 | 10.0 | 2.68 | 2.22 |
| 1939 | .. | .. | 909 | 7.85 | 2.85 | 2.88 | 167 | 10.1 | 3.23 | 2.22 |

| Year | (20) Sulfur Quantity Th. l.t. | Price $ per l.t. | (21) Pyrites Quantity Th. l.t. | Price $ per l.t. | (22) Phosphate Rock Quantity Mil. l.t. | Price $ per l.t. | (23) Potash Quantity Th. s.t. | Price $ per s.t. | (24) Fluorspar Quantity Th. s.t. | Price $ per s.t. |
|---|---|---|---|---|---|---|---|---|---|---|
| 1899 | 4.31 | 24.9 | 175 | 3.11 | 1.52 | 3.35 | .. | .. | 15.9 | 6.08 |
| 1900 | 3.15 | 28.0 | 205 | 3.67 | 1.70 | 3.59 | .. | .. | 18.4 | 5.12 |
| 1901 | 6.87 | 32.5 | 235 | 4.41 | 1.44 | 3.58 | .. | .. | 19.6 | 5.81 |
| 1902 | 5.00 | 20.4 | 228 | 4.26 | 1.50 | 3.15 | .. | .. | 48.0 | 5.66 |
| 1903 | 25.0 | 20.1 | 199 | 3.95 | 1.62 | 3.36 | .. | .. | 42.5 | 5.02 |
| 1904 | 85.0 | 20.9 | 207 | 3.93 | 1.99 | 3.51 | .. | .. | 36.5 | 6.44 |
| 1905 | 220 | 20.4 | 253 | 3.71 | 2.14 | 3.47 | .. | .. | 57.4 | 6.32 |
| 1906 | 295 | 17.3 | 261 | 3.56 | 2.00 | 4.12 | .. | .. | 40.8 | 5.98 |
| 1907 | 189 | 17.5 | 247 | 3.21 | 2.37 | 4.70 | .. | .. | 49.5 | 5.81 |
| 1908 | 364 | 18.1 | 223 | 3.85 | 2.66 | 4.78 | .. | .. | 38.8 | 5.83 |
| 1909 | 274 | 18.5 | 247 | 4.16 | 2.44 | 4.62 | .. | .. | 50.7 | 5.75 |
| 1910 | 247 | 18.0 | 242 | 4.05 | 2.63 | 4.11 | .. | .. | 69.4 | 6.20 |
| 1911 | 205 | 18.0 | 301 | 3.86 | 3.10 | 3.90 | .. | .. | 87.0 | 7.02 |
| 1912 | 788 | 17.3 | 351 | 3.80 | 3.19 | 3.93 | .. | .. | 117 | 6.60 |
| 1913 | 491 | 17.6 | 341 | 3.77 | 3.15 | 3.79 | .. | .. | 116 | 6.37 |
| 1914 | 418 | 18.2 | 337 | 3.81 | 2.65 | 3.51 | .. | .. | 95.1 | 5.99 |
| 1915 | 521 | 16.9 | 394 | 4.25 | 1.94 | 2.95 | .. | .. | 137 | 5.58 |
| 1916 | 650 | 16.0 | 439 | 4.64 | 2.17 | 2.97 | 3.99 | 485 | 156 | 5.92 |
| 1917 | 1,134 | 21.4 | 483 | 5.37 | 2.85 | 3.01 | 20.7 | 400 | 219 | 10.5 |
| 1918 | 1,354 | 22.0 | 464 | 5.69 | 2.28 | 3.30 | 39.7 | 382 | 264 | 20.7 |
| 1919 | 1,191 | 15.1 | 421 | 6.08 | 1.85 | 5.10 | { 21.6 / 25.4 | 232 } / 236 } | 138 | 25.5 |
| 1920 | 1,255 | 20.0 | 311 | 5.14 | 3.98 | 6.11 | 41.0 | 173 | 187 | 25.3 |
| 1921 | 1,879 | 17.8 | 157 | 4.53 | 2.43 | 5.94 | 7.20 | 93.3 | 35.0 | 20.7 |
| 1922 | 1,831 | 16.4 | 169 | 3.97 | 2.34 | 4.34 | 9.32 | 39.2 | 142 | 17.9 |
| 1923 | 2,036 | 16.1 | 182 | 3.64 | 2.94 | 3.85 | 18.0 | 38.6 | 121 | 20.7 |
| 1924 | 1,221 | 16.3 | 160 | 4.03 | 2.85 | 3.57 | { 19.4 / 22.9 | 38.1 } / 38.5 } | 125 | 19.6 |
| 1925 | 1,409 | 15.6 | 170 | 3.82 | 3.25 | 3.32 | 25.4 | 46.7 | 114 | 18.1 |
| 1926 | 1,890 | 18.0 | 167 | 3.70 | 3.59 | 3.39 | 23.4 | 43.2 | 129 | 18.2 |
| 1927 | 2,112 | 18.5 | 216 | 3.73 | 3.13 | 3.55 | 43.5 | 49.5 | 113 | 18.1 |
| 1928 | 1,982 | 18.0 | 182 | 3.33 | 3.52 | 3.55 | 59.9 | 50.2 | 140 | 18.9 |
| 1929 | 2,362 | 18.0 | { 164 / 333 | 3.75 } / 3.75 } | 3.79 | 3.50 | 61.6 | 51.9 | 146 | 19.1 |
| 1930 | 2,559 | 18.0 | 348 | 2.96 | 4.04 | 3.56 | 61.3 | 52.8 | 95.8 | 18.2 |
| 1931 | 2,129 | 18.0 | 331 | 2.95 | 2.67 | 3.66 | 63.9 | 48.4 | 53.5 | 17.4 |
| 1932 | 890 | 18.0 | 190 | 2.63 | 1.70 | 3.36 | 62.0 | 37.8 | 25.3 | 15.5 |
| 1933 | 1,406 | 18.0 | 284 | 2.71 | 2.36 | 3.16 | 143 | 38.1 | 72.9 | 14.2 |
| 1934 | 1,422 | 17.9 | 433 | 2.81 | 2.90 | 3.54 | 144 | 24.7 | 85.8 | 16.2 |
| 1935 | 1,633 | 17.9 | 514 | 3.08 | 3.16 | 3.60 | 193 | 22.2 | 124 | 15.0 |
| 1936 | 2,016 | 18.0 | 547 | 3.04 | 3.46 | 3.40 | 247 | 31.3 | 177 | 17.6 |
| 1937 | 2,742 | 18.0 | 584 | 3.04 | 4.26 | 3.28 | 284 | 33.8 | 181 | 20.2 |
| 1938 | 2,393 | 16.8 | 556 | 3.03 | 3.86 | 3.46 | 317 | 34.0 | 80.4 | 19.9 |
| 1939 | 2,091 | 15.9 | 516 | 3.00 | 3.99 | 3.27 | 312 | 32.8 | 183 | 20.3 |

| Year | (25) BORATES | | (26) BROMINE | | (27) SODIUM CAR-BONATES AND SUL-FATES (NATURAL) | | (28) MAGNESIUM CHLORIDE AND SULFATE | | (29) CALCIUM CHLORIDE | |
|---|---|---|---|---|---|---|---|---|---|---|
| | Quantity Th. s.t. | Price $ per s.t. | Quantity Mil. lb. | Price $ per lb. | Quantity Th. s.t. | Price $ per s.t. | Quantity Th. s.t. | Price $ per s.t. | Quantity Th. s.t. | Price $ per s.t. |
| 1899 | 24.1 | 21.0 | .433 | .25 | .. | .. | .. | .. | .. | .. |
| 1900 | 25.4 | 21.0 | .521 | .27 | .. | .. | .. | .. | .. | .. |
| 1901 | 23.2 | 17.6 | .552 | .28 | .. | .. | .. | .. | .. | .. |
| 1902 | 20.0 | 19.3 | .514 | .25 | .. | .. | .. | .. | .. | .. |
| 1903 | 34.4 | 19.2 | .598 | .28 | .. | .. | .. | .. | .. | .. |
| 1904 | 45.6 | 15.3 | .897 | .30 | .. | .. | .. | .. | .. | .. |
| 1905 | 46.3 | 22.0 | 1.19 | .15 | .. | .. | .. | .. | .. | .. |
| 1906 | 58.2 | 20.3 | .938 | .176 | .. | .. | .. | .. | .. | .. |
| 1907 | 52.8 | 21.2 | 1.00 | .195 | .. | .. | .. | .. | .. | .. |
| 1908 | 25.0 | 39.0 | .760 | .0971 | .. | .. | .. | .. | .. | .. |
| 1909 | 41.4 | 37.0 | .570 | .101 | .. | .. | .. | .. | 12.9 | 4.92 |
| 1910 | 42.4 | 28.4 | .245 | .129 | .. | .. | .. | .. | 11.0 | 6.81 |
| 1911 | 53.3 | 29.4 | .652 | .170 | .. | .. | .. | .. | 14.6 | 6.24 |
| 1912 | 42.3 | 26.7 | .647 | .225 | .. | .. | .. | .. | 18.6 | 6.32 |
| 1913 | 58.1 | 25.7 | .572 | .202 | .. | .. | .. | .. | 19.6 | 6.63 |
| 1914 | 62.4 | 23.5 | .577 | .352 | .. | .. | .. | .. | 19.4 | 6.28 |
| 1915 | 67.0 | 25.0 | .856 | 1.00 | .. | .. | .. | .. | 20.5 | 6.37 |
| 1916 | 104 | 23.3 | .729 | 1.31 | .. | .. | .. | .. | 27.7 | 8.12 |
| 1917 | 109 | 33.2 | .896 | .550 | .. | .. | .. | .. | 30.5 | 14.8 |
| 1918 | 88.8 | 25.5 | 1.73 | .562 | .. | .. | .. | .. | 26.6 | 18.9 |
| 1919 | 66.1 | 20.9 | 1.86 | .666 | 27.2 | 22.4 | .. | .. | 26.1 | 12.3 |
| 1920 | 120 | 18.1 | 1.16 | .642 | 40.2 | 29.4 | .. | .. | 27.8 | 19.4 |
| 1921 | 50.0 | 32.0 | .712 | .243 | 22.3 | 27.4 | .. | .. | 23.7 | 21.6 |
| 1922 | 85.2 | 31.7 | 1.01 | .150 | 38.6 | 18.8 | .. | .. | 33.1 | 17.3 |
| 1923 | 137 | 29.2 | .842 | .174 | 45.5 | 18.7 | .. | .. | 45.0 | 14.8 |
| 1924 | 116 | 27.4 | 2.03 | .292 | 61.1 | 16.5 | .. | .. | 58.8 | 19.8 |
| 1925 | 114 | 27.1 | 1.57 | .312 | 55.8 | 18.0 | 42.6 | 29.4 | 67.9 | 20.4 |
| 1926 | 116 | 27.0 | 1.25 | .343 | 76.4 | 17.3 | 38.3 | 27.2 | 82.3 | 20.8 |
| 1927 | 109 | 31.8 | 1.76 | .322 | 90.3 | 15.7 | 34.9 | 28.7 | 95.7 | 20.3 |
| 1928 | 131 | 30.5 | 2.16 | .300 | 86.4 | 18.8 | 35.5 | 28.8 | 102 | 19.5 |
| 1929 | 170 | 26.6 | 6.41 | .274 | 110 | 17.7 | 45.2 | 23.9 | 114 | 18.4 |
| 1930 | 177 | 30.2 | 8.46 | .249 | 123 | 14.6 | 36.6 | 29.2 | 116 | 19.0 |
| 1931 | 179 | 27.6 | 8.94 | .208 | 111 | 12.8 | 33.1 | 29.7 | 86.2 | 19.6 |
| 1932 | 182 | 16.6 | 5.73 | .206 | 87.6 | 12.5 | 29.7 | 30.1 | 66.3 | 17.6 |
| 1933 | 188 | 18.3 | 10.1 | .201 | 117 | 9.94 | 38.8 | 28.3 | 57.8 | 15.5 |
| 1934 | 242 | 19.9 | 15.3 | .210 | 105 | 13.4 | 42.5 | 29.8 | 76.7 | 15.0 |
| 1935 | 273 | 19.7 | 16.4 | .212 | 132 | 11.0 | 54.8 | 23.5 | 83.5 | 12.4 |
| 1936 | 314 | 19.6 | 20.6 | .196 | 154 | 9.34 | 63.8 | 25.5 | 126 | 15.2 |
| 1937 | 359 | 20.2 | 26.2 | .198 | 185 | 9.69 | 64.8 | 24.4 | { 102 / 97.1 | 12.8 / 13.3 |
| 1938 | 216 | 22.0 | 33.3 | .198 | 180 | 10.2 | 70.7 | 22.5 | 96.5 | 12.6 |
| 1939 | 245 | 23.2 | 37.9 | .201 | 262 | 9.75 | 85.8 | 22.2 | 108 | 12.1 |

## (30) SILICA AND SILICATES (MAINLY FOR USE AS ABRASIVES)

| Year | (A) GARNET Quantity Th. s.t. | Price $ per s.t. | (B) PUMICE AND PUMICITE Quantity Th. s.t. | Price $ per s.t. | (C) GROUND SAND AND SANDSTONE, AND QUARTZ Quantity Th. s.t. | Price $ per s.t. | (D) TRIPOLI Quantity Th. s.t. | Price $ per s.t. | (31) ABRASIVE SANDSTONE Quantity Th. s.t. | Price $ per s.t. |
|---|---|---|---|---|---|---|---|---|---|---|
| 1899 | 2.76 | 35.6 | .. | .. | 43.5 | 5.05 | .. | .. | .. | .. |
| 1900 | 3.18 | 38.8 | .. | .. | 47.0 | 2.71 | .. | .. | .. | .. |
| 1901 | 4.44 | 35.6 | .. | .. | 48.5 | 3.94 | .. | .. | .. | .. |
| 1902 | 3.93 | 33.8 | .700 | 3.93 | 51.5 | 4.44 | .. | .. | .. | .. |
| 1903 | 3.95 | 33.5 | .885 | 3.01 | 64.2 | 3.64 | .. | .. | .. | .. |
| 1904 | 3.85 | 30.5 | 1.53 | 3.54 | 84.2 | 2.08 | .. | .. | .. | .. |
| 1905 | 5.05 | 29.3 | 1.83 | 3.02 | 70.2 | 2.74 | .. | .. | .. | .. |
| 1906 | 4.65 | 33.8 | 12.2 | 1.37 | 90.8 | 4.02 | .. | .. | .. | .. |
| 1907 | 7.06 | 30.0 | 8.11 | 4.17 | 33.2 | 6.74 | .. | .. | .. | .. |
| 1908 | 2.00 | 32.4 | 10.6 | 3.72 | 47.3 | 4.02 | .. | .. | .. | .. |
| 1909 | 2.97 | 34.4 | 15.1 | 2.21 | 135 | 1.84 | .. | .. | .. | .. |
| 1910 | 3.81 | 29.8 | 23.3 | 4.08 | 63.6 | 3.05 | .. | .. | .. | .. |
| 1911 | 4.08 | 29.9 | 21.7 | 4.08 | 87.9 | 1.76 | .. | .. | .. | .. |
| 1912 | 4.95 | 33.0 | 27.1 | 3.19 | 97.9 | 1.96 | .. | .. | .. | .. |
| 1913 | 5.31 | 34.6 | 24.6 | 2.26 | { 97.9 / 205 } | { 2.06 / 3.26 } | 20.8 | 10.4 | .. | .. |
| 1914 | 4.23 | 34.4 | 27.6 | 2.14 | 153 | 2.35 | 17.2 | 8.27 | .. | .. |
| 1915 | 4.30 | 32.5 | 27.7 | 2.28 | 208 | 3.17 | 30.7 | 4.20 | .. | .. |
| 1916 | 6.17 | 33.8 | 33.3 | 2.47 | 199 | 3.68 | 43.3 | 4.98 | .. | .. |
| 1917 | 5.00 | 39.7 | 35.3 | 2.40 | 675 | 2.24 | { 26.1 / 26.1 } | { 3.55 / 13.0 } | 61.4 | 21.4 |
| 1918 | 4.70 | 52.8 | 30.6 | 2.98 | 171 | 5.15 | 20.0 | 10.0 | 66.3 | 29.6 |
| 1919 | 4.94 | 62.7 | 36.1 | 3.24 | 111 | 5.99 | 24.3 | 7.47 | 48.3 | 32.5 |
| 1920 | 5.48 | 79.3 | 41.8 | 2.74 | 227 | 6.64 | 40.2 | 14.2 | 54.6 | 35.5 |
| 1921 | 3.05 | 85.5 | 37.1 | 4.27 | 117 | 7.58 | 12.3 | 17.3 | 27.2 | 51.5 |
| 1922 | 7.05 | 80.4 | 45.3 | 3.88 | 174 | 6.68 | 30.2 | 10.5 | 27.5 | 44.2 |
| 1923 | 9.01 | 76.4 | 56.6 | 3.79 | 117 | 7.18 | 27.1 | 14.1 | 47.8 | 40.2 |
| 1924 | 8.29 | 81.3 | 43.7 | 4.36 | 228 | 7.32 | 28.5 | 13.7 | 39.2 | 49.1 |
| 1925 | 8.43 | 84.6 | 40.4 | 4.43 | 213 | 7.16 | 29.4 | 14.8 | 38.3 | 51.6 |
| 1926 | 6.40 | 81.9 | 53.9 | 3.87 | 224 | 7.47 | 31.4 | 16.7 | 40.0 | 52.4 |
| 1927 | 6.94 | 82.7 | 53.3 | 4.16 | 192 | 7.10 | 26.1 | 17.1 | 33.0 | 54.2 |
| 1928 | 6.62 | 69.4 | 57.4 | 4.85 | 190 | 7.30 | 34.0 | 16.3 | 34.2 | 50.8 |
| 1929 | 5.96 | 73.0 | 67.0 | 5.27 | 209 | 7.06 | 38.0 | 14.4 | 28.6 | 50.9 |
| 1930 | 5.00 | 62.8 | 56.8 | 5.91 | 169 | 6.69 | 32.4 | 15.6 | 19.4 | 46.9 |
| 1931 | 2.95 | 65.5 | 68.8 | 4.92 | 123 | 6.65 | 26.7 | 11.6 | 9.09 | 46.6 |
| 1932 | 1.95 | 75.6 | 53.2 | 4.42 | 158 | 5.93 | 14.8 | 15.8 | 8.00 | 38.9 |
| 1933 | 2.79 | 80.4 | 61.2 | 3.95 | 213 | 5.52 | 20.9 | 16.8 | 14.8 | 36.6 |
| 1934 | 2.59 | 82.9 | 56.2 | 3.69 | 250 | 5.72 | 20.5 | 16.0 | 13.0 | 42.8 |
| 1935 | 3.06 | 83.8 | 60.0 | 4.12 | 280 | 5.99 | 27.4 | 14.0 | 15.0 | 40.7 |
| 1936 | 3.82 | 82.7 | 72.9 | 4.50 | 367 | 6.04 | 28.5 | 13.8 | 13.9 | 44.5 |
| 1937 | 4.86 | 78.7 | 71.0 | 4.25 | 341 | 6.05 | 34.9 | 12.9 | 15.4 | 44.7 |
| 1938 | 2.67 | 71.8 | 65.7 | 4.76 | 256 | 5.92 | 22.2 | 14.8 | 6.72 | 55.1 |
| 1939 | 4.06 | 68.7 | 89.2 | 4.76 | 345 | 6.03 | 33.5 | 13.9 | 11.1 | 49.0 |

| Year | (32) ASPHALT AND RELATED BITUMENS | | (33) TALC | | (34) BARITE | | (35) MAGNESITE | | (36) FELD-SPAR | |
|---|---|---|---|---|---|---|---|---|---|---|
| | Quantity Th. s.t. | Price $ per s.t. | Quantity Th. s.t. | Price $ per s.t. | Quantity Th. s.t. | Price $ per s.t. | Quantity Th. s.t. | Price $ per s.t. | Quantity Th. l.t. | Price $ per l.t. |
| 1899 | 75.1 | 7.37 | 79.4 | 9.68 | 41.9 | 3.33 | 1.28 | 14.4 | 21.6 | 9.79 |
| 1900 | 54.4 | 7.65 | 91.4 | 9.66 | 67.7 | 2.78 | 2.25 | 8.6 | 22.2 | 8.17 |
| 1901 | 63.1 | 8.80 | 97.8 | 9.29 | 49.1 | 3.22 | 3.50 | 3.0 | 31.0 | 7.11 |
| 1902 | 84.6 | 5.46 | 98.0 | 11.6 | 61.7 | 3.29 | 2.83 | 3.0 | 40.4 | 6.19 |
| 1903 | 55.1 | 8.78 | 86.9 | 9.67 | 50.4 | 3.02 | 3.74 | 2.8 | 37.4 | 6.86 |
| 1904 | 64.2 | 6.56 | 91.2 | 10.3 | 65.7 | 2.66 | 2.85 | 3.3 | 40.3 | 6.60 |
| 1905 | 62.9 | 4.85 | 96.6 | 11.2 | 48.2 | 3.08 | 3.93 | 3.9 | 31.6 | 7.15 |
| 1906 | 73.1 | 9.24 | 121 | 11.9 | 50.2 | 3.19 | 7.80 | 3.0 | 64.9 | 6.19 |
| 1907 | 85.9 | 10.8 | 140 | 11.0 | 89.6 | 3.26 | 7.56 | 3.0 | 82.0 | 6.82 |
| 1908 | 78.6 | 6.59 | 117 | 11.9 | 38.5 | 3.13 | 6.59 | 3.0 | 62.9 | 6.81 |
| 1909 | 99.1 | 5.78 | 130 | 9.38 | 61.9 | 3.39 | 9.46 | 4.0 | 68.3 | 6.21 |
| 1910 | 98.9 | 8.64 | 151 | 10.6 | 43.0 | 2.83 | 12.4 | 6.0 | 72.4 | 6.94 |
| 1911 | 87.1 | 9.39 | 144 | 11.5 | 38.4 | 3.19 | 9.38 | 8.0 | 82.8 | 7.00 |
| 1912 | 95.2 | 9.09 | 159 | 10.7 | 37.5 | 4.09 | 10.5 | 8.0 | 77.3 | 6.73 |
| 1913 | 92.6 | 8.11 | 176 | 10.9 | 45.3 | 3.45 | 9.63 | 8.0 | 108 | 7.19 |
| 1914 | 79.9 | 8.04 | 172 | 10.8 | 52.7 | 2.95 | 11.3 | 11.0 | 121 | 5.21 |
| 1915 | 75.8 | 6.95 | 187 | 10.1 | 109 | 3.51 | 30.5 | 9.0 | 93.9 / 93.9 | 5.21 / 3.59 |
| 1916 | 98.5 | 9.38 | 213 | 10.6 | 222 | 4.56 | 155 | 8.99 | 118 | 3.42 |
| 1917 | 81.6 | 9.48 | 219 | 10.5 | 207 | 5.66 | 317 | 9.15 | 127 | 3.75 |
| 1918 | 60.0 | 13.0 | 208 | 12.9 | 155 | 6.73 | 232 | 7.83 | 88.5 | 4.86 |
| 1919 | 88.3 | 7.74 | 185 | 12.7 | 209 | 8.25 | 156 | 7.99 | 63.4 | 5.49 |
| 1920 | 198 | 6.12 | 211 | 14.4 | 228 | 9.39 | 304 | 9.05 | 136 | 6.28 |
| 1921 | 296 | 6.70 | 122 | 14.4 | 66.4 | 8.02 | 47.9 | 10.6 | 91.9 | 6.72 |
| 1922 | 328 | 6.87 | 199 | 14.4 | 155 | 7.25 | 55.8 | 10.2 | 117 | 7.21 |
| 1923 | 400 | 7.21 | 197 | 15.3 | 214 | 7.77 | 147 | 7.50 | 145 | 7.29 |
| 1924 | 562 | 7.04 | 204 / 178 | 17.2 / 12.5 | 196 | 7.85 | 120 | 8.67 | 205 | 7.37 |
| 1925 | 585 | 7.09 | 182 | 11.0 | 228 | 7.47 | 121 | 11.9 | 186 | 7.08 |
| 1926 | 715 | 6.27 | 182 | 11.6 | 238 | 7.45 | 134 | 8.99 | 210 | 7.65 |
| 1927 | 839 | 6.68 | 192 | 11.6 | 214 | 6.57 | 121 | 8.98 | 202 | 7.04 |
| 1928 | 808 | 6.41 | 203 | 12.5 | 260 | 6.51 | 127 | 8.64 | 211 | 6.73 |
| 1929 | 804 | 6.80 | 220 | 12.0 | 276 | 6.67 | 188 | 7.99 | 198 | 6.46 |
| 1930 | 703 | 6.35 | 179 | 11.8 | 238 | 6.55 | 129 | 7.99 | 172 | 6.21 |
| 1931 | 503 | 5.82 | 164 | 11.3 | 211 | 5.70 | 73.6 | 6.78 | 147 | 5.85 |
| 1932 | 340 | 5.71 | 123 | 11.0 | 134 | 5.74 | 38.5 | 7.37 | 105 | 5.15 |
| 1933 | 313 | 5.45 | 166 | 10.4 | 146 | 5.08 | 108 | 7.76 | 151 | 5.17 |
| 1934 | 441 | 5.37 | 138 | 10.5 | 178 | 5.29 | 101 | 7.24 | 154 | 5.53 |
| 1935 | 347 | 6.19 | 173 | 10.7 | 218 | 5.56 | 177 | 6.73 | 190 | 5.30 |
| 1936 | 581 | 5.61 | 216 | 10.8 | 274 | 5.91 | 207 | 6.82 | 245 | 5.32 |
| 1937 | 485 | 6.22 | 230 | 11.1 | 361 | 6.30 | 203 | 7.29 | 269 | 5.15 |
| 1938 | 478 | 6.02 | 213 | 10.8 | 335 | 6.47 | 97.0 | 7.47 | 196 | 4.56 |
| 1939 | 460 | 6.67 | 254 | 10.6 | 366 | 6.11 | 199 | 7.36 | 253 | 4.39 |

|  | (37) Mica (A) Uncut Sheet and Punch | | (B) Scrap | | (38) Asbestos | | (39) Graphite | |
|---|---|---|---|---|---|---|---|---|
| Year | Quantity Mil. lb. | Price $ per lb. | Quantity Th. s.t. | Price $ per s.t. | Quantity Th. s.t. | Price $ per s.t. | Quantity Th. s.t. | Price $ per s.t. |
| 1899 | .109 | .650 | 1.50 | 20.5 | .681 | 17.2 | 3.77 | 44.3 |
| 1900 | .456 | .203 | 5.50 | 10.0 | 1.05 | 15.5 | 3.37 | 58.7 |
| 1901 | .360 | .275 | 2.17 | 9.08 | .747 | 18.1 | 2.79 | 60.0 |
| 1902 | .373 | .225 | 1.40 | 25.0 | 1.00 | 16.1 | 6.71 | 27.2 |
| 1903 | .620 | .191 | 1.66 | 15.1 | .887 | 18.9 | 18.9 | 12.0 |
| 1904 | .668 | .164 | 1.10 | 9.90 | 1.48 | 17.4 | 19.8 | 16.3 |
| 1905 | .925 | .174 | 1.13 | 15.9 | 3.11 | 13.8 | 25.0 | 12.7 |
| 1906 | 1.42 | .177 | 1.49 | 15.3 | 1.70 | 16.9 | 19.8 | 17.2 |
| 1907 | 1.06 | .329 | 3.02 | 14.1 | .653 | 18.2 | 29.3 | 10.1 |
| 1908 | .973 | .241 | 2.42 | 14.0 | .936 | 21.0 | 2.59 | 80.4 |
| 1909 | 1.81 | .130 | 4.09 | 11.3 | 3.08 | 20.3 | 8.24 | 41.9 |
| 1910 | 2.48 | .115 | 4.06 | 13.1 | 3.69 | 18.5 | 4.20 | 79.8 |
| 1911 | 1.89 | .164 | 3.51 | 13.0 | 7.60 | 15.8 | 3.62 | 79.7 |
| 1912 | .845 | .335 | 3.23 | 15.2 | 4.40 | 20.0 | 3.84 | 57.5 |
| 1913 | 1.70 | .208 | 5.32 | 15.5 | 1.10 | 10.0 | 4.78 | 61.5 |
| 1914 | .557 | .500 | 3.73 | 13.8 | 1.25 | 15.2 | 4.34 | 74.8 |
| 1915 | .554 | .683 | 3.96 | 12.8 | 1.73 | 44.5 | 4.72 | 91.1 |
| 1916 | .866 | .606 | 4.43 | 15.8 | 1.64 | 110 | 8.09 | 116 |
| 1917 | 1.28 | .591 | 3.43 | 15.4 | 1.96 | 149 | 13.6 | 85.9 |
| 1918 | 1.64 | .445 | 2.29 | 14.5 | .998 | 119 | 13.0 | 117 |
| 1919 | 1.55 | .313 | 3.26 | 17.8 | 1.16 | 214 | 7.42 | 105 |
| 1920 | 1.68 | .325 | 5.72 | 29.2 | 1.65 | 412 | 9.51 | 65.8 |
| 1921 | .742 | .160 | 2.58 | 22.1 | .831 | 406 | 2.44 | 39.6 |
| 1922 | 1.08 | .180 | 4.76 | 18.2 | .067 | 151 | 3.12 | 34.7 |
| 1923 | 2.06 | .151 | 6.03 | 20.4 | .227 | 42.4 | 6.04 | 31.6 |
| 1924 | 1.46 | .145 | 4.71 | 18.5 | .300 | 142 | 4.97 | 17.6 |
| 1925 | 1.79 | .179 | 9.70 | 17.9 | 1.26 | 41.1 | 4.67 | 20.7 |
| 1926 | 2.17 | .184 | 7.04 | 19.4 | 1.36 | 99.2 | 5.47 | 40.1 |
| 1927 | 1.51 | .140 | 6.28 | 17.5 | 2.98 | 113 | 5.21 | 44.7 |
| 1928 | 1.68 | .137 | 7.76 | 17.1 | 2.24 | 157 | 5.61 | 52.9 |
| 1929 | 2.04 | .141 | 6.25 | 18.9 | 3.16 | 111 | 6.46 | 48.1 |
| 1930 | 1.47 | .121 | 6.73 | 16.2 | 4.24 | 68.2 | .. | .. |
| 1931 | .963 | .116 | 6.62 | 15.0 | 3.23 | 36.9 | .. | .. |
| 1932 | .339 | .135 | 7.04 | 11.9 | 3.56 | 29.6 | .. | .. |
| 1933 | .365 | .146 | 8.75 | 11.2 | 5.02 | 27.5 | .. | .. |
| 1934 | .584 | .155 | 7.72 | 12.9 | 6.54 | 31.1 | .. | .. |
| 1935 | .937 | .172 | 12.2 | 10.9 | 9.42 | 32.8 | .. | .. |
| 1936 | 1.32 | .155 | 12.7 | 10.5 | 10.9 | 28.4 | .. | .. |
| 1937 | 1.69 | .168 | 14.7 | 14.0 | 13.9 | 28.5 | .. | .. |
| 1938 | .940 | .148 | 13.7 | 12.4 | 12.9 | 23.7 | .. | .. |
| 1939 | .814 | .171 | 14.7 | 13.8 | 15.1 | 33.2 | .. | .. |

*General Note to Table A-1*

Output relates to production data where such figures are available, otherwise to sales or shipments. So far as possible prices are given in mine values, except in the cases of gold, silver, copper, lead and zinc, for which market prices are shown instead (see Appendix B for explanation).

Except where otherwise noted, all data come from *Mineral Resources of the United States* (published annually for 1899 to 1923 by the U. S. Geological Survey, and for 1924 to 1931 by the U. S. Bureau of Mines); and from *Minerals Yearbook* (published for 1932–33 and annually for 1934 to the present by the U. S. Bureau of Mines).

The following abbreviations are used in the table.

| | |
|---|---|
| Bbl. | barrel (42 gallons) |
| Th. | thousand |
| Mil. | million |
| L.t. | long ton (2,240 lb.) |
| S.t. | short ton (2,000 lb.) |
| F. oz. | fine ounce |
| Cu. ft. | cubic foot |

(1) Iron ore:

Quantity data relate to production. The fourfold breakdown is not entirely definitive, since for most years small amounts of each of the ores are known to have been wrongly classified. The data exclude ores containing more than 5 percent of manganese. For 1899–1905 figures differ from the totals in *Mineral Resources* because we have excluded such ores in order to maintain comparability with later years; prior to 1906 the *Mineral Resources* figures include ores containing up to 40 percent of manganese (see note on manganese ore, below).

Prices are unit values at the mine. They represent commercial selling prices only in part: most iron ore mined in the United States is smelted by the producers in their own furnaces, and the value placed upon such ore is an accounting rather than an actual sale value. For 1920 and later years prices for carbonate are not available, and the quantity data for this ore have been disregarded in the construction of the indexes.

(2) Manganese ore:

Quantity data refer to production in 1899–1910 and to shipments in all other years. Ores containing more than 5 percent of manganese are included here; those with less than 5 percent of manganese are regarded as iron ore. As noted, a slight change in classification occurs between 1914 and 1915, but the quantitative importance of the break is small; column (A) is treated as comparable with column (B), column (C) with columns (D) and (E).

For the years 1899–1905 *Mineral Resources* includes 5 to 40 percent manganese ores with iron ore and, therefore, does not present a distinct series for such ores. We derived our data for these years from figures found in the manganese chapters of *Mineral Resources* relating to the production of manganiferous silver ores and manganiferous ores used for fluxing. For 1906 figures for Colorado fluxing ores are not available: our data include estimates for such ores based on the data for 1905 and 1907. In 1919 two sets of figures are shown. That comparable with later years excludes ores used for fluxing and that comparable with earlier years includes such ores. Fluxing ores are of declining importance following 1919, and disappear entirely beginning with 1929. They are, however, important for some of the years (especially in the 10 to 35 percent group) but suitable value figures were not available.

(3)–(7) Gold, silver, copper, lead, and zinc:

See Appendix B for a discussion of some of the problems posed by the statistics for the industries producing these metals. In general the quantity data are official estimates of the recoverable metal content of the various metalliferous ores mined during the year. The "prices" are those used by the Bureau of Mines to value production, and relate to the manufactured product, either smelted or refined. However, the value data in Table A-2 are on a mine basis, and these values were used in combining indexes for the several nonferrous metal mining industries.

(3) Copper, 1904–39:

The quantity data comprise total copper production, together with gold and silver produced from copper ores. For copper in 1904 and 1905 smelter output alone was available. We estimated recoverable content of ores mined on the basis of the 1906 relationship between mine (recoverable content) and smelter output. The figures for 1904 and 1905 were not used in constructing indexes: see (7) below.

(4) Lode gold and silver, and lead and zinc outside the Mississippi Valley, 1906–39:

The quantity data comprise all gold and silver production except amounts derived from copper ore (see column 3) and placers (see column 6); together with all lead and zinc produced in states other than those included in the Mississippi Valley classification (see below). For lead and zinc in 1906 smelter or refinery output alone was available. We estimated the recoverable content of ores mined on the basis of the 1907 relationship between mine (recoverable content) and smelter output. For lead in 1928 and 1929, production in Virginia had to be estimated. For lead in 1930 and all later years, Tennessee's production has been included. No overlap is necessary because this state's 1929 production was zero. For zinc the second 1929 figure and data for all later years include Tennessee's production since it could not be segregated. The first 1929 figure and data for all earlier years exclude Tennessee's production, the output of Tennessee being estimated in 1928 and 1929.

(5) Lead and zinc in the Mississippi Valley, 1906–39:

The quantity data comprise all lead and zinc produced in Arkansas, Illinois, Iowa, Kansas, Kentucky, Missouri, Oklahoma, Tennessee, and Wisconsin. In the computation of productivity, fluorspar from Illinois and Kentucky has to be included in the measurement of this industry's output because the employment data cannot be segregated. However, in measuring mining output as a whole (Table A-7) we have omitted the fluorspar shown here, since it partly duplicates column (24). For lead and zinc in 1906 smelter output alone was available. We estimated the recoverable content of ores mined on the basis of the 1907 relationship between mine (recoverable content) and smelter output. For lead in 1930 and all later years, Tennessee's production has been excluded. No overlap is necessary because this state's 1929 production was zero. For zinc the second 1929 figure and data for all later years exclude Tennessee's production because it was not published separately. The first 1929 figure and data for all earlier years include Tennessee's production; the output of this state is estimated for 1928 and 1929.

(6) Placer gold and silver:

The quantity data comprise all gold and silver produced from placers.

(7) Lode gold and silver, and copper, lead and zinc, 1899–1906:

The data for years prior to 1906 do not permit the allocation of the total production of these metals to the several mining industries producing them. Total production, therefore, is expressed in terms of a breakdown according to product rather than according to industry. Furthermore, these figures relate to the metal recovered from domestic ores during the year as smelter or refinery products rather than to the recoverable content of ores mined during the year. It should be noted, too, that the totals duplicate 1904 and 1905 production in the copper industry; the figures shown in this column were used in constructing our indexes.

(8) Bauxite:

Quantity data relate to shipments for all years, but the latter are believed to approximate production closely, for bauxite is usually shipped as soon as mined.

*Footnotes to Table A-1 continued on next page.*

*Footnotes to Table A-1, continued.*

Bauxite is shipped in several forms—crude, dried, calcined, etc.—with widely varying moisture content. Consequently the actual tonnage shipped is not a perfect measure of the amount of bauxite shipped. However, the first set of 1934 figures and data for all earlier years relate to the actual tonnage of material as shipped. In the second set of 1934 figures and data for all later years the several forms of bauxite have been converted to a common product—the "dried bauxite equivalent" of the shipped material. For 1916 and earlier years the quantity data shown will be found only in *Mineral Resources, 1918*, Vol. I, p. 516. The data published in later reports of the Bureau of Mines are figures which, according to the text discussion on page 514 of the 1918 report, are not as accurate as the data we have used. The Bureau of Mines apparently continues to reproduce them because the differences are slight in most years, and the unrevised figures had already been widely quoted. Our price data for these years are derived from the unrevised quantity and value figures.

(9) Mercury (1 flask = 76 lbs.):

Quantity data relate to production for all years. The price series is for the average price of mercury on either the New York or the San Francisco market.

(10) Molybdenum:

Quantity data relate to the molybdenum content of concentrates, whether produced by molybdenum mines and mills, or as a byproduct of other activities such as copper mining. For 1914–26 quantity data relate to shipments and for 1927–39 to production. The serious beginning of a molybdenum industry apparently dates from 1914 since, according to *Mineral Resources, 1918*, Vol. I, p. 795, no molybdenum ore was produced in 1911, 1912 or 1913, and only small amounts were extracted before that time. For 1930 production figures were published only in terms of molybdenum sulfide; we converted the figure in question to a basis of molybdenum.

Prices for the entire period were derived from a comparison of the value and quantity of shipments; such values were in most cases estimated by the Bureau of Mines. Since no prices are available for 1923 and 1924, the price shown for 1925 was used in constructing output indexes for these years.

(11) Tungsten:

Quantity data relate to tungsten concentrates reduced to an equivalent of 60 percent tungsten trioxide ($WO_3$). For 1901–05 the tungsten trioxide equivalent of concentrates reported is not known exactly, and may have been somewhat higher than 60 percent. For the years 1900–36 the figures refer to shipments, for 1937–39 to production. However, we have transferred 191 tons of 60 percent $WO_3$ concentrates, valued at $87,000, from 1924 to 1919, for this amount was apparently produced in 1919 but not sold until 1924. There was some production prior to 1900 but it appears to have been insignificant (see *Mineral Resources, 1915*, Vol. I, p. 823). Prices for the entire period were derived from a comparison of the published value and quantity of shipments.

(12) Pennsylvania anthracite:

Quantity data relate to production in all years. Only anthracite mined in Pennsylvania is covered by the statistics. Small amounts of anthracite and subanthracite produced outside Pennsylvania are included with bituminous coal (see notes to column 13, bituminous coal). Bootleg production of Pennsylvania anthracite is not covered by the statistics.

(13) Bituminous coal:

Quantity data relate to production in all years. The figures cover all coal produced in the United States other than Pennsylvania anthracite. Included are the small quantities of hard coal produced outside Pennsylvania and the lignite of the Dakotas, Texas and Montana. (In 1938 such anthracite and lignite comprised only 0.97 percent of the total tonnage.) The Bureau of Mines does not attempt to include in the statistics the output of mines producing less than 1,000 tons a year.

Therefore, country coal banks have not been included and wagon mines have been canvassed (indirectly, through rail shipments) only in those years when prices were high enough to call forth sizable production on their part. The excluded output of these small, irregular operators is believed not to exceed 1 million tons a year. For 1916–39 production in Alaska has been excluded. In all other years Alaska is included because its production could not be segregated. Since its output is slight in all years the break in comparability in 1915 is of little importance.

The price series represents the average value of coal at the mine. It is not entirely based on commercial selling prices, since a large part of production is either used directly at the mine (for colliery fuel or the manufacture of coke) or is the output of "captive mines" which transfer the product to the parent concern in a bookkeeping transaction. The value of such production is estimated by the producer. For 1937 and years following the Bureau of Mines has revised the basis of its price series which now includes selling costs, and therefore differs from the earlier mine value series. For 1936 both prices are available. We have estimated mine values for 1937, 1938 and 1939, using the ratio of the two figures for 1936.

(14) Petroleum and natural gas (1 barrel of petroleum = 42 gals.):

Quantity data relate to the production of petroleum and natural gasoline and to the marketed production of natural gas. The production series do not each define a single industry. Natural gas and its byproduct, natural gasoline, are produced in part from oil wells and in part independently. A breakdown according to the two sources of production is not available. Data for Pennsylvania grade petroleum are estimates derived by combining published production figures for New York, Pennsylvania, West Virginia and southeastern and central Ohio.

For natural gas the quantity figures prior to 1906 are estimates by F. G. Tryon and were obtained from "contemporary estimates of the quantity of coal displaced by gas or of the value of gas sold" (see Arthur F. Burns, *Production Trends in the United States since 1870*, National Bureau of Economic Research, 1934, pp. 292, 333). We have derived unit values for these years by using the production figures shown in the table and Bureau of Mines estimates of the total value of gas sold, which may not be comparable. Prices shown for natural gas in 1899–1918, and the first price shown for 1919, relate to value at the point of consumption; the second price for 1919 and prices for 1920–39 refer to value at the well; such value was estimated for 1919–21 on the basis of its relation to value at the point of consumption in 1922.

Little or no natural gasoline was produced prior to 1911.

(15) and (16) Dimension and nondimension stone:

For a discussion of methods of classifying the stone industries, and for reasons underlying the choice of the short ton as a physical unit, see Appendix C. The breakdown between dimension and nondimension stone is made according to industry rather than product. Because nondimension marble and slate are primarily byproducts of the corresponding dimension stone, they are included as part of the output of the dimension industry. For a like reason dimension basalt is included as a product of the nondimension industry. The presentation of two sets of data for dimension and nondimension granite, limestone and basalt, and for nondimension sandstone, in 1916 is necessary because of a change in the manner in which the original data were published. In the first set of figures shown for 1916, and in the figures for all earlier years, the products labeled nondimension include only stone crushed for concrete aggregate, railroad ballast and road metal; while the products labeled dimension include, in addition to regular dimension stone, all other forms of nondimension stone. In the second set of figures for 1916, and in the figures for all later years, the product classification comprises only the regular products indicated. These products include, in the case of dimension stone, building stone (including rubble), monumental stone, paving blocks, curbing, flagging; and in the case of nondimension stone, riprap and all varieties of crushed and broken stone.

*Footnotes to Table A-1 continued on next page.*

*Footnotes to Table A-1, continued.*

(15) Dimension stone:

Quantity data relate to sales throughout.

A. Dimension granite. For 1915 and earlier years value of sales alone is available. Quantities were estimated by deflating these value figures by an average price derived from quantity and value data for important producing states. These states are: 1906–11, Vermont; 1912, Maine, Minnesota, New Hampshire and Vermont; 1913–15, Maine, Minnesota, New Hampshire, Vermont and Wisconsin. The prices so obtained were adjusted to a United States level by ratios derived in years when a United States price was available.

B. Dimension limestone. For 1915 and earlier years value of sales alone was reported. Quantities were estimated by deflating these value figures by an average price derived from quantity and value data for Lawrence and Monroe counties, Indiana, important dimension limestone producing centers. The prices so obtained were adjusted to a United States level by ratios derived in years when a United States price was available.

C. Dimension marble and D. Nondimension marble. For 1911–15 separate data for dimension and nondimension marble were not published. Our distribution between the two products was estimated by assuming that sales reported in cubic feet or in square feet referred to the dimension product, while those reported in short tons referred to nondimension stone. Sales reported in cubic feet were converted to short tons by a ratio derived in years when data were available in both forms. Sales reported in square feet were converted to short tons by dividing their value by the average price per ton for quantities reported in cubic feet, already so converted.

E. Dimension sandstone. For years prior to 1916 no data adequate for estimating quantities could be discovered.

F. Dimension slate. Most dimension slate is roofing slate; the remainder is called millstock, and includes electrical, structural and sanitary slate, grave vaults, blackboards and bulletin boards, billiard table tops and school slates. Quantity figures covering all millstock are not available for years prior to 1916. For 1907–15 quantity figures are available for the greater part of these sales, and value figures for the remainder. The quantity of this remainder was estimated by dividing its value by the price of blackboard slate. For 1899–1906 value figures only are available for millstock; its quantity was estimated by dividing its value by the average price of millstock for 1907–15. During this period millstock was usually less than 10 percent of all slate; the remaining 90 percent consisted of roofing slate, for which quantity and value data are available throughout. For 1918 and earlier years, however, quantity data for roofing slate and for millstock (where available) were reported in square feet only; their conversion to short tons was a simple matter, for the ratios (derived from later years) scarcely vary.

G. Nondimension slate (slate granules). No data are available prior to 1918.

H. Miscellaneous dimension stone. For 1917 no quantity data are available, and for 1916 and earlier years miscellaneous varieties of dimension stone were reported with such other categories as they resembled most closely. For 1918–31 rubble is not included, since it could not be separated from riprap.

(16) Nondimension stone:

For limestone used for lime and cement, quantity data refer to production; elsewhere they relate to sales. The figures for nondimension basalt, granite, limestone (not including limestone for lime) and sandstone include noncommercial production. Noncommercial production represents tonnages reported by states, counties, municipalities and other government agencies, produced either by themselves or by contractors expressly for their consumption, often with publicly owned equipment. Such production is not important prior to 1929: it can be segregated only for all varieties of stone taken together (see note k to Table A-5; also Appendix C).

For dimension basalt in 1915 and prior years, value of sales alone is available.

Quantities were estimated by applying the average price for 1916–38 to the value figures reported.

For nondimension limestone, including limestone for lime, prices were calculated from quantities and values reported for limestone other than that used for lime. For 1914 and earlier years quantities consumed in the manufacture of lime were estimated by multiplying lime production by an average ratio between limestone consumed and lime produced in years for which both kinds of data are available.

For limestone used in making cement (cement rock) quantity figures relate to material consumed in the manufacture of Portland and natural cements. For 1914 and earlier years such quantities were estimated by multiplying total cement production by the average ratio between limestone or cement rock consumed and cement produced in years for which both kinds of data are available. For years prior to 1909 this ratio did not seem adequate (because of a change in the composition of cement production) and no data are offered. Cement manufacturers usually quarry their own limestone, and it does not enter commercial channels; for this reason the output of limestone for cement is difficult to value. To obtain a price for index number weighting, we may either adopt that used for other nondimension limestone, or we may derive a price from that for cement. The latter procedure was chosen. The figure for 1929 comes from page 363 of "Mines and Quarries, 1929," *Fifteenth Census of the United States*. Prices for all other years were estimated by applying the ratio between this price and the 1929 price for manufactured cement to the cement price for the year, the latter calculated from quantity and value data in *Minerals Yearbook*. Because of the arbitrary character of the series it is shown in parentheses.

For miscellaneous nondimension stone in 1917 no quantity data are available, and for 1916 and earlier years miscellaneous varieties of nondimension stone were reported with such other categories as they most closely resembled. For 1918–31 miscellaneous varieties of rubble are treated as nondimension because they could not be separated from riprap.

(17) Sand and gravel:

Quantity data relate to sales throughout. Much sand and gravel is produced by noncommercial operators. These comprise government agencies, and contractors producing directly for government agencies, the output being reported by the latter. The first set of data for 1923, and data for earlier years, include noncommercial production, which cannot be segregated from commercial; the second set of figures for 1923, and data for later years, exclude such production. Data for noncommercial production, which has increased in importance in recent years, do not appear to be reliable: see *Statistical Appendix to Minerals Yearbook, 1932–33*, pp. 289-91. For 1902–04 data relating to the combined production of sand and gravel are available, but we have made no use of these figures, since they appear to suffer from serious undercoverage.

(18) Clay (including fuller's earth):

Quantity data relate to sales. The figures include only marketable clay, and do not cover much greater quantities of so-called common clay, mined by manufacturers of brick, tile and other heavy-clay products for their own use in nearby plants. For 1899–1903 we combined all varieties for which data are reported, except fuller's earth, into a single classification, because the breakdown given for these years did not seem satisfactory. The first set of data for 1902, and data for earlier years, include certain clays whose production is unreported in later years.

(19) Gypsum:

Quantity data relate to crude gypsum mined. With the exception of the years 1937–39 no value is available for crude gypsum, and even for these years the value is estimated by producers, since the material does not enter the market in this form. Our prices are, therefore, derived from data relating to the quantity and value of

*Footnotes to Table A-1 continued on next page.*

*Footnotes to Table A-1, continued.*

uncalcined gypsum products sold, since this represented the closest approximation to a crude unit value available in most years.

(20) Sulfur:

Quantity data relate to production in all years. The figures for 1902 and 1903 are unpublished data furnished to the authors by Mr. Robert H. Ridgway of the Bureau of Mines. (The revisions in the data for all years prior to 1918, according to additional information made available to the Geological Survey, apparently did not affect the figures for 1899–1901, since the unrevised figures for those years are still considered accurate by the Bureau of Mines.) Prices are derived from the quantity and value of sulfur shipped, except in 1902 and 1903. In these years the value of shipments is not available, and we have used a price derived from data in *The Mineral Industry, 1903* (The Engineering and Mining Journal, 1904), p. 315.

(21) Pyrites:

Quantity data relate to production of pyrite ores and concentrates. Since 1925 the production of pyrites as a byproduct of zinc operations in Wisconsin and of copper operations in Tennessee has been fairly important. We have excluded such production whenever possible, since it is included in the value weight assigned to these other industries. Thus the first set of data for 1929, and data for all earlier years, exclude byproduct pyrites. The second set of figures for 1929, and data for all later years include such production. For 1902 and 1903 data on both output and price are from *The Mineral Industry, 1903,* summary table.

(22) Phosphate rock:

Quantity figures relate to production in all years except 1899. The 1899 figure relates to sales. Prices for all years are from quantity and value of sales. Production is measured on a mixed wet and dry basis prior to 1926, on a dry basis for 1926–39 (see A. Porter Haskell, Jr. and O. E. Kiessling, *Phosphate-Rock Mining,* National Research Project, Philadelphia, 1938, note c to Table A-8, p. 108).

(23) Potash:

Quantity data relate to the potash ($K_2O$) equivalent of potassium salts produced. Prices are derived from quantity and value of sales of potassium salts (potash equivalent). There was no production of potash salts prior to 1915; in that year quantity data are not available. Potash comes from several sources. In addition to production from natural brines and bedded saline deposits, recovery from distillery waste, cement flue and blast furnace dust, etc., has been made from time to time. In recent years production from natural brines and bedded saline deposits has accounted for over 98 percent of total output, but during World War I and the early post-war period production from other sources was important. We have excluded such secondary production whenever possible. Thus the first set of figures for 1919, and data for earlier years, relate only to natural brine potash. The second set of 1919 data, and figures for 1920 through the first set of 1924 include, in addition, potash from cement mill and blast furnace dust which could not be segregated. Again, the second set of data for 1924, and data for all later years, include potash from all sources.

(24) Fluorspar:

Data relate to production prior to 1906 and to shipments in 1906 and later years.

(25) Borates:

Data relate to sales in all years. Quantity data for 1899 and 1900 are from *The Mineral Industry, 1900* (Scientific Publishing Co., 1901), p. 2. Prices in 1901 and 1902 come from *The Mineral Industry, 1901* (The Engineering and Mining Journal, 1902), p. 2.

(26) Bromine:

Quantity data relate to sales in all years and comprise the quantity of bromine recovered by producers from natural brines and the bromine content of compounds produced.

(27) Sodium carbonates and sulfates (natural):

Quantity data relate to sales of sodium carbonate and sulfate recovered from natural brines and saline deposits. No data are available for years before 1919: in that year sodium carbonates and sulfates are separated from sodium borate only in value terms, and the separation of quantities was therefore estimated.

(28) Magnesium chloride and sulfate:

Quantity data relate to sales of magnesium chloride and sulfate recovered from natural brines and saline deposits. No data are available for years before 1925. A slight discontinuity in the output series occurs between 1937 and 1938, because of the inclusion of brucite in 1938 and later years but not in 1937 and earlier years. Brucite was produced commercially as early as 1934 but production was very slight until 1938.

(29) Calcium chloride:

Quantity data relate to sales of calcium chloride and mixed calcium-magnesium chloride recovered from natural brines. Only since 1937 have quantity figures been expressed in a constant unit—75 percent $(Ca,Mg)Cl_2$—hence two sets of 1937 data are presented. The first figures for 1937 and data for earlier years are not expressed in this constant unit; the second 1937 figures and data for later years are so expressed.

(30) Silica and silicates (mainly for use as abrasives):

Quantity data relate to sales.

Some ground sand and sandstone is produced in the sand and gravel industry and is therefore already included in the statistics for that industry. However, the figures for ground sand and sandstone in the silica and abrasives chapters of *Minerals Yearbook* often include such production too. This is true of the data for the years 1923–32 and 1934–36. Quantity and value figures, excluding such production in these years, are available only for 1936 in the summary table to be found in the 1939 *Minerals Yearbook*. For the other years value figures alone, which exclude such production, are found in the annual summary tables. We have estimated quantities from these values, and from prices derived from quantity and value figures, including production in the sand and gravel industry. For years before 1913 data for ground sand and sandstone are not available, and figures for those years relate to quartz only: an overlap is provided in 1913.

Data for tripoli include Pennsylvania rottenstone. The first price shown for 1917, and prices for earlier years, relate to crude tripoli; the second 1917 price, and those for later years, refer to the product as sold, whether crude or finished.

(31) Abrasive sandstone:

Quantity data relate to sales and include grindstones, pulpstones, oilstones and related products. In 1917 the quantity of pulpstones is reported only as a number of pieces; this number we converted to short tons, using the 1918 ratio of short tons to pieces.

(32) Asphalt and related bitumens:

Quantity data apparently relate to sales of native asphalt and related bitumens. The figures are sometimes described as "production" and sometimes as "sales," but presumably the latter description is the more accurate (see, e.g., *Mineral Resources, 1930*, Vol. II, pp. 205-06).

(33) Talc:

Quantity data relate to sales, and include, in addition to talc, products with similar physical properties: pyrophyllite, a hydrous aluminum silicate, and (for certain

*Footnotes to Table A-1 continued on next page.*

*Footnotes to Table A-1, continued.*

years) soapstone, both dimension and ground. Ground soapstone is included in 1933 and later years and excluded in earlier years; no overlap is possible. Dimension soapstone was included until 1924 and has been excluded since then; an overlap is provided.

(34) Barite:

Quantity data relate to sales in 1899–1926 and to production in 1927–39. Prices are derived from quantity and value of sales in all years.

(35) Magnesite:

Data relate to crude magnesite mined. However, since most of the output is first sold after processing (either dead-burned or caustic calcined) the crude value as reported is largely estimated. For 1938 and 1939 quantities were partly estimated by the Bureau of Mines. (The figures do not include brucite which appears in column 28 with other magnesium compounds.)

(36) Feldspar:

Quantity data relate to sales of crude feldspar. Prices refer to feldspar as sold, whether crude or finished, in 1899–1914, and to crude feldspar in 1915–39. The first 1915 price is comparable with earlier years and relates to feldspar as sold; the second 1915 price is comparable with later years and relates to crude feldspar.

(37) Mica:

Data relate to sales.

A. Uncut sheet and punch. In earlier years some mica miners operated cutting plants and the value of finished products was included in the production statistics. Since 1920, however, the figures relate to the uncut product only.

B. Scrap. Our figures do not include mica recovered from schist and kaolin operations. In 1922 and 1923 the published figures include mica from schist; the amount of such production was estimated by us (using ratios of schist to all scrap mica in 1921 and 1924) and excluded.

(38) Asbestos:

Quantity data relate to sales in 1899–1932 and to production in 1933–39. Prices are derived from quantity and value of sales in all years.

(39) Graphite:

Data relate to combined sales of crystalline and amorphous graphite, and are not available for years after 1929. In 1922 the price shown includes our estimate of the price of amorphous graphite (mean of 1921 and 1923) for which product the Bureau of Mines gives no value data.

## VALUE OF MINERAL PRODUCTS

*Thousand dollars*

*This table, based largely on Table A-1, shows the value, at the mine or beneficiating plant, not only of products included in our indexes of output, but of others for which quantity data were lacking. In the case of minor minerals not reported in Table A-1, values were taken from the summary tables in the U. S. Bureau of Mines publications* Mineral Resources *and* Minerals Yearbook. *Where a different procedure was followed, the fact is indicated in footnotes.*

| Industry | 1899 | 1909 | 1919 | 1929 | 1937 |
|---|---|---|---|---|---|
| METALS, TOTAL | 189,057 | 328,699 | 539,200 | | |
| | | | 540,956 | 627,216 | 641,577 |
| Antimony[a] | 44 | 5 | 0 | 0 | 138 |
| Bauxite | 117[b] | 696[b] | 2,202 | 2,266 | 2,445 |
| Bismuth ore | 9 | 0 | 0 | 0 | 0 |
| Chromite | 1 | 8 | 129 | 4 | 15 |
| Iron ore[c] | 34,646 | 110,425 | 213,601 | 190,388 | 207,352 |
| Manganese[d] | 435 | 236 | 3,349 | 4,887 | 4,920 |
| Mercury | 1,453 | 958 | 1,934 | 2,893 | 1,489 |
| Molybdenum[e] | 1 | 0 | 342 | 2,326 | 20,091 |
| Nonferrous, major:[f] | | | | | |
| Copper | | 99,494 | 179,006 | 282,058 | 184,996 |
| Gold, placer | | 10,237 | 9,300 | 3,772 | 21,052 |
| Lead and zinc (Mississippi Valley) | 152,348 | 24,271 | 43,782 | 53,865 | 38,172 |
| Lode gold and silver, and lead and zinc (outside Mississippi Valley) | | 81,732 | 85,042 | 83,124 | 156,115 |
| Platinum[g] | 2 | 13 | 52 | 15 | 30 |
| Titanium ore (rutile) | 1 | 10 | 20 | [h] | [h] |
| Tungsten | 0 | 614 | 441 | 654 | 4,094 |
| Unspecified[i] | [j] | [j] | 1,756 | 964 | 668 |
| NONMETALS, TOTAL | 399,486 | 861,897 | | | |
| | | 887,814 | 2,750,347 | | |
| | | | 2,652,836 | 3,431,776 | |
| | | | | 3,428,130 | 3,153,179 |
| Asbestos | 12 | 63 | 248 | 351 | 345 |
| Asphalt and related bitumens | 554 | 573 | 683 | 5,470 | 3,019 |
| Barite[e] | 140 | 210 | 1,728 | 1,842 | 2,272 |
| Borates | 505[k] | 1,534 | 1,380 | 4,515 | 7,233 |
| Bromine | 108 | 58 | 1,235 | 1,759 | 5,180 |
| Calcium chloride | [j] | 63 | 322 | 2,097 | 1,295 |
| Clay (incl. fuller's earth) | 1,725 | 3,751 | 9,089 | 19,160 | 18,000 |
| Coal: | | | | | |
| Bituminous | 167,952 | 405,487 | 1,160,616 | 952,781 | 830,782[l] |
| Pennsylvania anthracite | 88,142 | 149,182 | 364,927 | 385,643 | 197,599 |
| Emery (excl. gems; incl. corundum) | 151 | 18 | 23 | 11 | 3 |
| Feldspar[m] | 212 | 425 | 585 | | |
| | | | 348 | 1,277 | 1,383 |
| Fluorspar | 97 | 292 | 3,526 | 2,791 | 3,667 |
| Gems and precious stones | 186 | 534 | 112 | [h] | [h] |
| Graphite | 167 | 346 | 779 | 311 | [h] |
| Gypsum[n] | 752 | 3,641 | 7,201 | 9,869 | |
| | | | | 5,589 | 4,783 |
| Magnesite | 18 | 38 | 1,248 | 1,500 | 1,483 |
| Magnesium chloride and sulfate | [j] | [j] | o | 1,082 | 1,579 |

**Table A-2—VALUE OF PRODUCTS (continued)**

| *Industry* | *1899* | *1909* | *1919* | *1929* | *1937* |
|---|---|---|---|---|---|
| Marl: | | | | | |
| Calcareous | 30 | 45 | 327 | 131 | 60 |
| Greensand | | | 4[p] | 256 | 211 |
| Mica | 101 | 281 | 542 | 404 | 490 |
| Millstones | 28 | 35 | 67 | 31 | 8 |
| Mineral waters | 6,948 | 6,894 | 4,880 | [h] | [h] |
| Monazite and zircon | 20 | 65 | [h] | 0 | 0 |
| Peat | [j] | 127 | 706 | [h] | 305 |
| Petroleum and natural gas[q] | 84,679 | 191,536 | 985,351 | | |
| | | | 886,101 | 1,596,423 | 1,733,922 |
| Phosphate rock[r] | 5,084 | 11,287 | 9,446 | 13,245 | 13,976 |
| Potash[s] | 0 | 0 | 5,980 | 3,199 | 9,613 |
| Pyrites[t] | 543 | 1,028 | 2,558 | 616 | |
| | | | | 1,250 | 1,778 |
| Sand and gravel[u] | [v] | 18,337 | 45,952 | | |
| | | | 45,317 | 125,080 | 79,114 |
| Silica and silicates (mainly for use as abrasives): | | | | | |
| Garnet | 98 | 102 | 310 | 435 | 383 |
| Pumice and pumicite | [j] | 33 | 117 | 353 | 302 |
| Ground sand and sandstone, and quartz[w] | 219 | 249 | 374 | | |
| | | | 662 | 1,473 | 2,063 |
| Diatomite | 37 | 122 | 532 | [h] | [h] |
| Tripoli[x] | | | 98 | | |
| | | | 182 | 546 | 451 |
| Abrasive silica stone products | 893 | 1,018 | 1,572 | 1,454 | 686 |
| Sodium carbonates and sulfates (natural) | [j] | [j] | 608 | 1,958 | 1,791 |
| Stone:[y] | | | | | |
| Basalt, nondimension | | 4,749 | 8,482 | | |
| | | | 8,822 | 18,876 | 12,480 |
| Basalt, dimension | | 385 | 463 | | |
| | | | 123 | 70 | 28 |
| Granite, nondimension | | 3,064 | 3,300 | | |
| | | | 3,783 | 8,856 | 8,741 |
| Granite, dimension | | 16,518 | 16,045 | | |
| | | | 15,563 | 25,369 | 11,452 |
| Limestone, nondimension (incl. limestone for lime) | | 22,975[z] | | | |
| | 35,245[z] | 26,600 | 47,333 | | |
| | | | 55,017 | 100,380 | 93,117 |
| Limestone, dimension | | 9,096 | 12,191 | | |
| | | | 4,733 | 21,501 | 5,309 |
| Marble, nondimension | | 6,549 | 258 | 534 | 321 |
| Marble, dimension | | | 7,784 | 16,011 | 5,135 |
| Miscellaneous, nondimension | | [aa] | 1,878 | 7,753 | 8,950 |
| Miscellaneous, dimension | | [aa] | 43 | 293 | 687 |
| Sandstone, nondimension | | 1,213 | 1,433 | | |
| | | | 2,680 | 5,737 | 5,795 |
| Sandstone, dimension | | 6,797 | 3,851 | | |
| | | | 2,604 | 5,287 | 1,721 |

| Industry | 1899 | 1909 | 1919 | 1929 | 1937 |
|---|---|---|---|---|---|
| Stone:[y] (cont.) | | | | | |
| Slate, nondimension | [j] | [j] | 1,155 | 2,498 | 1,578 |
| Slate, dimension | 3,963 | 5,441 | 4,876 | 8,747 | 4,027 |
| Limestone for cement | [j] | 3,797 | 9,543 | 18,135 | 12,278 |
| Sulfur | 108 | 5,074 | 17,996 | 42,455 | 49,249 |
| Talc[bb] | 769 | 1,222 | 2,353 | | |
| | | | 1,822 | 2,629 | 2,562 |
| Unspecified[cc] | [j] | [j] | 780 | 10,582 | 5,973 |
| TOTAL METALS AND NONMETALS | 588,543 | 1,190,596 | | | |
| | | 1,216,513 | 3,289,547 | | |
| | | | 3,193,792 | 4,058,992 | |
| | | | | 4,055,346 | 3,794,756 |

[a] Data relate to antimony ore and concentrates only; separate figures for metal obtained as a byproduct of lead are lacking, but the value of such metal is included among the products of the major nonferrous metal industries.

[b] Available only in *Mineral Resources, 1918*, Vol. I, p. 516. This figure seems more accurate than those presented in later reports of the Bureau of Mines.

[c] For all years but 1899 the values are estimates derived by applying unit values for hematite, brown ore, magnetite and carbonate to their respective quantities (see Table A-1). For 1929 and 1937 unit values for carbonate are not available; therefore its value, which is negligible, is excluded. In 1919 there was no production of carbonate, and for 1899 and 1909 carbonate is included. The 1899 figure as presented in *Mineral Resources* is slightly larger than that shown here—the difference is attributable to the inclusion of manganiferous ores, which we have classified with manganese.

[d] For 1919 and earlier years the value of ores used for fluxing is included. No adjustment for comparability is made because no such ores were produced in 1929. Our 1899 figure is larger than that in *Mineral Resources* because we have included manganiferous ores classified by the Geological Survey with iron ore.

[e] 1929 and 1937 values are estimates, derived by applying unit values from sales to production figures. Data for other years are sales values.

[f] For a discussion of the industrial breakdown the reader is referred to Appendix B. The value data here presented are intended to relate to the value of the industry's products at the mine or ore dressing plant and, therefore, run lower than similar figures computed from Table A-1 (where market prices for refined metal are quoted); for the same reason they run lower than values to be found in *Minerals Yearbook* or its predecessor *Mineral Resources*. However, they include the value of byproducts (see Table B-1, below), in addition to the value of the primary products of each industry, quantity data for which are given in Table A-1. The figures for 1909, 1919 and 1929 are based on data in the Census of Mines and Quarries for those years. In most cases we adjusted the raw data in order to keep the table internally consistent or to maintain comparability from year to year. For example, we adjusted the Census figures to exclude such byproducts as are already included in the value figures for other commodities. It should be noted, in addition, that although in the 1909 Census the distinction between mining and manufacturing is not too carefully observed, we have abstracted from that volume figures which we consider comparable with the data for other years. There were no Census canvasses in the years 1899 and 1937. Hence, figures for these years are our estimates based on the relationship between mine and smelter or refinery values in 1902 and 1939 respectively, the two closest Census years.

[g] Estimated by applying derived price to production (excluding Alaska) in 1919, 1929 and 1937. For other years taken directly from *Mineral Resources*.

[h] Included under "unspecified."

*Footnotes to Table A-2 continued on next page.*

*Footnotes to Table A-2, continued.*

[i] Includes, in 1937, tantalum, titanium, uranium and vanadium. Does not include iron ore sold for magnets for which value cannot be secured (however, this is of infinitesimal importance).

Includes, in 1929, tantalum, titanium, uranium, vanadium. Does not include iron ore sold for magnets (see above).

Includes, in 1919, cobalt, tantalum (columbite), titanium (ilmenite), uranium and vanadium. Does not include iron ore sold for magnets (see above).

[j] Data not available.

[k] From *The Mineral Industry, 1900* (Scientific Publishing Co., 1901), p. 2.

[l] Estimated value, excluding sales costs; see note to Table A-1.

[m] The figures for 1899 and 1909, and the upper figure for 1919, refer to the value of feldspar as sold, whether crude or finished; the lower figure for 1919, and the figures for 1929 and 1937, refer to the value of the crude mineral.

[n] The figures for 1899, 1909 and 1919, and the upper figure for 1929, were derived by applying the *Minerals Yearbook* unit value for uncalcined gypsum to total production figures; the lower figure for 1929, and the figure for 1937, are mine values. The latter were derived for 1929 by applying a Census unit value for crude gypsum to the *Minerals Yearbook* quantity figure; and for 1937 from quantity and value data reported in *Minerals Yearbook*.

[o] Cannot be traced; probably included in "unspecified."

[p] Estimate based on relationship between calcareous and greensand marl in 1920.

[q] Figures for 1899 and 1909, and the upper figure for 1919, include the delivered value of natural gas; the lower figure for 1919, and the figures for 1929 and 1937, include the value of natural gas at the well (see Table A-1).

[r] For years other than 1899 the figures are estimates derived by applying sales unit values to production figures. The 1899 figure refers to value of sales.

[s] Estimates derived by applying sales unit values to production figures; the industry began in 1914.

[t] Figures for 1899, 1909 and 1919, and the upper figure for 1929, do not include the value of byproduct pyrites recovered from zinc mining in Wisconsin and copper mining in Tennessee; the lower figure for 1929, and the figure for 1937, include such byproduct recovery.

[u] The figure for 1909, and the upper figure for 1919, include the value of noncommercial production; the lower figure for 1919, and the figures for 1929 and 1937, exclude such output (exclusion in 1919 based on relationship in 1923).

[v] No canvass of the industry was undertaken in 1899. Sand crushed from sandstone and used in the manufacture of glass is included in the stone industry, but the value of the sand so included cannot be determined separately.

[w] Figures for 1899 and 1909, and the upper figure for 1919, refer to quartz only; the lower figure for 1919, and the figures for 1929 and 1937, include ground sand and sandstone as well.

[x] Figures for 1899 and 1909, and the upper figure for tripoli in 1919, relate to its value in crude form; the lower figure for 1919, and figures for 1929 and 1937, relate to its value as sold, whether crude or finished.

[y] The numerous overlaps shown for 1919 result from a change in the manner of reporting the products of the various divisions of the industry, some crushed stone being included with dimension stone in the upper figures comparable with 1909 (see Table A-1 and notes to that table).

[z] Excludes limestone for lime, for which data are lacking in 1899.

[aa] No separate value is available, miscellaneous varieties of stone having been reported in whatever categories they most closely resembled.

[bb] Figures for 1899 and 1909, and the upper figure for 1919, include the value of dimension soapstone; the lower figure for 1919, and the figures for 1929 and 1937, exclude its value. In 1929 dimension soapstone is included under "unspecified," and in 1937 with miscellaneous dimension stone.

[cc] Includes, in 1937, iodine, lithium minerals, vermiculite, chats, sulfur ore for agricultural purposes, natural sulfonated bitumen, flint lining for tube mills, op-

tical fluorspar, pebbles for grinding, gems and precious stones, graphite, mineral waters, diatomite and brucite.

Includes, in 1929, chats, flint lining for tube mills and pebbles for grinding, gem feldspar, micaceous minerals, diatomite, gems and precious stones, mineral waters, peat, optical fluorspar, lithium minerals and dimension soapstone.

Includes, in 1919, chats, flint lining for tube mills, lithium minerals, pebbles for grinding, chert and monazite.

EMPLOYMENT

*A general note appears at the end of this table, followed by specific notes referring to individual industries or groups of industries.*

| Year | Total Mining Including Oil and Gas Wells | | | Total Mining Excluding Oil and Gas Wells | | | Metal Mining and Ore Dressing Total | | |
|---|---|---|---|---|---|---|---|---|---|
| | Men (thous.) | Mandays (mil.) | Man-hours (mil.) | Men (thous.) | Mandays (mil.) | Man-hours (mil.) | Men (thous.) | Mandays (mil.) | Man-hours (mil.) |
| 1899 | .. | .. | .. | .. | .. | .. | .. | .. | .. |
| 1900 | .. | .. | .. | .. | .. | .. | .. | .. | .. |
| 1901 | .. | .. | .. | .. | .. | .. | .. | .. | .. |
| 1902 | .. | .. | 1,500 | .. | 137.8 | 1,245 | .. | 35.2 | 330 |
| 1903 | .. | .. | .. | .. | .. | .. | .. | .. | .. |
| 1904 | .. | .. | .. | .. | .. | .. | .. | .. | .. |
| 1905 | .. | .. | .. | .. | .. | .. | .. | .. | .. |
| 1906 | .. | .. | .. | .. | .. | .. | .. | .. | .. |
| 1907 | .. | .. | .. | .. | .. | .. | .. | .. | .. |
| 1908 | .. | .. | .. | .. | .. | .. | .. | .. | .. |
| 1909 | .. | .. | .. | .. | .. | .. | .. | .. | .. |
| 1910 | .. | .. | .. | .. | .. | .. | .. | .. | .. |
| 1911 | .. | .. | .. | .. | { 205.5 226.1 } | .. | .. | .. | .. |
| 1912 | .. | .. | .. | .. | 232.4 | .. | .. | .. | .. |
| 1913 | .. | .. | .. | .. | 253.8 | .. | 183.3 | 54.1 | .. |
| 1914 | .. | .. | .. | .. | 217.8 | .. | 152.7 | 42.4 | .. |
| 1915 | .. | .. | .. | .. | 215.7 | .. | 152.2 | 44.0 | .. |
| 1916 | .. | .. | .. | .. | 247.2 | .. | 209.3 | 60.82 | .. |
| 1917 | .. | .. | .. | .. | 267.3 | .. | 208.0 | 61.01 | .. |
| 1918 | .. | .. | .. | .. | 266.6 | .. | 189.2 | 57.22 | .. |
| 1919 | .. | .. | .. | .. | { 219.2 220.3 } | { 1,674 1,818 } | 147.7 | 42.10 | 361.1 |
| 1920 | .. | .. | .. | .. | 241.0 | .. | 138.9 | 41.59 | .. |
| 1921 | .. | .. | .. | .. | 178.2 | .. | 89.0 | 21.31 | .. |
| 1922 | .. | .. | .. | .. | 166.9 | .. | 104.7 | 29.36 | .. |
| 1923 | .. | .. | .. | .. | 226.3 | .. | 125.4 | 37.72 | .. |
| 1924 | .. | .. | .. | .. | 208.2 | .. | 126.0 | 37.48 | .. |
| 1925 | .. | .. | .. | .. | 200.4 | .. | 129.3 | 38.73 | .. |
| 1926 | .. | .. | .. | .. | 223.3 | .. | 129.9 | 38.85 | .. |
| 1927 | .. | .. | .. | .. | 202.6 | .. | 121.0 | 35.43 | .. |
| 1928 | .. | .. | .. | .. | 189.4 | .. | 112.1 | 33.23 | .. |
| 1929 | 1,022 | .. | 2,047 | { .. 843 } | { 195.1 198.8 } | { 1,599 1,634 } | 120.1 | 35.98 | 298.4 |
| 1930 | .. | .. | .. | 811 | 168.6 | .. | 102.7 | 28.31 | .. |
| 1931 | .. | .. | .. | 733 | 129.2 | 1,057 | 78.2 | 18.58 | 154.0 |
| 1932 | .. | .. | .. | 627 | 97.9 | 797 | 48.8 | 10.30 | 84.9 |
| 1933 | .. | .. | .. | 625 | 107.6 | 867 | 51.6 | 10.40 | 83.7 |
| 1934 | .. | .. | .. | 678 | 127.0 | 952 | 61.7 | 13.69 | 109.6 |
| 1935 | 841 | .. | 1,203 | 702 | 131.3 | 967 | 84.1 | 19.59 | 155.7 |
| 1936 | 884 | .. | 1,410 | 729 | 151.1 | 1,118 | 95.0 | 24.76 | 198.9 |
| 1937 | 933 | .. | 1,472 | 765 | 156.8 | 1,148 | 115.2 | 30.42 | 243.1 |
| 1938 | .. | .. | 1,207 | .. | 121.2 | 884 | 96.1 | 22.85 | 182.6 |
| 1939 | 847 | .. | 1,240 | 694 | 132.8 | 967 | 102.6 | 25.68 | 203.9 |

| | METAL MINING AND ORE DRESSING (continued) | | | | | | OTHER NONFERROUS METALS | | |
| | IRON ORE | | | COPPER | | | | | |
| Year | Men (thous.) | Mandays (mil.) | Man-hours (mil.) | Men (thous.) | Mandays (mil.) | Man-hours (mil.) | Men (thous.) | Mandays (mil.) | Man-hours (mil.) |
|---|---|---|---|---|---|---|---|---|---|
| 1899 | .. | .. | .. | .. | .. | .. | .. | .. | .. |
| 1900 | .. | .. | .. | .. | .. | .. | .. | .. | .. |
| 1901 | .. | .. | .. | .. | .. | .. | .. | .. | .. |
| 1902 | 46.2 | 12.0 | 119 | .. | 8.4 | 75 | .. | 14.8 | 136 |
| 1903 | .. | .. | .. | .. | .. | .. | .. | .. | .. |
| 1904 | .. | .. | .. | .. | .. | .. | .. | .. | .. |
| 1905 | .. | .. | .. | .. | .. | .. | .. | .. | .. |
| 1906 | .. | .. | .. | .. | .. | .. | .. | .. | .. |
| 1907 | .. | .. | .. | .. | .. | .. | .. | .. | .. |
| 1908 | .. | .. | .. | .. | .. | .. | .. | .. | .. |
| 1909 | .. | .. | .. | .. | .. | .. | .. | .. | .. |
| 1910 | .. | .. | .. | .. | .. | .. | .. | .. | .. |
| 1911 | .. | .. | .. | .. | .. | .. | .. | .. | .. |
| 1912 | .. | .. | .. | .. | .. | .. | .. | .. | .. |
| 1913 | .. | .. | .. | .. | .. | .. | .. | .. | .. |
| 1914 | .. | .. | .. | .. | .. | .. | .. | .. | .. |
| 1915 | 43.4 | 11.81 | 105.5 | 54.5 | 16.6 | .. | .. | .. | .. |
| 1916 | 57.0 | 15.64 | 140.8 | 70.5 | 22.06 | .. | 81.7 | 23.12 | .. |
| 1917 | 60.6 | 16.97 | 153.6 | 72.6 | 22.85 | .. | 74.8 | 21.20 | .. |
| 1918 | 55.7 | 16.30 | 148.6 | 69.2 | 22.31 | .. | 64.4 | 18.61 | .. |
| 1919 | 51.8 | 14.48 | 131.1 | 44.7 | 13.72 | 115.3 | 51.2 | 13.90 | 114.8 |
| 1920 | 50.6 | 14.54 | 133.5 | 41.4 | 13.28 | .. | 46.9 | 13.77 | .. |
| 1921 | 32.3 | 6.75 | 61.1 | 20.9 | 4.88 | .. | 35.8 | 9.68 | .. |
| 1922 | 35.8 | 8.95 | 79.4 | 30.6 | 8.90 | .. | 38.3 | 11.51 | .. |
| 1923 | 41.3 | 11.80 | 107.6 | 38.0 | 12.19 | .. | 46.1 | 13.73 | .. |
| 1924 | 38.8 | 10.20 | 91.3 | 39.2 | 12.60 | .. | 48.1 | 14.68 | .. |
| 1925 | 35.8 | 9.67 | 86.3 | 39.8 | 12.74 | .. | 53.7 | 16.32 | .. |
| 1926 | 34.4 | 9.40 | 84.2 | 40.5 | 13.23 | .. | 55.0 | 16.22 | .. |
| 1927 | 34.8 | 9.18 | 82.0 | 37.3 | 11.91 | .. | 48.9 | 14.34 | .. |
| 1928 | 30.2 | 8.01 | 71.4 | 37.5 | 12.39 | .. | 44.3 | 12.83 | .. |
| 1929 | 30.8 | 8.64 | 77.1 | 44.6 | 14.56 | 118.9 | 44.8 | 12.78 | 102.3 |
| 1930 | 31.0 | 8.04 | 71.6 | 33.8 | 10.21 | .. | 37.9 | 10.06 | 80.8 |
| 1931 | 22.9 | 4.60 | 40.9 | 24.8 | 6.54 | 53.1 | 30.4 | 7.44 | 60.0 |
| 1932 | 12.6 | 1.83 | 16.4 | 12.7 | 2.95 | 24.0 | 23.5 | 5.53 | 44.5 |
| 1933 | 15.1 | 2.12 | 17.9 | 9.0 | 2.14 | 17.0 | 27.5 | 6.14 | 48.8 |
| 1934 | 16.5 | 3.19 | 25.5 | 10.3 | 2.40 | 19.2 | 34.8 | 8.10 | 65.0 |
| 1935 | 15.0 | 3.28 | 26.3 | 13.1 | 3.64 | 29.1 | 56.0 | 12.68 | 100.4 |
| 1936 | 20.3 | 4.62 | 37.2 | 17.7 | 5.55 | 44.5 | 57.0 | 14.59 | 117.2 |
| 1937 | 25.9 | 6.40 | 51.4 | 27.0 | 8.40 | 67.2 | 62.3 | 15.62 | 124.5 |
| 1938 | 19.8 | 3.81 | 30.6 | 21.6 | 5.56 | 44.4 | 54.7 | 13.48 | 107.6 |
| 1939 | 21.9 | 4.86 | 39.1 | 23.2 | 6.77 | 54.1 | 57.5 | 14.06 | 110.8 |

| Year | PENNSYLVANIA ANTHRACITE | | | BITUMINOUS COAL | | | OIL AND GAS WELLS | | |
| | Men (thous.) | Mandays (mil.) | Man-hours (mil.) | Men (thous.) | Mandays (mil.) | Man-hours (mil.) | Men (thous.) | Mandays (mil.) | Man-hours (mil.) |
|---|---|---|---|---|---|---|---|---|---|
| 1899 | 139.6 | 24.15 | .. | 271.0 | 63.42 | .. | .. | .. | .. |
| 1900 | 144.2 | 23.94 | .. | 304.4 | 71.22 | .. | .. | .. | .. |
| 1901 | 145.3 | 28.48 | 270.6 | 340.2 | 76.55 | .. | .. | .. | .. |
| 1902 | 148.1 | 17.18 | 163.2 | 370.1 | 85.11 | 749.0 | 32.3 | .. | 118.8 |
| 1903 | 150.5 | 31.00 | 279.0 | 415.8 | 93.55 | 813.9 | .. | .. | .. |
| 1904 | 155.9 | 31.17 | 280.5 | 437.8 | 88.44 | 760.6 | .. | .. | .. |
| 1905 | 165.4 | 35.56 | 320.1 | 460.6 | 97.19 | 835.9 | .. | .. | .. |
| 1906 | 162.4 | 31.66 | 284.9 | 478.4 | 101.90 | 876.4 | .. | .. | .. |
| 1907 | 167.2 | 36.79 | 331.1 | 513.3 | 120.10 | 1032.9 | .. | .. | .. |
| 1908 | 174.2 | 34.84 | 313.5 | 516.3 | 99.64 | 856.9 | .. | .. | .. |
| 1909 | 173.5 | 35.57 | 320.1 | 543.2 | 113.52 | 976.3 | .. | .. | .. |
| 1910 | 169.5 | 38.82 | 349.3 | 555.5 | 120.55 | 1036.7 | .. | .. | .. |
| 1911 | 172.6 | 42.46 | 382.1 | 549.8 | 116.00 | 997.6 | .. | .. | .. |
| 1912 | 174.0 | 40.20 | 361.8 | 548.6 | 122.34 | 1052.2 | .. | .. | .. |
| 1913 | 175.7 | 45.17 | 406.5 | 571.9 | 132.68 | 1141.0 | .. | .. | .. |
| 1914 | 179.7 | 44.02 | 396.2 | 583.5 | 113.78 | 978.5 | .. | .. | .. |
| 1915 | 176.6 | 40.56 | 365.0 | 557.5 | 112.92 | 971.1 | .. | .. | .. |
| 1916 | 159.9 | 40.47 | 344.0 | 561.0 | 129.24 | 1111.5 | .. | .. | .. |
| 1917 | 154.2 | 43.90 | 351.2 | 603.1 | 146.50 | 1215.9 | .. | .. | .. |
| 1918 | 147.1 | 43.14 | 345.2 | 615.1 | 153.29 | 1244.7 | .. | .. | .. |
| 1919 | 154.6 | 41.08 | 328.6 | 621.8 | 121.54 | 979.6 | .. | .. | .. |
| 1920 | 145.1 | 39.36 | 314.9 | 639.3 | 140.98 | 1133.5 | .. | .. | .. |
| 1921 | 159.5 | 43.15 | 345.2 | 663.4 | 99.11 | 796.9 | .. | .. | .. |
| 1922 | 156.8 | 23.64 | 189.1 | 687.5 | 97.82 | 788.4 | .. | .. | .. |
| 1923 | 157.7 | 42.20 | 337.6 | 704.6 | 125.95 | 1015.1 | .. | .. | .. |
| 1924 | 160.0 | 43.90 | 351.2 | 619.4 | 106.02 | 856.6 | .. | .. | .. |
| 1925 | 160.3 | 29.11 | 232.9 | 588.3 | 114.92 | 928.6 | .. | .. | .. |
| 1926 | 165.4 | 40.31 | 322.5 | 593.5 | 127.49 | 1028.8 | .. | .. | .. |
| 1927 | 165.3 | 37.21 | 297.7 | 593.8 | 113.67 | 918.5 | .. | .. | .. |
| 1928 | 160.7 | 34.79 | 278.3 | 522.0 | 105.78 | 854.7 | .. | .. | .. |
| 1929 | 151.5 | 34.10 | 272.8 | 502.8 | 110.34 | 891.6 | 179.0 | .. | 413.3 |
| 1930 | 150.8 | 31.57 | 252.5 | 493.1 | 92.30 | 749.9 | .. | .. | .. |
| 1931 | 139.4 | 25.92 | 208.4 | 450.1 | 72.06 | 585.5 | .. | .. | .. |
| 1932 | 121.2 | 19.49 | 156.9 | 406.3 | 59.36 | 480.3 | .. | .. | .. |
| 1933 | 104.6 | 19.04 | 152.3 | 418.6 | 69.84 | 564.1 | .. | .. | .. |
| 1934 | 109.0 | 22.57 | 180.6 | 457.9 | 81.70 | 591.4 | .. | .. | .. |
| 1935 | 103.3 | 19.49 | 155.7 | 462.3 | 82.78 | 581.9 | 139.6 | .. | 236.3 |
| 1936 | 102.1 | 19.59 | 156.1 | 477.1 | 95.05 | 668.4 | 155.0 | .. | 291.3 |
| 1937 | 99.1 | 18.74 | 135.9 | 491.7 | 94.99 | 667.5 | 167.2 | .. | 323.4 |
| 1938 | 96.4 | 16.53 | 115.9 | 441.2 | 71.30 | 502.1 | 163.4 | .. | 323.4 |
| 1939 | 93.1 | 17.04 | 119.8 | 445.0 | 78.94 | 554.8 | 153.6 | .. | 273.2 |

| | STONE QUARRYING | | | | | | | | |
|---|---|---|---|---|---|---|---|---|---|
| | TOTAL | | | DIMENSION STONE | | | NONDIMENSION STONE | | |
| Year | Men (thous.) | Mandays (mil.) | Man-hours (mil.) | Men (thous.) | Mandays (mil.) | Man-hours (mil.) | Men (thous.) | Mandays (mil.) | Man-hours (mil.) |
| 1899 | .. | .. | .. | .. | .. | .. | .. | .. | .. |
| 1900 | .. | .. | .. | .. | .. | .. | .. | .. | .. |
| 1901 | .. | .. | .. | .. | .. | .. | .. | .. | .. |
| 1902 | .. | .. | .. | .. | .. | .. | .. | .. | .. |
| 1903 | .. | .. | .. | .. | .. | .. | .. | .. | .. |
| 1904 | .. | .. | .. | .. | .. | .. | .. | .. | .. |
| 1905 | .. | .. | .. | .. | .. | .. | .. | .. | .. |
| 1906 | .. | .. | .. | .. | .. | .. | .. | .. | .. |
| 1907 | .. | .. | .. | ... | .. | .. | .. | .. | .. |
| 1908 | .. | .. | .. | .. | .. | .. | .. | .. | .. |
| 1909 | .. | .. | .. | .. | .. | .. | .. | .. | .. |
| 1910 | .. | .. | .. | .. | .. | .. | .. | .. | .. |
| 1911 | .. | 20.67 | .. | .. | .. | .. | .. | .. | .. |
| 1912 | .. | 21.72 | .. | .. | .. | .. | .. | .. | .. |
| 1913 | .. | 21.36 | .. | .. | .. | .. | .. | .. | .. |
| 1914 | .. | 17.24 | .. | .. | .. | .. | .. | .. | .. |
| 1915 | .. | 17.88 | .. | .. | .. | .. | .. | .. | .. |
| 1916 | .. | 16.23 | .. | .. | .. | .. | .. | .. | .. |
| 1917 | .. | 15.44 | .. | .. | .. | .. | .. | .. | .. |
| 1918 | .. | 12.62 | .. | .. | .. | .. | .. | .. | .. |
| 1919 | .. | 14.06 | 132.9 | .. | .. | .. | .. | .. | .. |
| 1920 | .. | 16.50 | .. | .. | .. | .. | .. | .. | .. |
| 1921 | .. | 13.04 | .. | .. | .. | .. | .. | .. | .. |
| 1922 | .. | 14.60 | .. | .. | 3.70 | .. | .. | 10.90 | .. |
| 1923 | .. | 18.88 | .. | .. | 4.58 | .. | .. | 14.29 | .. |
| 1924 | .. | 19.02 | .. | .. | 5.33 | .. | .. | 13.69 | .. |
| 1925 | .. | 15.83 | .. | .. | 4.22 | .. | .. | 11.61 | .. |
| 1926 | .. | 14.96 | .. | .. | 3.85 | .. | .. | 11.12 | .. |
| 1927 | .. | 14.65 | .. | .. | 3.64 | .. | .. | 11.01 | .. |
| 1928 | .. | 14.03 | .. | .. | 3.61 | .. | .. | 10.41 | .. |
| 1929 | { .. / 63.1 | 13.23 / 16.93 | 122.5 } / 157.0 } | .. | 3.36 | 30.2 | .. | { 9.87 / 13.57 | 92.2 / 126.8 |
| 1930 | 59.6 | 15.14 | 137.6 | .. | 2.88 | 25.6 | .. | 12.27 | 112.0 |
| 1931 | 60.8 | 11.80 | 100.9 | .. | 1.93 | 16.4 | .. | 9.87 | 84.5 |
| 1932 | 47.7 | 8.26 | 70.1 | .. | 1.15 | 9.53 | .. | 7.11 | 60.5 |
| 1933 | 46.4 | 7.66 | 61.0 | .. | 1.05 | 8.30 | .. | 6.61 | 52.7 |
| 1934 | 45.2 | 8.16 | 62.5 | .. | .873 | 6.43 | .. | 7.28 | 56.1 |
| 1935 | 47.9 | 8.45 | 65.3 | .. | 1.06 | 8.14 | .. | 7.39 | 57.2 |
| 1936 | 50.3 | 10.58 | 84.9 | .. | 1.46 | 11.6 | .. | 9.12 | 73.3 |
| 1937 | 54.5 | 11.37 | 91.2 | .. | 1.64 | 13.3 | .. | 9.73 | 77.9 |
| 1938 | 47.6 | 9.44 | 74.5 | .. | 1.41 | 11.3 | .. | 8.03 | 63.2 |
| 1939 | 48.3 | 10.04 | 79.0 | .. | 1.56 | 12.4 | .. | 8.49 | 66.6 |

| | GYPSUM MINING | | | PHOSPHATE ROCK MINING | | |
|---|---|---|---|---|---|---|
| Year | Men (thous.) | Mandays (mil.) | Manhours (mil.) | Men (thous.) | Mandays (mil.) | Manhours (mil.) |
| 1899 | .. | .. | .. | .. | .. | .. |
| 1900 | .. | .. | .. | .. | .. | .. |
| 1901 | .. | .. | .. | .. | .. | .. |
| 1902 | .. | .247 | 2.47 | .. | 1.85 | 19.0 |
| 1903 | .. | .. | .. | .. | .. | .. |
| 1904 | .. | .. | .. | .. | .. | .. |
| 1905 | .. | .. | .. | .. | .. | .. |
| 1906 | .. | .. | .. | .. | .. | .. |
| 1907 | .. | .. | .. | .. | .. | .. |
| 1908 | .. | .. | .. | .. | .. | .. |
| 1909 | .. | .. | .. | .. | .. | .. |
| 1910 | .. | .. | .. | .. | .. | .. |
| 1911 | 1.70 | .418 | 4.03 | .. | .. | .. |
| 1912 | .. | .438 | 4.21 | .. | .. | .. |
| 1913 | .. | .443 | 4.25 | .. | .. | .. |
| 1914 | .. | .411 | 3.94 | .. | .. | .. |
| 1915 | .. | .396 | 3.79 | .. | .. | .. |
| 1916 | 1.57 | .435 | 4.16 | .. | .. | .. |
| 1917 | .. | .442 | 4.25 | .. | .. | .. |
| 1918 | .. | .350 | 3.39 | .. | .. | .. |
| 1919 | 1.55 | .429 | 4.18 | 5.79 | 1.12 | 11.3 |
| 1920 | 1.77 | .510 | 4.90 | 7.05 | 2.06 | 20.9 |
| 1921 | 1.72 | .443 | 4.30 | 5.54 | 1.18 | 11.9 |
| 1922 | 1.98 | .573 | 5.60 | 3.79 | .899 | 9.15 |
| 1923 | 2.33 | .675 | 6.60 | 3.53 | .926 | 9.39 |
| 1924 | 2.59 | .730 | 7.12 | 3.78 | 1.06 | 10.6 |
| 1925 | 2.93 | .829 | 7.41 | 3.59 | .999 | 9.99 |
| 1926 | 2.75 | .782 | 6.81 | 3.33 | .951 | 9.66 |
| 1927 | 2.59 | .686 | 5.91 | 3.04 | .906 | 9.20 |
| 1928 | 2.28 | .613 | 5.31 | 3.24 | .909 | 9.32 |
| 1929 | 2.04 | .521 | 4.61 | 3.22 | .938 | 9.62 |
| 1930 | 1.44 | .326 | 2.78 | 3.28 | .937 | 9.73 |
| 1931 | 1.37 | .272 | 2.30 | 2.67 | .614 | 6.06 |
| 1932 | 1.02 | .140 | 1.12 | 1.90 | .380 | 3.64 |
| 1933 | 1.00 | .149 | 1.18 | 2.30 | .516 | 4.70 |
| 1934 | 1.06 | .186 | 1.42 | 2.91 | .694 | 5.99 |
| 1935 | .992 | .196 | 1.56 | 3.10 | .757 | 6.64 |
| 1936 | 1.22 | .280 | 2.21 | 3.23 | .883 | 7.84 |
| 1937 | 1.31 | .297 | 2.37 | 3.48 | .956 | 8.27 |
| 1938 | 1.11 | .242 | 1.92 | .. | .835 | 6.97 |
| 1939 | 1.24 | .312 | 2.47 | 3.31 | .827 | 6.68 |

*General Note to Table A-3*

For the most part the employment data shown in this table are derived for 1902 from the Census, and for other years from the accident statistics collected by the U. S. Bureau of Mines. Our chief concern is their comparability with output. In 1902 both output and employment are effectively derived from the same (Census) canvass, and therefore tend to have the same coverage. Even so, various adjustments all of which are described in the following notes, had to be made for 1902. For more recent years it will be seen that we use employment data collected quite independently of the reporting of output; these were gathered primarily in order to measure accident rates. Since employment and accidents are measured in the same canvass, complete coverage is not of first importance when the aim is to compute accident frequencies. For our purposes, however, the coverage of the accident employment data is obviously of vital significance. Our output data are practically complete; and our employment data must be equally comprehensive if accurate indexes of productivity are to result. With certain exceptions (which are noted) the coverage of these data appears to be satisfactory, by comparison with Census figures for employment and by other tests. In a few cases of patent undercoverage we have ventured to make adjustments.

Figures for men employed as collected by the Bureau of Mines are "active period averages," i.e., averages of monthly counts confined to the months in which the enterprise was active; or exceptionally, in recent years, they may represent an actual number of mandays taken from payroll records, divided by the number of days during the year that the mine operated. The latter is of course the superior method of measurement. Figures for mandays usually consist of the active period average number of employees reported, multiplied by the average number of days the mine was active (the computation is carried out separately for each enterprise by the Bureau of Mines); exceptionally, for recent years, they may include actual payroll records of mandays worked. Practically throughout, figures for manhours represent mandays multiplied by nominal hours worked per day (the computation is carried out, except where otherwise noted, by the Bureau of Mines for individual establishments), rather than a summation of hours recorded in payrolls. For further discussion of these measures, see pp. 272-75 above and Chapter 3 of the text.

In the special case of oil and gas wells, accident data on employment do not exist, and we depend almost entirely upon the few Census canvasses of the industry that have been made. The data differ from those for other industries also in covering wage earners only, instead of all persons subject to accident hazard; further, they are confined to average number of men and manhours worked. See notes below.

*Metal Mining and Ore Dressing, Total*

The metal mining industries have been defined to include not only the actual mining of metallic ores, but also subsequent ore dressing operations preliminary to smelting and refining.

Because of peculiarities in the data, employment totals for the group include certain nonmetals and exclude one metal mining industry. The excluded industry is placer gold mining. We have chosen not to include it in our indexes of employment and productivity because employment data are inadequate by reason of the prevalence of extremely small scale and migratory operations. Since there is no way of determining how the coverage of the industry has varied over time, it seemed best to exclude it.[1] The nonmetals included are fluorspar operations in Illinois and Kentucky, and pyrites. The former is included in the Bureau of Mines statistics of lead and zinc operations in Illinois and Kentucky because the products are often jointly produced, and because accident hazards in mines producing lead and zinc are similar to those in mines producing fluorspar. Pyrites has been included in the

[1] However, employment data for placer mining are included in the statistics of Chapter 3. See also Census reports; and Charles W. Merrill, Charles W. Henderson and O. E. Kiessling, *Small-Scale Placer Mines as a Source of Gold, Employment and Livelihood in 1935* (National Research Project, Philadelphia, 1937).

*Footnotes to Table A-3 continued on next page.*

*Footnotes to Table A-3, continued.*

Bureau of Mines statistics for miscellaneous metal mining because the cinder is used in some metallurgical works for its iron and copper content. Neither pyrites nor fluorspar can be excluded from the total without resort to rather rough estimates; since these products are very unimportant we have made no attempt to derive employment estimates which exclude them, but have preferred instead to include them in our output indexes.

For all years for which figures are given except 1902, the source for employment in mining (as distinct from milling or beneficiating) is the U. S. Bureau of Mines annual publication, "Metal-Mine Accidents in the United States." We have adjusted the published totals to exclude employment in Alaska and in placer mining. Figures for Alaska (including placer employment) are published separately and have been subtracted. For 1912–16 and 1924–39 placer employment (including Alaska) also is given separately and may be subtracted. (In so doing we deduct figures for placers in Alaska twice over, and as we wish to do this only once, the amount concerned must be added back. For most of these years unpublished data on persons employed at placers in Alaska were supplied to us in a special tabulation by Mr. W. W. Adams of the U. S. Bureau of Mines.) For 1911 and 1917–23 we estimated the number of placer miners to be excluded on the basis of gold production from placers in these years.

Except for 1902, employment at milling and ore dressing establishments is derived from the series of annual reports by the U. S. Bureau of Mines entitled "Accidents at Metallurgical Works in the United States." For metal mining as a whole these are available back to 1913, though separate figures for copper, for example, date from 1915. We have subtracted Alaska from the totals. The chief defect of these data is that employment at auxiliary works connected with mills (which we wish to include) is not separated from employment at such works attached to smelters (which we wish to exclude).[2] A single series covers both, because auxiliary works sometimes serve both mills and smelters. It is therefore difficult to secure a figure for the number of mandays or manhours associated with the one or with the other separately. We have attempted to estimate the amount of employment at such works which should be included with that at mills. These estimates were based on figures for recent years kindly furnished by Mr. W. W. Adams. In his letter to us Mr. Adams explained that the Bureau of Mines received separate figures for mill and smelter auxiliary works in most instances, but that some large operators reported a combined figure. The figures he forwarded to us gave the distribution of auxiliary works reported separately for mills and smelters. On the basis of this partial distribution of auxiliary employment, we derived a figure for all auxiliary employment associated with milling in 1935–39. For earlier years we extrapolated the ratio of mill auxiliary employment to total auxiliary employment derived from these data. Such estimates were carried through in terms of mandays, and active period averages for men employed were then adjusted on the basis of the manday relationships. The calculation for mandays—our basic measure—is shown in Worksheets I and II. For 1911 and 1912 employment at mills is not available; for these years the manday index for metal mining and milling in Table A-5 was derived by extrapolating the 1913 figure, with the use of employment data relating to mines only (Worksheet II, column 1).

[2] Auxiliary works are described, not very specifically, as "yards, shops, construction, etc., in connection with mills and smelters." Their nature is further suggested by the statement that ladders, scaffolds, railway cars and hand tools are causes of accidents. Probably they are concerned chiefly with maintenance or development work. (See e.g., U. S. Bureau of Mines, *Technical Paper 395*, "Accidents at Metallurgical Works, 1924," pp. 7–8.)

Worksheet I

Derivation of Mandays at Mills and Auxiliary Works Attached to Them,
Metal Mining, 1916–39[a]
*Thousand mandays, except columns (3) and (6).*

| Year | (1) Mills[b] | (2) All Auxiliary Works[b] | (3) Ratio of Mandays at Mill Auxiliary Works to Mandays at All Auxiliary Works[c] | (4) Auxiliary Works Attached to Mills[d] | (5) Mills and Auxiliary Works Attached to Them[e] | (6) Ratio of Mandays at Mills and Auxiliary Works Attached to Them to Mandays at Mills Only[f] |
|---|---|---|---|---|---|---|
| 1916 | 7,041 | 4,729 | .. | 1,366 | 8,407 | 1.1940 |
| 1917 | *7,311 | 5,104 | .. | 1,475 | 8,786 | 1.2018 |
| 1918 | 6,755 | 6,033 | .. | 1,743 | 8,498 | 1.2580 |
| 1919 | 5,059 | 4,852 | .. | 1,402 | 6,461 | 1.2771 |
| 1920 | 5,044 | 5,509 | .. | 1,592 | 6,636 | 1.3156 |
| 1921 | 2,411 | 2,493 | .. | 720 | 3,131 | 1.2986 |
| 1922 | 3,315 | 4,221 | .. | 1,219 | 4,534 | 1.3677 |
| 1923 | 4,435 | 5,412 | .. | 1,564 | 5,999 | 1.3526 |
| 1924 | 4,828 | 5,287 | .. | 1,528 | 6,356 | 1.3165 |
| 1925 | 5,125 | 5,844 | .. | 1,688 | 6,813 | 1.3294 |
| 1926 | 5,215 | 5,776 | .. | 1,669 | 6,884 | 1.3200 |
| 1927 | 4,693 | 5,386 | .. | 1,556 | 6,249 | 1.3316 |
| 1928 | 3,707 | 4,800 | .. | 1,387 | 5,094 | 1.3742 |
| 1929 | 4,280 | 5,130 | .. | 1,482 | 5,762 | 1.3463 |
| 1930 | 3,339 | 3,971 | .. | 1,147 | 4,486 | 1.3435 |
| 1931 | 2,310 | 2,554 | .. | 738 | 3,048 | 1.3195 |
| 1932 | 1,274 | 1,809 | .. | 523 | 1,797 | 1.4105 |
| 1933 | 1,311 | 1,787 | .. | 516 | 1,827 | 1.3936 |
| 1934 | 1,746 | 2,195 | .. | 634 | 2,380 | 1.3631 |
| 1935 | 2,817 | 3,062 | .28892 | 885 | 3,702 | 1.3142 |
| 1936 | 3,414 | 3,823 | .29851 | 1,141 | 4,555 | 1.3342 |
| 1937 | 4,031 | 4,886 | .31056 | 1,517 | 5,548 | 1.3763 |
| 1938 | 2,956 | 3,892 | .33337 | 1,297 | 4,253 | 1.4388 |
| 1939 | 3,453 | 4,029 | .34543 | 1,392 | 4,845 | 1.4031 |

[a] Data for mills include Alaska; there were apparently no auxiliary works in Alaska.

[b] U. S. Bureau of Mines annual publication, "Accidents at Metallurgical Works," and bulletins on "Health and Safety Statistics."

[c] Ratios based on a breakdown of mandays at auxiliary works between mills and smelters supplied by Mr. W. W. Adams of the Bureau of Mines. This breakdown has a coverage (in manday terms) of all auxiliary works as follows: 1935, 98 percent; 1936, 88 percent; 1937, 86 percent; 1938 and 1939, 87 percent.

[d] For 1916–35, column (2) × .28892; 1936–39, columns (2) × (3). The alternative to this use of a constant (1935) ratio for 1935 and all earlier years is to make the segregation depend upon mandays at mills and smelters respectively (see Vivian E. Spencer, *Mineral Extractive Industries*, National Research Project, Philadelphia, 1940, p. 124). However, corresponding ratios obtained in this fashion run much higher (e.g., .40454 for 1935) than those available for recent years from the sample data quoted, and would appear to lead to the overestimation of the employment we wish to include.

[e] (1) + (4).

[f] (5) ÷ (1). This ratio is used in Worksheet IV below.

*Footnotes to Table A-3 continued on next page.*

*Footnotes to Table A-3, continued.*

Worksheet II

Derivation of Mandays at Mines and Mills, Including Auxiliary Works
Attached to Mills, Metal Mining, 1913–39

*Thousand mandays*

| Year | (1)<br>Mines Only[a] | (2)<br>Mills, including<br>Alaska[b] | (3)<br>Mills,<br>Alaska[c] | (4)<br>Mills, excluding<br>Alaska[d] | (5)<br>Mines and<br>Mills[e] |
|---|---|---|---|---|---|
| 1911 | 42,406 | .. | .. | .. | .. |
| 1912 | 43,397 | .. | .. | .. | .. |
| 1913 | 49,298 | .. | .. | 4,846[f] | 54,144 |
| 1914 | 37,860 | .. | 76 | 4,491[f] | 42,351 |
| 1915 | 38,388 | .. | 159 | 5,573[f] | 43,961 |
| 1916 | 52,742 | 8,407 | 333 | 8,074 | 60,816 |
| 1917 | 52,367 | 8,786 | 140 | 8,647 | 61,014 |
| 1918 | 48,837 | 8,498 | 112 | 8,386 | 57,223 |
| 1919 | 35,771 | 6,461 | 134 | 6,327 | 42,098 |
| 1920 | 35,120 | 6,636 | 167 | 6,469 | 41,589 |
| 1921 | 18,355 | 3,131 | 176 | 2,955 | 21,310 |
| 1922 | 24,924 | 4,534 | 94 | 4,441 | 29,365 |
| 1923 | 31,879 | 5,999 | 163 | 5,836 | 37,715 |
| 1924 | 31,219 | 6,356 | 93 | 6,263 | 37,482 |
| 1925 | 32,070 | 6,813 | 154 | 6,658 | 38,728 |
| 1926 | 32,131 | 6,884 | 163 | 6,721 | 38,852 |
| 1927 | 29,329 | 6,249 | 150 | 6,099 | 35,428 |
| 1928 | 28,277 | 5,094 | 137 | 4,957 | 33,234 |
| 1929 | 30,356 | 5,762 | 141 | 5,621 | 35,977 |
| 1930 | 23,953 | 4,486 | 133 | 4,354 | 28,307 |
| 1931 | 15,646 | 3,048 | 112 | 2,936 | 18,582 |
| 1932 | 8,611 | 1,797 | 105 | 1,692 | 10,303 |
| 1933 | 8,652 | 1,827 | 79 | 1,748 | 10,400 |
| 1934 | 11,390 | 2,380 | 78 | 2,301 | 13,691 |
| 1935 | 15,981 | 3,702 | 91 | 3,611 | 19,592 |
| 1936 | 20,325 | 4,555 | 119 | 4,436 | 24,761 |
| 1937 | 24,999 | 5,548 | 124 | 5,424 | 30,423 |
| 1938 | 18,730 | 4,253 | 133 | 4,120 | 22,850 |
| 1939 | 20,943 | 4,845 | 105 | 4,741 | 25,684 |

[a] U. S. Bureau of Mines, "Metal-Mine Accidents in the United States." Totals
have been adjusted, as described in accompanying notes, to exclude employment
in Alaska and at placer mines.

[b] Worksheet I, column (5). Data include estimated employment at auxiliary works
attached to mills.

[c] U. S. Bureau of Mines, "Accidents at Metallurgical Works" and bulletins on
"Health and Safety Statistics." There are apparently no auxiliary works in Alaska.

[d] (2) — (3).

[e] (1) + (4).

[f] U. S. Bureau of Mines, "Accidents at Metallurgical Works" and bulletins on
"Health and Safety Statistics." Auxiliary works appear to have been included in
the published figures for mills in these years, but coverage may not have been
complete.

Data on manhours in metal mining are shown for all the years for which reasonably good figures can be obtained. Their reliability is compromised chiefly by the fact that figures for hours per day (used to convert mandays to manhours) usually relate to nominal rather than actual hours worked. For 1931–39 manhours in mining (as distinguished from milling) are taken directly from "Metal-Mine Accidents in the United States." For the same period manhours at mills (excluding auxiliaries) were taken directly from "Accidents at Metallurgical Works" and "Health and Safety Statistics." Manhours at auxiliaries attached to mills were estimated separately as follows: mandays at auxiliaries attached to mills (Worksheet I, column 4) were multiplied by average hours per day at all auxiliaries, the source being the same as for mill employment. For 1929 we derived manhours in mining by summing data for iron ore, copper, and other nonferrous metals (see below); and we obtained manhours in milling (including auxiliaries) by multiplying mandays (Worksheet II, column 4) by hours per shift at all mills, derived from "Accidents at Metallurgical Works, 1929." For 1919 manhours in mining and milling (including auxiliary works) are the sum of the data for iron ore, copper and other nonferrous metals (see below).

For 1902 the basic source is the Census (*Special Reports*, "Mines and Quarries, 1902"). The data for average employment of wage earners found in that volume are not comparable with our figures for later years for two reasons. (1) The latter figures, based on accident reports, are intended to cover all persons subject to mine hazards, and to exclude clerical workers and others not so subject. It seems probable that this concept is slightly more inclusive than the "wage earners" of Census reports. Accordingly, in deriving figures for 1902 from the Census of that year, we have included the salaried category *Superintendents, managers, foremen, surveyors*; but we have excluded the salaried categories *General officers* and *Clerks*. (2) Our data for men, based on Bureau of Mines statistics for all years except 1902, are "active period averages," i.e., averages of monthly counts confined to the months in which the enterprise was active. The 1902 Census figures for wage earners, on the other hand, are full year averages derived in a rather unusual manner. Where an enterprise worked fewer than 300 days, say 253, the number of wage earners reported was multiplied by 253/300 in the course of editing the schedules, to yield an indicated number of 300-day wage earners. Where an enterprise worked more than 300 days in 1902 the Census refrained from making such an adjustment. (See "Mines and Quarries, 1902," pp. 1122-23.) Totals for each industry in this Census therefore represent a combination of averages for individual establishments, partly as originally reported, partly as adjusted by the Census personnel. Since there is no way of unscrambling the result, active period average employment cannot be derived for 1902. Mandays and manhours were estimated as follows: First, we estimated true 300-day averages for each industry. That is, in industries in which some firms reported more than 300 days' operation we made a slight upward adjustment of the wage earner total: if one fifth of the firms worked 315 days (i.e., were reported in the group 300-330 days; "Mines and Quarries, 1902," p. 109), and the remainder 300 days or fewer, the wage earner average was multiplied by 303/300. (Note: $300 \times 4 + 315 = 1,515$; $1,515 \div 5 = 303$ days active implicit in Census average.) This estimate of the true number of wage earners was multiplied by 300 to yield the number of wage earner mandays. The number of superintendents, etc. (see above) was then multiplied by the average number of days all firms in the industry were active to yield the salary earner mandays which we have to include. The two sets of mandays (wage and salary) were then added together. Mandays were converted into manhours with the help of the distribution of firms by nominal hours per shift ("Mines and Quarries, 1902," p. 110). These calculations were performed separately for each metal mining industry distinguished by the Census, and are indicated in Worksheet III.

*Footnotes to Table A-3 continued on next page.*

Worksheet III

Derivation of Employment Estimates For Metal Mining and Ore Dressing, 1902

| Industry | (1) Wage Earners (Census Average)[c] | (2) Days Active Implicit in Census Average[d] | (3) Superintendents, Managers, Surveyors, Foremen[e] | (4) Days Mine Was Active[d] | (5) Total Mandays[f] (thous.) | (6) Estimated Hours per Shift[g] | (7) Total Manhours[h] (thous.) |
|---|---|---|---|---|---|---|---|
| Iron ore | 38,851 | 300 | 1,628 | 260[j] | 12,008[j] | 9.9 | 118,879 |
| Copper | 26,007 | 315 | 737 | 250 | 8,376 | 8.95 | 74,965 |
| Lead and zinc | 9,067[k] | 300 | 729 | 185 | 2,855 | 8.9 | 25,410 |
| Gold and silver[a] | 34,041[l] | 310 | 2,436[m] | 200 | 11,040 | 9.2 | 101,568 |
| Mercury | 1,329 | 323 | 74 | 288 | 450 | 9.5 | 4,275 |
| Bauxite | 150 | 300 | 32 | 259 | 53 | 10 | 530 |
| Pyrites[b] | 970 | 306 | 38 | 261 | 307 | 9.8 | 3,009 |
| Manganese | 194 | 300 | 16 | 138 | 130[n] | 10 | 1,300 |
| TOTAL | | | | | 35,219 | | 329,936 |

[a] Deep mines only.
[b] Includes sulfur from which it cannot be separated; however, production of sulfur was unimportant in 1902.
[c] *Special Reports*, "Mines and Quarries, 1902," p. 93.
[d] *Ibid.*, p. 109. Days were weighted by number of mines.
[e] *Ibid.*, see individual chapters.
[f] (1) × (2) + (3) × (4).
[g] "Mines and Quarries, 1902," p. 110. Hours per shift were weighted by number of mines.
[h] (5) × (6).
[i] N. Yaworski and others, *Iron Mining* (National Research Project, Philadelphia, 1940), p. 215, footnote h.
[j] The indicated amount is 12,078 thousand mandays. However the Census industry produced 35,554 thousand long tons of which only 35,347 thousand long tons were true iron ore, the remainder being manganiferous ore included by us under manganese. A proportion-

ate adjustment reduces employment to 12,008 thousand mandays as shown.

[k] The 6,835 wage earners reported for Kansas and Missouri were increased to 8,021 for undercoverage: ratio based on value of products. See "Mines and Quarries, 1902," pp. 19-20, 446, 463-65; *Thirteenth Census*, "Mines and Quarries, 1909," p. 15.

[l] The 33,821 wage earners reported for the industry were increased to 34,041 to allow for undercoverage: ratio based on value of products. See "Mines and Quarries, 1902," pp. 510, 512.

[m] Of 1,725 superintendents, etc., in gold and silver mines ("Mines and Quarries, 1902," p. 578) 1,586 were allocated to deep mines on the basis of the ratio for "other salaried employees" (p. 512); to these were added 850 foremen working below ground.

[n] Includes 70 thousand mandays in the mining of manganiferous iron ore: see note j.

*Iron Ore Mining and Beneficiating*

Employment totals, which include both mining and milling (or beneficiating), are available for all years since 1915, and our figures for these years are therefore directly transcribed from other sources. For the years 1923–39 the data are from the iron chapters in recent issues of *Minerals Yearbook*, especially the 1937 *Yearbook*, p. 600. The data for these years are also to be found in the National Research Project report on the industry prepared by N. Yaworski and others (*Iron Mining*, Philadelphia, 1940). In addition, this report presents comparable data for the period 1915–22. According to a letter from Mr. Yaworski, now with the Bureau of the Census, the NRP data for 1915–22 were compiled from the original reports submitted by companies to the Bureau of Mines. He states that the data for 1915–22 are fully comparable with those for later years. For practically all years the employment totals are estimates based on a coverage close to 100 percent. In addition, manhours were estimated for some of the mines in all years. (See *Iron Mining*, Table A-6, pp. 218, 225.)

For 1902, data were derived by the method described above in the note on "Metal mining" (see Worksheet III).

For 1911–14, data on employment at mills are not available. For these years the manday index in Table A-5 was derived by extrapolation of the 1915 index with the use of employment data relating to mines only. The figures, taken from "Metal-Mine Accidents in the United States," are:

|      | Men<br>(thous.) | Mandays<br>(mil.) |
|------|------|-------|
| 1911 | 46.0 | 12.75 |
| 1912 | 45.7 | 13.04 |
| 1913 | 51.1 | 15.06 |
| 1914 | 44.8 | 11.75 |
| 1915 | 39.4 | 10.71 |

*Copper Mining and Milling*

As with other metal mining industries, the nonmanufacturing activities of the copper industry include ore dressing (or milling) as well as mining. For 1902 the derivation of the data has already been described. For years since 1911 the basic sources are the U. S. Bureau of Mines annual publications, "Metal-Mine Accidents in the United States" and "Accidents at Metallurgical Works in the United States." Employment in Alaska is of course excluded. For copper mills, separate data are available back to 1915; however, as with metal mining as a whole, employment at auxiliary works connected with mills is not separated from similar employment attached to smelters. A single series covers both. We therefore estimated the former (which alone we wish to include), using ratios already derived for metal mining as a whole. The computations are shown in Worksheet IV, and were carried through in terms of mandays only. Active period averages for men employed were then adjusted on the basis of the manday relationships. The procedure for manhours is discussed below.

For 1911–14 employment at copper milling establishments is not available. For these years the manday index in Table A-5 was derived by extrapolating the 1915 figure, and employment data relating exclusively to mines were used. The figures for these years, taken from "Metal-Mine Accidents in the United States," are:

|      | Men<br>(thous.) | Mandays<br>(mil.) |
|------|------|-------|
| 1911 | 44.7 | 13.77 |
| 1912 | 51.3 | 15.69 |
| 1913 | 55.7 | 17.22 |
| 1914 | 44.1 | 12.68 |
| 1915 | 46.5 | 13.98 |

*Footnotes to Table A-3 continued on next page.*

Worksheet IV

Derivation of Manday Employment in Copper Mining and Milling, 1915–39
*Thousand mandays, except column (3)*

| | (1) | (2) | (3) | (4) Mills and | (5) Mines and |
|------|------------|--------|--------|------------------------|------------------|
| Year | Mines Only[a] | Mills[b] | Ratio[c] | Auxiliary Works[d] | Mills[e] |
| 1915 | 13,984 | .. | .. | 2,651[f] | 16,635 |
| 1916 | 18,680 | 2,827 | 1.1940 | 3,375 | 22,055 |
| 1917 | 18,829 | 3,343 | 1.2018 | 4,018 | 22,847 |
| 1918 | 18,900 | 2,711 | 1.2580 | 3,411 | 22,311 |
| 1919 | 11,632 | 1,636 | 1.2771 | 2,089 | 13,721 |
| 1920 | 10,930 | 1,787 | 1.3156 | 2,351 | 13,281 |
| 1921 | 4,318 | 435 | 1.2986 | 565 | 4,883 |
| 1922 | 7,326 | 1,154 | 1.3677 | 1,578 | 8,904 |
| 1923 | 10,071 | 1,565 | 1.3526 | 2,117 | 12,188 |
| 1924 | 10,023 | 1,956 | 1.3165 | 2,576 | 12,599 |
| 1925 | 10,059 | 2,018 | 1.3294 | 2,683 | 12,742 |
| 1926 | 10,332 | 2,199 | 1.3200 | 2,902 | 13,234 |
| 1927 | 9,464 | 1,838 | 1.3316 | 2,447 | 11,911 |
| 1928 | 9,765 | 1,911 | 1.3742 | 2,626 | 12,391 |
| 1929 | 11,849 | 2,010 | 1.3463 | 2,707 | 14,556 |
| 1930 | 8,136 | 1,546 | 1.3435 | 2,076 | 10,212 |
| 1931 | 5,040 | 1,138 | 1.3195 | 1,502 | 6,542 |
| 1932 | 2,277 | 476 | 1.4105 | 672 | 2,949 |
| 1933 | 1,689 | 324 | 1.3936 | 451 | 2,140 |
| 1934 | 1,840 | 411 | 1.3631 | 560 | 2,400 |
| 1935 | 2,774 | 657 | 1.3142 | 863 | 3,637 |
| 1936 | 4,333 | 914 | 1.3342 | 1,219 | 5,552 |
| 1937 | 6,467 | 1,406 | 1.3763 | 1,935 | 8,402 |
| 1938 | 4,301 | 871 | 1.4388 | 1,254 | 5,555 |
| 1939 | 5,255 | 1,077 | 1.4031 | 1,511 | 6,766 |

[a] U. S. Bureau of Mines, "Metal-Mine Accidents in the United States." In the exclusion of Alaska, when data for copper mining in that territory were not given explicitly they could be obtained by deducting employment in gold, silver and miscellaneous metal mining from employment in all metal mining in Alaska.

[b] U. S. Bureau of Mines, "Accidents at Metallurgical Works" and bulletins on "Health and Safety Statistics." Data do not include employment at auxiliary works. Copper mills, if any, in Alaska are included; but employment at such mills is slight and (according to a letter from Mr. W. W. Adams of the Bureau of Mines) in 1939 was zero. For 1930 and earlier years figures cover only mills employing 30 or more persons; for 1931, 28 or more persons. For 1932–39 coverage is believed to be complete. Figures available for 1932 suggest that the number of persons employed at mills with fewer than 28 employees is negligible.

[c] Ratio of mandays at mills and auxiliary works attached to them to mandays at mills only, all metal mining. See Worksheet I column (6).

[d] (2) × (3).

[e] (1) + (4).

[f] U. S. Bureau of Mines, "Accidents at Metallurgical Works." This figure apparently includes auxiliaries.

Data on manhours are shown for all years for which reasonably good figures can be constructed. Their reliability is compromised chiefly by the fact that figures on hours per day (used to convert mandays to manhours) usually relate to nominal rather than to actual hours worked. For 1931–39 manhours in copper mining are given in "Metal-Mine Accidents." For 1932–39 manhours at mills (excluding auxiliaries) were taken from "Accidents at Metallurgical Works"; manhours at auxiliaries were estimated by multiplying mandays at copper auxiliaries (column 4 minus column 2, Worksheet IV) by average hours per day reported for all auxiliary works. For 1931 manhours at copper mills and auxiliaries were derived by multiplying mandays at such establishments (see Worksheet IV) by average hours per day reported for all mills and auxiliary works. (In years when hours per day at all mills, and at copper mills only, were both available, they were close enough to warrant our following this procedure to obtain the estimate for 1931.) For 1919 and 1929 the manhour estimates are based on average (nominal) hours per day for copper mining, taken from the Census of Mines and Quarries for those years; these averages rest on distributions of mines working a given number of hours per week. Average hours per week were then divided by an estimate of days worked per week from the 1929 Census. (For 1929 it was possible also to derive an hours figure from "Metal-Mine Accidents." The Census figure was considered preferable because of the apparently incomplete coverage of the hours data reported for that year in "Accidents.") The figure for manhours in 1902 was derived above in the note on metal mining as a whole (see Worksheet III).

*Other Nonferrous Metals*

This classification is essentially a catch-all for metal mining other than iron ore and copper (both of which are discussed above). It includes especially lead, zinc, gold, silver, mercury, bauxite, pyrites and manganese. Employment at milling establishments as well as at mines is covered. As already explained, placer mining has not been included. Much the most important industries in the group are lode gold and silver, and lead and zinc. However, the only breakdown by industries in which separate employment and output figures can be related is a partial one, viz., lead and zinc mining (not including milling) in the Mississippi Valley, and mercury mining and recovery. For these two divisions separate employment data are given in Table A-4 below.

In good part the figures for employment at other nonferrous metal mines in Table A-3 have been derived by subtracting data given there for iron ore and copper from the totals for metal mining and milling. Here we shall note only those cases where this procedure was not followed, and where figures for the group were obtained separately. Thus the derivation of the figures for 1902 has already been given in Worksheet III above. There remains the question of manhours.

For 1919 we estimated manhours by multiplying our manday figure by an estimate of hours per day from the Census of that year. For 1929 and 1930 we obtained manhours in mining by multiplying mandays in mining by a figure for average hours per shift derived from data in the accident reports. This computation was made separately for the following accident bulletin classifications: lead and zinc (Mississippi Valley); and gold, silver and miscellaneous metal mines. Manhours in milling in 1929 and 1930 were derived by subtracting estimated manhours in copper and iron ore milling from manhours in all metal milling. (Manhours in all metal mills and auxiliaries were estimated in these years in the manner described for 1929 in the note on "Metal mining" above.)

For 1911–15 employment at mills is not available. For these years we derived the manday index in Table A-5 by extrapolating the 1916 figure, using employment data relating to mines only. The figures, based on "Metal-Mine Accidents in the United States," are:

*Footnotes to Table A-3 continued on next page.*

*Footnotes to Table A-3, continued.*

|      | Men (thous.) | Mandays (mil.) |
|------|------|-------|
| 1911 | 58.2 | 15.88 |
| 1912 | 53.7 | 14.67 |
| 1913 | 61.5 | 17.01 |
| 1914 | 49.0 | 13.43 |
| 1915 | 48.3 | 13.69 |
| 1916 | 69.8 | 19.19 |

### Pennsylvania Anthracite

Data for men employed are from *Minerals Yearbook* and its predecessor *Mineral Resources*. These figures are available also in U. S. Bureau of Mines, "Coal-Mine Accidents in the United States," but for the years 1909, 1911, 1933-35 and 1938 the two sources differ slightly. For 1909 both took their figures from the Census of Mines and Quarries of that year, but the latter used a preliminary figure only. In 1911 the two sources made separate canvasses; the same is true for years after 1930. Where slight differences occurred between the two sources, we chose the *Minerals Yearbook* data, in order to obtain employment figures from the same source as those for output.

Mandays were derived as follows. For 1899–1911, the average number employed was multiplied by average days active, both from *Mineral Resources*. For 1912–32, the data were taken directly from "Coal-Mine Accidents." For 1933–34, the average number employed was multiplied by average days active, both from *Minerals Yearbook*. For 1935–39, mandays were derived directly from *Minerals Yearbook*.

Manhours in 1901 and 1902 were obtained by multiplying mandays by 9.5, the average hours per shift derived by the National Research Project from 1902 Census material (Vivian E. Spencer, *Mineral Extractive Industries, 1880–1938*, Philadelphia, 1940, p. 154). For 1903–29, the figures represent multiplication of mandays by the established length of the shift: 9.0 hours from 1903 to 1915, 8.5 for 1916 (hours per shift changed from 9 to 8 in May), 8.0 from 1917 to 1929. (See *ibid.*, p. 117.) For 1930–39, data are from accident bulletins; where our manday figure differed from the bulletin figure, we adjusted manhours according to the ratio of the two.

### Bituminous Coal

Data for men employed are from *Minerals Yearbook* and its predecessor *Mineral Resources*. These figures are also available in "Coal-Mine Accidents," but for the years 1909, 1911, 1913, 1931 and 1933–39 the two sources differ slightly. For 1909 both sources took their figures from the Census of that year, but the latter used a preliminary figure only. In 1911 the two sources made separate canvasses, and in 1913 the bulletins printed an unrevised *Mineral Resources* figure. From 1930 onward the two sources again made separate canvasses. Where slight differences occurred between the sources, we chose the *Minerals Yearbook* (or National Research Project) data, in order to obtain employment figures from the same source as those for output.

Mandays were derived as follows. For 1899–1911 and 1913, the average number employed was multiplied by average days active, both of which came from *Mineral Resources*. For 1912 and 1914 to 1925, the data were taken directly from "Coal-Mine Accidents." For 1926–33, mandays were taken from a special Bureau of Mines tabulation whose results appear in Willard E. Hotchkiss and others, *Bituminous-Coal Mining* (National Research Project, Philadelphia, 1939), Vol. II, p. 358. For 1934–38, *Minerals Yearbook*. Through 1925 days active or mandays were apparently derived by states; for 1926 and later years by individual mines.

To obtain manhours in 1902 we multiplied mandays by 8.8, a figure for hours per shift derived from the 1902 Census. For 1903–29 mandays were multiplied by the U.S. Geological Survey's series on average hours per day. ("Coal-Mine Accidents" also gives a manhour figure for most of these years, but we have preferred the former method. The manday figure used in the accident calculations is simply the product of average numbers employed and average days active for each state, summed to yield a United States total. See William W. Adams, "Coal-Mine Fatalities in the United States, 1927," U. S. Bureau of Mines, *Bulletin 293*, pp. 62-63. For years since 1926 the manday figures we have used are presumably derived for individual mines.) For 1930–38, manhours were taken from "Coal-Mine Accidents," but were adjusted by the ratio of *Minerals Yearbook* mandays to accident bulletin mandays, for comparability with the former.

For 1939, only accident bulletin data are available. We have used them without adjustment, since they differ only slightly from *Minerals Yearbook* data through 1938.

*Oil and Gas Wells*

Prior to the Census of Mineral Industries for 1939 there was no comprehensive survey of employment in the petroleum and natural gas industry. Bureau of Mines statistics similar to those we have used for most other important mineral industries are not available except for a few recent years. For years prior to 1939, information from the decennial Censuses is either lacking altogether, or deficient. In 1929, for instance, no attempt whatever was made to cover the industry. In the reports on the industry in 1909 and 1919 a very important part of total operations —that conducted by contractors—remain untouched. Only in the Census of 1902 was information collected in anything approaching as comprehensive a fashion as that of the Census of 1939. Since we wish to cover the operations of contractors as well as of regular producers (see the discussion in Chapter 10), 1902 and 1939 represent benchmarks in our employment estimates for this industry.

In relatively recent years data purporting to cover the industry have appeared in several places. For the period 1935–38, for example, figures on employment at oil and gas wells and at natural gasoline plants were published in *Minerals Yearbook*. These figures represent a brave beginning, but unfortunately they suffer from deficiencies common to most surveys of the industry—incomplete coverage of contract employment. The same defect is found to exist in the Bureau of Labor Statistics index of employment in crude petroleum production. This defect could be overlooked if contract employment were of relatively small magnitude, or if its relative importance remained unchanged over the period. We know that neither of these conditions is satisfied. Hence the level of contract employment must somehow be estimated. The Petroleum Code Authority under NRA made an attempt to do this. The estimates made covered contract employment in drilling (the chief activity of contractors) and related to representative dates in 1929, 1933 and 1934. These estimates can be found in the Temporary National Economic Committee hearings on the petroleum industry (Part 16, 1940, p. 9285), together with comparable figures for 1936 and 1938 estimated by regional production committees of the American Petroleum Institute. Unfortunately we know too little of the methods used in making these estimates to find them useful here. It is difficult, moreover, to convert them into annual averages.

The most ambitious attempt yet made to estimate total industrial employment (including that incidental to work performed on a contract basis) is that by the National Research Project (O. E. Kiessling and others, *Petroleum and Natural-Gas Production*, Philadelphia, 1939), in Table A-11 (p. 327) of its report. The figures in this table represent the abstract of an enormous amount of research, details of which are to be found in underlying worksheets placed at our disposal by Dr. Kiessling. For the most part we have reproduced the NRP data. In some cases we have chosen to make slight alterations, indicated in the following notes. In other cases we have preferred to omit data for certain years as apparently less reliable.

The data relate to wage earners only. In this regard they differ from figures for other industries which are based on mine accident statistics, and include all persons subject to mine hazards. Figures for men employed are full year averages. Since the production of petroleum and natural gas is a continuous process, there

*Footnotes to Table A-3 continued on next page.*

*Footnotes to Table A-3, continued.*

is little if any difference between a full year and an active period average in this industry. (The Census reported a full year average of 153,559 persons and an active period average of 163,717 for 1939. These figures exclude nonproducing operations and some small producers.) For reasons set forth in Chapter 3, no figures are presented for mandays. The derivation of the data is explained in Worksheet v. Estimates for employment in 1909 and 1919 will be found in the NRP report. We have not reproduced the NRP figures for these years because we believe that the basic data used for the estimate of contract manhours, although the best available, were not really adequate for our purpose.

Worksheet v

Derivation of Employment Estimates for Petroleum, Natural Gas and Natural Gasoline

| | Regular Producers | | Contractors | | Total | |
|---|---|---|---|---|---|---|
| Year | Wage Earners | Manhours (thous.) | Wage Earners | Manhours (thous.) | Wage Earners | Manhours (thous.) |
| 1902 | 22,230[a] | 81,824[b] | 10,040[c] | 36,955[d] | 32,270 | 118,779 |
| 1929 | .. | 328,032[b] | .. | 85,288[b] | 179,000[b] | 413,320 |
| 1935 | 108,735[b] | 187,727[b] | 30,870[e] | 48,533[b] | 139,610 | 236,260 |
| 1936 | 119,100[b] | 228,600[b] | 35,870[e] | 62,700[f] | 155,000 | 291,300 |
| 1937 | 126,800[b] | 250,700[b] | 40,370[e] | 72,700[f] | 167,200 | 323,400 |
| 1938 | 122,400[g] | 247,700[g] | 41,050[e] | 75,700[f] | 163,400 | 323,400 |
| 1939 | 113,498[h] | 206,712[h] | 40,061[h] | 66,479[h] | 153,559 | 273,191 |

[a] U. S. Bureau of the Census, *Special Reports*, "Mines and Quarries, 1902," p. 93.

[b] O. E. Kiessling and others, *Petroleum and Natural-Gas Production* (National Research Project, Philadelphia, 1939), p. 327.

[c] The 11,217 employees reported by contractors ("Mines and Quarries, 1902," p. 104) apparently include some salary earners. We assumed this figure included at least foremen, supervisors, etc. For regular producers this class of salaried worker represented 10.49 percent of wage earners plus foremen, supervisors, etc. We therefore reduced the count of 11,217 employees reported by contractors by this percentage, i.e., to 10,040.

[d] Calculated on the assumption that average hours per year were the same as for wage earners engaged in regular production.

[e] Derived from manhour data in the next column. The 1939 Census reports hours per year at 1,659 for contract wage earners and 1,821 for regular wage earners. For 1935–38 hours per year for regular wage earners, derived from the two preceding columns, were adjusted downward in the ratio mentioned to yield an estimate of hours per year for contract wage earners.

[f] Derived from manhours of wage earners employed by regular producers in a preceding column. The ratio of manhours in contract employment to manhours in regular employment was interpolated between 1935 and 1939 along a straight line. There is evidence that the share of contract operations in oil and gas well operations as a whole has increased rather steadily in recent years.

[g] For 1938, *Minerals Yearbook* reports 117,570 persons working 237,857 thousand manhours in petroleum, 8,090 persons working 16,416 thousand manhours in natural gas, and 9,205 persons working 18,818 thousand manhours in natural gasoline production. These figures apparently include salary earners. If we exclude the latter, using ratios for 1935 from Kiessling and others, *op. cit.*, p. 318, we have 108,365 wage earners working 219,235 thousand manhours in petroleum, 5,856 wage earners working 11,884 thousand manhours in natural gas, and 8,134 wage earners working 16,629 thousand manhours in natural gasoline production.

[h] From preliminary releases of Census of Mineral Industries, 1939; see also Table A-19 below. For the sake of comparability with other years employment at nonproducing operations, and at enterprises classed by the Census as "small producers," has been excluded. In general small producers have a value of products less than $2,500.

*Stone Quarrying*

Some peculiarities of this industry ought first to be noted. Employment at non-commercial operations—during the past decade these have been of increasing importance in the case of crushed stone—is still largely unrecorded. The statistics shown here are therefore confined to commercial quarries. Employment reported at "outside works" (i.e. stone dressing plants) has been included in the case of non-dimension, and excluded in the case of dimension, stone. It so happens that dimension trap rock (basalt) is mainly a byproduct of nondimension quarrying, and that, contrariwise, crushed marble and slate come chiefly from dimension quarries. Employment reported for dimension trap rock quarries has therefore been included with the nondimension industry; while nondimension marble and slate quarries (such as they are) have been classified with the corresponding dimension establishments. (A corresponding treatment was adopted in constructing the indexes of output, all basalt being classed as crushed, all marble and slate as dimension; see Table A-1.)

The construction of indexes of employment for the stone industries actually involved a more complicated series of operations than in the case of nonferrous metals, although the latter are much larger employers of labor. The difficulties we encountered stemmed from the generally unsatisfactory character of the data, and especially from their obvious and serious variations in coverage. A critique of the data, and a discussion of the problem of matching output and employment in these industries, will be found in Appendix C. In the following notes we shall merely indicate the steps actually performed in the derivation of the estimates, without making any detailed attempt to explain why particular assumptions were chosen. The methods adopted were, for the most part, the result of extensive correspondence, both with authors of National Research Project reports and with officials of the Bureau of Mines. The reader who is interested in the general question of ways and means to estimate employment at stone quarries, rather than in the derivation of the actual estimates offered here, should turn to Appendix C.

The computations were carried out mainly in terms of mandays; figures for the number of men employed (active period averages) and for the number of manhours worked were usually obtained indirectly from the manday estimates. Moreover, in discussing productivity, we have relied mainly on manday measures. For these reasons, and for the sake of brevity, the detailed description to follow will be confined to mandays, with only the barest indication as to how figures for men or manhours were derived.

For 1902, no employment estimates are offered here (see, however, Chapter 3, where some figures for quarry employment in 1902 will be found). The omission is to be charged to the impossibility of constructing satisfactory output indexes for stone in that year.

For 1911–39, the basic source of employment data for the stone industries is the Bureau of Mines annual publication "Quarry Accidents in the United States." The manner in which the figures there given were converted into estimates suitable for our purpose is shown in the series of Worksheets VI–XI.

For the years 1911–21 employment at dimension and nondimension quarries is combined for the several kinds of stone (granite, limestone, etc.). The reports began to show employment separately at the two kinds of quarry from the year 1922. Since we wished to include employment at nondimension "outside works" (especially crushing plants), but to exclude the operations of outside works at dimension quarries (the latter engaged in stone dressing—a form of manufacturing), a segregation between the two kinds of outside works had to be attempted. The various steps in the construction of estimates for these years are indicated in Worksheet VI.

*Footnotes to Table A-3 continued on next page.*

**Worksheet VI**

**Derivation of Mandays at Dimension and Nondimension Stone Quarries, 1911–21[a]**

*Thousand mandays*

| Year | Cement Rock[b] | | Granite | | | | Limestone[e] | | | | |
|---|---|---|---|---|---|---|---|---|---|---|---|
| | (1) | (2) | (3) | (4) | (5) | (6) | (7) | (8) | (9) | (10) | (11) |
| | At Quarries | At Quarries and Crushers[f] | At Quarries | At All Outside Works | At Nondimension Outside Works[g] | Total (3) + (5) | At Quarries | At All Outside Works | At Nondimension Outside Works Including Limekilns[h] | At Limekilns[i] | Total (7) + (9) − (10) |
| 1911 | 1,651 | 1,929 | 3,004 | 1,524 | 408 | 3,412 | 9,137 | 3,104 | 2,747 | 1,508 | 10,376 |
| 1912 | 1,034 | 1,208 | 2,976 | 1,684 | 451 | 3,427 | 10,080 | 3,787 | 3,352 | 1,543 | 11,889 |
| 1913 | 1,354 | 1,582 | 2,799 | 1,485 | 398 | 3,197 | 9,491 | 3,607 | 3,193 | 1,547 | 11,137 |
| 1914 | 1,142 | 1,334 | 2,509 | 886 | 237 | 2,746 | 7,626 | 2,318 | 2,052 | 1,432 | 8,246 |
| 1915 | 1,190 | 1,391 | 2,871 | 1,500 | 402 | 3,272 | 8,015 | 2,226 | 1,970 | 1,512 | 8,473 |
| 1916 | 1,189 | 1,390 | 2,380 | 1,161 | 311 | 2,692 | 7,739 | 2,704 | 2,393 | 1,676 | 8,456 |
| 1917 | 1,180 | 1,379 | 2,102 | 1,090 | 292 | 2,394 | 7,371 | 2,651 | 2,346 | 1,536 | 8,181 |
| 1918 | 902 | 1,054 | 1,494 | 749 | 201 | 1,695 | 6,790 | 2,410 | 2,133 | 1,282 | 7,641 |
| 1919 | 938 | 1,096 | 1,761 | 736 | 197 | 1,959 | 6,711 | 3,206 | 2,838 | 1,314 | 8,235 |
| 1920 | 1,232 | 1,440 | 2,093 | 794 | 213 | 2,306 | 7,343 | 3,812 | 3,374 | 1,541 | 9,176 |
| 1921 | 959 | 1,121 | 1,572 | 531 | 142 | 1,714 | 5,728 | 3,091 | 2,736 | 1,206 | 7,258 |

*For footnotes see pp. 330-31.*

Derivation of Mandays at Dimension and Nondimension Stone Quarries, 1911–21[a]

*Thousand mandays*

| Year | Marble[d] (12) At Quarries | Sandstone (13) At Quarries | Sandstone (14) At All Outside Works | Sandstone (15) At Nondimension Outside Works[j] | Sandstone (16) Total (13) + (15) | Slate[d] (17) At Quarries | Trap Rock[e] (18) At Quarries and Outside Works | Grand Total (19) (2) + (6) + (11) + (12) + (16) + (17) + (18) |
|---|---|---|---|---|---|---|---|---|
| 1911 | 639 | 1,758 | 551 | 195 | 1,953 | 1,005 | 1,359 | 20,673 |
| 1912 | 942 | 1,535 | 533 | 189 | 1,724 | 1,072 | 1,459 | 21,721 |
| 1913 | 737 | 1,602 | 448 | 158 | 1,760 | 947 | 2,000 | 21,360 |
| 1914 | 693 | 1,611 | 248 | 88 | 1,699 | 955 | 1,563 | 17,236 |
| 1915 | 744 | 1,405 | 537 | 190 | 1,595 | 1,019 | 1,386 | 17,880 |
| 1916 | 596 | 1,001 | 403 | 142 | 1,143 | 877 | 1,080 | 16,234 |
| 1917 | 458 | 718 | 502 | 178 | 896 | 831 | 1,300 | 15,439 |
| 1918 | 272 | 547 | 391 | 138 | 685 | 488 | 781 | 12,616 |
| 1919 | 333 | 575 | 212 | 75 | 650 | 579 | 1,207 | 14,059 |
| 1920 | 453 | 820 | 243 | 86 | 905 | 765 | 1,459 | 16,504 |
| 1921 | 569 | 551 | 167 | 59 | 610 | 626 | 1,147 | 13,045 |

*For footnotes see pp. 330-31.*

*Footnotes to Table A-3, continued.*

ᵃ Columns (1), (3), (4), (7), (8), (12), (13), (14), (17) and (18) are transcribed directly from U. S. Bureau of Mines, "Quarry Accidents in the United States," with the following exceptions. For 1911–14 employment between quarries and outside works is distinguished only in terms of men. Where necessary, therefore, we allocated total mandays as published for these years between quarries and outside works in the proportion in which men employed were so divided for the year in question. For 1917 all California quarries were reported in the totals for granite, and for 1918 in the figures for sandstone. Accordingly we reduced the published data for granite in 1917 and for sandstone in 1918, and increased the other categories correspondingly, as follows (figures in thousands of mandays are based on the known distribution of California employment at different types of quarry in 1916):

|  | 1917 | | 1918 | |
|---|---|---|---|---|
|  | At Quarries | At Outside Works | At Quarries | At Outside Works |
| Deducted from published figures: |  |  |  |  |
| Granite | 280 | 413 | .. | .. |
| Sandstone | .. | .. | 404 | 1,055 |
| Added to published figures: |  |  |  |  |
| Cement rock | 82 | 326 | 73 | 653 |
| Granite | .. | .. | 155 | 228 |
| Limestone | 77 | 46 | 69 | 93 |
| Marble | 7 | .. | 6 | .. |
| Sandstone | 3 | .. | .. | .. |
| Trap rock | 111 | 40 | 99 | 79 |

In 1919 and 1920 employment at trap rock quarries in California is included in the reported figure for granite. On the basis of the relative values of granite and trap rock produced in California in these years, the following adjustments were made (in thousand mandays):

|  | 1919 | | 1920 | |
|---|---|---|---|---|
|  | At Quarries | At Outside Works | At Quarries | At Outside Works |
| Deducted from granite as published and added to trap rock | 96 | 56 | 202 | 109 |

In 1917 and 1918 all Colorado quarries are included under limestone, but we considered the distortion so introduced too slight to warrant an adjustment.

ᵇ Consists chiefly of limestone used for making cement.

ᶜ Except limestone for cement.

ᵈ Since marble and slate quarries produce little but dimension stone, no allowance is made for employment at nondimension outside works.

ᵉ Because trap rock quarries produce little but nondimension stone, all outside works are regarded as nondimension, and all of such employment is included.

ᶠ Column (1) multiplied by 1.1686. This is the ratio of mandays at quarries and crushers to mandays at quarries, from "Quarry Accidents in the United States, 1925." (An alternative procedure would be to distribute employment recorded for outside works between crushers and cement mills, using a similar ratio; but figures for cement rock outside works, prior to 1925, exhibit symptoms of undercoverage, and the method indicated was chosen.)

ᵍ Column (4) multiplied by .26787. This is the ratio of 175,485 mandays reported for nondimension outside works in 1922 to 655,123 mandays for all outside works in that year. (Employment reported at "all other and not stated" outside works in 1922 was allocated to dimension.)

ʰ Column (8) multiplied by .88510. This is the ratio of 3,284,197 mandays reported for nondimension and "all other and not stated" outside works in 1922 to 3,710,537 mandays for all outside works in that year. (Employment at "all other and not stated" outside works was allocated to nondimension in all years.)

ⁱ See Worksheet VII.

ʲ Column (14) multiplied by .35379. This is the ratio of 95,744 mandays reported for nondimension outside works in 1922 to 270,626 mandays for all outside works in that year. (The category "all other and not stated" does not appear for sandstone in 1922, in which year all employment was definitely distributed between dimension and nondimension.)

In the case of limestone, employment at all outside works through 1921, and at nondimension outside works for 1922 and later years, includes the operation of limekilns—a form of fabrication. Estimates of the limekiln employment which has to be deducted are offered in Worksheet vii.

Although dimension and nondimension quarries and outside works began to be segregated in 1922, it happens that employment in the two kinds of production was not always clearly distinguished in the reports submitted, for in all years since 1922 figures are given also for employment at a group of establishments labeled "all other and not stated." Fortunately it is often possible to judge by inspection whether "all other and not stated" employment for a particular variety of stone is predominantly either dimension or nondimension in character. Such a judgment is based upon the distribution given for this employment between quarries (proper) and outside works (i.e. stone dressing plants). For outside works are far more important in connection with dimension than with nondimension operations. Frequently we included "all other and not stated" employment either in the total for dimension, or for nondimension, on this basis. In other years or for other kinds of stone the distribution could not be made by inspection, whereupon we adopted what seemed to us the simplest assumption, as follows. Let $a$ and $b$ be ratios of mandays in quarries to mandays in quarries and outside works, for dimension and nondimension quarries respectively, as determined in each year and for each kind of stone by that portion of the data for which the distribution is available. We know in each case $Q$ and $O$, mandays reported as "all other and not stated" at quarries and outside works respectively. Put $D = \dfrac{bO - (1 - b)Q}{b - a}$ and $N = \dfrac{(1 - a)Q - aO}{b - a}$,

where $D$ and $N$ are the "all other and not stated" mandays to be allocated respectively to dimension and to nondimension quarries. This assumes that the ratios $a$ and $b$ are the same for "all other and not stated" as for the establishments for which the distribution between quarries and outside works is reported. $D$ may then be apportioned $aD$ to quarries, and $(1 - a)D$ to outside works; and $N$ apportioned $bN$ to quarries and $(1 - b)N$ to outside works.

With the help of this device the figures reported in "Quarry Accidents" for "all other and not stated" in 1922–39 are segregated into nondimension quarries and outside works (crushers) in Worksheet viii and dimension quarries in Worksheet xi. (Employment at dimension outside works we exclude from the totals.)

There remains the question of changing coverage, discussed in Appendix C below. Adjustment of the data on this account is possible only for nondimension stone and for the years 1929–39 alone. The elaborate study undertaken by the National Research Project (see Harry S. Kantor and Geoffrey A. Saeger, *Crushed-Stone Industry*, Philadelphia, 1939) makes it very clear that the "Quarry Accident" coverage of nondimension stone (including neither cement rock nor limestone for lime) increased rapidly from but 50 to nearly 100 percent during the 1930's; and comparison with the Census of Mineral Industries for 1939 suggests that the coverage of the accident data is now substantially complete. For cement rock a Bureau of Mines canvass of cement manufacturers makes possible a similar analysis of changing coverage in this branch of quarrying. Adjustments, based upon these investigations, to the accident data in Worksheet viii are carried out for 1929–39 in Worksheets ix and x.

The above discussion, in conjunction with the accompanying worksheets, describes the construction of our manday estimates. For men employed (active period averages) we made rough estimates for 1929–39 only. The data are not used to construct indexes of employment and productivity, but only to obtain totals for men

*Footnotes to Table A-3 continued on next page.*

*Footnotes to Table A-3, continued.*

employed in mining as a whole. They were derived by adjusting the accident bulletin figures for men employed by the ratios of our manday totals for dimension and nondimension stone to the "Quarry Accident" totals.

Manhours are shown for all the years for which estimates could be made. For 1919, we derived them by multiplying our manday figures by a figure for average hours per shift (9.45) from Vivian E. Spencer, *Mineral Extractive Industries* (National Research Project, Philadelphia, 1940), p. 137. For dimension stone in 1931–39 manhours are for the most part given explicitly in "Quarry Accidents." However, the division of "all other and not stated" between dimension and nondimension was carried out in manday terms (see Worksheets VIII and XI). The mandays affected we converted to manhours, using separate data for hours per shift at "all other and not stated" for each variety of stone. For 1929 and 1930 hours per shift data for each variety were extracted from "Quarry Accidents."

For nondimension stone in 1929–39 manhours were derived as follows. For 1929–36 granite, sandstone, trap rock and limestone (except limestone for lime and cement rock) are from the National Research Project (see Worksheet IX); for 1937–39 mandays were multiplied by an average hours per shift for each year, from "Quarry Accidents." For cement rock manhours come from the same source as mandays. The same is true of limestone for lime and dimension trap rock for the years 1931–39. For 1929 and 1930 manhours at quarries and crushers producing limestone for lime are from U. S. Bureau of Mines, "Health and Safety Statistics," No. 141. Mandays in dimension trap rock for the same two years were multiplied by figures on hours per shift for such operations from "Quarry Accidents." A figure for nondimension manhours in 1929, comparable with earlier years, is shown only because it was used in obtaining the corresponding item for total stone. It was derived by multiplying the manday figure by an average hours per shift for nondimension stone from data comparable with later years.

Worksheet VII

Derivation of Mandays at Limekilns, 1911–39

| Year | (1)<br>Average Number[a]<br>Employed | (2)<br>Lime<br>Sales[b]<br>(th.s.t.) | (3)<br>Output per<br>Wage Earner[c]<br>(s.t.) | (4)<br>Mandays at<br>Limekilns[d]<br>(thous.) |
|---|---|---|---|---|
| 1909 | 13,725 | 3,485 | 253.9 | .. |
| 1910 | 13,579 | 3,506 | 258.2 | .. |
| 1911 | 12,926 | 3,393 | 262.5 | 1,508 |
| 1912 | 13,231 | 3,530 | 266.8 | 1,543 |
| 1913 | 13,261 | 3,595 | 271.1 | 1,547 |
| 1914 | 12,275 | 3,381 | 275.4 | 1,432 |
| 1915 | 12,967 | 3,623 | 279.4 | 1,512 |
| 1916 | 14,367 | 4,073 | 283.5 | 1,676 |
| 1917 | 13,169 | 3,786 | 287.5 | 1,536 |
| 1918 | 10,995 | 3,206 | 291.6 | 1,282 |
| 1919 | 11,264 | 3,330 | 295.6 | 1,314 |
| 1920 | 13,212 | 3,570 | 270.2 | 1,541 |
| 1921 | 10,345 | 2,532 | 244.8 | 1,206 |
| 1922 | 12,630 | 3,640 | 288.2 | 1,473 |
| 1923 | 12,290 | 4,076 | 331.7 | 1,433 |
| 1924 | 11,464 | 4,072 | 355.2 | 1,337 |
| 1925 | 12,095 | 4,581 | 378.8 | 1,410 |
| 1926 | 11,639 | 4,560 | 391.8 | 1,357 |
| 1927 | 10,903 | 4,415 | 404.9 | 1,271 |
| 1928 | 9,863 | 4,458 | 452.0 | 1,150 |
| 1929 | 8,554 | 4,270 | 499.2 | 997[e] |
| 1930 | 7,504 | 3,388 | 451.5 | 875[e] |
| 1931 | 6,706 | 2,708 | 403.8 | 782 |
| 1932 | .. | .. | .. | 540 |
| 1933 | .. | .. | .. | 680 |
| 1934 | .. | .. | .. | 808 |
| 1935 | .. | .. | .. | 877 |
| 1936 | .. | .. | .. | 1,072 |
| 1937 | .. | .. | .. | 1,141 |
| 1938 | .. | .. | .. | 992 |
| 1939 | .. | .. | .. | 1,073 |

[a] For 1909, 1914, 1919, 1921, 1923, 1925, 1927, 1929 and 1931, Census of Manufactures. For other years, column (2) divided by column (3).

[b] U. S. Bureau of Mines, *Mineral Resources* and *Minerals Yearbook*.

[c] For 1909, 1914, 1919, 1921, 1923, 1925, 1927, 1929 and 1931, column (2) divided by column (1). For other years, by straight line interpolation.

[d] 1931–39, "Quarry Accidents in the United States," extrapolated back to 1911 by means of column (1).

[e] Figures for 1929 and 1930 more accurately comparable with later years are 1,083 th. and 969 th. mandays respectively. This extrapolation is based on manhour figures in U. S. Bureau of Mines, "Health and Safety Statistics," Nos. 141 and 235.

*Footnotes to Table A-3 continued on next page.*

Derivation of Mandays at Nondimension Stone Quarries, Before Adjustment for Changing Coverage, 1922-39[a]

*Thousand mandays*

| | Cement Rock[b] | | | | | Granite | | | Limestone[f] | | | | | | |
| | At Quarries (1) | At All Outside Works (2) | At Cement Mills (3) | At Crushers[e] (4) | Total[d] (5) | At Quarries and Outside Works | | Total (6)+ (7) (8) | At Quarries and Outside Works | | At Lime-kilns[i] (11) | Cement Rock to be Excluded[j] (12) | Total[k] (13) | For Lime[l] (14) | Total, excl. Limestone for Lime (15) |
| *Year* | | | | | | As Given (6) | Not Stated[e] (7) | | As Given[g] (9) | Not Stated[h] (10) | | | | | |
|---|---|---|---|---|---|---|---|---|---|---|---|---|---|---|---|
| 1922 | 1,072 | .. | .. | .. | 1,253 | 727 | .. | 727 | 8,766 | 76 | 1,473 | .. | 7,369 | .. | .. |
| 1923 | 1,301 | .. | .. | .. | 1,520 | 743 | .. | 743 | 11,080 | 205 | 1,433 | .. | 9,852 | .. | .. |
| 1924 | 1,340 | .. | .. | .. | 1,566 | 575 | .. | 575 | 10,494 | 620 | 1,337 | .. | 9,777 | .. | .. |
| 1925 | 1,388 | 5,356 | .. | 234 | 1,622 | 860 | .. | 860 | 8,402 | 752 | 1,410 | .. | 7,744 | .. | .. |
| 1926 | 1,474 | 5,854 | .. | 256 | 1,730 | 409 | .. | 409 | 8,265 | 742 | 1,357 | .. | 7,649 | .. | .. |
| 1927 | 1,309 | 5,962 | .. | 260 | 1,569 | 463 | .. | 463 | 7,831 | 1,092 | 1,271 | .. | 7,652 | .. | .. |
| 1928 | 1,185 | 5,957 | .. | 260 | 1,445 | 353 | .. | 353 | 7,926 | 644 | 1,150 | .. | 7,420 | .. | .. |
| 1929 | 1,057 | 5,456 | .. | 238 | 1,296 | 396 | .. | 396 | 7,119 | 934 | { 997 / 1,083 | 1,301 | 7,056 / 5,669 | 1,469 | 4,200 |
| 1930 | 918 | 5,047 | .: | 221 | 1,139 | 279 | .. | 279 | 6,568 | 585 | 969 | 1,529 | 4,655 | 1,315 | 3,340 |
| 1931 | 814 | 4,143 | 3,962 | .. | 995 | 260 | .. | 260 | 4,426 | 601 | 782 | 329 | 3,916 | 1,061 | 2,855 |
| 1932 | 597 | 2,961 | 2,813 | .. | 745 | 157 | .. | 157 | 3,116 | 565 | 540 | .. | 3,141 | 658 | 2,483 |
| 1933 | 604 | 3,357 | 3,197 | .. | 764 | 225 | .: | 225 | 3,818 | 190 | 680 | .. | 3,328 | 557 | 2,771 |
| 1934 | 772 | 4,784 | 4,522 | .. | 1,034 | 341 | 53 | 394 | 4,163 | 333 | 808 | .. | 3,688 | 695 | 2,993 |
| 1935 | 746 | 4,800 | 4,504 | .. | 1,042 | 345 | 53 | 397 | 3,354 | 59 | 877 | .. | 4,725 | 1,312 | 3,413 |
| 1936 | 1,073 | 5,993 | 5,641 | .. | 1,425 | 510 | .. | 510 | 4,198 | 60 | 1,072 | .. | 5,818 | 1,561 | 4,258 |
| 1937 | 1,042 | 6,522 | 6,041 | .. | 1,523 | 556 | 135 | 691 | 4,435 | 60 | 1,141 | .. | 6,263 | 1,768 | 4,495 |
| 1938 | 843 | 5,673 | 5,260 | .. | 1,256 | 542 | 180 | 722 | 3,601 | 89 | 992 | .. | 5,074 | 1,384 | 3,690 |
| 1939 | 890 | 6,202 | 5,730 | .. | 1,362 | 619 | 126 | 745 | 3,779 | 99 | 1,073 | .. | 5,515 | 1,638 | 3,878 |

*For footnotes see p. 336.*

Worksheet VIII (concluded)

Derivation of Mandays at Nondimension Stone Quarries, Before Adjustment for Changing Coverage, 1922–39[a]

*Thousand mandays*

| Year | Sandstone | | | Trap Rock | | | | Grand Total (23) |
|---|---|---|---|---|---|---|---|---|
| | At Quarries and Outside Works | | Total (16) + (17) (18) | At Quarries and Outside Works | | Reported for Dimension Quarries (21) | Total (22) | |
| | As Given (16) | Not Stated[e] (17) | | As Given (19) | Not Stated[h] (20) | | | |
| 1922 | 390 | .. | 390 | 754 | 359 | 42 | 1,156 | 10,895 |
| 1923 | 573 | 3 | 576 | 946 | 641 | 15 | 1,601 | 14,292 |
| 1924 | 482 | 10 | 492 | 1,165 | 17 | 95 | 1,277 | 13,687 |
| 1925 | 385 | 66 | 451 | 749 | 172 | 15 | 937 | 11,614 |
| 1926 | 439 | 16 | 455 | 725 | 132 | 18 | 875 | 11,118 |
| 1927 | 358 | 52 | 410 | 742 | 159 | 14 | 915 | 11,009 |
| 1928 | 281 | 60 | 340 | 699 | 134 | 23 | 856 | 10,414 |
| 1929 | 301 | 23 | 324 | 633 | 121 | 43 | 796 | 9,868 |
| 1930 | 211 | 10 | 220 | 600 | 83 | 28 | 712 | .. |
| 1931 | 114 | 35 | 149 | 454 | 116 | 10 | 581 | .. |
| 1932 | 79 | 8 | 88 | 428 | 43 | 0 | 472 | .. |
| 1933 | 112 | 10 | 122 | 340 | 35 | 12 | 387 | .. |
| 1934 | 135 | 10 | 145 | 406 | 33 | 4 | 443 | .. |
| 1935 | 231 | 30 | 261 | 522 | 15 | 0 | 537 | .. |
| 1936 | 376 | 15 | 391 | 565 | 16 | 0 | 580 | .. |
| 1937 | 422 | 11 | 433 | 537 | 0 | 3 | 540 | .. |
| 1938 | 284 | 22 | 306 | 542 | 8 | 2 | 552 | .. |
| 1939 | 343 | 2 | 345 | 513 | 1 | 3 | 517 | .. |

See Worksheet x

*For footnotes see p. 336.*

335

*Footnotes to Table A-3, continued.*

ᵃ The coverage of the data in this table, taken with minor exceptions from "Quarry Accidents in the United States," is not complete. For years prior to 1929 it does not seem possible to make any adjustment on this score. But in Worksheet x (see below) the figures for cement rock, granite, limestone, sandstone and trap rock are adjusted to what appears to be 100 percent coverage. Columns (1), (2), (3), (6), (9), (10), (16), (19), (20) and (21) are transcribed directly from "Quarry Accidents."

ᵇ Consists chiefly of limestone used for making cement.

ᶜ Column (2) multiplied by .0437. This is the ratio of mandays at crushers (995 th. — 814 th. = 181 th.) to mandays at all outside works (4,143 th.) in 1931.

ᵈ For 1922–24, column (1) multiplied by 1.1686. This is the ratio of total mandays (1,622 th.) to mandays at quarries (1,388 th.) in 1925. (See note f to Worksheet vi.) For 1925–30, column (1) plus column (4). For 1931–39, columns (1) plus (2) minus (3).

ᵉ Shows portion of "all other and not stated" allocated to nondimension stone according to formula already given.

ᶠ Except limestone for cement.

ᵍ 1922–34, includes limestone for lime; 1935–39 no longer includes limestone for lime which is for the first time given separately for these years (columns 11 and 14).

ʰ We allocated the whole of employment designated "all other and not stated" to nondimension quarries, and this column is therefore a simple transcription from "Quarry Accidents."

ⁱ See Worksheet vii.

ʲ Correspondence with the Bureau of Mines established that some cement rock employment is included with limestone in these years. The amount to be deducted was derived from a comparison of "Quarry Accidents" and *Minerals Yearbook* data, and, so far as it consists of quarry employment, is added back in column (2) of Worksheet x.

ᵏ 1922–34, columns (9) plus (10) minus (11) minus (12). 1935-39, columns (9) plus (10) plus (14).

ˡ Obtained by deducting mandays at limekilns (Worksheet vii) from total mandays engaged in the production of limestone for lime. For 1929–34 the latter were estimated by dividing corresponding figures for manhours (U. S. Bureau of Mines, "Health and Safety Statistics," Nos. 141 and 235) by hours per day at limekilns derived from "Quarry Accidents."

Worksheet IX

Derivation of Coverage Adjustment for Nondimension Stone, 1929–36[a]

| Year | (1) Granite | (2) Limestone[b] | (3) Sandstone | (4) Trap Rock | (5) Resulting Total | (6) Full Coverage[c] | (7) Adjustment Ratio (6) ÷ (5) |
|---|---|---|---|---|---|---|---|
| | | | *Thousand mandays* | | | | |
| 1929 | 396 | 4,200 | 324 | 754 | 5,673 | .. | .. |
| 1930 | 279 | 3,340 | 221 | 683 | 4,523 | .. | .. |
| 1931 | 260 | 2,855 | 149 | 570 | 3,834 | .. | .. |
| | | | *Thousand manhours* | | | | |
| 1929 | .. | .. | .. | .. | 52,759 | 95,873 | 1.8172 |
| 1930 | .. | .. | .. | .. | 41,159 | 84,496 | 2.0529 |
| 1931 | 2,247 | 24,090 | 1,317 | 4,894 | 32,548 | 64,591 | 1.9845 |
| 1932 | 1,279 | 20,943 | 782 | 4,023 | 27,028 | 47,535 | 1.7587 |
| 1933 | 1,882 | 22,286 | 1,006 | 3,059 | 28,232 | 42,220 | 1.4955 |
| 1934 | 2,994 | 23,829 | 1,146 | 3,450 | 31,419 | 43,911 | 1.3976 |
| 1935 | 3,075 | 27,029 | 2,113 | 4,234 | 36,451 | 39,838 | 1.0929 |
| 1936 | 4,337 | 34,753 | 3,287 | 4,788 | 47,165 | 50,390 | 1.0684 |

[a] The derivation of columns (1) to (5) is as follows. For mandays in granite, limestone and sandstone see Worksheet VIII. Mandays in trap rock quarries are transcribed directly from "Quarry Accidents," and differ from figures for trap rock in Worksheet VIII because they do not cover dimension quarries. For 1931–36 manhours were obtained by methods similar to mandays: see notes to Worksheet VIII. For 1929 and 1930 manhours were derived from mandays as follows. Hours per day as shown were 8.5 in 1931. From Vivian E. Spencer, *Mineral Extractive Industries* (National Research Project, Philadelphia, 1940), Table A-26, columns (7) and (8) corresponding figures of 8.6, 9.2 and 9.4 may be obtained for 1931, 1930 and 1929 respectively. Accordingly, manhours are found by multiplying mandays by 8.5 × 9.2/8.6 in 1930 and 8.5 × 9.4/8.6 in 1929.

[b] Excluding cement rock and limestone for lime.

[c] Data for commercial operations only, from Harry S. Kantor and Geoffrey A. Saeger, *Crushed-Stone Industry* (National Research Project, Philadelphia, 1939), Table 4, p. 18 (average number of men employed at commercial operations multiplied by average hours per man per year at such operations).

*Footnotes to Table A-3 continued on next page.*

Worksheet x

Adjustment of Mandays at Nondimension Stone Quarries for Coverage, 1929–39*

*Thousand mandays*

| Year | Cement Rock[b] | | | Unadjusted Data | | | | | Adjustment Ratio[e] (9) | Column (8) Adjusted[f] (10) | Limestone for Lime (11) | Dimension Trap Rock[g] (12) | Grand Total[h] (13) |
| --- | --- | --- | --- | --- | --- | --- | --- | --- | --- | --- | --- | --- | --- |
| | Un-adjusted (1) | Adjust-ment[e] (2) | Total (3) | Granite (4) | Lime-stone[d] (5) | Sand-stone (6) | Trap Rock (7) | Total (8) | | | | | |
| 1929 | 1,296 | 449 | 1,745 | 396 | 4,200 | 324 | 754 | 5,674 | 1.8172 | 10,311 | 1,469 | 43 | 13,567 |
| 1930 | 1,139 | 500 | 1,639 | 279 | 3,340 | 221 | 683 | 4,523 | 2.0529 | 9,285 | 1,315 | 28 | 12,268 |
| 1931 | 995 | 191 | 1,186 | 260 | 2,855 | 149 | 570 | 3,834 | 1.9845 | 7,609 | 1,061 | 10 | 9,866 |
| 1932 | 745 | 81 | 826 | 157 | 2,483 | 87 | 471 | 3,198 | 1.7587 | 5,624 | 658 | .. | 7,108 |
| 1933 | 764 | 55 | 819 | 225 | 2,771 | 122 | 375 | 3,493 | 1.4955 | 5,224 | 557 | 12 | 6,611 |
| 1934 | 1,034 | .. | 1,034 | 394 | 2,993 | 145 | 439 | 3,971 | 1.3976 | 5,550 | 695 | 4 | 7,284 |
| 1935 | 1,042 | .. | 1,042 | 398 | 3,413 | 261 | 537 | 4,609 | 1.0929 | 5,037 | 1,312 | .. | 7,392 |
| 1936 | 1,425 | .. | 1,425 | 510 | 4,258 | 391 | 580 | 5,739 | 1.0684 | 6,132 | 1,561 | .. | 9,118 |
| 1937 | 1,523 | .. | 1,523 | 691 | 4,495 | 433 | 537 | 6,156 | 1.0456 | 6,437 | 1,768 | 3 | 9,731 |
| 1938 | 1,256 | .. | 1,256 | 722 | 3,690 | 306 | 550 | 5,268 | 1.0228 | 5,388 | 1,384 | 2 | 8,030 |
| 1939 | 1,362 | .. | 1,362 | 745 | 3,878 | 345 | 515 | 5,483 | 1.0000 | 5,483 | 1,638 | 3 | 8,486 |

a Since adjustments shown here cannot be applied to years prior to 1929, there is a discontinuity in the data for which we allow by overlap. Columns (1), (4), (5), (6), (7), (11) and (12) are taken from Worksheet VIII.

b Consists chiefly of limestone used for making cement.

c According to a communication from Mr. W. W. Adams of the U. S. Bureau of Mines, the "Quarry Accidents" data for cement rock for years prior to 1933 include chiefly quarries operated in conjunction with cement mills; they do not fully cover other quarries producing limestone for cement, some of which were probably classified with regular crushed limestone quarries. Figures for employment at quarries and crushers (including miscellaneous employment; especially baggers, truckmen, shippers, and construction workers) obtained by a canvass of cement manufacturers and published in Minerals Yearbook (see Table C-4 below) are reported by Mr. Adams to be practically complete. Accordingly, for 1929–33 we have substituted these figures (column 3) for the "Quarry Accidents" data (column 1); the adjustment shown is the difference between the two sets of data for these years. In part we are adding back employment deducted in column (12) of Worksheet VIII; that deduction consisted partly of cement mill employment, and was therefore larger than the adjustment shown here.

d Except limestone for cement and limestone for lime.

e For 1929–36 see Worksheet IX. Comparison with employment data from the Census of Mineral Industries, 1939, suggests that coverage of our figures (based on "Quarry Accidents") for commercial operations had become virtually complete in that year, the ratio consequently being unity. We assumed coverage increased steadily between 1936 and 1939, and the ratios shown for 1937 and 1938 are therefore interpolated along a straight line.

f Column (8) multiplied by column (9): assumed to represent complete coverage.

g Quarries only; does not include outside works. Only small amounts of employment are reported for dimension trap rock quarries, and these are included with nondimension (as dimension trap rock output is included with nondimension).

h Columns (3) + (10) + (11) + (12).

Footnotes to Table A-3, continued.

Worksheet XI

Derivation of Mandays at Dimension Stone Quarries, 1922–39[a]

*Thousand mandays*

| | Granite | | | | Marble | | | |
|---|---|---|---|---|---|---|---|---|
| | | | | *Limestone*[c] | | | Reported for Nondimension | |
| *Year* | As Given (1) | Not Stated[b] (2) | Total (3) | As Given (4) | As Given (5) | Not Stated[d] (6) | Quarries[e] (7) | Total (8) |
| 1922 | 867 | 38 | 905 | 849 | 602 | 22 | 143 | 767 |
| 1923 | 1,462 | 85 | 1,547 | 984 | 655 | 38 | 41 | 734 |
| 1924 | 1,635 | 143 | 1,778 | 1,355 | 658 | 3 | 104 | 766 |
| 1925 | 1,324 | 102 | 1,426 | 792 | 638 | 44 | 28 | 710 |
| 1926 | 924 | 358 | 1,282 | 489 | 586 | 70 | 30 | 686 |
| 1927 | 881 | 429 | 1,310 | 571 | 696 | 62 | 35 | 793 |
| 1928 | 952 | 444 | 1,396 | 537 | 742 | 6 | 33 | 780 |
| 1929 | 920 | 291 | 1,211 | 589 | 636 | 111 | 25 | 772 |
| 1930 | 807 | 260 | 1,067 | 545 | 588 | 14 | 25 | 627 |
| 1931 | 581 | 233 | 815 | 265 | 430 | 5 | 15 | 450 |
| 1932 | 426 | 98 | 524 | 136 | 269 | 5 | 14 | 288 |
| 1933 | 365 | 147 | 511 | 121 | 234 | 3 | 28 | 265 |
| 1934 | 401 | 129 | 530 | 58 | 120 | 1 | 20 | 141 |
| 1935 | 438 | 102 | 540 | 78 | 137 | 6 | 27 | 170 |
| 1936 | 565 | 140 | 704 | 152 | 180 | 7 | 31 | 219 |
| 1937 | 640 | 32 | 672 | 218 | 250 | 7 | 31 | 288 |
| 1938 | 511 | 15 | 526 | 171 | 249 | 39 | 24 | 313 |
| 1939 | 515 | 35 | 549 | 205 | 282 | 34 | 16 | 332 |

Worksheet XI (concluded)

Derivation of Mandays at Dimension Stone Quarries, 1922–39[a]

*Thousand mandays*

| | Sandstone | | | Slate | | | | |
|---|---|---|---|---|---|---|---|---|
| | | | | | | Non-dimension | | *Grand* |
| *Year* | As Given (9) | Not Stated[b] (10) | Total (11) | As Given (12) | Not Stated[d] (13) | Quarries[e] (14) | Total (15) | *Total* (16) |
| 1922 | 439 | .. | 439 | 742 | 2 | .. | 744 | 3,704 |
| 1923 | 483 | .. | 483 | 836 | .. | .. | 836 | 4,584 |
| 1924 | 626 | 8 | 634 | 774 | 24 | .. | 798 | 5,331 |
| 1925 | 545 | 9 | 554 | 697 | 18 | 20 | 735 | 4,217 |
| 1926 | 505 | 28 | 532 | 837 | 20 | 0 | 858 | 3,847 |
| 1927 | 322 | .. | 322 | 626 | 16 | 4 | 646 | 3,642 |
| 1928 | 307 | .. | 307 | 567 | 24 | 1 | 592 | 3,612 |
| 1929 | 232 | 23 | 255 | 526 | 12 | 0 | 538 | 3,365 |
| 1930 | 274 | 19 | 293 | 325 | 15 | 5 | 345 | 2,877 |
| 1931 | 146 | 2 | 147 | 233 | 22 | 2 | 257 | 1,934 |
| 1932 | 83 | .. | 83 | 111 | 2 | 3 | 116 | 1,147 |
| 1933 | 42 | .. | 42 | 104 | 3 | 3 | 110 | 1,049 |
| 1934 | 54 | .. | 54 | 74 | 3 | 14 | 90 | 873 |
| 1935 | 74 | .. | 74 | 117 | 0 | 75 | 193 | 1,055 |
| 1936 | 119 | .. | 119 | 174 | .. | 89 | 263 | 1,457 |
| 1937 | 121 | .. | 121 | 233 | 18 | 89 | 341 | 1,640 |
| 1938 | 122 | .. | 122 | 168 | 37 | 69 | 274 | 1,406 |
| 1939 | 141 | 1 | 141 | 224 | 31 | 74 | 329 | 1,556 |

<sup>a</sup> For dimension stone, employment reported at quarries is included, but not employment at outside works (i.e. stone dressing establishments). Columns (1), (4), (5), (7), (9), (12) and (14) are transcribed directly from "Quarry Accidents."

<sup>b</sup> Mandays reported for "all other and not stated" (i.e. not distributed between dimension and nondimension quarries) were allocated according to the formula already given.

<sup>c</sup> Mandays reported for "all other and not stated" were allocated wholly to non-dimension establishments: see Worksheet VIII.

<sup>d</sup> Mandays reported for "all other and not stated" were distributed between dimension and nondimension establishments according to the formula already given. Although, in the case of marble and slate, both dimension and nondimension employment are included, the allocation has still to be made, in order that (small amounts of) employment at nondimension outside works may be included.

<sup>e</sup> The nondimension output of marble and slate is mostly a byproduct of dimension; few marble and slate quarries are classified as nondimension establishments. Therefore employment reported for nondimension marble and slate quarries and outside works (like the output of nondimension marble and slate) has been included with dimension.

---

*Gypsum*

Employment covers the mining, but not the calcining or processing, of the mineral. For 1911, 1916 and 1919–38, data are derived from Robinson Newcomb and Knute Peterson, "Production, Employment and Output per Man in Gypsum Mining," Information Circular 7134 (U. S. Bureau of Mines, 1940). This survey covers between 67 and 100 percent of output; accordingly employment figures there given were written up by the ratio of total output to output covered by the survey. The 1902 figures are based on output and are derived from the same source, it being assumed that productivity in 1902 was equal to productivity in 1900. (The Census report for 1902 does not clearly distinguish between mining and manufacturing, and for this reason was not used.) Figures for 1912–15 and 1917–18 are based on output, with the help of productivity ratios interpolated along straight lines between 1911 and 1916, and 1916 and 1919, respectively. The 1939 data come from a preliminary release of the Census of Mineral Industries, 1939.

*Phosphate Rock*

For 1902, figures were derived from the Census of Mines and Quarries. For 1919–37, we employed Bureau of Mines sample data as given in A. P. Haskell, Jr. and O. E. Kiessling, *Phosphate-Rock Mining* (National Research Project, Philadelphia, 1938), p. 99. We derived figures for mandays and manhours by stepping up sample mandays and manhours by the ratio of total numbers employed to sample numbers employed. For 1939, the data come from a preliminary release of the Census of Mineral Industries, 1939. For 1938 mandays and manhours are based on output, output per manday and per manhour being taken as the mean of 1937 and 1939.

Owing to the absence of comparable data for 1911, figures shown for phosphate rock employment in 1902 are not included in the totals.

Table A-4

ADDITIONAL EMPLOYMENT DATA[a]

| Year | Lead and Zinc Mining, Mississippi Valley[b] | | Mercury Mining[c] | |
|------|---------------------|---------------------|---------------------|---------------------|
|      | Mandays (mil.) | Manhours (mil.) | Mandays (mil.) | Manhours (mil.) |
| 1902 | .. | .. | .450 | 4.28 |
| 1911 | 3.20 | .. | .. | .. |
| 1912 | 3.78 | .. | .. | .. |
| 1913 | 3.23 | .. | .. | .. |
| 1914 | 2.78 | .. | .. | .. |
| 1915 | 3.35 | .. | .. | .. |
| 1916 | 5.44 | .. | .. | .. |
| 1917 | 4.99 | .. | .415 | .. |
| 1918 | 3.52 | .. | .. | ..⌐ |
| 1919 | 3.27 | .. | .. | .. |
| 1920 | 3.30 | .. | .. | .. |
| 1921 | 1.63 | .. | .. | .. |
| 1922 | 2.50 | .. | .. | .. |
| 1923 | 2.96 | .. | .. | .. |
| 1924 | 3.70 | .. | .123 | .985 |
| 1925 | 3.61 | .. | .107 | .860 |
| 1926 | 3.83 | .. | .112 | .899 |
| 1927 | 3.18 | .. | .200 | 1.60 |
| 1928 | 2.60 | .. | .257 | 2.09 |
| 1929 | 2.74 | 22.0 | .325 | 2.63 |
| 1930 | 1.84 | 14.8 | .284 | 2.46 |
| 1931 | 1.17 | 9.46 | .297 | 2.42 |
| 1932 | .683 | 5.53 | .122 | .979 |
| 1933 | .703 | 5.66 | .109 | .864 |
| 1934 | .985 | 7.85 | .142 | 1.06 |
| 1935 | 1.19 | 9.59 | .160 | 1.23 |
| 1936 | 1.53 | 12.3 | .. | .. |
| 1937 | 1.83 | 14.7 | .. | .. |
| 1938 | 1.33 | 10.6 | .. | .. |
| 1939 | 1.57 | 12.4 | .180 | 1.41 |

[a] Data in this table are included in, but do not exhaust, the category "Metal mining and ore dressing—other nonferrous metals" in Table A-3.

[b] Arkansas, Illinois, Iowa, Kansas, Kentucky, Missouri, Oklahoma, Tennessee, Wisconsin. Data are from U. S. Bureau of Mines, "Metal-Mine Accidents in the United States," and include fluorspar mining in Illinois and Kentucky. Figures cover mining only and do not include milling.

[c] The 1902 data are from the Census: see notes to metal mining, Table A-3. For 1939 figures are from preliminary releases of the Census of Mineral Industries. Data for other years are from sample material collected by the Bureau of Mines and published in *Minerals Yearbook;* data were adjusted by us to full coverage by ratios (varying from 1.049 to 1.380) of total output to output covered by study. Employment at recovery plants is included.

OTAL MINING AND INDIVIDUAL MINING INDUSTRIES

dexes of Output,[a] Employment[b] and Productivity[c]

*29:100*

| ar | TOTAL, INCLUDING OIL AND GAS WELLS[d] | | | TOTAL, EXCLUDING OIL AND GAS WELLS[e] | | | | |
|---|---|---|---|---|---|---|---|---|
| | Output | Manhours of Employment | Output per Manhour | Output | Mandays of Employment | Manhours of Employment | Output per Manday | Output per Manhour |
| 99 | 26.3 | .. | .. | 43.0 | .. | .. | .. | .. |
| 00 | 28.4 | .. | .. | 46.0 | .. | .. | .. | .. |
| 01 | 30.0 | .. | .. | 48.6 | .. | .. | .. | .. |
| 02 | 31.3 | 73.3 | 43 | 49.8 | 78.1 | 84.5 | 64 | 59 |
| 03 | 35.4 | .. | .. | 56.6 | .. | .. | .. | .. |
| 04 | 36.0 | .. | .. | 56.9 | .. | .. | .. | .. |
| 05 | 40.2 | .. | .. | 63.6 | .. | .. | .. | .. |
| 06 | 41.8 | .. | .. | 66.4 | .. | .. | .. | .. |
| 07 | 45.4 | .. | .. | 71.6 | .. | .. | .. | .. |
| 08 | 42.1 | .. | .. | 65.0 | .. | .. | .. | .. |
| 09 | 47.8 | .. | .. | 74.5 | .. | .. | .. | .. |
| 10 | 50.8 | .. | .. | 78.6 | .. | .. | .. | .. |
| 11 | 50.0 | .. | .. | 76.9 | 116.5 | .. | 66 | .. |
| 12 | 53.4 | .. | .. | 82.4 | 119.7 | .. | 69 | .. |
| 13 | 56.6 | .. | .. | 87.0 | 130.7 | .. | 67 | .. |
| 14 | 52.7 | .. | .. | 78.8 | 112.2 | .. | 70 | .. |
| 15 | 57.7 | .. | .. | 86.8 | 111.1 | .. | 78 | .. |
| 16 | 66.6 | .. | .. | 101.1 | 127.3 | .. | 79 | .. |
| 17 | 70.0 | .. | .. | 104.6 | 137.7 | .. | 76 | .. |
| 18 | 70.5 | .. | .. | 104.4 | 137.4 | .. | 76 | .. |
| 19 | 61.0 | .. | .. | 83.6 | 112.9 | 113.6 | 74 | 74 |
| 20 | 70.8 | .. | .. | 96.4 | 123.5 | .. | 78 | .. |
| 21 | 57.7 | .. | .. | 70.0 | 91.4 | .. | 77 | .. |
| 22 | 61.9 | .. | .. | 71.7 | 85.5 | .. | 84 | .. |
| 23 | 85.5 | .. | .. | 99.8 | 116.0 | .. | 86 | .. |
| 24 | 80.3 | .. | .. | 91.0 | 106.7 | .. | 85 | .. |
| 25 | 83.0 | .. | .. | 91.8 | 102.7 | .. | 89 | .. |
| 26 | 89.9 | .. | .. | 102.4 | 114.5 | .. | 89 | .. |
| 27 | 92.0 | .. | .. | 96.1 | 103.8 | .. | 93 | .. |
| 28 | 91.8 | .. | .. | 94.6 | 97.0 | .. | 97 | .. |
| 29 | 100.0 | 100.0 | 100 | 100.0 | 100.0 | 100.0 | 100 | 100 |
| 30 | 88.1 | .. | .. | 85.6 | 84.8 | .. | 101 | .. |
| 31 | 73.8 | .. | .. | 66.8 | 65.0 | 64.7 | 103 | 103 |
| 32 | 60.1 | .. | .. | 49.4 | 49.3 | 48.8 | 100 | 101 |
| 33 | 65.3 | .. | .. | 52.1 | 54.1 | 53.1 | 96 | 98 |
| 34 | 70.8 | .. | .. | 59.1 | 63.9 | 58.2 | 92 | 101 |
| 35 | 76.3 | 58.8 | 130 | 62.6 | 66.0 | 59.2 | 95 | 106 |
| 36 | 89.0 | 68.9 | 129 | 76.6 | 76.0 | 68.4 | 101 | 112 |
| 37 | 100.1 | 71.9 | 139 | 83.8 | 78.9 | 70.3 | 106 | 119 |
| 38 | 85.6 | 59.0 | 145 | 64.2 | 61.0 | 54.1 | 105 | 119 |
| 39 | 94.7 | 60.6 | 156 | 75.7 | 66.8 | 59.2 | 113 | 128 |

r footnotes see pp. 351-52.

| | METAL MINING AND ORE DRESSING | | | | | | | | |
| | TOTAL[f] | | | | | IRON ORE | | | |
| Year | Output | Man-days of Employ-ment | Man-hours of Employ-ment | Out-put per Man-day | Out-put per Man-hour | Output | Man-days of Employ-ment | Man-hours of Employ-ment | Out-put per Man-day | Out pu pe Ma ho |
|---|---|---|---|---|---|---|---|---|---|---|
| 1899 | 39.1 | .. | .. | .. | .. | 33.6 | .. | .. | .. | |
| 1900 | 42.8 | .. | .. | .. | .. | 37.3 | .. | .. | .. | . |
| 1901 | 43.2 | .. | .. | .. | .. | 39.1 | .. | .. | .. | |
| 1902 | 47.2 | 97.9 | 110.6 | 48 | 43 | 48.3 | 139.0 | 154.2 | 35 | |
| 1903 | 47.1 | .. | .. | .. | .. | 47.6 | .. | .. | .. | |
| 1904 | 49.1 | .. | .. | .. | .. | 37.6 | .. | .. | .. | |
| 1905 | 55.4 | .. | .. | .. | .. | 57.9 | .. | .. | .. | |
| 1906 | 58.2 | .. | .. | .. | .. | 65.2 | .. | .. | .. | |
| 1907 | 56.9 | .. | .. | .. | .. | 70.7 | .. | .. | .. | |
| 1908 | 54.3 | .. | .. | .. | .. | 49.0 | .. | .. | .. | |
| 1909 | 66.6 | .. | .. | .. | .. | 70.2 | .. | .. | .. | |
| 1910 | 68.3 | .. | .. | .. | .. | 78.1 | .. | .. | .. | |
| 1911 | 64.9 | 129.5[g] | .. | 50 | .. | 60.2 | 162.7[g] | .. | 37 | |
| 1912 | 72.2 | 132.5[g] | .. | 55 | .. | 75.7 | 166.4[g] | .. | 46 | . |
| 1913 | 75.3 | 150.5 | .. | 50 | .. | 85.1 | 192.3[g] | .. | 44 | . |
| 1914 | 67.4 | 117.7 | .. | 57 | .. | 56.8 | 149.9[g] | .. | 38 | . |
| 1915 | 83.4 | 122.2 | .. | 68 | .. | 76.0 | 136.7 | 136.8 | 56 | |
| 1916 | 104.2 | 169.0 | .. | 62 | .. | 103.0 | 181.0 | 182.5 | 57 | |
| 1917 | 102.3 | 169.6 | .. | 60 | .. | 103.2 | 196.4 | 199.2 | 53 | |
| 1918 | 98.7 | 159.1 | .. | 62 | .. | 95.3 | 188.7 | 192.7 | 51 | |
| 1919 | 72.7 | 117.0 | 121.0 | 62 | 60 | 83.5 | 167.6 | 170.0 | 50 | |
| 1920 | 77.1 | 115.6 | .. | 67 | .. | 92.6 | 168.3 | 173.1 | 55 | |
| 1921 | 38.4 | 59.2 | .. | 65 | .. | 40.4 | 78.1 | 79.3 | 52 | |
| 1922 | 61.3 | 81.6 | .. | 75 | .. | 64.5 | 103.7 | 103.0 | 62 | |
| 1923 | 84.6 | 104.8 | .. | 81 | .. | 94.8 | 136.6 | 139.5 | 69 | |
| 1924 | 82.1 | 104.2 | .. | 79 | .. | 74.2 | 118.1 | 118.4 | 63 | |
| 1925 | 89.7 | 107.6 | .. | 83 | .. | 84.6 | 111.9 | 111.9 | 76 | |
| 1926 | 93.2 | 108.0 | .. | 86 | .. | 92.6 | 108.8 | 109.2 | 85 | |
| 1927 | 88.4 | 98.5 | .. | 90 | .. | 84.7 | 106.2 | 106.4 | 80 | |
| 1928 | 91.3 | 92.4 | .. | 99 | .. | 85.2 | 92.7 | 92.6 | 92 | |
| 1929 | 100.0 | 100.0 | 100.0 | 100 | 100 | 100.0 | 100.0 | 100.0 | 100 | 1 |
| 1930 | 78.2 | 78.7 | .. | 99 | .. | 80.2 | 93.0 | 92.9 | 86 | |
| 1931 | 53.6 | 51.6 | 51.6 | 104 | 104 | 42.7 | 53.2 | 53.1 | 80 | |
| 1932 | 29.3 | 28.6 | 28.4 | 102 | 103 | 13.5 | 21.2 | 21.3 | 64 | |
| 1933 | 34.0 | 28.9 | 28.1 | 118 | 121 | 24.0 | 24.6 | 23.2 | 98 | 1 |
| 1934 | 43.2 | 38.0 | 36.7 | 113 | 118 | 33.7 | 36.9 | 33.0 | 91 | 1 |
| 1935 | 56.1 | 54.5 | 52.2 | 103 | 107 | 41.9 | 38.0 | 34.1 | 110 | 1 |
| 1936 | 76.0 | 68.8 | 66.7 | 110 | 114 | 66.9 | 53.4 | 48.3 | 125 | 1 |
| 1937 | 98.2 | 84.6 | 81.5 | 116 | 121 | 98.8 | 74.0 | 66.7 | 133 | 1 |
| 1938 | 67.2 | 63.5 | 61.2 | 106 | 110 | 38.9 | 44.2 | 39.7 | 88 | |
| 1939 | 86.2 | 71.4 | 68.3 | 121 | 126 | 70.7 | 56.3 | 50.6 | 126 | 1 |

*For footnotes see pp. 351-52.*

| | METAL MINING AND ORE DRESSING (continued) | | | | | | | | | |
| | COPPER[h] | | | | | OTHER NONFERROUS METALS[i] | | | | |
| Year | Output | Man-days of Employment | Man-hours of Employment | Output per Man-day | Output per Man-hour | Output | Man-days of Employment | Man-hours of Employment | Output per Man-day | Output per Man-hour |
|---|---|---|---|---|---|---|---|---|---|---|
| 1899 | .. | .. | .. | .. | .. | .. | .. | .. | .. | .. |
| 1900 | .. | .. | .. | .. | .. | .. | .. | .. | .. | .. |
| 1901 | .. | .. | .. | .. | .. | .. | .. | .. | .. | .. |
| 1902 | 35.6 | 57.5 | 63.0 | 62 | 56 | 66.2 | 116.1 | 133.0 | 57 | 50 |
| 1903 | 37.6 | .. | .. | .. | .. | 63.5 | .. | .. | .. | .. |
| 1904 | 43.7 | .. | .. | .. | .. | 66.9 | .. | .. | .. | .. |
| 1905 | 47.3 | .. | .. | .. | .. | 68.4 | .. | .. | .. | .. |
| 1906 | 48.8 | .. | .. | .. | .. | 70.0 | .. | .. | .. | .. |
| 1907 | 45.0 | .. | .. | .. | .. | 68.1 | .. | .. | .. | .. |
| 1908 | 50.4 | .. | .. | .. | .. | 66.0 | .. | .. | .. | .. |
| 1909 | 59.5 | .. | .. | .. | .. | 75.4 | .. | .. | .. | .. |
| 1910 | 57.1 | .. | .. | .. | .. | 76.9 | .. | .. | .. | .. |
| 1911 | 57.3 | 112.6[g] | .. | 51 | .. | 79.8 | 149.7[g] | .. | 53 | .. |
| 1912 | 63.9 | 128.2[g] | .. | 50 | .. | 81.9 | 138.3[g] | .. | 59 | .. |
| 1913 | 63.5 | 140.8[g] | .. | 45 | .. | 85.1 | 160.3[g] | .. | 53 | .. |
| 1914 | 58.6 | 103.7[g] | .. | 57 | .. | 86.7 | 126.6[g] | .. | 68 | .. |
| 1915 | 72.8 | 114.3 | .. | 64 | .. | 102.8 | 129.1[g] | .. | 80 | .. |
| 1916 | 97.4 | 151.5 | .. | 64 | .. | 114.6 | 180.9 | .. | 63 | .. |
| 1917 | 92.6 | 157.0 | .. | 59 | .. | 115.3 | 165.8 | .. | 70 | .. |
| 1918 | 94.2 | 153.3 | .. | 61 | .. | 105.8 | 145.6 | .. | 73 | .. |
| 1919 | 59.5 | 94.3 | 96.9 | 63 | 61 | 81.5 | 108.7 | 112.2 | 75 | 73 |
| 1920 | 58.7 | 91.2 | .. | 64 | .. | 87.4 | 107.7 | .. | 81 | .. |
| 1921 | 20.9 | 33.6 | .. | 62 | .. | 62.0 | 75.7 | .. | 82 | .. |
| 1922 | 45.4 | 61.2 | .. | 74 | .. | 80.9 | 90.0 | .. | 90 | .. |
| 1923 | 71.2 | 83.7 | .. | 85 | .. | 94.1 | 107.4 | .. | 88 | .. |
| 1924 | 78.6 | 86.6 | .. | 91 | .. | 95.8 | 114.9 | .. | 83 | .. |
| 1925 | 82.6 | 87.5 | .. | 94 | .. | 104.7 | 127.7 | .. | 82 | .. |
| 1926 | 85.0 | 90.9 | .. | 94 | .. | 106.2 | 126.9 | .. | 84 | .. |
| 1927 | 81.6 | 81.8 | .. | 100 | .. | 101.1 | 112.2 | .. | 90 | .. |
| 1928 | 90.2 | 85.1 | .. | 106 | .. | 98.2 | 100.4 | .. | 98 | .. |
| 1929 | 100.0 | 100.0 | 100.0 | 100 | 100 | 100.0 | 100.0 | 100.0 | 100 | 100 |
| 1930 | 70.6 | 70.2 | .. | 101 | .. | 86.4 | 78.7 | 78.9 | 110 | 109 |
| 1931 | 52.6 | 44.9 | 44.6 | 117 | 118 | 66.6 | 58.2 | 58.6 | 114 | 114 |
| 1932 | 23.8 | 20.3 | 21.2 | 117 | 118 | 53.7 | 43.2 | 43.5 | 124 | 124 |
| 1933 | 20.1 | 14.7 | 14.3 | 137 | 140 | 58.8 | 48.0 | 47.7 | 122 | 123 |
| 1934 | 25.4 | 16.5 | 16.1 | 154 | 158 | 71.0 | 63.4 | 63.5 | 112 | 112 |
| 1935 | 40.1 | 25.0 | 24.4 | 161 | 164 | 86.9 | 99.2 | 98.1 | 88 | 89 |
| 1936 | 63.5 | 38.1 | 37.4 | 167 | 170 | 100.2 | 114.1 | 114.5 | 88 | 88 |
| 1937 | 86.4 | 57.7 | 56.5 | 150 | 153 | 114.0 | 122.2 | 121.6 | 93 | 94 |
| 1938 | 58.2 | 38.2 | 37.3 | 152 | 156 | 104.0 | 105.5 | 105.1 | 99 | 99 |
| 1939 | 77.0 | 46.5 | 45.5 | 166 | 169 | 111.7 | 110.0 | 108.2 | 102 | 103 |

*For footnotes see pp. 351-52.*

| Year | Output | Mandays of Employment | Manhours of Employment | Output per Manday | Output per Manhour |
|------|--------|----------------------|------------------------|-------------------|--------------------|
| | | COAL MINING TOTAL | | | |
| 1899 | 45.5 | 60.6 | .. | 75 | .. |
| 1900 | 47.7 | 65.9 | .. | 72 | .. |
| 1901 | 52.3 | 72.7 | .. | 72 | .. |
| 1902 | 51.1 | 70.8 | 78.3 | 72 | 65 |
| 1903 | 63.0 | 86.2 | 93.9 | 73 | 67 |
| 1904 | 62.0 | 82.8 | 89.4 | 75 | 69 |
| 1905 | 68.7 | 91.9 | 99.3 | 75 | 69 |
| 1906 | 71.4 | 93.2 | 99.7 | 77 | 72 |
| 1907 | 83.0 | 108.6 | 117.1 | 76 | 71 |
| 1908 | 72.8 | 93.1 | 100.5 | 78 | 72 |
| 1909 | 79.5 | 103.2 | 111.3 | 77 | 71 |
| 1910 | 86.2 | 110.3 | 119.0 | 78 | 72 |
| 1911 | 86.1 | 109.7 | 118.5 | 78 | 73 |
| 1912 | 91.1 | 112.5 | 121.4 | 81 | 75 |
| 1913 | 97.4 | 123.1 | 132.9 | 79 | 73 |
| 1914 | 88.8 | 109.3 | 118.1 | 81 | 75 |
| 1915 | 91.3 | 106.3 | 114.8 | 86 | 80 |
| 1916 | 100.1 | 117.5 | 125.0 | 85 | 80 |
| 1917 | 110.7 | 131.8 | 134.6 | 84 | 82 |
| 1918 | 115.1 | 136.0 | 136.5 | 85 | 84 |
| 1919 | 94.6 | 112.6 | 112.4 | 84 | 84 |
| 1920 | 111.3 | 124.9 | 124.4 | 89 | 90 |
| 1921 | 87.3 | 98.5 | 98.1 | 89 | 89 |
| 1922 | 79.0 | 84.1 | 84.0 | 94 | 94 |
| 1923 | 111.2 | 116.4 | 116.2 | 96 | 96 |
| 1924 | 97.8 | 103.8 | 103.7 | 94 | 94 |
| 1925 | 93.7 | 99.7 | 99.8 | 94 | 94 |
| 1926 | 109.2 | 116.2 | 116.1 | 94 | 94 |
| 1927 | 100.1 | 104.5 | 104.5 | 96 | 96 |
| 1928 | 96.0 | 97.3 | 97.3 | 99 | 99 |
| 1929 | 100.0 | 100.0 | 100.0 | 100 | 100 |
| 1930 | 89.2 | 85.8 | 86.1 | 104 | 104 |
| 1931 | 74.0 | 67.8 | 68.2 | 109 | 109 |
| 1932 | 60.5 | 54.6 | 54.7 | 111 | 111 |
| 1933 | 63.4 | 61.5 | 61.5 | 103 | 103 |
| 1934 | 69.7 | 72.2 | 66.3 | 96 | 105 |
| 1935 | 69.7 | 70.8 | 63.4 | 99 | 110 |
| 1936 | 80.0 | 79.4 | 70.8 | 101 | 113 |
| 1937 | 79.9 | 78.7 | 69.0 | 102 | 116 |
| 1938 | 64.7 | 60.8 | 53.1 | 106 | 122 |
| 1939 | 72.8 | 66.4 | 57.9 | 110 | 126 |

*For footnotes see pp. 351-52.*

| | COAL MINING (continued) | | | | | | | | |
| | PENNSYLVANIA ANTHRACITE | | | | | BITUMINOUS COAL | | | |
| ar | Output | Man-days of Employment | Man-hours of Employment | Output per Man-day | Output per Man-hour | Output | Man-days of Employment | Man-hours of Employment | Output per Man-day | Output per Man-hour |
|---|---|---|---|---|---|---|---|---|---|---|
| 99 | 81.8 | 70.8 | .. | 116 | .. | 36.1 | 57.5 | .. | 63 | .. |
| 00 | 77.7 | 70.2 | .. | 111 | .. | 39.7 | 64.6 | .. | 61 | .. |
| 01 | 91.4 | 83.5 | 99.2 | 109 | 92 | 42.2 | 69.4 | .. | 61 | .. |
| 02 | 56.0 | 50.4 | 59.8 | 111 | 94 | 48.6 | 77.1 | 84.0 | 63 | 58 |
| 03 | 101.1 | 90.9 | 102.3 | 111 | 99 | 52.9 | 84.8 | 91.3 | 62 | 58 |
| 04 | 99.1 | 91.4 | 102.8 | 108 | 96 | 52.1 | 80.2 | 85.3 | 65 | 61 |
| 05 | 105.2 | 104.3 | 117.3 | 101 | 90 | 58.9 | 88.1 | 93.8 | 67 | 63 |
| 06 | 96.6 | 92.8 | 104.5 | 104 | 92 | 64.1 | 92.4 | 98.3 | 69 | 65 |
| 07 | 116.0 | 107.9 | 121.4 | 107 | 96 | 73.8 | 108.8 | 115.8 | 68 | 64 |
| 08 | 112.8 | 102.2 | 114.9 | 110 | 98 | 62.2 | 90.3 | 96.1 | 69 | 65 |
| 09 | 109.8 | 104.3 | 117.4 | 105 | 94 | 71.0 | 102.9 | 109.5 | 69 | 65 |
| 10 | 114.4 | 113.8 | 128.1 | 101 | 89 | 78.0 | 109.2 | 116.3 | 71 | 67 |
| 11 | 122.5 | 124.5 | 140.1 | 98 | 87 | 75.9 | 105.1 | 111.9 | 72 | 68 |
| 12 | 114.3 | 117.9 | 132.6 | 97 | 86 | 84.2 | 110.9 | 118.0 | 76 | 71 |
| 13 | 124.0 | 132.5 | 149.0 | 94 | 83 | 89.4 | 120.2 | 128.0 | 74 | 70 |
| 14 | 123.0 | 129.1 | 145.2 | 95 | 85 | 79.0 | 103.1 | 109.8 | 77 | 72 |
| 15 | 120.5 | 119.0 | 133.8 | 101 | 90 | 82.8 | 102.3 | 108.9 | 81 | 76 |
| 16 | 118.6 | 118.7 | 126.1 | 100 | 94 | 94.0 | 117.1 | 124.7 | 80 | 75 |
| 17 | 134.9 | 128.8 | 128.8 | 105 | 105 | 103.2 | 132.8 | 136.4 | 78 | 76 |
| 18 | 133.9 | 126.5 | 126.5 | 106 | 106 | 108.3 | 138.9 | 139.6 | 78 | 78 |
| 19 | 119.3 | 120.5 | 120.5 | 99 | 99 | 87.1 | 110.2 | 109.9 | 79 | 79 |
| 920 | 121.4 | 115.4 | 115.4 | 105 | 105 | 106.3 | 127.8 | 127.1 | 83 | 84 |
| 921 | 122.6 | 126.6 | 126.6 | 97 | 97 | 77.7 | 89.8 | 89.4 | 87 | 87 |
| 922 | 74.0 | 69.3 | 69.3 | 107 | 107 | 78.9 | 88.6 | 88.4 | 89 | 89 |
| 923 | 126.4 | 123.8 | 123.8 | 102 | 102 | 105.5 | 114.1 | 113.9 | 92 | 93 |
| 924 | 119.1 | 128.8 | 128.8 | 92 | 92 | 90.4 | 96.1 | 96.1 | 94 | 94 |
| 925 | 83.7 | 85.4 | 85.4 | 98 | 98 | 97.2 | 104.2 | 104.2 | 93 | 93 |
| 926 | 114.4 | 118.2 | 118.2 | 97 | 97 | 107.2 | 115.5 | 115.4 | 93 | 93 |
| 927 | 108.5 | 109.1 | 109.1 | 99 | 99 | 96.8 | 103.0 | 103.0 | 94 | 94 |
| 928 | 102.1 | 102.0 | 102.0 | 100 | 100 | 93.6 | 95.9 | 95.9 | 98 | 98 |
| 929 | 100.0 | 100.0 | 100.0 | 100 | 100 | 100.0 | 100.0 | 100.0 | 100 | 100 |
| 930 | 94.0 | 92.6 | 92.6 | 102 | 102 | 87.4 | 83.6 | 84.1 | 104 | 104 |
| 931 | 80.8 | 76.0 | 76.4 | 106 | 106 | 71.4 | 65.3 | 65.7 | 109 | 109 |
| 932 | 67.5 | 57.2 | 57.5 | 118 | 117 | 57.9 | 53.8 | 53.9 | 108 | 107 |
| 933 | 67.1 | 55.8 | 55.8 | 120 | 120 | 62.4 | 63.3 | 63.3 | 99 | 99 |
| 934 | 77.4 | 66.2 | 66.2 | 117 | 117 | 67.2 | 74.0 | 66.3 | 91 | 101 |
| 935 | 70.6 | 57.2 | 57.1 | 124 | 124 | 69.6 | 75.0 | 65.3 | 93 | 107 |
| 936 | 73.9 | 57.4 | 57.2 | 129 | 129 | 82.1 | 86.1 | 75.0 | 95 | 109 |
| 937 | 70.2 | 55.0 | 49.8 | 128 | 141 | 83.3 | 86.1 | 74.9 | 97 | 111 |
| 938 | 62.4 | 48.5 | 42.5 | 129 | 147 | 65.1 | 64.6 | 56.3 | 101 | 116 |
| 939 | 69.7 | 50.0 | 43.9 | 140 | 159 | 73.5 | 71.5 | 62.2 | 103 | 118 |

or footnotes see pp. 351-52.

| Year | OIL AND GAS WELLS[j] | | | STONE QUARRYING[k] TOTAL | | | | |
| | Output | Manhours of Employment | Output per Manhour | Output | Mandays of Employment | Manhours of Employment | Output per Manday | Output per Manhour |
| --- | --- | --- | --- | --- | --- | --- | --- | --- |
| 1899 | 8.1 | .. | .. | .. | .. | .. | .. | .. |
| 1900 | 9.0 | .. | .. | .. | .. | .. | .. | .. |
| 1901 | 9.6 | .. | .. | .. | .. | .. | .. | .. |
| 1902 | 11.1 | 28.7 | 39 | .. | .. | .. | .. | .. |
| 1903 | 12.0 | .. | .. | .. | .. | .. | .. | .. |
| 1904 | 13.0 | .. | .. | .. | .. | .. | .. | .. |
| 1905 | 14.3 | .. | .. | .. | .. | .. | .. | .. |
| 1906 | 14.2 | .. | .. | 62.9 | .. | .. | .. | .. |
| 1907 | 16.3 | .. | .. | 64.5 | .. | .. | .. | .. |
| 1908 | 16.8 | .. | .. | 62.2 | .. | .. | .. | .. |
| 1909 | 18.3 | .. | .. | 69.9 | .. | .. | .. | .. |
| 1910 | 20.1 | .. | .. | 73.0 | .. | .. | .. | .. |
| 1911 | 20.4 | .. | .. | 72.2 | 156.2 | .. | 46 | .. |
| 1912 | 21.4 | .. | .. | 72.6 | 164.1 | .. | 44 | .. |
| 1913 | 23.0 | .. | .. | 76.2 | 161.4 | .. | 47 | .. |
| 1914 | 24.0 | .. | .. | 70.4 | 130.2 | .. | 54 | .. |
| 1915 | 25.2 | .. | .. | 69.4 | 135.1 | .. | 51 | .. |
| 1916 | 27.9 | .. | .. | 73.5 | 122.7 | .. | 60 | .. |
| 1917 | 31.4 | .. | .. | 63.2 | 116.7 | .. | 54 | .. |
| 1918 | 32.5 | .. | .. | 48.6 | 95.3 | .. | 51 | .. |
| 1919 | 34.7 | .. | .. | 50.8 | 106.2 | 108.5 | 48 | 47 |
| 1920 | 40.3 | .. | .. | 59.0 | 124.7 | .. | 47 | .. |
| 1921 | 42.6 | .. | .. | 51.1 | 98.6 | .. | 52 | .. |
| 1922 | 50.0 | .. | .. | 64.1 | 110.3 | .. | 58 | .. |
| 1923 | 66.7 | .. | .. | 79.6 | 142.6 | .. | 56 | .. |
| 1924 | 66.6 | .. | .. | 80.9 | 143.7 | .. | 56 | .. |
| 1925 | 71.7 | .. | .. | 89.0 | 119.6 | .. | 74 | .. |
| 1926 | 74.0 | .. | .. | 91.6 | 113.1 | .. | 81 | .. |
| 1927 | 86.3 | .. | .. | 97.6 | 110.7 | .. | 88 | .. |
| 1928 | 87.8 | .. | .. | 97.2 | 106.0 | .. | 92 | .. |
| 1929 | 100.0 | 100.0 | 100 | 100.0 | 100.0 | 100.0 | 100 | 100 |
| 1930 | 91.3 | .. | .. | 89.1 | 89.4 | 87.6 | 100 | 102 |
| 1931 | 84.5 | .. | .. | 65.8 | 69.7 | 64.3 | 94 | 102 |
| 1932 | 77.4 | .. | .. | 44.5 | 48.8 | 44.6 | 91 | 100 |
| 1933 | 86.5 | .. | .. | 40.8 | 45.2 | 38.8 | 90 | 105 |
| 1934 | 88.4 | .. | .. | 46.4 | 48.2 | 39.8 | 96 | 117 |
| 1935 | 96.8 | 57.2 | 169 | 43.6 | 49.9 | 41.6 | 87 | 105 |
| 1936 | 106.9 | 70.5 | 152 | 63.7 | 62.5 | 54.1 | 102 | 118 |
| 1937 | 123.8 | 78.2 | 158 | 66.1 | 67.2 | 58.1 | 98 | 114 |
| 1938 | 118.2 | 78.2 | 151 | 57.2 | 55.7 | 47.4 | 103 | 121 |
| 1939 | 123.2 | 66.1 | 186 | 67.2 | 59.3 | 50.3 | 113 | 134 |

*For footnotes see pp. 351-52.*

| | STONE QUARRYING[k] (continued) | | | | | | | | | |
| | DIMENSION STONE | | | | | NONDIMENSION STONE | | | | |
| ear | Output | Man-days of Employ-ment | Man-hours of Employ-ment | Out-put per Man-day | Out-put per Man-hour | Output | Man-days of Employ-ment | Man-hours of Employ-ment | Out-put per Man-day | Out-put per Man-hour |
|---|---|---|---|---|---|---|---|---|---|---|
| 899 | .. | .. | .. | .. | .. | .. | .. | .. | .. | .. |
| 900 | .. | .. | .. | .. | .. | .. | .. | .. | .. | .. |
| 901 | .. | .. | .. | .. | .. | .. | .. | .. | .. | .. |
| 902 | .. | .. | .. | .. | .. | .. | .. | .. | .. | .. |
| 903 | .. | .. | .. | .. | .. | .. | .. | .. | .. | .. |
| 904 | .. | .. | .. | .. | .. | .. | .. | .. | .. | .. |
| 905 | .. | .. | .. | .. | .. | .. | .. | .. | .. | .. |
| 906 | 111.0 | .. | .. | .. | .. | 41.2 | .. | .. | .. | .. |
| 907 | 106.8 | .. | .. | .. | .. | 46.3 | .. | .. | .. | .. |
| 908 | 112.6 | .. | .. | .. | .. | 39.4 | .. | .. | .. | .. |
| 909 | 117.3 | .. | .. | .. | .. | 49.2 | .. | .. | .. | .. |
| 910 | 110.0 | .. | .. | .. | .. | 57.2 | .. | .. | .. | .. |
| 911 | 107.5 | .. | .. | .. | .. | 57.1 | .. | .. | .. | .. |
| 912 | 101.3 | .. | .. | .. | .. | 60.9 | .. | .. | .. | .. |
| 913 | 100.3 | .. | .. | .. | .. | 66.9 | .. | .. | .. | .. |
| 914 | 97.3 | .. | .. | .. | .. | 59.2 | .. | .. | .. | .. |
| 915 | 87.0 | .. | .. | .. | .. | 63.0 | .. | .. | .. | .. |
| 916 | 95.6 | .. | .. | .. | .. | 64.9 | .. | .. | .. | .. |
| 917 | 71.5 | .. | .. | .. | .. | 59.6 | .. | .. | .. | .. |
| 918 | 47.0 | .. | .. | .. | .. | 48.6 | .. | .. | .. | .. |
| 919 | 59.5 | .. | .. | .. | .. | 47.1 | .. | .. | .. | .. |
| 920 | 64.0 | .. | .. | .. | .. | 56.6 | .. | .. | .. | .. |
| 921 | 61.8 | .. | .. | .. | .. | 46.6 | .. | .. | .. | .. |
| 922 | 75.5 | 110.1 | .. | 69 | .. | 59.1 | 110.4 | .. | 54 | .. |
| 923 | 91.8 | 136.2 | .. | 67 | .. | 74.2 | 144.8 | .. | 51 | .. |
| 924 | 93.8 | 158.4 | .. | 59 | .. | 75.1 | 138.7 | .. | 54 | .. |
| 925 | 100.2 | 125.3 | .. | 80 | .. | 83.9 | 117.7 | .. | 71 | .. |
| 926 | 95.6 | 114.3 | .. | 84 | .. | 89.7 | 112.7 | .. | 80 | .. |
| 927 | 98.5 | 108.2 | .. | 91 | .. | 97.2 | 111.6 | .. | 87 | .. |
| 928 | 98.7 | 107.3 | .. | 92 | .. | 96.4 | 105.5 | .. | 91 | .. |
| 929 | 100.0 | 100.0 | 100.0 | 100 | 100 | 100.0 | 100.0 | 100.0 | 100 | 100 |
| 930 | 88.5 | 85.5 | 84.6 | 104 | 104 | 89.3 | 90.4 | 88.3 | 99 | 101 |
| 931 | 60.2 | 57.5 | 54.4 | 105 | 111 | 68.4 | 72.7 | 66.6 | 94 | 103 |
| 932 | 40.6 | 34.1 | 31.5 | 119 | 129 | 46.0 | 52.4 | 47.7 | 88 | 96 |
| 933 | 31.1 | 31.2 | 27.5 | 100 | 113 | 45.8 | 48.7 | 41.5 | 94 | 110 |
| 934 | 29.1 | 25.9 | 21.3 | 112 | 137 | 55.3 | 53.7 | 44.2 | 103 | 125 |
| 935 | 29.5 | 31.4 | 26.9 | 94 | 109 | 50.8 | 54.5 | 45.1 | 93 | 113 |
| 936 | 40.5 | 43.3 | 38.4 | 93 | 105 | 75.7 | 67.2 | 57.8 | 113 | 131 |
| 937 | 42.7 | 48.7 | 44.1 | 88 | 97 | 78.0 | 71.7 | 61.4 | 109 | 127 |
| 938 | 40.1 | 41.8 | 37.5 | 96 | 107 | 66.0 | 59.2 | 49.8 | 112 | 133 |
| 939 | 48.8 | 46.2 | 41.1 | 106 | 119 | 76.8 | 62.6 | 52.5 | 123 | 146 |

*For footnotes see pp. 351-52.*

| | GYPSUM | | | | | PHOSPHATE ROCK | | | | |
|---|---|---|---|---|---|---|---|---|---|---|
| Year | Output | Man-days of Employment | Man-hours of Employment | Output per Man-day | Output per Man-hour | Output | Man-days of Employment | Man-hours of Employment | Output per Man-day | Output per Man-hour |
| 1899 | 9.7 | .. | .. | .. | .. | 40.0 | .. | .. | .. | . |
| 1900 | 11.8 | .. | .. | .. | .. | 44.9 | .. | .. | .. | . |
| 1901 | 12.6 | .. | .. | .. | .. | 38.0 | .. | .. | .. | . |
| 1902 | 16.3 | 47.4 | 53.6 | 34 | 30 | 39.6 | 197.1 | 198.0 | 20 | 2 |
| 1903 | 20.8 | .. | .. | .. | .. | 42.7 | .. | .. | .. | . |
| 1904 | 18.8 | .. | .. | .. | .. | 52.6 | .. | .. | .. | . |
| 1905 | 20.8 | .. | .. | .. | .. | 56.5 | .. | .. | .. | . |
| 1906 | 30.7 | .. | .. | .. | .. | 52.8 | .. | .. | .. | . |
| 1907 | 34.9 | .. | .. | .. | .. | 62.5 | .. | .. | .. | . |
| 1908 | 34.3 | .. | .. | .. | .. | 70.3 | .. | .. | .. | . |
| 1909 | 44.9 | .. | .. | .. | .. | 64.5 | .. | .. | .. | . |
| 1910 | 47.4 | .. | .. | .. | .. | 69.4 | .. | .. | .. | . |
| 1911 | 46.3 | 80.2 | 87.3 | 58 | 53 | 81.9 | .. | .. | .. | . |
| 1912 | 49.9 | .. | .. | .. | .. | 84.2 | .. | .. | .. | . |
| 1913 | 51.8 | .. | .. | .. | .. | 83.2 | .. | .. | .. | . |
| 1914 | 49.4 | .. | .. | .. | .. | 70.0 | .. | .. | .. | . |
| 1915 | 48.8 | .. | .. | .. | .. | 51.1 | .. | .. | .. | . |
| 1916 | 55.0 | 83.5 | 90.3 | 66 | 61 | 57.3 | .. | .. | .. | . |
| 1917 | 53.8 | .. | .. | .. | .. | 75.3 | .. | .. | .. | . |
| 1918 | 41.0 | .. | .. | .. | .. | 60.3 | .. | .. | .. | . |
| 1919 | 48.2 | 82.3 | 90.6 | 59 | 53 | 48.9 | 119.2 | 117.7 | 41 | 4 |
| 1920 | 62.4 | 97.8 | 106.2 | 64 | 59 | 105.0 | 219.7 | 217.4 | 48 | 4 |
| 1921 | 57.6 | 84.9 | 93.3 | 68 | 62 | 64.1 | 125.6 | 123.9 | 51 | 5 |
| 1922 | 75.4 | 109.8 | 121.4 | 69 | 62 | 61.7 | 95.8 | 95.2 | 64 | 6 |
| 1923 | 94.8 | 129.5 | 143.0 | 73 | 66 | 77.7 | 98.7 | 97.6 | 79 | 8 |
| 1924 | 100.5 | 140.0 | 154.5 | 72 | 65 | 75.1 | 112.6 | 110.7 | 67 | 6 |
| 1925 | 113.2 | 159.0 | 160.6 | 71 | 70 | 85.9 | 106.5 | 103.9 | 81 | 8 |
| 1926 | 112.3 | 149.9 | 147.5 | 75 | 76 | 94.8 | 101.4 | 100.5 | 93 | 9 |
| 1927 | 106.6 | 131.6 | 128.1 | 81 | 83 | 82.6 | 96.6 | 95.6 | 85 | 8 |
| 1928 | 101.7 | 117.6 | 115.2 | 86 | 88 | 93.0 | 96.9 | 97.0 | 96 | 9 |
| 1929 | 100.0 | 100.0 | 100.0 | 100 | 100 | 100.0 | 100.0 | 100.0 | 100 | 10 |
| 1930 | 69.2 | 62.5 | 60.3 | 111 | 115 | 106.6 | 99.9 | 101.2 | 107 | 10 |
| 1931 | 51.0 | 52.2 | 49.9 | 98 | 102 | 70.4 | 65.5 | 63.0 | 108 | 11 |
| 1932 | 28.2 | 26.8 | 24.4 | 105 | 116 | 44.8 | 40.5 | 37.8 | 111 | 11 |
| 1933 | 26.6 | 28.6 | 25.7 | 93 | 104 | 62.3 | 55.0 | 48.9 | 113 | 12 |
| 1934 | 30.6 | 35.6 | 30.8 | 86 | 99 | 76.5 | 74.0 | 62.2 | 103 | 12 |
| 1935 | 38.0 | 37.6 | 33.9 | 101 | 112 | 83.4 | 80.7 | 69.0 | 103 | 12 |
| 1936 | 54.1 | 53.7 | 47.8 | 101 | 113 | 91.4 | 94.1 | 81.5 | 97 | 11 |
| 1937 | 61.0 | 56.9 | 51.3 | 107 | 119 | 112.5 | 101.9 | 86.0 | 110 | 13 |
| 1938 | 53.5 | 46.4 | 41.7 | 115 | 128 | 101.9 | 89.0 | 72.5 | 114 | 14 |
| 1939 | 64.3 | 59.9 | 53.5 | 107 | 120 | 105.3 | 88.2 | 69.5 | 119 | 15 |

*For footnotes see pp. 351-52.*

ᵃ The indexes of output shown in this table were computed from data in Tables A-1 and A-2 after the fashion described at the beginning of this appendix. They are set up on an industry rather than a product basis (a distinction important only in the case of nonferrous metals), and include only those industries for which both output and employment data are available. More comprehensive output indexes (especially for industries omitted from this table owing to absence of employment data), and indexes on a product basis (in the case of nonferrous metals), will be found in Table A-7.

ᵇ The indexes of employment, in terms of mandays and of manhours, are computed from the data in Table A-3.

ᶜ The indexes of productivity (output per manday and output per manhour) are obtained in every case by dividing the index of output by the corresponding index of employment—and multiplying by 100. This operation implies a degree of comparability between our measures of output and employment which unfortunately cannot be taken for granted. The results are probably most reliable in the case of iron ore and coal mining. The data on productivity in copper mining and other nonferrous metals appear to be somewhat less satisfactory, owing to uncertainties in measuring both output and employment. Least securely founded, perhaps, are the indexes for oil and gas wells (owing to uncertainties of employment coverage), and for stone quarrying (in which both output and employment are difficult to measure). For further details the reader is referred to the notes to Tables A-1 and A-3 in this appendix; and to Appendices B, C and D.

ᵈ Includes all industries shown in this table, i.e., those numbered (1) through (5), (7) through (16), (19), (21) and (22) in Table A-1. Excluded are: the stone industries prior to 1906 for lack of output data; the placer mining of gold and silver, and numerous minor nonmetals, for lack of employment data.

ᵉ Includes all industries shown in this table except oil and gas wells.

ᶠ Combination of iron ore, copper, and other nonferrous metal mining. Does not include placer gold mining; includes pyrites and the production of fluorspar in Illinois and Kentucky.

ᵍ For these years mandays of employment at beneficiating plants are not available; the index is extrapolated by means of data for the mining section of the industry only. See notes to Table A-3.

ʰ The indexes are for the copper mining industry—(3) in Table A-1—and not for the product "copper": for further explanation, see Appendix B. Some doubts arise concerning the reliability of the indexes of productivity obtained for this industry. Changes may have occurred in the quality of the product (ore or concentrates) which are not reflected in our output index (see Appendix D); also, the segregation of employment between milling (included) and smelting (excluded) is somewhat artificial (see notes to Table A-3).

ⁱ Includes the industries numbered (2), (4), (5), (7) through (11), and (21) in Table A-1. Indexes for output, employment and productivity for two constituents of this group, lead and zinc mining in the Mississippi Valley and mercury mining, will be found in Table A-6. The data for this industry are weakened by some uncertainties of coverage. In particular, numerous minor nonferrous metals are included in the output index whose coverage in the employment statistics may be more ostensible than real. In 1902 correction was made for undercoverage of employment data at small lead and zinc and gold and silver mines (see notes to Table A-3).

ʲ Manhours at oil and gas wells refer to wage earners only. The series shown for output includes petroleum, natural gas and natural gasoline. Output data for this industry appear to be satisfactory, but employment figures leave much to be desired. As explained in notes to Table A-3, employment given by contractors was canvassed only in 1902 and in 1939; the 1902 canvass was probably defective. The reader should note, however, that if employment in 1902 is understated, the rise in productivity was even greater than that reported in the table.

ᵏ After 1929 noncommercial production of crushed stone, for which we have no employment data, is excluded. If this production is included, the output indexes for total and crushed, or nondimension, stone read as follows:

*Footnotes to Table A-5 continued on next page.*

*Footnotes to Table A-5, concluded.*

|      | Total | Nondimension |
|------|-------|--------------|
| 1929 | 100.0 | 100.0 |
| 1930 | 89.6  | 89.9 |
| 1931 | 67.1  | 70.2 |
| 1932 | 47.1  | 49.8 |
| 1933 | 43.2  | 49.0 |
| 1934 | 52.2  | 63.6 |
| 1935 | 49.1  | 58.6 |
| 1936 | 74.7  | 91.5 |
| 1937 | 76.4  | 92.8 |
| 1938 | 71.1  | 86.2 |
| 1939 | 84.8  | 102.4 |

The indexes of productivity in stone quarrying are among the least satisfactory we have, because of the problem of weighting different kinds of dimension stone which vary greatly in unit value; the difficulty of excluding employment in stone dressing establishments; and undercoverage of the employment data, especially for crushed stone. For further comment on these matters, see Appendix C.

EAD AND ZINC, AND MERCURY MINING

ndexes of Output, Employment and Productivity[a]

1929:100

| | LEAD AND ZINC MINING, MISSISSIPPI VALLEY[b] | | | | | MERCURY MINING[c] | | | | |
|---|---|---|---|---|---|---|---|---|---|---|
| ar | Output | Man-days of Employment | Man-hours of Employment | Output per Man-day | Output per Man-hour | Output | Man-days of Employment | Man-hours of Employment | Output per Man-day | Output per Man-hour |
| 02 | .. | .. | .. | .. | .. | 145.8 | 138.3 | 162.5 | 105 | 90 |
| 11 | 55.6 | 117.0 | .. | 47 | .. | 88.6 | .. | .. | .. | .. |
| 12 | 59.1 | 138.3 | .. | 43 | .. | 104.4 | .. | .. | .. | .. |
| 13 | 57.6 | 117.9 | .. | 49 | .. | 84.2 | .. | .. | .. | .. |
| 14 | 58.3 | 101.6 | .. | 57 | .. | 69.0 | .. | .. | .. | .. |
| 15 | 71.5 | 122.5 | .. | 58 | .. | 87.6 | .. | .. | .. | .. |
| 16 | 86.8 | 198.9 | .. | 44 | .. | 124.7 | .. | .. | .. | .. |
| 17 | 98.6 | 182.5 | .. | 54 | .. | 150.7 | 127.4 | .. | 118 | .. |
| 18 | 95.4 | 128.6 | .. | 74 | .. | 137.0 | .. | .. | .. | .. |
| 19 | 90.0 | 119.5 | .. | 75 | .. | 89.2 | .. | .. | .. | .. |
| 20 | 97.9 | 120.6 | .. | 81 | .. | 55.8 | .. | .. | .. | .. |
| 21 | 66.1 | 59.6 | .. | 111 | .. | 26.4 | .. | .. | .. | .. |
| 22 | 93.0 | 91.4 | .. | 102 | .. | 26.6 | .. | .. | .. | .. |
| 23 | 103.3 | 108.3 | .. | 95 | .. | 33.1 | .. | .. | .. | .. |
| 24 | 111.4 | 135.1 | .. | 82 | .. | 42.0 | 37.8 | 37.4 | 111 | 112 |
| 25 | 122.4 | 132.0 | .. | 93 | .. | 38.2 | 33.0 | 32.7 | 116 | 117 |
| 26 | 122.8 | 140.0 | .. | 88 | .. | 31.8 | 34.6 | 34.2 | 92 | 93 |
| 27 | 104.5 | 116.1 | .. | 90 | .. | 47.0 | 61.6 | 60.9 | 76 | 77 |
| 28 | 96.5 | 95.0 | .. | 102 | .. | 75.5 | 79.1 | 79.2 | 95 | 95 |
| 29 | 100.0 | 100.0 | 100.0 | 100 | 100 | 100.0 | 100.0 | 100.0 | 100 | 100 |
| 30 | 77.2 | 67.1 | 67.2 | 115 | 115 | 91.0 | 87.4 | 93.3 | 104 | 98 |
| 31 | 50.8 | 42.8 | 42.9 | 119 | 118 | 105.3 | 91.1 | 92.0 | 116 | 114 |
| 32 | 37.3 | 25.0 | 25.1 | 149 | 149 | 53.3 | 37.6 | 37.2 | 142 | 143 |
| 33 | 42.6 | 25.7 | 25.7 | 166 | 166 | 40.8 | 33.4 | 32.8 | 122 | 124 |
| 34 | 46.3 | 36.0 | 35.6 | 129 | 130 | 65.2 | 43.6 | 40.4 | 150 | 161 |
| 35 | 56.3 | 43.6 | 43.5 | 129 | 129 | 74.0 | 49.2 | 46.6 | 150 | 159 |
| 36 | 65.9 | 56.0 | 55.9 | 118 | 118 | 70.0 | .. | .. | .. | .. |
| 37 | 75.9 | 67.0 | 66.7 | 113 | 114 | 69.7 | .. | .. | .. | .. |
| 38 | 58.7 | 48.6 | 48.0 | 121 | 122 | 76.0 | .. | .. | .. | .. |
| 39 | 73.2 | 57.2 | 56.5 | 128 | 130 | 78.7 | 55.2 | 53.5 | 143 | 147 |

[a] Data in this table are included in, but do not exhaust, the category "Metal mining and ore ressing—other nonferrous metals" in Table A-5. The indexes of output were computed from ata in Tables A-1 and A-2 after the fashion described at the beginning of the appendix. The ndexes of employment are derived from Table A-4.

[b] Arkansas, Illinois, Iowa, Kansas, Kentucky, Missouri, Oklahoma, Tennessee, Wisconsin. Includes fluorspar mining in Illinois and Kentucky. Employment data cover mining alone and do ot include milling.

[c] Employment at recovery plants is included.

TABLE A-7

GROUPS AND INDIVIDUAL MINERALS

Indexes of Output[a]

*1929:100*

| Year | Total Mining[b] | Metals[c] | Fuels[d] | Other Nonmetals[e] | Copper, Lead and Zinc | Copper | Lead |
|------|------|------|------|------|------|------|------|
| 1899 | 25.7 | 39.7 | 23.0 | 19.7 | 27.9 | 29.2 | 32.0 |
| 1900 | 27.8 | 43.4 | 24.5 | 21.3 | 30.4 | 31.1 | 41.4 |
| 1901 | 29.4 | 44.0 | 26.8 | 20.7 | 30.5 | 30.9 | 41.0 |
| 1902 | 30.6 | 47.7 | 27.1 | 22.8 | 33.2 | 33.8 | 42.4 |
| 1903 | 34.5 | 47.7 | 32.5 | 25.3 | 34.9 | 35.7 | 44.5 |
| 1904 | 35.4 | 49.7 | 32.8 | 29.4 | 40.0 | 41.6 | 47.2 |
| 1905 | 39.6 | 56.1 | 36.2 | 36.3 | 43.3 | 45.3 | 48.8 |
| 1906 | 41.2 | 59.1 | 37.3 | 43.7 | 44.7 | 46.6 | 53.3 |
| 1907 | 44.6 | 57.7 | 43.3 | 45.5 | 42.9 | 43.0 | 55.9 |
| 1908 | 41.6 | 55.3 | 39.5 | 44.0 | 45.7 | 48.7 | 50.6 |
| 1909 | 47.4 | 67.7 | 43.1 | 50.3 | 54.4 | 57.4 | 59.0 |
| 1910 | 50.2 | 69.4 | 46.8 | 52.0 | 53.7 | 55.5 | 58.6 |
| 1911 | 49.4 | 66.0 | 47.0 | 51.5 | 55.0 | 55.6 | 65.3 |
| 1912 | 53.0 | 73.2 | 49.6 | 54.8 | 61.3 | 62.4 | 67.7 |
| 1913 | 55.9 | 76.3 | 53.0 | 55.4 | 62.6 | 62.1 | 74.0 |
| 1914 | 52.1 | 68.5 | 50.3 | 50.8 | 60.0 | 57.7 | 77.3 |
| 1915 | 56.7 | 84.3 | 52.1 | 49.9 | 75.6 | 71.7 | 83.0 |
| 1916 | 65.4 | 105.0 | 57.2 | 54.9 | 96.0 | 96.5 | 92.0 |
| 1917 | 69.0 | 102.9 | 63.6 | 55.5 | 94.2 | 92.4 | 96.1 |
| 1918 | 69.4 | 99.1 | 66.0 | 48.3 | 92.0 | 94.2 | 86.1 |
| 1919 | 60.1 | 73.3 | 59.6 | 46.4 | 63.5 | 59.6 | 65.7 |
| 1920 | 69.8 | 77.5 | 70.3 | 56.8 | 65.9 | 59.0 | 76.0 |
| 1921 | 57.2 | 39.3 | 61.6 | 48.7 | 30.7 | 20.9 | 63.4 |
| 1922 | 61.5 | 61.5 | 61.9 | 59.2 | 54.0 | 45.4 | 73.1 |
| 1923 | 84.8 | 85.1 | 86.1 | 75.6 | 75.6 | 71.2 | 83.8 |
| 1924 | 79.8 | 82.3 | 79.8 | 76.1 | 82.1 | 78.4 | 91.2 |
| 1925 | 82.7 | 89.9 | 81.1 | 83.3 | 89.3 | 82.1 | 104.7 |
| 1926 | 89.6 | 93.5 | 89.0 | 88.2 | 92.7 | 84.8 | 104.7 |
| 1927 | 91.9 | 88.7 | 92.3 | 93.6 | 88.6 | 81.6 | 101.8 |
| 1928 | 91.8 | 91.4 | 91.4 | 95.1 | 92.5 | 90.5 | 96.9 |
| 1929 | 100.0 | 100.0 | 100.0 | 100.0 | 100.0 | 100.0 | 100.0 |
| 1930 | 88.4 | 78.4 | 90.5 | 90.4 | 75.2 | 70.5 | 85.3 |
| 1931 | 73.6 | 54.0 | 79.6 | 67.8 | 55.4 | 53.0 | 61.7 |
| 1932 | 59.2 | 30.2 | 69.3 | 43.6 | 30.9 | 23.9 | 44.7 |
| 1933 | 64.2 | 35.0 | 75.4 | 43.9 | 31.1 | 19.5 | 41.6 |
| 1934 | 69.7 | 44.2 | 79.8 | 49.4 | 36.1 | 24.3 | 43.9 |
| 1935 | 75.4 | 57.4 | 84.1 | 52.2 | 48.0 | 38.1 | 50.6 |
| 1936 | 88.5 | 77.4 | 94.5 | 71.4 | 64.4 | 61.0 | 57.0 |
| 1937 | 99.6 | 99.7 | 103.4 | 78.0 | 82.5 | 84.4 | 71.1 |
| 1938 | 85.3 | 70.0 | 92.7 | 66.9 | 59.4 | 55.6 | 56.5 |
| 1939 | 94.3 | 89.0 | 99.1 | 75.3 | 74.1 | 74.5 | 63.3 |

[a] This table provides output indexes additional to those given in Tables A-5 and A-6. All data in this table are derived from Tables A-1 and A-2. In the case of many series shown, comparable employment data are not available. Indexes of output comparable with employment will be found in Tables A-5 and A-6.

[b] Includes all items shown in Table A-1.

[c] Gold, silver, copper, lead, zinc, iron ore, manganese, tungsten, molybdenum, mercury, bauxite. For separate indexes of copper, lead, zinc, gold, silver and manganese, see columns to right. For iron ore, see Table A-5.

354

| Zinc | Gold | Silver | Manganese | Petroleum | Natural Gas | Sand and Gravel[f] | Clay[g] |
|---|---|---|---|---|---|---|---|
| 20.1 | 192.6 | 93.6 | 12.7 | 8.7 | 11.6 | .. | 12.0 |
| | | | | | | | |
| 19.3 | 206.3 | 99.6 | 24.4 | 9.8 | 12.4 | .. | 17.0 |
| 22.0 | 209.0 | 95.8 | 29.9 | 10.4 | 13.8 | .. | 19.2 |
| 24.5 | 208.7 | 95.6 | 21.2 | 12.4 | 14.7 | .. | 23.8 |
| 24.9 | 192.1 | 93.0 | 19.0 | 13.4 | 15.5 | .. | 27.5 |
| 29.1 | 206.0 | 92.4 | 12.4 | 14.9 | 16.2 | .. | 26.0 |
| 31.8 | 208.4 | 93.0 | 13.4 | 16.1 | 18.3 | 12.1 | 30.1 |
| 31.2 | 216.0 | 94.7 | 11.2 | 15.3 | 20.3 | 16.9 | 33.3 |
| 34.9 | 195.5 | 86.7 | 11.2 | 18.2 | 21.2 | 21.1 | 34.7 |
| 32.3 | 208.0 | 84.0 | 7.2 | 19.2 | 21.0 | 18.7 | 27.8 |
| 41.7 | 226.4 | 94.7 | 6.6 | 20.0 | 25.1 | 29.5 | 34.3 |
| | | | | | | | |
| 44.8 | 226.0 | 95.1 | 6.1 | 22.4 | 26.6 | 33.6 | 38.1 |
| 45.8 | 229.9 | 100.4 | 4.7 | 23.1 | 26.8 | 33.0 | 36.3 |
| 53.2 | 216.0 | 108.5 | 4.7 | 23.7 | 29.3 | 33.4 | 40.5 |
| 57.1 | 211.2 | 117.3 | 7.6 | 26.0 | 30.3 | 38.4 | 42.9 |
| 57.4 | 217.1 | 114.6 | 9.7 | 27.2 | 30.9 | 38.2 | 37.6 |
| 81.2 | 234.4 | 118.0 | 20.3 | 28.5 | 32.8 | 36.8 | 40.1 |
| 97.1 | 212.8 | 128.3 | 54.5 | 30.2 | 39.3 | 42.6 | 51.2 |
| 98.5 | 189.5 | 115.0 | 125.4 | 33.4 | 41.5 | 37.1 | 54.6 |
| 87.8 | 163.6 | 111.3 | 231.6 | 35.3 | 37.6 | 30.0 | 52.5 |
| 75.8 | 136.5 | 84.9 | 56.9 | 37.6 | 38.9 | 34.0 | 44.0 |
| | | | | | | | |
| 81.1 | 117.5 | 92.0 | 106.2 | 44.0 | 41.6 | 39.7 | 59.3 |
| 35.4 | 116.1 | 75.5 | 9.0 | 46.9 | 34.5 | 38.2 | 37.4 |
| 65.2 | 114.9 | 100.2 | 44.8 | 55.3 | 39.8 | 45.8 | 55.8 |
| 84.3 | 125.6 | 115.2 | 105.1 | 72.7 | 52.5 | 67.0 | 69.3 |
| 88.1 | 127.1 | 105.0 | 85.1 | 70.9 | 59.5 | 74.3 | 74.2 |
| 98.1 | 118.8 | 109.3 | 140.4 | 75.8 | 62.0 | 80.5 | 83.0 |
| 106.9 | 113.3 | 102.3 | 101.7 | 76.5 | 68.5 | 85.5 | 86.2 |
| 99.2 | 108.1 | 97.7 | 108.0 | 89.5 | 75.4 | 92.0 | 87.7 |
| 96.0 | 107.9 | 95.1 | 92.1 | 89.5 | 81.8 | 96.9 | 93.0 |
| 100.0 | 100.0 | 100.0 | 100.0 | 100.0 | 100.0 | 100.0 | 100.0 |
| | | | | | | | |
| 82.2 | 102.7 | 78.4 | 81.7 | 89.1 | 101.3 | 85.7 | 95.4 |
| 56.6 | 104.8 | 48.9 | 39.2 | 84.5 | 87.9 | 62.6 | 68.5 |
| 39.4 | 109.1 | 37.3 | 10.2 | 77.9 | 81.1 | 41.4 | 43.2 |
| 53.0 | 109.0 | 38.0 | 20.6 | 89.9 | 81.1 | 32.0 | 51.8 |
| 60.6 | 133.1 | 54.0 | 26.3 | 90.1 | 92.3 | 36.5 | 57.5 |
| 71.5 | 164.4 | 79.9 | 46.1 | 98.9 | 99.9 | 41.0 | 72.7 |
| 79.4 | 192.6 | 100.5 | 72.8 | 109.2 | 113.0 | 58.1 | 89.3 |
| 86.5 | 207.2 | 117.4 | 101.4 | 127.0 | 125.5 | 60.7 | 98.6 |
| 71.3 | 214.0 | 101.4 | 32.2 | 120.6 | 119.7 | 51.2 | 68.3 |
| 80.6 | 237.4 | 106.3 | 63.5 | 125.6 | 129.2 | 57.5 | 89.6 |

[d] Pennsylvania anthracite, bituminous coal, petroleum, natural gas and natural gasoline. For breakdown, see columns to right and Table A-5.

[e] Asbestos, asphalt, barite, borates, bromine, fluorspar, tripoli, garnet, pumice, ground sand, sand, gravel, sodium salts, calcium chloride, abrasive sandstone, clay, fuller's earth, stone (dimension and nondimension), talc, gypsum, pyrites, sulfur, mica, potash, magnesite, other magnesium compounds, graphite, feldspar, phosphate rock. Indexes for stone, gypsum and phosphate rock will be found in Table A-5.

[f] For 1923–39 the series covers commercial production only.

[g] Does not include common clay.

TABLE A-8

COPPER, LEAD AND ZINC: SECONDARY OUTPUT, 1907-39[a]
*Thousand short tons*

| | Copper | | | | |
|---|---|---|---|---|---|
| *Year* | New | Old | Total | *Lead* | *Zinc*[b] |
| 1907 | .. | .. | 30 | 26 | .. |
| 1908 | .. | .. | 12 | 18 | .. |
| 1909 | .. | .. | 45 | 42 | 42 |
| 1910 | .. | .. | 94 | 55 | 62 |
| 1911 | .. | .. | 107 | 54 | 68 |
| 1912 | .. | .. | 138 | 67 | 85 |
| 1913 | .. | .. | 136 | 73 | 80 |
| 1914 | .. | .. | 128 | 61 | 72 |
| 1915 | .. | .. | 196 | 79 | 93 |
| 1916 | .. | .. | 350 | 96 | 114 |
| 1917 | .. | .. | 383 | 94 | 116 |
| 1918 | 176 | 177 | 353 | 97 | 121 |
| 1919 | 135 | 153 | 287 | 122 | 108 |
| 1920 | 143 | 169 | 312 | 125 | 116 |
| 1921 | 85 | 132 | 217 | 104 | 78 |
| 1922 | 133 | 203 | 336 | 160 | 140 |
| 1923 | 140 | 271 | 411 | 194 | 139 |
| 1924 | 122 | 266 | 388 | 204 | 132 |
| 1925 | 129 | 291 | 420 | 227 | 128 |
| 1926 | 143 | 337 | 480 | 277 | 141 |
| 1927 | 151 | 339 | 490 | 276 | 140 |
| 1928 | 171 | 365 | 536 | 309 | 149 |
| 1929 | 222 | 404 | 627 | 311 | 143 |
| 1930 | 125 | 342 | 467 | 256 | 99 |
| 1931 | 86 | 261 | 347 | 235 | 72 |
| 1932 | 67 | 181 | 248 | 198 | 48 |
| 1933 | 78 | 260 | 338 | 224 | 88 |
| 1934 | 66 | 311 | 377 | 208 | 66 |
| 1935 | 87 | 362 | 449 | 270 | 94 |
| 1936 | 102 | 383 | 485 | 263 | 122 |
| 1937 | 123 | 409 | 532 | 275 | 127 |
| 1938 | 93 | 267 | 360 | 225 | 87 |
| 1939 | 213 | 287 | 500 | 242 | 135 |

[a] All data are from U. S. Bureau of Mines, *Minerals Yearbook,* or its predecessor *Mineral Resources.*

[b] Amount recovered as metal or in alloys; does not include zinc recovered in chemical products.

BITUMINOUS COAL: UNDERGROUND AND OPEN PIT MINES, 1914–36[a]
Output, Employment and Productivity

| Year | Underground Mines | | | Open Pit Mines | | | All Mines | | |
|---|---|---|---|---|---|---|---|---|---|
| | Output[b] (thous. tons) | Employment, Mandays[b] (thous.) | Output per Manday (tons) | Output[c] (thous. tons) | Employment, Mandays[d] (thous.) | Output per Manday[e] (tons) | Output[f] (thous. tons) | Employment, Mandays[g] (thous.) | Output per Manday (tons) |
| 1914 | 421,423 | 113,531 | 3.71 | 1,281 | 253 | 5.06 | 422,704 | 113,784 | 3.71 |
| 1915 | 439,791 | 112,441 | 3.91 | 2,832 | 478 | 5.93 | 442,623 | 112,919 | 3.92 |
| 1916 | 498,626 | 128,618 | 3.88 | 3,881 | 625 | 6.21 | 502,507 | 129,243 | 3.89 |
| 1917 | 546,253 | 145,500 | 3.75 | 5,484 | 999 | 5.49 | 551,737 | 146,499 | 3.77 |
| 1918 | 571,361 | 151,831 | 3.76 | 7,949 | 1,456 | 5.46 | 579,310 | 153,287 | 3.78 |
| 1919 | 460,413 | 120,569 | 3.82 | 5,386 | 974 | 5.53 | 465,799 | 121,543 | 3.83 |
| 1920 | 560,430 | 139,619 | 4.01 | 8,176 | 1,358 | 6.02 | 568,606 | 140,977 | 4.03 |
| 1921 | 411,239 | 98,482 | 4.18 | 4,606 | 630 | 7.31 | 415,845 | 99,112 | 4.20 |
| 1922 | 412,891 | 96,456 | 4.28 | 9,298 | 1,361 | 6.83 | 422,189 | 97,817 | 4.32 |
| 1923 | 553,358 | 124,468 | 4.45 | 11,087 | 1,478 | 7.50 | 564,445 | 125,946 | 4.48 |
| 1924 | 470,403 | 104,517 | 4.50 | 13,184 | 1,500 | 8.79 | 483,587 | 106,017 | 4.56 |
| 1925 | 503,473 | 113,371 | 4.44 | 16,497 | 1,550 | 10.64 | 519,970 | 114,921 | 4.52 |
| 1926 | 557,197 | 125,785 | 4.43 | 16,083 | 1,702 | 9.45 | 573,280 | 127,487 | 4.50 |
| 1927 | 499,792 | 111,878 | 4.47 | 17,867 | 1,792 | 9.97 | 517,659 | 113,670 | 4.55 |
| 1928 | 481,488 | 104,086 | 4.63 | 19,131 | 1,698 | 11.27 | 500,619 | 105,784 | 4.73 |
| 1929 | 515,121 | 108,822 | 4.73 | 19,767 | 1,519 | 13.01 | 534,888 | 110,341 | 4.85 |
| 1930 | 448,468 | 90,941 | 4.93 | 18,938 | 1,360 | 13.92 | 467,406 | 92,301 | 5.06 |
| 1931 | 363,459 | 70,881 | 5.13 | 18,524 | 1,174 | 15.78 | 381,983 | 72,055 | 5.30 |
| 1932 | 290,148 | 58,121 | 4.99 | 19,459 | 1,242 | 15.67 | 309,607 | 59,363 | 5.22 |
| 1933 | 315,470 | 68,425 | 4.61 | 18,065 | 1,415 | 12.77 | 333,535 | 69,840 | 4.78 |
| 1934 | 338,791 | 80,014 | 4.23 | 20,469 | 1,690 | 12.11 | 359,260 | 81,704 | 4.40 |
| 1935 | 348,987 | 80,703 | 4.32 | 23,267 | 2,076 | 11.21 | 372,254 | 82,779 | 4.50 |
| 1936 | 411,472 | 92,871 | 4.43 | 27,479 | 2,181 | 12.60 | 438,951 | 95,052 | 4.62 |

[a] This table underlies the discussion of Chapter 8 and contains material on which Chart 38 is based. No output was recorded from open pit mines prior to 1914. Figures for 1937 and later years not available. Tons are short tons.

[b] By difference.

[c] Willard E. Hotchkiss and others, *Bituminous-Coal Mining* (National Research Project, Philadelphia, 1939), Vol. I, p. 106.

[d] Derived from adjacent columns.

[e] Hotchkiss and others, *op. cit.*, Vol. II, p. 366.

[f] Table A-1.

[g] Table A-3.

# Table A-10

## COPPER MINING: UNDERGROUND AND OPEN PIT MINES, 1914-36[a]
### Output, Employment and Productivity

| Year | Underground Mines | | | Open Pit Mines | | | All Mines | | |
|---|---|---|---|---|---|---|---|---|---|
| | Output, Recoverable Content (mil. lb.) | Employment, Mandays (mil.) | Output per Manday (lb.) | Output, Recoverable Content (mil. lb.) | Employment, Mandays (mil.) | Output per Manday (lb.) | Output, Recoverable Content (mil. lb.) | Employment, Mandays (mil.) | Output per Manday (lb.) |
| 1914 | 909 | 11.64 | 78 | 223 | 1.21 | 185 | 1,132 | 12.85 | 88 |
| 1915 | 1,175 | 12.98 | 91 | 281 | 1.24 | 226 | 1,456 | 14.22 | 102 |
| 1916 | 1,630 | 17.61 | 93 | 358 | 1.32 | 270 | 1,988 | 18.93 | 105 |
| 1917 | 1,507 | 17.61 | 86 | 386 | 1.48 | 261 | 1,893 | 19.09 | 99 |
| 1918 | 1,517 | 17.61 | 86 | 393 | 1.50 | 263 | 1,910 | 19.10 | 100 |
| 1919 | 979 | 10.90 | 90 | 231 | .957 | 241 | 1,210 | 11.86 | 102 |
| 1920 | 975 | 10.25 | 95 | 237 | .934 | 253 | 1,212 | 11.18 | 108 |
| 1921 | 390 | 4.28 | 91 | 64.1 | .184 | 349 | 454 | 4.46 | 102 |
| 1922 | 765 | 7.14 | 107 | 162 | .363 | 445 | 927 | 7.50 | 124 |
| 1923 | 1,036 | 9.11 | 114 | 352 | 1.19 | 295 | 1,388 | 10.31 | 135 |
| 1924 | 1,115 | 8.83 | 126 | 415 | 1.40 | 297 | 1,531 | 10.23 | 150 |
| 1925 | 1,175 | 8.82 | 133 | 425 | 1.60 | 265 | 1,600 | 10.42 | 154 |
| 1926 | 1,143 | 8.90 | 128 | 479 | 1.61 | 297 | 1,622 | 10.51 | 154 |
| 1927 | 1,089 | 8.28 | 131 | 461 | 1.34 | 343 | 1,550 | 9.63 | 161 |
| 1928 | 1,139 | 8.40 | 136 | 552 | 1.51 | 367 | 1,691 | 9.90 | 171 |
| 1929 | 1,279 | 10.27 | 125 | 561 | 1.71 | 328 | 1,840 | 11.98 | 154 |
| 1930 | 1,003 | 7.18 | 140 | 339 | 1.07 | 319 | 1,343 | 8.25 | 163 |
| 1931 | 757 | 4.35 | 174 | 292 | .729 | 401 | 1,049 | 5.08 | 207 |
| 1932 | 352 | 1.95 | 180 | 122 | .341 | 358 | 474 | 2.29 | 207 |
| 1933 | 258 | 1.41 | 183 | 120 | .281 | 425 | 377 | 1.69 | 224 |
| 1934 | 298 | 1.46 | 204 | 172 | .381 | 452 | 470 | 1.84 | 255 |
| 1935 | 438 | 2.33 | 188 | 251 | .455 | 551 | 689 | 2.79 | 247 |
| 1936 | 677 | 3.61 | 187 | 452 | .740 | 612 | 1,129 | 4.35 | 259 |

[a] This table underlies the discussion of Chapter 12 and contains material on which Charts 38 and 46 are based. Data are from Y. S. Leong and others, *Copper Mining* (National Research Project, Philadelphia, 1940), pp. 252-53. Owing to difficulty of segregation, figures for output and employment at open pit mines are minimum esti- mates, for figures for underground mines contain some open pit output and employment. However, figures for output and employ- ment are comparable as shown. Data for other years are not avail- able. Since this table covers mining only and does not include ore dressing figures for employment run lower than in Table A-3.

TABLE A-11

COPPER: CONSUMPTION BY USE, 1919–40[a]
*Thousand short tons*

| Year | Electrical Industries[b] | Automobiles[c] | Buildings | Manufactures for Export | Other Uses[d] | Total |
|------|------|------|------|------|------|------|
| 1919 | 246 | 49 | 31 | 100 | 196 | 621 |
| 1920 | 306 | 61 | 34 | 107 | 176 | 684 |
| 1921 | 246 | 48 | 22 | 49 | 95 | 460 |
| 1922 | 285 | 75 | 37 | 48 | 94 | 539 |
| 1923 | 397 | 105 | 38 | 53 | 145 | 738 |
| 1924 | 434 | 95 | 40 | 55 | 142 | 766 |
| 1925 | 458 | 108 | 47 | 58 | 170 | 840 |
| 1926 | 513 | 104 | 50 | 51 | 191 | 910 |
| 1927 | 473 | 101 | 53 | 57 | 178 | 862 |
| 1928 | 542 | 127 | 62 | 67 | 192 | 991 |
| 1929 | 674 | 138 | 59 | 75 | 214 | 1,160 |
| 1930 | 580 | 87 | 50 | 71 | 168 | 956 |
| 1931 | 382 | 62 | 45 | 48 | 113 | 650 |
| 1932 | 203 | 32 | 29 | 23 | 81 | 368 |
| 1933 | 198 | 49 | 36 | 16 | 116 | 415 |
| 1934 | 208 | 63 | 36 | 26 | 131 | 463 |
| 1935 | 266 | 95 | 49 | 30 | 136 | 575 |
| 1936 | 376 | 108 | 71 | 32 | 162 | 749 |
| 1937 | 460 | 112 | 70 | 45 | 172 | 860 |
| 1938 | 323 | 55 | 68 | 39 | 124 | 608 |
| 1939 | 413 | 85 | 89 | 52 | 162 | 801 |
| 1940 | 522 | 103 | 102 | 148 | 195 | 1,070 |

[a] See Chart 14. For 1919–26, annual issues for the years 1926 to 1930 of the *Yearbook* of the American Bureau of Metal Statistics. For 1927–31, *Mineral Resources, 1931*, Vol. I, p. 599. For 1932–40, annual issues of *Minerals Yearbook*. Data not available prior to 1919. Figures are for total consumption, whether of primary or of secondary origin.

[b] Electrical manufactures (generators, motors, electric locomotives, switchboards, light bulbs, etc.), telephones and telegraphs, light and power lines (transmission and distribution wire and bus bars), other wire, radio receiving sets.

[c] Does not include starter, generator and transmission equipment.

[d] Wire cloth, ammunition, castings (bearings, bushings, lubricators, valves and fittings), clocks and watches, coinage, copper-bearing steel, fire-fighting apparatus, radiators, railway equipment, refrigerators, shipbuilding, washing machines, water heaters, other uses.

TABLE A-12

LEAD: CONSUMPTION BY USE, 1919-40[a]

*Thousand short tons*

| Year | Storage Batteries | Cable Coverings | Buildings | White Lead, Red Lead and Litharge[b] | Other Uses[c] | Total |
|------|------|------|------|------|------|------|
| 1919 | 100 | 53 | 68 | 143 | 184 | 548 |
| 1920 | 108 | 79 | 71 | 162 | 185 | 605 |
| 1921 | 87 | 67 | 48 | 160 | 159 | 521 |
| 1922 | 130 | 93 | 71 | 186 | 203 | 683 |
| 1923 | 143 | 131 | 75 | 176 | 243 | 768 |
| 1924 | 170 | 138 | 83 | 184 | 237 | 812 |
| 1925 | 180 | 156 | 88 | 173 | 259 | 856 |
| 1926 | 190 | 185 | 94 | 156 | 276 | 901 |
| 1927 | 175 | 161 | 88 | 164 | 253 | 841 |
| 1928 | 220 | 180 | 96 | 154 | 281 | 931 |
| 1929 | 210 | 220 | 96 | 150 | 297 | 972 |
| 1930 | 163 | 208 | 67 | 116 | 215 | 769 |
| 1931 | 157 | 117 | 40 | 96 | 158 | 568 |
| 1932 | 138 | 56 | 22 | 86 | 115 | 417 |
| 1933 | 147 | 31 | 26 | 97 | 148 | 450 |
| 1934 | 163 | 35 | 30 | 106 | 153 | 488 |
| 1935 | 175 | 39 | 32 | 128 | 166 | 539 |
| 1936 | 191 | 61 | 40 | 140 | 202 | 634 |
| 1937 | 192 | 90 | 45 | 143 | 209 | 679 |
| 1938 | 167 | 60 | 36 | 114 | 169 | 546 |
| 1939 | 198 | 74 | 50 | 132 | 212 | 667 |
| 1940 | 220 | 107 | 65 | 125 | 264 | 782 |

[a] See Chart 15. For 1919, the *Yearbook* for 1927 of the American Bureau of Metal Statistics. For 1920-40, annual issues of *Mineral Resources,* and its successor *Minerals Yearbook.* Data not available prior to 1919. Figures include antimonial lead, and are for total consumption, whether of primary or of secondary origin.

[b] Used chiefly for pigments.

[c] Includes automobiles, railway equipment, shipbuilding, ammunition, terneplate, foil, bearing metal, solder, type metal, calking, castings, tetrethyl lead for motor fuel, and other uses.

TABLE A-13

ZINC: CONSUMPTION BY USE, 1908–40
*Thousand short tons*

| Year | Galvanizing | Brassmaking | Rolled Zinc | Other Uses[b] | Total |
|------|-------------|-------------|-------------|-------------|-------|
| 1908 | 119 | 33 | 27 | 12 | 192 |
| 1909 | 164 | 48 | 33 | 17 | 262 |
| 1910 | 162 | 54 | 30 | 24 | 270 |
| 1916 | 200 | 175 | 48 | 28 | 450 |
| 1917 | 190 | 170 | 57 | 28 | 445 |
| 1919 | 163 | 155 | 55 | 29 | 402 |
| 1920 | 192 | 144 | 53 | 35 | 424 |
| 1921 | 138 | 75 | 30 | 19 | 262 |
| 1922 | 205 | 145 | 54 | 36 | 440 |
| 1923 | 235 | 175 | 56 | 49 | 515 |
| 1924 | 240 | 155 | 61 | 56 | 512 |
| 1925 | 283 | 165 | 71 | 60 | 579 |
| 1926 | 290 | 180 | 86 | 66 | 622 |
| 1927 | 280 | 160 | 74 | 69 | 583 |
| 1928 | 291 | 174 | 74 | 88 | 626 |
| 1929 | 290 | 185 | 68 | 91 | 634 |
| 1930 | 217 | 120 | 51 | 62 | 451 |
| 1931 | 168 | 98 | 49 | 55 | 370 |
| 1932 | 109 | 66 | 40 | 44 | 259 |
| 1933 | 148 | 94 | 41 | 67 | 350 |
| 1934 | 152 | 98 | 41 | 69 | 360 |
| 1935 | 195 | 124 | 56 | 98 | 473 |
| 1936 | 242 | 165 | 55 | 120 | 582 |
| 1937 | 256 | 169 | 58 | 127 | 610 |
| 1938 | 198 | 102 | 46 | 75 | 421 |
| 1939 | 275 | 175 | 62 | 114 | 626 |
| 1940 | 287 | 232 | 58 | 142 | 719 |

[a] See Chart 16. All data from annual issues of *Mineral Resources* and its successor *Minerals Yearbook*. Data not available prior to 1919 except for years shown. Figures are for total consumption, whether of primary or of secondary origin.

[b] Includes die castings; and slab zinc used for the manufacture of French oxide, zinc for wet batteries, castings and the desilverization of lead.

TABLE A-14

BITUMINOUS COAL: CONSUMPTION BY USE, 1917–40[a]
*Million short tons*

| Year | Electric Utilities[b] | Locomo-tive Fuel[c] | Byproduct Coke | Beehive Coke | All Other Domestic Uses[d] | Exports | Total |
|------|------|------|------|------|------|------|------|
| 1917 | 34 | 133 | 32 | 52 | 279 | 24 | 553 |
| 1918 | 34 | 134 | 37 | 48 | 277 | 22 | 553 |
| 1919 | 35 | 120 | 36 | 30 | 261 | 20 | 502 |
| 1920 | 37 | 135 | 44 | 32 | 260 | 39 | 547 |
| 1921 | 32 | 108 | 29 | 8 | 215 | 23 | 415 |
| 1922 | 34 | 113 | 41 | 13 | 225 | 12 | 439 |
| 1923 | 39 | 131 | 54 | 30 | 264 | 21 | 540 |
| 1924 | 38 | 117 | 49 | 16 | 264 | 17 | 501 |
| 1925 | 40 | 118 | 57 | 17 | 267 | 17 | 517 |
| 1926 | 41 | 123 | 64 | 19 | 286 | 35 | 568 |
| 1927 | 42 | 116 | 63 | 11 | 268 | 18 | 518 |
| 1928 | 41 | 112 | 70 | 7 | 268 | 16 | 515 |
| 1929 | 45 | 114 | 77 | 10 | 274 | 17 | 537 |
| 1930 | 43 | 98 | 66 | 4 | 244 | 16 | 471 |
| 1931 | 39 | 82 | 47 | 2 | 203 | 12 | 384 |
| 1932 | 30 | 66 | 31 | 1 | 178 | 9 | 316 |
| 1933 | 31 | 66 | 39 | 1 | 185 | 9 | 331 |
| 1934 | 34 | 70 | 44 | 2 | 197 | 11 | 358 |
| 1935 | 35 | 71 | 49 | 1 | 204 | 10 | 370 |
| 1936 | 42 | 81 | 63 | 3 | 234 | 11 | 433 |
| 1937 | 45 | 83 | 70 | 5 | 227 | 13 | 442 |
| 1938 | 40 | 69 | 45 | 1 | 189 | 10 | 355 |
| 1939 | 46 | 74 | 61 | 2 | 194 | 12 | 390 |
| 1940 | 53 | 79 | 77 | 5 | 217 | 16 | 447 |

[a] See Chart 21. All data from *Mineral Resources,* and its successor *Minerals Year-book.* Data not available prior to 1917.
[b] Represents all coal consumed by public utility power plants in power genera-tion, including a small amount of anthracite.
[c] Class I railroads only; excludes switching and terminal companies.
[d] Includes colliery fuel, bunker coal, manufacturing, domestic and miscellaneous uses.

Table A-15

PETROLEUM: OUTPUT OF PRINCIPAL REFINED PRODUCTS, 1917–40[a]

*Million barrels of 42 gallons*

| Year | Gasoline | Fuel Oil[b] | Kerosene | Lubricants |
|------|----------|-------------|----------|------------|
| 1917 | 68 | 155 | 41 | 18 |
| 1918 | 85 | 174 | 43 | 20 |
| 1919 | 94 | 182 | 56 | 20 |
| 1920 | 116 | 211 | 55 | 25 |
| 1921 | 123 | 230 | 46 | 21 |
| 1922 | 148 | 255 | 55 | 23 |
| 1923 | 180 | 287 | 56 | 26 |
| 1924 | 213 | 320 | 60 | 27 |
| 1925 | 260 | 365 | 60 | 31 |
| 1926 | 303 | 365 | 62 | 32 |
| 1927 | 334 | 393 | 56 | 32 |
| 1928 | 381 | 427 | 59 | 35 |
| 1929 | 439 | 449 | 56 | 34 |
| 1930 | 441 | 372 | 49 | 34 |
| 1931 | 437 | 337 | 42 | 27 |
| 1932 | 400 | 301 | 44 | 22 |
| 1933 | 408 | 316 | 49 | 24 |
| 1934 | 424 | 335 | 54 | 26 |
| 1935 | 468 | 360 | 56 | 28 |
| 1936 | 516 | 414 | 56 | 31 |
| 1937 | 572 | 459 | 65 | 35 |
| 1938 | 569 | 447 | 65 | 31 |
| 1939 | 611 | 468 | 69 | 35 |
| 1940 | 616 | 500 | 74 | 37 |

[a] See Chart 22. All data from *Mineral Resources,* and its successor *Minerals Yearbook.* Data not available prior to 1917. Other products not listed are wax and coke.
[b] Includes gas oil.

TABLE A-16

DIMENSION STONE OUTPUT AND BUILDING CONSTRUCTION,
1915–39[a]

| Year | Dimension Stone Output[b] (1915:100) | Value of Building Construction, Current Prices[c] ($ mil.) | Building Costs[d] (1913:100) | Physical Volume of Building Construction[e] (1915:100) |
|---|---|---|---|---|
| 1915 | 100 | 1,646 | 95.3 | 100 |
| 1916 | 109.9 | 1,976 | 130.9 | 87.4 |
| 1917 | 82.2 | 1,867 | 166.8 | 64.8 |
| 1918 | 54.0 | 1,606 | 159.1 | 58.4 |
| 1919 | 68.4 | 2,841 | 158.8 | 103.6 |
| 1920 | 73.6 | 3,675 | 207.2 | 102.7 |
| 1921 | 71.0 | 3,508 | 166.1 | 122.3 |
| 1922 | 86.9 | 4,724 | 154.9 | 176.6 |
| 1923 | 105.6 | 5,861 | 186.0 | 182.5 |
| 1924 | 107.8 | 6,402 | 185.8 | 199.5 |
| 1925 | 115.3 | 7,170 | 182.7 | 227.2 |
| 1926 | 109.9 | 7,650 | 185.0 | 239.4 |
| 1927 | 113.2 | 7,366 | 186.1 | 229.2 |
| 1928 | 113.5 | 7,092 | 188.0 | 218.4 |
| 1929 | 115.0 | 6,705 | 190.9 | 203.4 |
| 1930 | 101.8 | 4,325 | 185.4 | 135.1 |
| 1931 | 69.3 | 3,147 | 169.4 | 107.6 |
| 1932 | 46.7 | 1,590 | 140.9 | 65.3 |
| 1933 | 35.8 | 1,021 | 147.8 | 40.0 |
| 1934 | 33.4 | 1,240 | 166.7 | 43.1 |
| 1935 | 33.9 | 1,639 | 165.8 | 57.3 |
| 1936 | 46.5 | 2,673 | 172.2 | 89.9 |
| 1937 | 49.1 | 3,237 | 196.2 | 95.5 |
| 1938 | 46.1 | 3,056 | 196.8 | 89.9 |
| 1939 | 56.1 | 3,656 | 197.4 | 107.2 |

[a] See Chart 24.
[b] Table A-5.
[c] For 1915–28, Lowell J. Chawner, *Construction Activity in the United States, 1915–37* (U. S. Department of Commerce, 1938), Tables 1 and 3. For 1929–39, *Survey of Current Business*, February 1942, p. 36. Includes new residential and nonresidential private and public building construction; does not include farm, highway, sewage, water supply or other public utility construction, military and naval construction, or conservation projects.
[d] *Engineering News-Record*, April 23, 1942, p. 124.
[e] Value of building construction divided by building costs.

Table A-17

CRUSHED STONE OUTPUT AND HIGHWAY CONSTRUCTION, 1905–39[a]

| Year | Crushed Stone Used for Concrete Aggregate and Road Metal[b] (Th. sh. tons) | (1915:100) | Value of New Highway Construction, Current Prices[c] ($ mil.) | Highway Construction Costs[d] (1925–29:100) | Highway Construction, Physical Volume[e] (1915:100) |
|---|---|---|---|---|---|
| 1905 | 17,755 | .. | .. | .. | .. |
| 1906 | 19,205 | .. | .. | .. | .. |
| 1907 | 23,953 | .. | .. | .. | .. |
| 1908 | 26,145 | .. | .. | .. | .. |
| 1909 | 29,144 | .. | .. | .. | .. |
| 1910 | 33,053 | .. | .. | .. | .. |
| 1911 | 34,226 | .. | .. | .. | .. |
| 1912 | 34,512 | .. | .. | .. | .. |
| 1913 | 36,873 | .. | .. | .. | .. |
| 1914 | 37,460 | .. | .. | .. | .. |
| 1915 | 37,641 | 100.0 | 298 | 56.1 | 100 |
| 1916 | 37,421 | 99.4 | 308 | 78.6 | 74 |
| 1917 | 31,680 | 84.2 | 313 | 109.9 | 54 |
| 1918 | 22,104 | 58.7 | 288 | 114.7 | 47 |
| 1919 | 26,868 | 71.4 | 415 | 120.3 | 65 |
| 1920 | 32,824 | 87.2 | 640 | 152.4 | 79 |
| 1921 | 36,766 | 97.7 | 840 | 122.4 | 129 |
| 1922 | 42,426 | 112.7 | 851 | 105.8 | 151 |
| 1923 | 51,048 | 135.6 | 783 | 117.9 | 125 |
| 1924 | 57,684 | 153.2 | 951 | 113.1 | 158 |
| 1925 | 62,824 | 166.9 | 1,056 | 107.3 | 185 |
| 1926 | 66,893 | 177.7 | 1,039 | 103.4 | 189 |
| 1927 | 78,544 | 208.7 | 1,190 | 101.9 | 220 |
| 1928 | 74,384 | 197.6 | 1,270 | 95.3 | 251 |
| 1929 | 76,175 | 202.4 | 1,248 | 92.1 | 255 |
| 1930 | 74,293 | 197.4 | 1,481 | 85.7 | 325 |
| 1931 | 65,812 | 174.8 | 1,323 | 76.8 | 324 |
| 1932 | 48,021 | 127.6 | 916 | 61.0 | 283 |
| 1933 | 40,857 | 108.5 | 675 | 74.1 | 172 |
| 1934 | 55,244 | 146.8 | 821 | 84.0 | 184 |
| 1935 | 49,488 | 131.5 | 622 | 80.6 | 145 |
| 1936 | 79,337 | 210.8 | 876 | 82.9 | 199 |
| 1937 | 80,272 | 213.3 | 850 | 79.4 | 202 |
| 1938 | 88,787 | 235.9 | 837 | 72.8 | 217 |
| 1939 | 96,894 | 257.4 | 884 | 72.6 | 229 |

[a] See Chart 26.

[b] *Mineral Resources* and its successor, *Minerals Yearbook*. Noncommercial production is included.

[c] For 1915–28, Lowell J. Chawner, *Construction Activity in the United States, 1915–37* (U. S. Department of Commerce, 1938), Table 41; 1929–39, *Survey of Current Business*, February 1942, p. 36.

[d] For 1922–39, *Engineering News-Record*, April 23, 1942, p. 174; extrapolated back to 1915 with the construction cost index, *ibid.*, p. 124.

[e] Value of new highway construction divided by highway construction costs.

PETROLEUM: DISCOVERIES AND RESERVES, 1900–42[a]

*Billion barrels of 42 gallons*

| Year | Discoveries During Year | Cumulated Discoveries, January 1 | Cumulated Production, January 1 | Proved Reserves, January 1 |
|---|---|---|---|---|
| 1900 | .46 | 3.4 | .9 | 2.5 |
| 1901 | .17 | 3.9 | 1.0 | 2.9 |
| 1902 | .29 | 4.1 | 1.1 | 3.0 |
| 1903 | .30 | 4.4 | 1.2 | 3.2 |
| 1904 | .32 | 4.7 | 1.3 | 3.4 |
| 1905 | .33 | 5.0 | 1.4 | 3.6 |
| 1906 | .13 | 5.3 | 1.5 | 3.8 |
| 1907 | .27 | 5.4 | 1.6 | 3.8 |
| 1908 | .28 | 5.7 | 1.8 | 3.9 |
| 1909 | .38 | 6.0 | 2.0 | 4.0 |
| 1910 | .51 | 6.4 | 2.2 | 4.2 |
| 1911 | .72 | 6.9 | 2.4 | 4.5 |
| 1912 | .62 | 7.6 | 2.6 | 5.0 |
| 1913 | .35 | 8.2 | 2.8 | 5.4 |
| 1914 | .17 | 8.6 | 3.1 | 5.5 |
| 1915 | .38 | 8.7 | 3.3 | 5.4 |
| 1916 | .70 | 9.1 | 3.6 | 5.5 |
| 1917 | .34 | 9.8 | 3.9 | 5.9 |
| 1918 | .66 | 10.2 | 4.3 | 5.9 |
| 1919 | .88 | 10.8 | 4.6 | 6.2 |
| 1920 | .94 | 11.7 | 5.0 | 6.7 |
| 1921 | 1.07 | 12.6 | 5.4 | 7.2 |
| 1922 | .36 | 13.7 | 5.9 | 7.8 |
| 1923 | .73 | 14.1 | 6.5 | 7.6 |
| 1924 | .61 | 14.8 | 7.2 | 7.6 |
| 1925 | 1.76 | 15.4 | 7.9 | 7.5 |
| 1926 | 1.07 | 17.2 | 8.7 | 8.5 |
| 1927 | 2.60 | 18.2 | 9.4 | 8.8 |
| 1928 | 1.40 | 20.8 | 10.3 | 10.5 |
| 1929 | 3.21 | 22.2 | 11.2 | 11.0 |
| 1930 | 1.30 | 25.5 | 12.3 | 13.2 |
| 1931 | .25 | 26.7 | 13.1 | 13.6 |
| 1932 | .09 | 27.0 | 14.0 | 13.0 |
| 1933 | .61 | 27.1 | 14.8 | 12.3 |
| 1934 | 1.09 | 27.7 | 15.7 | 12.0 |
| 1935 | 1.22 | 28.8 | 16.6 | 12.2 |
| 1936 | 1.76 | 30.0 | 17.6 | 12.4 |
| 1937 | 3.72 | 31.8 | 18.7 | 13.1 |
| 1938 | 3.06 | 35.5 | 20.0 | 15.5 |
| 1939 | 2.40 | 38.5 | 21.2 | 17.3 |
| 1940 | 1.89 | 40.9 | 22.5 | 18.5 |
| 1941 | 1.97 | 42.8 | 23.8 | 19.0 |
| 1942 | .. | 44.8 | 25.2 | 19.6 |

[a] See Chart 43. Data on discoveries compiled by American Petroleum Institute and reproduced with permission from unpublished material. Figures for production by U. S. Bureau of Mines; see also Table A-1 above. Reserves are obtained by difference.

For a definition of proved reserves, and for a description of the methods used in compiling estimates of the kind shown in this table, see National Resources Committee, *Energy Resources and National Policy* (1939), pp. 127-33.

# TABLE A-19

## OIL AND GAS WELLS, 1939

### Derivation of Employment Estimates in Table 7 and Comparison with Table A-3[a]

| Industry | 300-Day Wage Earners | Wage Earners, Census Average | Salaried Employees | Proprietors and Firm Members | Total Engaged[b] | Wage Earners, Active Period Average | Wage Earners, Census Average (Table A-3) |
|---|---|---|---|---|---|---|---|
| *Petroleum and Natural Gas* | | | | | | | |
| Producing and nonproducing operations, Census figure | .. | 105,505 | 30,546 | 6,294 | 142,345 | 112,678 | .. |
| Producing and nonproducing operations, 300-day wage earners[c] | 105,505 | .. | .. | .. | .. | .. | 105,166 |
| Producing operations only, Census figure | .. | .. | .. | .. | .. | .. | .. |
| Small producers, Census figure | 2,179 | 2,179 | .. | 1,242 | 3,421 | 2,179 | .. |
| *Natural Gasoline* | | | | | | | |
| Census figure | .. | 8,332 | 2,005 | 10 | 10,347 | 8,608 | 8,332 |
| 300-day wage earners[d] | 9,928 | .. | .. | .. | .. | .. | .. |
| Small producers, Census figure | 8 | 8 | .. | 37 | 45 | 8 | .. |
| *Field Services (Contractors)* | | | | | | | |
| Census figure | .. | 40,061 | 5,153 | 1,725 | 46,939 | 43,308 | 40,061 |
| 300-day wage earners[e] | 41,720 | .. | .. | .. | .. | .. | .. |
| TOTAL | 159,340 | 156,085 | 37,704 | 9,308 | 203,097 | 166,781 | 153,559 |

[a] Except where otherwise indicated, all figures in this table are transcribed directly from preliminary releases of the Census of Mineral Industries, 1939. For small producers, neither value of products, nor expenses, nor outlay for buildings and equipment, nor cost of drilling amounted to as much as $2,500.

[b] Sum of three preceding columns.

[c] Assumed to equal Census average wage earners; no data on number of days in operation are available.

[d] Natural gasoline plants operated 346 days in 1939; 8,608 × 346 ÷ 300 = 9,928.

[e] Field services operated 289 days in 1939; 43,308 × 289 ÷ 300 = 41,720.

# The Classification of the Nonferrous Metal Mining Industries

THE BASIC sources, and the methods employed in the construction of our indexes of production and employment are set forth in notes to the tables in Appendix A. In some cases, however, special difficulties of measurement were encountered, and these call for more extended treatment. Accordingly we shall discuss in this appendix certain peculiarities of the more important nonferrous metal mining industries, i.e. of those industries in which gold, silver, copper, lead and zinc—singly or in combination—predominate in value.

## Industrial Classification

With the exception of the decennial Censuses of mining industries, physical output data for minerals are collected on a commodity, rather than on an industry, basis. In most types of mining a single commodity rather adequately defines a mining industry, and where this is the case no difficulties of classification arise. The nonferrous metals mentioned are peculiar, however, in that it is impossible to identify total production of any one of them with the output of a single mining industry.

Let us take copper, for example. The total production of copper from domestic ores is not synonymous with the output of the copper mining industry. For copper comes from gold and silver mines (among others), while copper mines produce other minerals besides copper. It happens that the major portion of our supply of nonferrous metals originates in mines in which a combination of metals is found.

For Census purposes a mine is classified according to the metal that contributes the largest share to the value of its products. Thus a copper mine would be one in which copper is the predominant metal; and the Census statistics for the copper mining industry would include all of the products issuing from this mine, and copper employment data would include all of the men engaged in bringing forth these products. Obviously, the metal that predominates at one time may not be the chief product at another time, so that the industrial classification of a given mine may alter.[1]

Census statistics are available for a few years only, and at best are

[1] ". . . the classification of individual mines [changes] from time to time, because of price changes and because the relative proportion of metals contained in the ores of many mines is different in different parts of the mines in ores mined at different

valuable as a check or to provide auxiliary information. Our problem is to take the commodity output data collected annually by the Bureau of Mines and available in *Minerals Yearbook,* and to arrange them in a manner that will make them as comparable as possible with the employment data found in the accident bulletins which are also published by the Bureau of Mines. The latter are presented on an industry basis, the classification being made according to the metal of predominant value. As a result, employment falls into three groups: (1) copper mines; (2) lead and zinc mines in the Mississippi Valley, including fluorspar mines in Illinois and Kentucky; (3) miscellaneous metal mines, including the remaining lead and zinc mines, gold and silver mines, and mines where certain minor metals are produced. The problem of fitting production data to these categories may be considered next.

Detailed data on the distribution of nonferrous metal production among the several metal mining industries, as classified by the Census, are available only for 1929. They are presented in Tables B-1 and B-2. In 1929, in the copper industry, copper contributed 93.0 percent of the total value of products; and, what is more significant, 99.2 percent of

TABLE B-1

NONFERROUS METAL MINES

Distribution of Products, by Industry, 1929

| | | Copper Industry | Lead Industry | Zinc Industry | Gold (lode) Industry | Gold (placer) Industry | Silver Industry |
|---|---|---|---|---|---|---|---|
| Mine value of ∫ $ thousand | | 283,517 | 67,562 | 44,866 | 17,650 | 3,779 | 8,457 |
| products ⎰ percent | | 100.0 | 100.0 | 100.0 | 100.0 | 100.0 | 100.0 |
| Mine value of copper, lead, zinc, gold and silver | percent | 99.5 | 97.0 | 97.7 | 95.7 | 99.8 | 98.6 |
| Copper | " | 93.0 | 2.0 | 1.0 | .7 | 0 | 2.6 |
| Lead | " | .5 | 71.8 | 17.0 | .4 | 0 | 9.6 |
| Zinc | " | .9 | 11.2 | 77.7 | b | 0 | 8.0 |
| Gold | " | 2.4 | 1.7 | .6 | 91.6 | 99.8 | 12.3 |
| Silver | " | 2.7 | 10.3 | 1.5 | 3.0 | b | 66.1 |
| Value of other products[a] | " | 0.5 | 3.0 | 2.3 | 4.3 | 0.2 | 1.4 |

*Source: Fifteenth Census,* "Mines and Quarries, 1929," p. 291.
[a] These include manganese, pyrites, cadmium, platinum; and custom milling.
[b] Less than 0.05.

times. Thus, certain large enterprises classified as copper mines for the year 1909 were classified as lead and zinc mines for 1919, and some mines which are essentially zinc mines were classified as silver mines for 1919 when, on account of the low price for zinc and the high price for silver, only the ores richer in silver could be profitably mined." *Fourteenth Census,* Vol. XI, "Mines and Quarries, 1919," p. 355. The quantitative effect of such shifts cannot be determined. However, the broader the classification adopted, the less is the importance of statistical migration of enterprises from one industry to another.

all copper was produced in copper mining establishments. The latter figure indicates that for comparisons of output and employment it is safe to present statistics for total copper production as representing copper produced in the copper mining industry.

## TABLE B-2

NONFERROUS METALS
Distribution by Industry, 1929

|  |  | Copper | Lead | Zinc | Gold | Silver |
|---|---|---|---|---|---|---|
| Mine value of metal ⌠ $ thousand | | 265,885 | 58,390 | 45,577 | 29,255 | 21,336 |
| from all sources ⌡ percent | | 100.0 | 100.0 | 100.0 | 100.0 | 100.0 |
| From copper mines | " | 99.2 | 2.3 | 5.5 | 23.4 | 35.6 |
| From lead mines | " | 0.5 | 83.1 | 16.6 | 4.0 | 32.6 |
| From zinc mines | " | 0.2 | 13.1 | 76.5 | 0.9 | 3.1 |
| From gold mines[a] | " | b | 0.1 | b | 68.2 | 2.4 |
| From silver mines | " | 0.1 | 1.4 | 1.5 | 3.5 | 26.2 |

Source: Fifteenth Census, "Mines and Quarries, 1929," p. 292.
[a] Both lode and placer.
[b] Less than 0.05.

Gold and silver are the next largest items in the total value of the output of copper mines; in 1929 they contributed 2.4 percent and 2.7 percent, respectively. (These amounts represented 23.4 percent of total gold production and 35.6 percent of total silver production.) In compiling annual series, we can allocate an approximately correct amount of gold and silver production to the copper mining industry with the help of a breakdown of gold and silver production by type of ore, available in the annual issues of *Minerals Yearbook*. Thus gold and silver derived from copper ores are treated as products of copper mining. Such a procedure is not entirely justifiable, however, from two points of view: (1) copper ores may be, and probably are, mined by establishments other than copper mines; (2) other ores such as lead-copper, lead-zinc-copper, lead-zinc, etc., all of which yield some copper, may be mined by copper mining establishments. The overstatement resulting from the first circumstance is in a measure offset by the understatement attributable to the second.[2] The remaining 1.9 percent of

[2] In an attempt to test the accuracy of allocating gold and silver production to copper mining establishments on the basis of amounts derived from copper ores, percentages were computed on the basis of ore figures and compared with the percentages shown for 1929 in Table B-2. Ore figures indicate that 27.2 percent of gold production was derived from copper ores, whereas in fact only 23.4 percent of gold production came from copper mines. Likewise, in silver, copper ore yielded 29.1 percent of total silver production whereas copper mines were responsible for 35.6 percent. Thus, the use of available data would yield only a rough approximation, with a bias, the direction of which cannot be determined. It is well to note, though, that relative to the total value of products of copper mining, the percentage of error would be negligible. An error of approximately 25 percent in a figure which constitutes 2.1 percent of the industry's value of products is of slight importance. (Figures by type of ore are from *Mineral Resources, 1929;* see also Table A-1 above.)

the copper industry's output in 1929 consisted mainly of lead and zinc, but there is no means of allocating the required amounts of these metals to the industry on an annual basis. Our series for the output of copper mining therefore consist of the nation's entire output of copper, plus such amounts of gold and silver as come from copper ores.

Lead and zinc mining are usually linked together. This is so because of the fact that the two metals are generally found in the same mineralized area. Table B-2 indicates that although only 83.1 percent of lead production was contributed by lead mines, and only 76.5 percent of zinc production came from zinc mines, lead and zinc mines together yielded 96.2 percent of total lead production and 93.1 percent of total zinc production. These figures refer, of course, to the continental United States and for this reason do not serve to indicate the varying relationships which obtain on a regional basis and which are particularly pertinent to this discussion.

Because of the nature of the ores worked, in the far western states the mining of lead and zinc is closely associated with the mining of gold and silver. In this area the mining of complex ores plays a large role, and this fact makes it unwise to adopt separate industry classifications for any of the four metals chiefly involved. In any case we have no way of breaking down the corresponding employment totals; indeed, as published by the Bureau of Mines, these are still more comprehensive and include the mining of mercury, molybdenum and other metals, as well as lead, zinc, gold and silver.

In the Mississippi Valley, on the other hand, the situation is quite different. Lead and zinc production in this region involves the extraction of nonargentiferous ores. The complex mixed ores of the far western states are not encountered here, and therefore the classification "lead and zinc mining" has real meaning when used with reference to this region.[3] For this region lead and zinc production are taken to represent a distinct mining industry. So as to secure comparability with employment, furthermore, fluorspar produced in these states is also included. For the far western states, on the other hand, the remaining lead and zinc is grouped with the remaining gold and silver to represent mixed mining in this area. To derive an index for comparison with employment all other nonferrous metals must also be included. This makes "mixed ore mining" so heterogeneous in character that, in presenting indexes, we have preferred to consolidate it

[3] A breakdown of the data in Table B-2 by states shows that in Kansas, Missouri, Oklahoma and Wisconsin (the only Mississippi Valley states listed separately by the Census) 1929 production of lead and zinc came almost entirely either from lead or from zinc mines. The indexes for lead and zinc mining in the Mississippi Valley are shown in Appendix Table A-6.

with lead and zinc mining in the Mississippi Valley under the rubric "other nonferrous metals": see Appendix Table A-5.

Besides the three industrial divisions already outlined—copper mining, mixed ore mining, and lead-zinc mines in the Mississippi Valley —a fourth group, placer mines producing gold (and a little silver), may conveniently be distinguished. While the output of these mines is of course included in our comprehensive indexes (Table A-7), we were not able to assemble employment data for the industry.

*Copper Mining*

As explained in Chapter 12 and Appendix D, we measure output in terms of metal produced. Two series are available for this purpose: (1) smelter output of copper from domestic ores, which is available back to 1845; (2) recoverable content of copper-bearing ores mined, available only since 1906. The smelter series is superior to the mines series in that the former is a measure of actual output, whereas the latter is merely an estimate of recoverable content.[4] Besides being more accurate, the smelter figure offers the more comprehensive figure of total copper production from domestic ores, for certain lead and zinc ores and siliceous ores of the precious metals contain so little copper that the mines are not paid for it and do not report it. Such amounts are included in smelter, but are omitted from mine, output.[5] Against this, it must be noted that the mines figure is superior to the smelter figure with respect to its time reference. A period of perhaps three months is consumed by transportation from mine to smelter, and by the operation of smelting; and since stocks of ore and concentrates vary from year to year, smelter output may exceed, or fall short of, mine output. Both series represent practically complete coverage, at least in the case of copper.[6] We have chosen to use the mine output series, for copper and other nonferrous metals since 1906, but have resorted to smelter figures for years prior to that date (Table A-1). Similarly, the mine output of gold and silver from copper ores is allocated to the industry for years since 1906.

All these products have to be valued in order that physical output

[4] It should be remembered that the mines figure does not refer to copper content of ore. Rather, it takes into account estimated losses in milling and smelting. These losses are calculated on the basis of past experience and the estimates are, therefore, probably quite accurate. This method of estimation is used not only in the case of copper but also for the other metals to be discussed.

[5] U. S. Bureau of Mines, *Mineral Resources, 1930*, Vol. I, pp. 701-02. However, such amounts would probably not be considered part of the product of the copper mining industry.

[6] Y. S. Leong, "Statistics on Copper in the United States," *Journal of the American Statistical Association*, Vol. 31 (Dec. 1936), p. 665.

series may be combined. The value of products shown in Table A-2 for copper mining is derived from Census sources and represents net value at the mill. This is equivalent to the smelter value of the mineral minus the cost of transporting the ores and concentrates to the smelter, and minus all smelter charges (estimated, if the smelter is owned by the mine).[7] The determination of unit mine values for individual products of the industry involves the allocation of joint costs and is difficult to carry out. However, the Bureau of the Census made such estimates for the year 1929, and these are reproduced in Table B-3.[8] Since we have to use market prices (Table A-1), which are roughly equivalent to smelter values, in combining individual products within each industrial division, it is evident that (if the relationships of Table B-3 are representative of other years) our procedure overweights silver in relation to copper and gold, and copper in relation to gold. However, in combining the output of copper mining with the output of other industries, we used the mine values shown in Table A-2.

TABLE B-3

COPPER MINING
Mine and Market Values Compared, 1929

| Unit Values | | At Mine[a] | At Market[b] | Ratio of Value at Market to Value at Mine |
|---|---|---|---|---|
| Copper | $ per lb. | 0.136 | 0.176 | 1.29 |
| Gold | $ per fine oz. | 17.39 | 20.67 | 1.19 |
| Silver | $ per fine oz. | 0.354 | 0.533 | 1.51 |

[a] Fifteenth Census, "Mines and Quarries, 1929," p. 292.
[b] Minerals Yearbook; see Table A-1 above.

Lead and Zinc Mining in the Mississippi Valley

As already explained, the segregation from mixed ore mining of lead and zinc mining in the Mississippi Valley states (Arkansas, Iowa, Kansas, Kentucky, Missouri, Oklahoma, Tennessee, Wisconsin and Illinois) has for its purpose the utilization of the corresponding breakdown available in the data for employment.

As in the case of copper, so with lead and zinc we have a choice be-

[7] Fifteenth Census, "Mines and Quarries, 1929," pp. 288-89.
[8] The mine value of the products of any mine was computed as indicated above. In general, this total was apportioned among individual products according to percentages of total smelter value contributed by each. However, if the individual mine was able to report actual cost attributable to each metal, these figures were accepted by the Census.

tween series for mine and for smelter output.[9] Again, we have chosen the mine output series, which measures recoverable content of ore and concentrates. Mine output is in the case of these two metals a superior measure, since it includes sizable amounts of lead and zinc used directly for pigments which never find their way to the smelter. In addition, we are forced to use mine rather than smelter output in allocating production on a regional basis;[10] consequently the segregation of the output of lead and zinc mining in the Mississippi Valley from the output of the remaining nonferrous industrial division, mixed ore mining, can be achieved only for years since 1906.

As with copper mining, the mine value of products shown in Table A-2 is derived from Census sources. Moreover, for 1929 we can make a comparison of mine and smelter unit values as estimated by the Bureau of the Census. It is plain that the use of market prices to weight the two metals, which is forced upon us by lack of data on mine value in other years than 1929, overweights zinc in relation to lead (Table B-4). In combining the industry with others we are, however, able to use the mine values in Table A-2.

TABLE B-4

LEAD AND ZINC MINING (MISSISSIPPI VALLEY)
Mine and Market Values Compared, 1929

| Unit Values | | At Mine[a] | At Market[b] | Ratio of Value at Market to Value at Mine |
|---|---|---|---|---|
| Lead | $ per lb. | 0.055 | 0.063 | 1.15 |
| Zinc | $ per lb. | 0.036 | 0.066 | 1.83 |

[a] *Fifteenth Census*, "Mines and Quarries, 1929," pp. 292-93. Data relate only to Kansas, Missouri, Oklahoma and Wisconsin, which are the more important Mississippi Valley states.
[b] *Minerals Yearbook;* see Table A-1 above.

The Bureau of Mines employment series (Table A-4) include workers engaged in mining fluorspar in Illinois and Kentucky. (Fluorspar is classed as a nonmetallic mineral and is used mainly as a fluxing agent in the manufacture of steel.) Consequently our production data for lead and zinc mining in the Mississippi Valley, as well as for wider indus-

[9] Although the term smelter output is used in connection with lead, the data actually refer to refinery output. Also, the data for mine output (recoverable content) allow for refining as well as for smelting losses (*Mineral Resources, 1923*, Vol. I, p. 134). In these respects the data for lead differ from the data for copper and zinc.

[10] State data for the smelter series are not available after 1931. In any case, "details of the geographic distribution of output are shown more precisely by statistics of mine production than by those of smelter and refinery production" (*Mineral Resources, 1930*, Vol. I, p. 701).

trial groupings which include this industry (Table A-5), have been computed so as to include the output of fluorspar in these two states.

## Mixed Ore Mining

This division contains two distinct groups of mines: enterprises in the western states producing gold, silver, lead and zinc, mainly from argentiferous ores; and lead and zinc mines in the eastern and southeastern states that lie outside the Mississippi Valley. It is thus rather heterogeneous, and in fact indexes are not shown separately for mixed ore mining, but only for nonferrous mining other than copper—a group in which lead and zinc mining in the Mississippi Valley and mixed ore mining are combined (Tables A-3 and A-5). Mixed ore mining furnishes all gold and silver produced outside the copper industry and apart from placer operations. Together with Mississippi lead and zinc, it includes all lead and zinc production. At the same time it excludes copper entirely.[11] As in former cases, the breakdown of mine output is

TABLE B-5

MIXED ORE MINING
Mine and Market Values Compared, 1929

| | Unit Values | At Mine[a] | At Market[b] | Ratio of Value at Market to Value at Mine |
|---|---|---|---|---|
| Gold | $ per fine oz. | 17.39 | 20.67 | 1.19 |
| Silver | $ per fine oz. | 0.354 | 0.533 | 1.51 |
| Lead | $ per lb. | 0.038[c] | 0.063 | 1.66 |
| Zinc | $ per lb. | 0.028[c] | 0.066 | 2.36 |

[a] *Fifteenth Census,* "Mines and Quarries, 1929," pp. 292-93.
[b] *Minerals Yearbook;* see Table A-1 above.
[c] Data relate to all states except Kansas, Missouri, Oklahoma and Wisconsin. It is not possible to exclude other Mississippi Valley states.

available only for years since 1906. Prior to 1906 it is necessary to rely on smelter output for each of the metals concerned. Once again, market values must be used to weight the various constituents of the output index for the industry, while this index can then be combined with those for other industries on the basis of the mine values given in Table A-2. It is evident from Table B-5 that this procedure overweights zinc and underweights gold; but no alternative is available.

[11] Not all copper comes from copper mines, and the copper mining industry yields sizable amounts of lead and zinc. Since it is impossible to allocate these amounts, except for 1929, we are compelled to assume that copper mines produce all of the copper and none of the lead and zinc obtained domestically. Hence mixed ore mining yields none of the copper but does supply (together with Mississippi Valley mines) all of the lead and zinc.

*Placer Gold Mining*

As in the other divisions of nonferrous metal mining, the two products of this industry—gold and a little silver—are combined by means of market prices; and this index is then combined with other industries with the help of the mine values in Table A-2. The output of Alaska is excluded. No satisfactory employment data are available. Thus the Census takes no account of itinerant individuals and of miners employing no help.[12] The exclusion of such individuals would be of little importance in other types of mining; but in placer mining this is not the case. It appears from a recent study that 28,022 individuals were engaged in 1935, in the continental United States, in the type of mining which the Census excludes. These individuals worked, on an average, 45 days a year and produced 57,557 fine ounces of gold.[13] Nor does the Bureau of Mines furnish employment data in this field. Since we have no measure of employment, the output of placer operations is omitted from the indexes in Table A-5, which seek to measure productivity. In the comprehensive indexes of output in Table A-7, however, placer mining is included.

[12] *Fifteenth Census,* "Mines and Quarries, 1929," p. 3.
[13] C. W. Merrill, C. W. Henderson and O. E. Kiessling, *Small-Scale Placer Mines* (National Research Project, Philadelphia, 1937), p. 4.

# Appendix C

# The Statistical Treatment of Stone Quarrying

THE PROBLEM of measuring output, employment and productivity in stone quarrying is complicated by a number of defects in the statistical record which call for comment. The chief of these derives from a failure to distinguish between mining and manufacturing as separate stages in the productive process whenever a single establishment carries production through both stages. The difficulty occurs with enterprises that quarry and also cut dimension stone; and with enterprises that quarry limestone and convert it into cement or lime. Other problems are the segregation of noncommercial output in the case of crushed stone, and the need to adjust for undercoverage in the employment data. The methods we developed to handle these various matters are described in the following sections. Details of the actual construction of the estimates of stone output will be found in notes to Table A-1, and of the estimates of quarry employment in notes to Table A-3.

## Mining and Manufacturing

Let us first draw a line of separation between the operations we wish to include in "mining," and those which we regard as a form of manufacture and therefore outside the scope of this report. Our definition is of course conditioned by the purpose it is intended to serve,[1] in this case the construction for stone quarrying of indexes of output and employment which do not overlap the statistics of manufactures. Since the basis of the distinction is essentially statistical in character, and since the basic data are those collected by the Bureau of the Census, we shall use the definitions adopted by that agency.[2]

[1] To one who is interested solely in distinguishing between extraction and fabrication from a purely technical standpoint, "mining" ends as soon as the stone is extracted from the quarry bed: all further processing is considered "manufacturing." Another whose interests lie only in industrial organization need merely note the distinction between mining and manufacturing when extraction and fabrication are performed by separate establishments; when the two activities are undertaken by the same establishment an interesting example of integration occurs, but no special problems arise.

[2] The National Bureau of Economic Research has already constructed index numbers of physical output in manufacturing which include the Census of Manufactures classification "Marble, granite, slate, and other stone, cut and shaped." See Solomon Fabricant, *The Output of Manufacturing Industries, 1899–1937* (1940); also the same author's *Employment in Manufacturing, 1899-1939: An Analysis of Its Relation to the Volume of Production* (1942).

The distinction between mining and manufacturing made by the Bureau of the Census is indicated in the following quotation from the 1929 Census of Mines and Quarries:

Relatively little stone is used rough as obtained from the quarry but at most quarries the stone is broken, crushed, shaped, dressed, ground, or otherwise prepared. The breaking of stone into rubble and riprap, and the crushing of stone for road work, ballast, concrete, or for other construction purposes are quite general and are closely connected with the quarrying operation, and data for these operations are included in the statistics for the several stone industries. On the other hand, the cutting, sawing, finishing, and polishing of stone for monumental, building, or other purposes, are considered as manufacturing operations and fall within the scope of the census of manufactures.[3]

To conform strictly to the definition of mining implicit in this quotation we should evidently have to exclude all fabricational processes from our statistics of production and employment in dimension stone, while the processing of nondimension or crushed stone would be considered a form of mining activity.[4] In general, definitions of mining followed in other Censuses were similar to that employed in 1929.[5] Nevertheless, it can readily be shown that the distinction in question is not definitive. Indeed it cannot be so, in view of the mixed character—extractive and fabricational—of many of the enterprises in the quarrying industry. The line of separation drawn by the Census Bureau is admittedly an ideal at which to aim in collecting statistics, rather than a touchstone of universal application.

Thus a certain amount of duplication is inevitable, especially in the

[3] *Fifteenth Census,* "Mines and Quarries, 1929," pp. 328-29.

[4] A minor difficulty of classification arises from the fact that, following the practice of the Bureau of Mines, we have found it convenient to regard rubble as a form of dimension stone. (Rubble consists of irregularly shaped pieces of stone, with perhaps one good face, used for building purposes, especially in foundations.) Theoretically, at least, the breaking of stone into rubble is excluded from our indexes, even though the Census Bureau regards it as a mining operation.

[5] The distinction between mining and manufacturing is not drawn as clearly in the Census of 1909 as it is in the Censuses of 1902, 1919 and 1929. From preliminary releases, it appears that the Census of 1939 used definitions similar to those of 1929, although there are references, for example in the report on sandstone, to "rough dimension stone trimming operations" which are included as a form of quarrying, i.e. mining, activity. These operations probably refer to "scabbling," the process whereby blocks are trimmed to uniform rectangular shape before shipment, in order to avoid freight charges on waste. See Oliver Bowles, *The Stone Industries* (McGraw-Hill, 1934), p. 53.

statistics for nondimension or crushed stone.[6] So far as possible, however, the definition of "mining" utilized in this analysis will conform
to the practice of the two most recent Censuses of Mines and Quarries
—1929 and 1939—and will exclude only the processing of dimension
stone. The processing of crushed stone (but not the manufacture of
cement or lime) will be considered a form of mining activity.[7] The
methods whereby Bureau of Mines figures for dimension stone are
made to conform to this definition will be discussed first with regard
to physical output and then with regard to employment.

### Dimension Stone—Output

Bureau of Mines statistics on quantity and value of dimension stone
are cross-classified according to two criteria. (1) Figures for stone are
divided according to variety: granite, marble, sandstone (including
bluestone), limestone, slate, and a miscellaneous category whose composition may vary somewhat from year to year. (2) Each of these varieties is then classified according to use: rough building stone, cut building stone, monumental stone, paving blocks, curbing, etc. It follows
that various degrees of detail may be adopted in computing an index
of physical output. Since the formula we use (see Appendix A) involves
essentially a comparison in constant prices, and since prices or unit
values differ markedly both as between varieties and as between uses
of stone, it follows that different breakdowns will yield differing measures of output. In principle, one of three alternatives may be selected:

---

[6] For example, we read that "in the stone-quarrying industries the establishments
included in both the mining and manufacturing statistics were chiefly producers of
crushed and ground stone and were classified by the census of manufactures as in
the roofing and paving-material industries" (*Fourteenth Census*, Vol. XI, "Mines and
Quarries, 1919," p. 13). It is easy to see, too, that an establishment which quarries,
cuts and polishes dimension stone would find it difficult to place a valuation on the
quarried product before fabrication when such a product never enters the market,
and might be unable to segregate its employment records. Censuses of Mines and
Quarries have in the past included substantial amounts of manufacturing operations in the statistics they report, but the Bureau of the Census has achieved progressively greater success in its attempt to exclude manufacturing from the statistics
of mining.

[7] It is difficult to determine to what extent our indexes of crushed stone will duplicate the indexes of manufacturing. It is certainly true that only a portion of stone
crushing is included in the statistics of manufactures whereas all dimension stone
processing is so covered. This is because the Census of Manufactures classifies dimension stone processing as a manufacturing industry, but includes stone crushing
only when it is incidental to manufacturing industries covered in the manufactures
data. In this sense the inclusion of stone crushing is similar to the inclusion of quarrying in the manufacturing statistics for dimension stone processing. (See discussion
under "Marble, granite, slate, and other stone, cut and shaped," in the 1937 Census
of Manufactures.)

i   A breakdown by variety without regard to use.

ii  A breakdown by use without regard to variety.

iii A simultaneous breakdown both by variety and by use.

Table C-1, relating to four of the dimension stone industries, indicates the different results yielded by the alternative methods of combination of products.

TABLE C-1

DIMENSION STONE
Alternative Indexes of Physical Output[a]
*1929:100*

| Industry | Single Production Series (in short tons) | | | Breakdown According to Use (all uses converted to short tons) | | |
|---|---|---|---|---|---|---|
| | 1919 | 1929 | 1937 | 1919 | 1929 | 1937 |
| Granite | 65.5 | 100.0 | 43.9 | 89.0 | 100.0 | 60.6 |
| Marble | 55.5 | 100.0 | 29.5 | 57.0 | 100.0 | 29.4 |
| Limestone | 42.8 | 100.0 | 41.9 | 31.8 | 100.0 | 44.5 |
| Sandstone | 66.3 | 100.0 | 35.3 | 59.3 | 100.0 | 33.5 |
| TOTAL | 57.0 | 100.0 | 39.0 | 61.0 | 100.0 | 45.3 |

[a] Comparisons are made throughout with the Edgeworth formula (see Appendix A).

The total index numbers secured correspond to those described under alternatives i and iii. Alternative ii yields the following indexes on the 1929 base: 1919:61.9; 1937:48.2. These correspond quite closely with the results under alternative iii. The only index of dimension stone output published to date, so far as the authors are aware, is that given by Vivian E. Spencer, *The Mineral Extractive Industries, 1880–1938* (National Research Project, Philadelphia, 1940), pp. 88-91, in which method ii is adopted.

Results will, of course, differ according to the degree of detail in the breakdown utilized. Also, it can be seen that differences may be obscured in the total because of the diverse movements of the individual components. This is particularly clear in 1919—the total indexes diverge slightly because even though those for granite, limestone and sandstone diverge considerably, the directions of the divergences differ.

It might be thought that method iii, which uses the greatest detail and the largest amount of information, would give the best result. But this is not necessarily the case, for some of the detail may establish distinctions irrelevant to our purpose. What we desire is an index of output which takes full account of differences in the grade of stone quarried, but gives no weight to "quality" differences wrought by manufacturing processes.

The various enterprises from which the Bureau of Mines collects statistics of production and value are described as follows:

Dimension-stone producers fall in three main groups upon the basis of plant operation: (1) those who quarry stone and sell it as rough blocks or slabs; (2) those who quarry stone and manufacture it into finished products; and (3) those who have no quarries but who buy their rough stock and manufacture it into finished products. The Bureau of Mines statistical canvass covers the first and second groups, but as the third group comprises manufacturers rather than quarrymen it is canvassed by the Bureau of the Census. Bureau of Mines statistics are compiled from reports of tonnages and values of original sales, hence they include some material sold as rough blocks and some sold as finished products.[8]

It is clear that producers in the second group report a fabricated product, and that the value of a block of stone produced by them exceeds its value as taken from the quarry. In fact, for these producers, differences in value per short ton among uses of a given variety of stone probably arise in good part from variations in value added by manufacture to a relatively constant "mine" value of mineral (i.e. value as it leaves the quarry), and are not the result of any considerable differences in the grade of stone quarried.[9]

These considerations imply that, at least for the part of the industry reporting fabricated products, the breakdown of dimension stone output by use is not one that it is desirable to employ if we are interested in measuring quarrying rather than manufacturing output. Only by using a single production series for each variety of stone, even though a detailed breakdown by use is available, can the pull which fabrication might otherwise exert on the index of physical output be avoided. For this reason method 1 has been used in the construction of our indexes of the physical output of dimension stone.

While this method—the adoption of a breakdown by variety but not by use—appears to approximate most closely what we actually wish to measure, it also has certain defects which we must briefly notice. Thus the use of a single output series (in short tons) effectively eliminates the influence of manufacturing, but it also obscures actual quality differences in stone quarried. Such differences exist, even though we can take no account of them. For example, first class monumental granite in unfinished blocks commands a premium over other unfinished granite.[10] Similarly, price differentials for sandstone derive from the nature of the cementing material between the grains, and from the

[8] *Minerals Yearbook, 1940*, p. 1164.

[9] This point is substantiated in a letter from Mr. Oliver Bowles of the United States Bureau of Mines. Commenting on the fact that in 1929 among the several uses of granite the unit values per short ton were: building stone, $15.86; paving blocks, $10.22; monumental stone, $43.39, etc., he states that "the differences in value . . . are due chiefly to differences in the degree of fabrication" and not to differences in the quality of the stone.

[10] Bowles, *The Stone Industries*, pp. 156-57.

degree of cementation.[11] Accordingly, the assumption that rough stone is uniform in quality within a single variety represents a shortcoming of our indexes.[12]

When we combine the series for individual varieties a further defect becomes apparent, for the prices of each variety include value added by manufacture in varying degrees. Judged by evidence of the extent to which finishing is done by mills attached to quarries, the degree of fabrication included in our data is greatest in slate (with marble and sandstone next), and least in granite and limestone. It seems likely, therefore, that in the output index for dimension stone slate is accorded too great a weight, and granite and limestone are given too small a weight. Although the evidence quoted is for recent years, conditions in this regard do not seem to have changed materially.[13]

We may summarize as follows. (1) Although manufacturing is eliminated from the indexes for the several varieties, this is achieved only by adopting the unreal assumption of uniform quality of stone within a single variety. (2) The values used in combining individual varieties into an index for stone output as a whole include substantial amounts of value added by manufacture. It follows (3) that the value of quarry products (Table A-2) is somewhat overstated, and therefore also the importance of quarrying in relation to other forms of mining in the computation of indexes for mining output as a whole.

*Dimension Stone—Employment*

Although the problem here is basically the same as in the measurement of production, the data seem to allow a simpler approach. The quarry accident totals [14] for number of persons employed, mandays and manhours (the latter since 1931 only) are divided for each variety of stone into two groups—quarries and "outside works." This breakdown fortunately provides a ready-made approximation to the distribution of employment between mining and manufacturing.

In constructing our indexes of employment for the several varieties of dimension stone and for the total, we have excluded all employment outside of quarries. Such treatment of the data is subject to the ob-

---

[11] *Ibid.*, p. 68.

[12] Nor is this all. The quantity data relate to stone that has already been cut and shaped. Since some stone is wasted in the process, this quantity is smaller than that which would have been reported by the quarry had it shipped stone to an independent mill for finishing. The difference is minimized where scabbling is practiced (see footnote 5 above).

[13] Bowles, *op. cit.*, p. 31. Additional information was received through correspondence with Mr. Bowles.

[14] U. S. Bureau of Mines annual publication, "Quarry Accidents in the United States."

vious criticism that "outside" employees include truckmen, shippers, construction workers and others engaged in similar capacities, who are not clearly associated with either the manufacturing or the mining end of an integrated establishment. To exclude such employment entirely is, therefore, to underestimate the actual numbers engaged in mining.[15]

It is of course impossible to determine exactly the magnitude of the understatement in the employment figures arising from our exclusion of all outside workers. For the period beginning in 1931, however, there are available data that permit us to determine the maximum possible error. This can be done by comparing employment in rock dressing for 1931-39 (which is a minimum figure for manufacturing in the sense that it includes the basic manufacturing employment but excludes employment common to both mining and manufacturing) with employment in outside dimension works (the total of which was excluded from our employment indexes). This comparison and other pertinent figures are summarized in the Table C-2.

TABLE C-2

EMPLOYMENT AT ALL DIMENSION STONE QUARRIES, 1931-39
*Thousand mandays*

| Year | (1) Outside Works[a] | (2) Rock Dressing Plants[b] | (3) Difference (1) — (2) | (4) Quarries[a] | (5) Ratio (3) ÷ (4) |
|---|---|---|---|---|---|
| 1931 | 2,619 | 2,483 | 136 | 1,905 | .071 |
| 1932 | 2,012 | 1,925 | 87 | 1,123 | .077 |
| 1933 | 1,609 | 1,583 | 26 | 1,023 | .025 |
| 1934 | 1,202 | 1,175 | 27 | 841 | .032 |
| 1935 | 1,224 | 1,195 | 29 | 946 | .031 |
| 1936 | 1,979 | 1,885 | 94 | 1,329 | .071 |
| 1937 | 1,992 | 1,919 | 73 | 1,497 | .049 |
| 1938 | 1,688 | 1,643 | 45 | 1,238 | .036 |
| 1939 | 1,882 | 1,837 | 45 | 1,403 | .032 |

[a] Includes employment actually listed under dimension stone in the accident bulletins and estimated dimension employment included under "all other and not stated." The employment shown for quarries (column 4) is included in Table A-3; that shown for outside works (column 1) is excluded. The totals for the dimension industry in Table A-3 also include nondimension marble and slate quarries, and therefore exceed the figures shown here.
[b] U. S. Bureau of Mines, "Quarry Accidents in the United States."

The table shows that in all years total employment in outside works exceeds total employment in rock dressing by only a small margin.

[15] That too many employees are excluded becomes most apparent when one considers quarries which produce only rough stone. They too have outside employees (engaged in the type of work indicated above) who clearly should be included under mining, in contrast to such workers in integrated establishments whose status in this regard is uncertain. However, when industry totals alone are available, it is impossible to treat these establishments separately.

What this means essentially is that, at the most, quarry employment should be increased by 7.1 percent in 1931, 7.7 percent in 1932, 2.5 percent in 1933, and so on, if mining is to be completely covered. Actually, of course, the amount of understatement is considerably less (and probably more stable) than these maximum figures indicate.

### Limestone for Cement and Lime—Output

All but a small fraction of the limestone used in cement and lime manufacture is quarried by the cement and lime companies for use in their own plants. Hence it becomes necessary to define the limits of manufacturing and mining, as in the case of dimension stone. The problem of defining the respective spheres is relatively simple here, since the actual production of the stone for manufacture into cement and lime is, broadly speaking, part of the crushed stone industry. This means that we may consider as pertaining to mining all fabrication preliminary to the burning of crushed limestone into lime, or preliminary to the addition of crushed limestone to the other components of the mixture to be manufactured into cement. In other words, quarrying and crushing of the stone are considered mining, while operations in the cement mill and the limekiln are included under manufacturing.

Adequate data on quantity of physical output are available from 1915 onward. For these years the Bureau of Mines presents quantity data for both limestone manufactured into cement and limestone manufactured into lime. For years prior to 1915 quantity figures have been estimated by us according to the methods indicated in footnotes to Table A-1. Since a single production series seems adequate for each industry, no problem of weighting arises and a suitable index of physical output may be derived in each case.

The weighting factor assumes importance when these two industries are combined with the other stone industries into an index of physical output for the total. Here lack of a unit value for mine or quarry gives rise to a problem identical with that encountered in combining the indexes for the several varieties of dimension stone. In the case of limestone for cement and lime, the difficulty is more serious because the only unit values available are for the final products—cement and lime—and therefore relate specifically to manufacturing. Under such circumstances it becomes necessary to attempt to approximate the unit mine values.

Since limestone for lime and cement are varieties of crushed limestone, the question which naturally arises is whether their unit values are sufficiently like the average unit value for the remainder of crushed limestone (for which a mine value is available) to allow the use of that value. This appears to be the case in lime, but not in cement.[16] We have, therefore, added quantity data on limestone for lime to those for regular crushed limestone, and used a unit value derived from quantity and value figures for the latter (before the inclusion of limestone for lime) as the price coefficient for the total.

In the case of cement we employed a far more dubious procedure, which nevertheless seemed the most adequate method available. In the 1929 Census of Mines and Quarries there are quantity and value data relating to limestone quarried by cement manufacturers and used in the manufacture of cement.[17] The unit value derived from these figures was used as the 1929 price; for all other years this price was extrapolated by the Bureau of Mines unit value for total cement produced during the year.

### Limestone for Cement and Lime—Employment

The employment figures for both limestone for lime and limestone for cement (referred to as limestone, chief product lime, and cement rock, respectively, in the accident bulletins) include limekilns and cement mills when these are attached to quarries. The two stages of production are usually combined in a single establishment and it is to be expected, therefore, that the bulk of manufacturing employment is included in the statistics.

The breakdown between quarries and outside works which approximated the distribution of employment between mining and manufacturing in the case of dimension stone cannot be similarly utilized in these two industries. It will be remembered that crushers are included in our definition of mining and a good percentage of the outside workers are employed at crushers. Only that portion of outside employment accounted for by cement mills and limekilns is excluded from our data.

[16] Oliver Bowles deals with this point in the following paragraph quoted from a letter in response to the above question: "As to unit values, it is difficult to arrive at a value per ton of stone used for cement and lime manufacture because the material does not enter the market except in the form of finished lime and cement. The cost of quarrying and crushing limestone for cement manufacture is in general lower than the cost of preparing similar stone for crushed stone uses because for the latter uses the stone must be crushed to produce a minimum of fines and the crusher product must be screened and possibly washed, whereas for cement manufacture the object is to secure a product as fine as dust. For lime burning the stone is selected carefully and is prepared in specified sizes, therefore, the quarrying costs are about the same as though the stone were prepared for crushed stone uses."

[17] Table 26, p. 363. The unit value of limestone used for cement in 1929 was $0.42 per short ton. In Table 27 on the same page there are similar data relating to limestone for lime. Here the unit value was $0.84 per short ton. The unit value for the remainder of crushed limestone (Table 28, p. 364) was $0.88 per short ton. It will be seen that these results are in general agreement with the statement in the preceding footnote.

For some of the more recent years (since 1931 for limekilns and since 1929 for cement mills) data relating to such employment are available; for all other years the numbers employed at limekilns and cement mills (which we need to deduct) have been estimated according to methods described in the footnotes to Table A-3.[18]

### Undercoverage of the Employment Data—Crushed Stone

The employment data collected by the Bureau of Mines in connection with the annual survey of accidents extend back to 1911. However, the Bureau's descriptions of the data throughout this period suggest that the canvass of the industry has not been complete. The 1911 report states that replies were received from 88 percent of the names on the list (the list did not necessarily include all producers) but that all of the large producers replied, so that the statistics are highly representative when measured by production.[19] In subsequent years the same general note of caution concerning coverage is repeated, although no attempt to estimate undercoverage is made. It seems certain that the data are to some extent incomplete over the entire period. Since the coverage may have changed, we are naturally concerned as to both the year-to-year and the long-time comparability of the series. This problem can be handled best if crushed stone, limestone for cement and lime, and dimension stone are considered separately.

In the case of crushed stone (other than limestone for cement or lime), the first real attempt to approximate 100 percent coverage was made by the National Research Project. Since the Project had access to the original production and employment schedules filed by producers with the Bureau of Mines, they were able to derive productivity measures from matched reports for representative samples. Employment (manhours) was then estimated from production for the remaining operations by use of figures for average productivity of quarries,

[18] In the discussion of the dimension stone statistics it was pointed out that employment in rock dressing is adequate only as an approximation to total manufacturing employment in dimension stone. The same point must be made with regard to the cement mill and limekiln data. The miscellaneous employees who cannot be clearly classified in either mining or manufacturing are automatically included with mining when only the numbers employed in cement mills and limekilns proper are deducted from total employment, whereas in dimension stone they were automatically included with manufacturing (since total outside employment was excluded). Data that provide some indication of the size of this group of employees are available only for workers in limestone for cement (*Minerals Yearbook, 1940*, pp. 1142-43). The mandays (in thousands) of all such employees were about 138 in 1934, 114 in 1935, and 116 in 1936; total employment at quarries and crushers (including these miscellaneous workers) for the same three years was 1,034, 1,042 and 1,425 respectively, which indicates a maximum error of small proportions.

[19] Albert H. Fay, "Quarry Accidents in the United States, 1911," U. S. Bureau of Mines, *Technical Paper 46*, p. 3.

similar in both size and location, for which the matched data were available.[20] Although the Kantor-Saeger estimates are available only for the years 1929–36, a comparison of their figures with the accident data for employment discloses marked changes in the coverage of the latter even over so short a period. This may be seen from Table C-3

TABLE C-3

CRUSHED STONE EMPLOYMENT, 1929–36[a]
Comparison of Accident Bulletin and Kantor-Saeger Figures
*Thousand manhours*

| Year | (1) Accident Bulletins[b] | (2) Kantor-Saeger[c] | (3) Ratio (2) ÷ (1) |
|---|---|---|---|
| 1929 | 52,759[d] | 95,873 | 1.82 |
| 1930 | 41,159[d] | 84,496 | 2.05 |
| 1931 | 32,548 | 64,591 | 1.98 |
| 1932 | 27,028 | 47,535 | 1.76 |
| 1933 | 28,232 | 42,220 | 1.50 |
| 1934 | 31,419 | 43,911 | 1.40 |
| 1935 | 36,451 | 39,838 | 1.09 |
| 1936 | 47,165 | 50,390 | 1.07 |

[a] See p. 337 above.
[b] Includes nondimension granite, sandstone, basalt (trap rock) and limestone (manhours actually listed under nondimension and estimated nondimension included under "all other and not stated"). For the years 1929–34 limestone had to be adjusted to exclude limestone for lime and for 1929–31 it had to be adjusted to exclude also some cement rock incorrectly classified under limestone in the accident bulletins: see pp. 334-36 above.
[c] Kantor and Saeger, *op. cit.*, Table 4, p. 18 (average number of men employed at commercial operations multiplied by average hours per man per year at such operations).
[d] Derived as mandays and converted to manhours.

Evidently the coverage of the Bureau of Mines data increased sharply during the years shown in the table, but we have no information as to coverage in other years. Accordingly, our indexes of crushed stone employment for the years 1929–36 are based upon the Kantor-Saeger estimates. For years after 1936 the Bureau of Mines data were adjusted to total coverage according to the procedure described in footnotes to Table A-3 above. For years prior to 1929 no adequate method of adjustment seemed possible.

There is reason to suspect that employment figures for other sections of the stone industry are also defective in coverage. In the case of limestone for cement, there are available data that permit a quantitative

[20] H. S. Kantor and G. A. Saeger, *Crushed-Stone Industry* (National Research Project, Philadelphia, 1939), p. 129, note 4. This note fails to mention that the estimates were based on limestone (by far the most important component of the total) and that the results were applied to total crushed stone (not including limestone for cement and lime). This procedure, noted by Mr. Kantor in a letter to us, was prompted by lack of adequate data for the other varieties.

evaluation of the undercoverage. Thus employment for the entire cement industry can be derived for the years 1928–38.[21] These figures cover 100 percent of the industry only in 1934, 1937 and 1938. For other years we have assumed, in deriving column (2) of Table C-4, that output per manday was the same in those establishments for which production data alone are available and those in which production and employment data are available.[22] These data of course include employment in cement manufacture as well as in quarrying operations, but it is possible to approximate the latter by deducting cement-mill employment (given separately) from the total. Figures thus derived from *Minerals Yearbook* are compared with the accident bulletin figures in Table C-4. It will be seen that *Yearbook* data exceed the bulletin figures for the 1928–33 period, while for all later years the relationship is reversed. The varying nature of the relationship is apparently explained by two factors. (1) Since 1933 both the accident bulletin and the *Yearbook* figures represent complete coverage. The excess of the former is accounted for by the fact that accident bulletin data include employment in the production of natural cement, and also some employment in construction work, both of which are excluded from the *Yearbook* figures for all years.[23] (2) In 1928–33 the *Yearbook* figures are complete, while the accident bulletin figures fall short of total coverage for two reasons. First, and most important, is the fact that a number of quarries producing limestone for cement were incorrectly classified under crushed limestone; since we present no separate employment indexes for limestone for cement, this causes us no concern. Second is the actual failure to include all producers within the scope of the canvass—the same weakness encountered in the case of the regular crushed stone data.[24]

Our employment data for limestone for cement are derived from both sources. For years since 1934 we have used the accident bulletin data, for 1929–33 the *Yearbook* figures, and for all years prior to 1929 we used accident bulletin figures in the absence of more reliable data.[25] Our employment figures are clearly most reliable for the period since 1929. Even during this period a minor difficulty is encountered because

[21] *Minerals Yearbook, 1940,* pp. 1142-43.

[22] Coverage is fairly high in all years. In 1935 and 1936 it is slightly less than 100 percent and in 1928–33 it varies between 87.3 percent and 89.0 percent.

[23] Construction work is very often reported under miscellaneous, in which case it is included in the *Yearbook* figures. Construction is excluded only when separate figures are available.

[24] This information was supplied by Mr. W. W. Adams of the U. S. Bureau of Mines.

[25] See pp. 338-39 above. Since the data have to be spliced in 1929, it is not feasible to use the available *Yearbook* figure for 1928 in the construction of the employment index.

of the exclusion of employment in natural cement and in some construction work from the *Yearbook* totals, but it appears unlikely that these omissions have had any noticeable effect on the movement of the index.[26] For years preceding 1929 little more than guesswork can be used as a guide to the adequacy of the index. There is no doubt that under-

TABLE C-4

LIMESTONE FOR CEMENT
Employment at Quarries and Crushers, 1928–38
*Thousand mandays*

| | (1) Accident Bulletins[a] | (2) Estimates Derived *from* Minerals Yearbook[b] | (3) Ratio (2) ÷ (1) |
|---|---|---|---|
| 1928 | 1,445 | 2,009 | 1.39 |
| 1929 | 1,296 | 1,745 | 1.35 |
| 1930 | 1,139 | 1,639 | 1.44 |
| 1931 | 995 | 1,186 | 1.19 |
| 1932 | 745 | 826 | 1.11 |
| 1933 | 764 | 819 | 1.07 |
| 1934 | 1,034 | 1,031 | .997 |
| 1935 | 1,042 | 998 | .96 |
| 1936 | 1,425 | 1,365 | .96 |
| 1937 | 1,523 | 1,339 | .88 |
| 1938 | 1,256 | 1,173 | .93 |

[a] See p. 334 above.
[b] See text.

coverage is severe; however, nothing is known of changes in the degree of undercoverage. Table C-4 suggests a tapering off in the degree of undercoverage after the violent change between 1930 and 1931. If the level of coverage in 1928–30 is representative of earlier years, the movement of the index may be a fairly faithful reflection of the true movement of employment, although it cannot be proved that this is the case. If the coverage of the data varied, it seems more likely on general grounds that an improvement in coverage followed the passage of time than that a deterioration occurred: in which case our measures (Table A-5) understate the rise in the productivity of stone quarrying prior to 1929.

[26] Examination reveals that the importance of the employment excluded from the *Yearbook* totals is slight in 1934, 1935 and 1936, and becomes greater in 1937 and 1938. (See Table C-4, col. 3.) Since natural cement is relatively unimportant in all these years the variation is most probably due to differences in the reporting of construction workers. (See footnote 23 above.) If, as the trend suggests, construction was reported under miscellaneous in the earlier years, it is safe to conclude that undercoverage is very slight from 1929 to 1933, the years for which we use *Yearbook* figures.

Since limestone for lime has been included under crushed limestone no separate index of employment has been constructed for it. It should be noted, however, that our estimates of undercoverage in crushed stone exclude limestone for lime because the Kantor-Saeger figures do not include it. An independent estimate of the adequacy of the employment data in this branch of quarrying is called for, but there are no means by which such an estimate may be assembled. As in the case of limestone for cement, the chief difficulty connected with the employment figures on limestone for lime is obviated by its inclusion with crushed limestone. Under such circumstances the incorrect classification, under crushed limestone, of an enterprise quarrying limestone for lime, is of no consequence. Nevertheless the problem that arises from actual deficiencies in the scope of the canvass still remains, and we are ignorant of its effect on the index for crushed limestone.

### Undercoverage of the Employment Data—Dimension Stone

We may suppose that employment data for dimension stone are subject to the same weaknesses as employment figures for the other stone industries. Unfortunately, in the case of dimension stone, data similar to the Kantor-Saeger figures mentioned above, which would enable us to derive a more or less precise measure of the degree of undercoverage, are lacking. Nevertheless, we can say something about the adequacy of the data in this part of the field.

It was pointed out above that in the dimension stone industry employees who are reported under the heading "outside works" are largely engaged in manufacturing. Therefore such employment was not included by us, with the result that our employment indexes for dimension stone relate solely to quarry workers. The exclusion of outside employment now assumes added importance because the problem of changing coverage in the "Quarry Accident" figures for dimension stone is especially pronounced with regard to such outside employment. This is not to say that the reported employment at quarries represents complete industrial coverage, but rather that changes in coverage for quarries and outside works as a whole are attributable mainly to the lack of uniformity in reporting employment in stone dressing over a period of years.[27]

[27] Miss Vivian E. Spencer of the Census of Mines and Quarries suggested that this was the case in a letter explaining the treatment of stone employment by the National Research Project (see Spencer, *The Mineral Extractive Industries, 1880–1938*, Philadelphia, 1940). She stated, in part, "Dimension-stone quarrying data as collected by all agencies (at least prior to taking the present Census [1939]) are fairly nebulous. All of them included some, but did not completely cover, dimension-stone dressing at plants operated in conjunction with the quarries."

The data at our disposal permit a rather simple demonstration of changing accident bulletin coverage of outside works since 1922 (the year when total stone employment was for the first time divided into dimension and nondimension). If the relationship between employment at outside works (which we exclude) and total employment is examined for this period (see Table C-5) a very definite rise in the percentage of total employment accounted for by outside works is indicated. Such a result must certainly stem from changing coverage, since

TABLE C-5

DIMENSION STONE QUARRIES
Ratio of Mandays at Outside Works to Total Mandays, 1922–1939[a]

| Year | Marble | Granite | Limestone | Sandstone |
|------|--------|---------|-----------|-----------|
| 1922 | .51 | .33 | .33 | .28 |
| 1923 | .55 | .27 | .22 | .29 |
| 1924 | .55 | .27 | .21 | .19 |
| 1925 | .59 | .37 | .37 | .23 |
| 1926 | .61 | .43 | .44 | .24 |
| 1927 | .58 | .40 | .53 | .45 |
| 1928 | .61 | .43 | .55 | .44 |
| 1929 | .64 | .46 | .53 | .42 |
| 1930 | .64 | .50 | .52 | .45 |
| 1931 | .66 | .53 | .59 | .55 |
| 1932 | .74 | .52 | .67 | .54 |
| 1933 | .73 | .50 | .66 | .67 |
| 1934 | .73 | .52 | .61 | .69 |
| 1935 | .71 | .45 | .62 | .62 |
| 1936 | .77 | .45 | .66 | .50 |
| 1937 | .69 | .50 | .58 | .47 |
| 1938 | .66 | .51 | .65 | .45 |
| 1939 | .66 | .51 | .63 | .43 |

[a] U. S. Bureau of Mines, "Quarry Accidents in the United States." Total mandays comprise mandays at quarries and at outside works. The ratios were computed from the data as published, and take no account of employment reported as "All other and not stated," i.e., not distributed between dimension and nondimension.

there has been no tendency toward a greater degree of fabrication by quarry companies during this period. The changes in coverage, in turn, are at least partially accounted for by the fact that accident bulletin coverage of outside employment has increased considerably during the period, whereas there has been no similar change with regard to quarry workers. Such changes as have taken place in the coverage of quarry statistics must have been of a much lower order of magnitude. In addition, it is possible that in the accident reports the segregation of employment between quarries and outside works has tended to improve over the period. To the extent that this has happened, our indexes suffer from lack of comparability over time.

### Crushed Stone Output—Noncommercial Production

During the past decade increasing amounts of crushed stone have been quarried by local government units, mainly for highway construction and repair. These amounts are included in the output data for crushed stone shown in Table A-1. The employment statistics collected by the Bureau of Mines cover only commercial enterprises.[28] To make our measure of output comparable with employment we therefore have to exclude noncommercial production for years after 1929. For this purpose we have used over-all value data, for no segregation in terms of physical output is available for individual varieties. For years since 1929, according to Bureau of Mines figures, the percentage contribution of commercial to total crushed stone production (excluding limestone for cement, which is produced only commercially) ran as follows, in value terms:

| | |
|------|------|
| 1929 | 95.1 |
| 1930 | 94.3 |
| 1931 | 92.3 |
| 1932 | 87.1 |
| 1933 | 88.3 |
| 1934 | 81.7 |
| 1935 | 81.2 |
| 1936 | 77.2 |
| 1937 | 78.6 |
| 1938 | 71.0 |
| 1939 | 69.3 |

Accordingly, the index for crushed stone (excluding limestone for cement) computed from the data in Table A-1 was adjusted for 1930 and later years as follows: for 1930 it was multiplied by 94.3/95.1, for 1931 by 92.3/95.1, and so forth. The resulting index was then combined with an index for limestone for cement to yield an index for total commercial crushed stone; this was in turn combined with the index for dimension stone to provide an index of the output of commercial stone quarrying as a whole (Table A-5).

### Conclusion

We have examined the adequacy both of the output and of the employment data in stone quarrying, and have indicated the choices we

---

[28] Since 1936 the Bureau of Mines has begun to collect employment data for noncommercial crushed stone operations, but the figures are incomplete and of unknown coverage.

made and the kinds of adjustment we found necessary. We have also mentioned the remaining weaknesses of the data, for which no adjustments could be devised. The defects in the figures for output appear to be much less serious than the weaknesses of the employment data. Any reservations we may have concerning the productivity measures for the stone industries (Table A-5) relate chiefly to the adequacy of the latter and for this reason we have devoted considerable space to the subject. It is probable that our indexes understate rather than overstate the rise which has occurred in the productivity of stone quarrying.

# The Statistical Treatment of the Nonferrous Metal Mining Industries, with Special Reference to Copper

THE NONFERROUS metal mining industries, as defined in this study, ordinarily furnish two broad groups of products: ores and concentrates. The ores represent the part of the product that passes directly from the mine to the smelter and receives no further processing by the mining industry. The concentrates account for that part of the industry's product which was unsuitable for smelting as it came from the mine, and which had to be further treated by concentration and perhaps separation before the industry could dispose of it to the smelter.[1]

The natural unit for measuring the output of such industries is the tonnage of ores and concentrates produced. Where the grade of ores and concentrates varies widely, and also shifts from year to year, as it does in these industries, the ideal index would be based on a breakdown of output sufficiently detailed to make for homogeneous groupings. As we point out in Chapter 12, the ideal index of copper mining, for example, would be derived by aggregating such output data with suitable unit values as weights. Unfortunately, such data are not available for copper or any of the other important nonferrous metals, and hence such an index of physical output must be approximated otherwise.

Usually two broad classes of data may be used to measure the output of these metals: total tonnage of ore, and recovered or recoverable metallic content of ore. Ordinarily, therefore, we must choose one of these two series. To use tonnage of ore as a measure of physical output we should at least require assurance that the average grade of ore mined had changed but little during our period of study. But we know that among nonferrous metals this condition has not been fulfilled. In fact, the average grade of nonferrous ore mined has continually declined, and it is quite clear that the average ton of ore today is much different from the average ton of ore at the turn of the century. For example, half of the nation's copper now comes from deposits that were known in 1900 but were then considered valueless because of their low metal content.[2]

---

[1] Often mines (with mills) and smelters are under identical ownership so that no sale is involved; but the distinction of principle remains.

[2] A. V. Corry and O. E. Kiessling, *Grade of Ore* (National Research Project, Philadelphia, 1938), p. 84.

Evidently these changes vitiate a simple tonnage aggregate when it is used as a measure of mineral production. We are left, therefore, with recoverable metallic content of the ore as a gauge of production in these industries.[3] Series that relate to metal contained in the ores and concentrates are free from difficulties of measurement caused by changes in grade of ore; a unit of copper metal, for example, remains more or less constant over time. However, the use of such series does not free us entirely from problems of measurement.

To begin with, we cannot escape the influence of declining grade of ore by the simple expedient of using something other than ore as a measure of output. For to the extent that ore has declined in grade, so must our measure of productivity (the ratio of output to employment) be subject to varying interpretations. Thus to insist that a man produce a given recoverable content is obviously, under such circumstances, a more stringent condition than to require of him a stated ore tonnage. Clearly our test of what constitutes a rise of productivity is strict in proportion as our definition of output is circumscribed. This must be borne in mind, but it is more a matter of interpretation than a defect in measurement. Of greater relevance is the fact that recoverable content of ore itself does not yield an unambiguous index of physical output in mining. In the first place, a given amount of metal in highly concentrated form is plainly more valuable to the smelter than the same quantity in low grade form, that is, dispersed through a much larger mass of gangue (waste matter). Recoverable content makes no allowance for differences of this sort in the quality of the product. In the second place, because of advances in metallurgy a greater percentage of metal is being recovered from ore today than formerly. If the total metallurgical process were part of mining, as defined, this would not concern us. However, the processes of smelting and refining fall within the scope of manufacturing; therefore, to the extent that improvements in these techniques have altered the ratio of recovery, our indexes are biased upward as measures of physical output in mining.

It so happens that in the case of copper the available statistics allow us to test the importance of these considerations. We shall therefore examine briefly the adequacy of recoverable content as a measure of output, or at least we shall note the differences which would result from the use of other principles of measurement. To do this we must restrict ourselves to sample data, and for simplicity we shall consider the product, copper, rather than the industry, copper mining. The comparison of alternative measures of output has special relevance in the case of copper because of the decline that has occurred in the grade of

---

[3] We use recoverable content rather than recovered content (i.e., smelter output) for reasons set forth in Appendix B.

copper ore, and the technological revolution that has accompanied this decline. We may start with several remarks designed to clarify certain of the concepts with which we shall deal.

We have seen that copper ore must pass through several stages of production before copper metal emerges as a product. The reader will recall that most copper ores are milling ores, that is, they are too lean to be smelted before they are concentrated; the remainder consist of high grade or direct smelting ores. Thus for the smelter product to emerge, the material must pass through either two or three phases of the production cycle. At the conclusion of each of these phases the product is different from that at the conclusion of each of the other phases. Recoverable content—our measure of output—relates to the product which emerges at the end of the smelting operations. How shall we determine whether an index based on this measure of output is similar to an index which might be based on output measured at some other stage of production? More precisely, how may we determine whether output measured at this stage will differ significantly from output measured at the conclusion of those operations which we have called mining?

Having once adopted metallic content as a measure of output we may reconsider the problem just raised in another fashion. Ore, when mined, contains a certain amount of metal. This is its *actual* content as distinguished from its recoverable content. The latter is smaller by reason of losses of metal in concentrating and smelting. A certain portion of this ore is concentrated before smelting. The concentrates produced also contain a certain amount of metal—their *actual* content. This is a smaller amount of metal than was contained in the ore, but a greater amount than will appear as smelter output. We are obviously confronted here by a choice between several principles of measurement. Conceivably, physical output can be measured by either the actual content of the ore, the actual content of the concentrates (assuming all the ores to be "milling ores"), or the recoverable content of the ores or concentrates (the measure of output we have used throughout).

Ordinarily we do not have at hand the several types of information mentioned. But if we did, and were to convert the data to index form, what would the resultant indexes mean? An index based on the actual content of ore could be used to measure output in mining (narrowly defined to include only those processes in which the ore is broken and brought to the surface). An index based on the actual content of concentrates could be used to measure physical output in the mining and concentrating of "milling ores." (Such an index is actually the sum of two components: an index of mining in the narrow sense used above and a net index of milling or concentrating.[4]) This index would come closest to measuring output for the bulk of the copper mining industry, and we should therefore be particularly interested in observing the differences between this index and that based on recoverable content.

The data which we have gathered for copper enable us to construct index numbers of the type described. The remainder of this Appendix deals with the behavior of the alternative indexes derived, and relates the lessons of their behavior to the questions raised several paragraphs above.

First, we may ask, how do indexes of copper content of ore, copper content of concentrates, and of ore itself, differ from one another? As pointed out, we must content ourselves with sample data for an undetermined section of the industry. Because of variations in coverage, the indexes we obtain are without interest in themselves: but since the coverage of each index is the same in any given year, the relations between them are significant. These indexes are shown, on a 1911 base, in Table D-2 and Chart 50. We must remember that these figures are concerned only with milling ores, and that they take no account of products of the copper mining industry other than copper itself.

Over the period as a whole, tonnage of ore mined rises in relation to its copper content. The ratio of the latter to the former is of course a measure of grade of ore; a growing spread between these two curves, in a relative sense, is an indication of declining grade (for further evidence on this point, see Table 22 above). It will be noticed that the ratio diminishes somewhat in years of low output: the improvement in grade in such years is no doubt occasioned by a temporary return to more selective mining methods.

Considered as a measure of output of the copper mining industry (if we exclude ore dressing), tonnage of ore is clearly subject to an upward bias, for it takes no account of the apparent decline in the quality of the product. The actual copper content of the ore mined may afford a suitable measure of the output of mining activity proper, but it is evident that it does not do so if we define the industry to include the dressing of ore. For the product of the "copper mining and ore dressing industry" consists for the most part of concentrates,[5] and the output of concentrates, measured by copper content, moved differently from either of the other two indexes shown in the chart. From 1911 to 1918 the content of concentrates, and the content of ore from which they were derived, moved together: it would appear that during this

---

[4] See Solomon Fabricant, *The Output of Manufacturing Industries, 1899–1937* (National Bureau of Economic Research, 1940), for a discussion of the concept of net indexes of physical output.

[5] In 1939, 80 percent of all copper came from milling ores; the remainder came from ores smelted directly or leached.

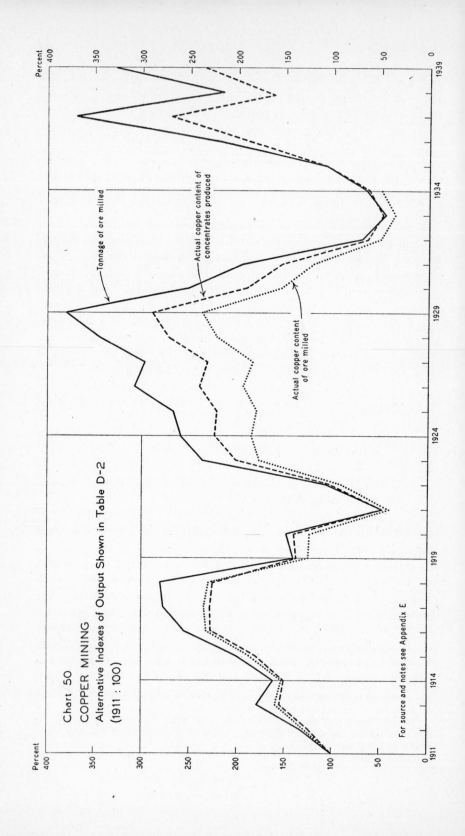

Chart 50

COPPER MINING
Alternative Indexes of Output Shown in Table D-2
(1911 : 100)

Tonnage of ore milled

Actual copper content of
concentrates produced

Actual copper content
of ore milled

Percent

For source and notes see Appendix E

period milling techniques were making small progress in overcoming the effects of the decline in the grade of ore. After 1918, however, perhaps with the general introduction of flotation and refinements in the technique, the ratio of content of concentrates to content of ore rises rather steadily: the increasing efficiency of the ore dressing process is reflected very clearly in the rising percentage of mill recovery shown in Table D-3.[6]

Next we may consider how the index of recoverable content would differ from the index of actual content of concentrates. It will be remembered that the former is the index on which we have relied in this volume, whereas (for concentrating ores) the latter is the index we should have preferred to show.[7] Unfortunately, we are not able to derive a series on recoverable content comparable with the series we have worked with in this appendix. Hence we cannot make the comparison which would directly reveal the differences in behavior of the two indexes. We are, however, able at least to cast some light on the probable behavior of the two indexes relative to each other.

In Table D-1 we have brought together scattered figures on smelter recovery for that portion of the industry covered in this appendix, and, for more recent years, for some direct smelting ores. It can be seen from these figures that smelter recovery of metal from concentrates has been remarkably constant over the period treated by our analysis. We may contrast this with the change in mill recovery indicated in the first two columns of Table D-3. Smelter recovery was very high at the beginning of our period and increased but little in succeeding years, while mill recovery jumped from about 70 percent to over 90 percent. This comparison suggests rather strongly that (so far as concentrating or milling ores are concerned) the advances in metallurgy making for a higher recovery of the metallic content of the ore have been almost

---

[6] Ordinarily the index based on content of concentrates lies somewhere between the extremes represented by ore on the one hand, and content of ore on the other. In 1921 and 1933, however, the two years of lowest output, the index of content of concentrates actually stood somewhat higher than the index of ore—when 1911 is used as a base. Such a result is not unexpected in years of low output in view of the high degree of selectivity in mining in such years. The narrowing in the gap between the index of ore and content in these two years—observed in the preceding paragraph—reflects the relative rise in grade. This shift in grade has combined with a ratio of recovery much higher than that in the base year to produce the results observed. Whether such a combination will cause the index of content of concentrates to exceed the index of ore must depend in good part on the choice of the base year. Obviously, the higher the grade in the base year, the less is the likelihood that even the combination of highly selective mining and relatively greater recovery will result in an index of content which stands higher than the index of ore.

[7] We may recall that this discussion deals chiefly with the concentrating ores. For ores that are not concentrated the proper index of physical output (in this context) would be based on actual content of ores. For these ores, too, we have relied on recoverable content.

wholly in milling and not in smelting: i.e., in mining, as defined here, and not in manufacturing. The gains which have been made in smelter recovery are too slight to have caused much of a difference between indexes of actual and recoverable content of concentrates. It follows that an output index for copper mining and ore dressing based upon actual copper content of concentrates and direct smelting ores would not differ significantly from the indexes (Tables A-5 and A-7) based upon data for recoverable content (Table A-1).[8]

Some further qualifications are necessary. Even in a purely technical sense the percentage of mill recovery is not a perfect measure of the efficiency of ore dressing; nor is metal content a perfect measure of the output of concentrates. We should also consider the ratio of concentration (tonnage of ore to tonnage of concentrates derived therefrom) in the one connection; and percentage copper content of concentrates in the other. Thus the higher the ratio of concentration for a given mill recovery, the more efficient is the ore dressing process; while the smaller the weight of concentrates necessary to contain a given weight of copper, the higher is the quality of the product which the mining industry passes along to the smelter.

Such evidence as we could collect on this topic is given in Table D-3. There are some suggestions of a rising tendency, both in the ratio of concentration and in the percentage copper content of concentrates: but in neither case is any conclusive statement possible. However, the clear absence of any *decline* in concentration ratios, coupled with the equally clear improvement in mill recovery, appears further to substantiate our judgment concerning the increased technical efficiency of milling.[9] Meanwhile, any rise that may have occurred over the period in the percentage copper content of concentrates, along with the greater relative importance of concentrates in the total output, suggests the presence of a downward bias in our index of output, based as it is upon metallic content. For copper in more available and less bulky form represents a better product, and we should like to allow for this improvement in quality in our index. Clearly, we cannot do so. The improvement in the grade of concentrates appears to have been rather moderate: however, the relative importance of high grade concentrates

[8] At least so far as the milling or concentrating ores are concerned. Probably this conclusion is not sound with regard to the direct smelting ores. The period 1929–39 covered by the data in Table D-1 is too recent to be of much value for any judgment on this point. For that segment of copper mining output an index of recoverable content may, in fact, be a measure that is biased upward.

[9] This means that the relative contribution of milling activity to the output of mining and milling combined has probably risen over the period. In other words, the *net* output of milling appears to have risen in relation to the output of mining. In addition, such advances in the efficiency of milling may have resulted in an improvement in the grade of concentrates produced.

has increased a good deal, so that there may be a substantial bias in our index on this account.

We may conclude that, so far as milling ores are concerned, output could best be measured by actual content of concentrates; and by actual content of ore, in the case of direct smelting ores. However, no important change appears to have occurred in percentage rates of recovery by smelters, at least with respect to concentrating ores. We may therefore regard recoverable content as an acceptable substitute, in a statistical sense, for actual content of metal. Put otherwise, our indexes for copper (Tables A-5 and A-7) do reflect changes in the output of mining and ore dressing, and are probably undistorted by developments in smelting and refining. The grade of direct smelting ores appears to have changed little (Table 22). The grade of concentrates may have risen (Table D-3), and certainly their relative importance has increased. This represents an improvement in the quality of the product —an improvement which we have no means of incorporating in our indexes of output. Meanwhile, to obtain a ton of copper more tons of ore must be mined than formerly; but the increase in the amount of ore required is less than that suggested by the decline in its copper content. For the deterioration which has occurred in the grade of concentrating ores has been offset in large measure, though not completely, by improvements in the ratio of mill recovery.[10]

[10] While it is true that the grade of ore mined by the copper mining industry has declined during the past forty years (Table 22), the grade of the material which constitutes the input of the smelting industry appears, if anything, to have improved in quality. (See Table D-3 for content of concentrates; Table 22 for content of direct smelting ores.) Nor have smelter recovery ratios changed appreciably over the period (Table D-1). Consequently, there seems to be no evidence (at least so far as concerns copper) that the net output of the smelting and refining industries has increased more rapidly than their gross output (see Fabricant, op. cit., p. 279).

TABLE D-1

COPPER

Smelter Recovery

*Percent of copper recovered from ores or concentrates smelted*

| Year | From Ore Mined at Individual Properties[a] | | | | From Ore Mined in Nine Western States[b] | |
| | Ray (Arizona) | Chino (New Mexico) | Morenci (Arizona) | Miami (Arizona) | Direct Smelting Ores | Concentrates |
|---|---|---|---|---|---|---|
| 1909 | .. | .. | 94.3 | .. | .. | .. |
| 1910 | .. | .. | .. | .. | .. | .. |
| 1911 | .. | .. | 92.6 | 95 | .. | .. |
| 1912 | .. | 95 | .. | 95 | .. | .. |
| 1913 | 96.6 | 95 | .. | 95 | .. | .. |
| 1914 | 96.5 | 95 | 96.4 | 95 | .. | .. |
| 1915 | 96.5 | 95 | 94.1 | 95 | .. | .. |
| 1916 | 96.3 | 95.5 | 95.2 | 95 | .. | .. |
| 1917 | 96.1 | 95.6 | 94.4 | 95 | .. | .. |
| 1918 | 96.2 | 95.4 | 93.4 | 95 | .. | .. |
| 1919 | 96.9 | 95.7 | 94.0 | 95 | .. | .. |
| 1920 | 96.8 | 95.6 | .. | 95 | .. | .. |
| 1921 | 95.8 | 96.1 | .. | 95 | .. | .. |
| 1922 | 96.0 | 96.3 | .. | 95 | .. | .. |
| 1923 | 96.4 | 96.0 | .. | 95 | .. | .. |
| 1924 | 96.3 | 96.1 | .. | 95 | .. | .. |
| 1925 | 96.4 | 96.0 | .. | 95 | .. | .. |
| 1926 | .. | .. | .. | 97 | .. | .. |
| 1927 | .. | .. | .. | 97 | .. | .. |
| 1928 | .. | .. | .. | 97 | .. | .. |
| 1929 | .. | .. | .. | 97 | 93.3 | 95.8 |
| 1930 | .. | .. | .. | 97 | 93.7 | 96.1 |
| 1931 | .. | .. | .. | 97 | 93.1 | 95.8 |
| 1932 | .. | .. | .. | .. | 95.5 | 95.7 |
| 1933 | .. | .. | .. | .. | 96.5 | 96.0 |
| 1934 | .. | .. | .. | .. | 95.8 | 96.6 |
| 1935 | .. | .. | .. | .. | 94.1 | 96.7 |
| 1936 | .. | .. | .. | .. | 94.1 | 95.5 |
| 1937 | .. | .. | .. | .. | 94.1 | 96.3 |
| 1938 | .. | .. | .. | .. | 94.2 | 96.6 |
| 1939 | .. | .. | .. | .. | 94.5 | 96.6 |

[a] Obtained from annual reports of individual companies: Ray Consolidated Copper Co. (Ray and Chino), Phelps Dodge Corp. (Morenci), Miami Copper Co. (Miami).

[b] Obtained from data collected by U. S. Bureau of Mines and published in successive annual issues of *Minerals Yearbook*. States included are Arizona, California, Colorado, Idaho, Montana, Nevada, New Mexico, Utah, Washington.

COPPER

Alternative Indexes of Output[a]

*1911:100*

| Year | Tonnage of Ore Milled | Actual Copper Content of Ore Milled | Actual Copper Content of Concentrates Produced |
|---|---|---|---|
| 1911 | 100 | 100 | 100 |
| 1912 | 134 | 128 | 126 |
| 1913 | 178 | 160 | 155 |
| 1914 | 162 | 153 | 151 |
| 1915 | 199 | 187 | 181 |
| 1916 | 255 | 232 | 227 |
| 1917 | 277 | 234 | 228 |
| 1918 | 280 | 230 | 226 |
| 1919 | 140 | 125 | 138 |
| 1920 | 148 | 124 | 140 |
| 1921 | 47 | 41 | 49 |
| 1922 | 106 | 90 | 104 |
| 1923 | 237 | 177 | 202 |
| 1924 | 259 | 186 | 224 |
| 1925 | 268 | 181 | 222 |
| 1926 | 308 | 194 | 240 |
| 1927 | 297 | 184 | 232 |
| 1928 | 346 | 222 | 272 |
| 1929 | 381 | 237 | 289 |
| 1930 | 252 | 154 | 191 |
| 1931 | 195 | 121 | 153 |
| 1932 | 70 | 50 | 64 |
| 1933 | 46 | 36 | 47 |
| 1934 | 66 | 49 | 63 |
| 1935 | 107 | .. | 107 |
| 1936 | 221 | .. | 191 |
| 1937 | 371 | .. | 271 |
| 1938 | 216 | .. | 162 |
| 1939 | 328 | .. | 235 |

[a] Because of year-to-year variations in coverage, the three indexes of output shown in this table must not be regarded as applicable, either to the entire copper mining industry, or to the product, copper. For comparisons between successive years, however, the three indexes have the same coverage, so that they are comparable among themselves. The data are confined to milling (as distinct from direct smelting) ores.

For 1911–29 the indexes were obtained by aggregating the results of individual properties, as follows: Ray (1911–25) and Chino (1912–25), Ray Consolidated Copper Co.; Nevada (1912–29), Ray (1926–29) and Chino (1926–29), Nevada Consolidated Copper Co.; Morenci (1911–19) and Copper Queen (1924–29), Phelps Dodge Corp.; Miami (1911–29), Miami Copper Co.; Utah (1911–29), Utah Copper Co. Data were taken from annual reports of the companies concerned. In years in which the number of properties changed the indexes were spliced. Coverage varies from 33 to 46 percent of all milling ores.

For 1929–39 the figures relate to all milling ores produced in Arizona, California, Colorado, Idaho, Montana, Nevada, New Mexico, Utah and Washington, as collected by U. S. Bureau of Mines and published in successive annual issues of *Minerals Yearbook*. In 1939 copper from milling ores in these states represented slightly more than 90 percent of all copper produced from milling ores, or about three quarters of total copper production from domestic ores.

The indexes for 1929–39 were spliced to those computed for 1911–29.

TABLE D-3

COPPER

Mill Recovery and Ratio of Concentration

| Year | Mill Recovery[a] (percent) | | Ratio of Concentration[d] | | | | Actual Copper Content of Concentrates (percent) | | | |
|------|----------------------------|----------------------|-------------------------|----------------|------------------|----------------------|--------------------------------------------------|---------------|------------------|----------------------|
| | Corporate Sample[b] | Nine Western States[c] | Morenci[e] (Arizona) | Utah[e] (Utah) | Miami[e] (Arizona) | Nine Western States[c] | Morenci[e] (Arizona) | Utah[e] (Utah) | Miami[e] (Arizona) | Nine Western States[c] |
| 1909 | .. | .. | 6.6 | .. | .. | .. | 15.8 | .. | .. | .. |
| 1910 | .. | .. | 6.8 | 26.6 | .. | .. | 15.4 | 27.3 | .. | .. |
| 1911 | 70 | .. | 7.6 | 24.4 | 22.2 | .. | 15.9 | 25.6 | 40.4 | .. |
| 1912 | 68 | .. | 7.1 | 22.9 | 22.3 | .. | 16.7 | 20.8 | 37.0 | .. |
| 1913 | 67 | .. | 7.7 | 21.7 | 23.3 | .. | 15.8 | 17.3 | 38.1 | .. |
| 1914 | 68 | .. | 7.6 | 19.3 | 24.6 | .. | 15.7 | 18.2 | 39.3 | .. |
| 1915 | 67 | .. | 6.8 | 20.8 | 25.7 | .. | 13.5 | 19.2 | 41.9 | .. |
| 1916 | 67 | .. | 7.1 | 20.9 | 27.8 | .. | 12.1 | 18.7 | 42.5 | .. |
| 1917 | 67 | .. | 6.8 | 20.4 | 30.6 | .. | 11.2 | 16.6 | 43.0 | .. |
| 1918 | 68 | .. | 7.8 | 20.1 | 27.8 | .. | 11.3 | 16.1 | 40.1 | .. |
| 1919 | 76 | .. | 6.8 | 20.1 | 25.9 | .. | 12.8 | 19.9 | 43.5 | .. |
| 1920 | 78 | .. | .. | 17.5 | 27.0 | .. | .. | 16.4 | 43.9 | .. |
| 1921 | 82 | .. | .. | 21.9 | 25.6 | .. | .. | 21.3 | 38.4 | .. |
| 1922 | 79 | .. | .. | 23.3 | 26.8 | .. | .. | 23.5 | 43.6 | .. |
| 1923 | 79 | .. | .. | 20.5 | 29.5 | .. | .. | 18.6 | 42.0 | .. |
| 1924 | 84 | .. | .. | 19.6 | 30.4 | .. | .. | 18.1 | 39.5 | .. |

| Year | | | | | | | | |
|---|---|---|---|---|---|---|---|---|
| 1925 | 85 | .. | 19.6 | 29.9 | .. | 17.5 | 27.9 | .. |
| 1926 | 86 | .. | 19.4 | 37.2 | .. | 17.1 | 28.0 | .. |
| 1927 | 87 | .. | 28.8 | 51.6 | .. | 25.1 | 34.3 | .. |
| 1928 | 85 | .. | 37.1 | 65.7 | .. | 31.5 | 38.4 | .. |
| 1929 | 84 | 87.5 | 37.6 | 60.0 | 20.2 | 32.1 | 36.2 | 23.7 |
| 1930 | 86 | 89.0 | 37.2 | 60.4 | 19.7 | 32.2 | 34.1 | 23.1 |
| 1931 | 89 | 90.5 | 37.2 | 69.6 | 21.2 | 32.6 | 40.9 | 25.8 |
| 1932 | .. | 92.0 | 35.7 | .. | 19.6 | 32.4 | .. | 27.5 |
| 1933 | .. | 93.9 | 35.4 | .. | 17.8 | 33.8 | .. | 28.3 |
| 1934 | .. | 93.7 | .. | .. | 19.0 | .. | .. | 28.4 |
| 1935 | .. | .. | .. | .. | 17.1 | .. | .. | 26.3 |
| 1936 | .. | .. | .. | .. | 21.9 | .. | .. | 29.1 |
| 1937 | .. | .. | .. | .. | 25.3 | .. | .. | 28.4 |
| 1938 | .. | .. | .. | .. | 22.5 | .. | .. | 25.8 |
| 1939 | .. | .. | .. | .. | 24.7 | .. | .. | 27.3 |

ᵃ Ratio of actual copper content of concentrates to actual copper content of ore concentrated.

ᵇ Ratio obtained by aggregating results at individual properties as follows: Ray (1911–25) and Chino (1912–25), Ray Consolidated Copper Co.; Nevada (1912–29), Ray (1926–29) and Chino (1926–29), Nevada Consolidated Copper Co.; Morenci (1911–19) and Copper Queen (1924–29), Phelps Dodge Corp.; Miami (1911–31), Miami Copper Co.; Utah (1911–31), Utah Copper Co. Data were taken from annual reports of the companies concerned. Dispersion of the ratio among individual properties was so slight as to make splicing unnecessary. Properties concerned produce from 33 to 46 percent of all milling ores.

ᶜ States included are Arizona, California, Colorado, Idaho, Montana, Nevada, New Mexico, Utah and Washington. Figures based on data collected by U. S. Bureau of Mines and published in successive annual issues of *Minerals Yearbook.* In 1939 copper from milling ores in these states represented slightly more than 90 percent of all copper produced from milling ores, or about three quarters of total copper production from domestic ores.

ᵈ Ratio of tonnage of milling ores to tonnage of concentrates derived therefrom.

ᵉ Obtained from annual reports of individual companies: Phelps Dodge Corp. (Morenci), Utah Copper Co. (Utah), Miami Copper Co. (Miami).

# Appendix E

# Charts: Sources and Notes

1 National Bureau index (NBER), Appendix Table A-7; Day's index, *Review of Economic Statistics*, Vol. VI (July 1924), p. 200; National Research Project index, Vivian E. Spencer, *The Mineral Extractive Industries, 1880–1938* (National Research Project, Philadelphia, 1940), p. 9; Federal Reserve Board index, *Federal Reserve Bulletin*, August 1940, p. 764.

2 Output indexes from Table 1; population figures from Harold Barger and Hans H. Landsberg, *American Agriculture, 1899–1939: A Study of Output, Employment and Productivity* (National Bureau of Economic Research, 1942), pp. 399-400.

3 Table 1; population figures, as in Chart 2.

4 Copper, lead and zinc, Appendix Table A-7; iron ore, Appendix Table A-5.

5 Iron ore output, Appendix Table A-5; steel production and consumption of scrap, annual issues of *Minerals Yearbook* (U. S. Bureau of Mines).

6 The total represents steel production as in Chart 5; production of alloy ingots and castings from *Annual Statistical Reports* of the American Iron and Steel Institute.

7 Iron ore, Appendix Table A-5; manganese, Appendix Table A-7.

8 Appendix Table A-7. Data shown in this chart refer to the output of the commodity copper, and not of the copper mining industry; and so forth. The distinction is elucidated in Appendix B.

9 Appendix Table A-1.

10⎤
11⎟ Primary output, Appendix Table A-1; secondary output, Appendix
12⎬ dix Table A-8.
13⎦

14 Appendix Table A-11.

15 Appendix Table A-12.

16 Appendix Table A-13.

17 Appendix Table A-1.

18 Petroleum, Appendix Table A-7; natural gas, bituminous and anthracite coal, Appendix Table A-1.

19⎤ *Minerals Yearbook, 1937*, pp. 807-08; *1940*, p. 789. Water power
20⎦ is included at constant fuel equivalent (4.02 pounds per kilowatt-

hour). The heat values employed by the Bureau of Mines are as follows: anthracite, 13,600 BTU per pound; bituminous coal, 13,100 BTU per pound; petroleum, 6,000,000 BTU per barrel; natural gas, 1,075 BTU per cubic foot. One BTU is the quantity of heat required to raise the temperature of one pound of water one degree Fahrenheit. The BTU values mentioned are determined by complete combustion in a calorimeter, and therefore represent the maximum energy obtainable provided there were no losses in fuel consumption.

21 Appendix Table A-14.

22 Appendix Table A-15.

23 Appendix Table A-5; for the inclusion of noncommercial output, see footnote k to that table.

24 Appendix Table A-16.

25 Appendix Table A-1. The indexes shown here represent simple tonnage aggregates for each variety of stone; they are not computed from data broken down by use (see discussion in Appendix C above).

26 Appendix Table A-17.

27 Clay, and sand and gravel, Appendix Table A-7; other items, Appendix Table A-1.

28 Appendix Table A-5. Comprises all metal mining except placers; bituminous coal; anthracite; gypsum; phosphate rock; and, for the period after 1911, stone quarrying.

29 Appendix Table A-5. "Metals" does not include placer mining; "coal" comprises bituminous coal and Pennsylvania anthracite; the coverage of "total mining" is the same as in Chart 28.

30 Appendix Table A-5. "Other metals" does not include placer mining.

31 Mercury, Appendix Table A-6; total metals, Appendix Table A-5. The latter does not include placer mining.

32 Appendix Table A-5. The coverage of "total mining" is the same as in Chart 28.

33 ⎤ Based on material to be found in Robert Peele and John A.
34 ⎬ Church, *Mining Engineers' Handbook* (3rd ed., John Wiley, 1941);
35 ⎦ Robert S. Lewis, *Elements of Mining* (2nd ed., John Wiley, 1941); and Y. S. Leong and others, *Copper Mining* (National Research Project, Philadelphia, 1940). In Charts 34 and 35 the vertical distance between the original surface line and the top of the ore (i.e., the thickness of the capping) has been greatly reduced for convenience in presentation.

36 For 1880–1899, Spencer, *The Mineral Extractive Industries,* p. 153; for 1899–1939, Appendix Table A-5.

37 Output per manhour and per manday, Appendix Table A-5; output per man computed from data in Appendix Tables A-3 and A-5.

38 Appendix Tables A-9 and A-10. For copper mines output per manday is computed from data which do not include employment at ore dressing plants.

39 Based on material to be found in Peele and Church, *Mining Engineers' Handbook;* and Lewis, *Elements of Mining.*

40 For 1880–1899, Spencer, *The Mineral Extractive Industries,* p. 154; for 1899–1939, Appendix Table A-5.

41 Output per manhour and per manday, Appendix Table A-5; output per man computed from data in Appendix Tables A-3 and A-5. The relatively low levels of output per man in 1902, 1922 and 1925 are attributable to strike conditions in those years.

42 Appendix Table A-5.

43 Appendix Table A-18. At any given moment, proved reserves are the difference between discoveries and production, each cumulated over the life of the industry to date.

44 For 1880–1902, Spencer, *The Mineral Extractive Industries,* p. 155; for 1902–1939, Appendix Table A-5.

45 For 1880–1902, Leong and others, *Copper Mining,* p. 214; for 1902–1939, Appendix Table A-5.

46 Appendix Table A-10. It should be observed that employment at ore dressing plants is not included in the calculation of output per manday, a fact which serves to explain differences between this chart and Chart 45.

47 Appendix Table A-5. Data are for commercial operations only.

48 Appendix Table A-5.

49 Appendix Table A-5. Data are for commercial operations only.

50 Appendix Table D-2. Data apply to a sample of the industry, which varies somewhat in composition over the period. While changes in coverage have been allowed for through the use of overlapping data, the alternative indexes shown measure the output of this sample rather than of the copper mining industry as a whole.

# Glossary of Minerals and Mining Terms

> *For minerals, this glossary attempts to provide information concerning (1) physical characteristics, (2) principal uses and (3) source. In addition, mining terms used in the text of the report are briefly explained in nontechnical language. The glossary is based on Albert H. Fay, A Glossary of the Mining and Mineral Industry (U. S. Bureau of Mines, 1920); and Minerals Yearbook (U. S. Bureau of Mines, issued annually).*

*Abrasives:* substances used industrially for grinding and polishing. Natural abrasives include those composed of silica (diatomite, tripoli, quartz, grindstones, oilstones, millstones, ground sand); silicates (pumice, garnet); alumina (corundum, emery) and carbon (industrial diamonds). Artificial abrasives are of increasing commercial importance, and include silicon carbide, aluminum oxide and metallic substances.

*Agate:* a variegated, waxy quartz in which the colors are in bands, in clouds, or in distinct groups.

*Aggregate:* the mineral material, such as sand, gravel, shells, slag, but more usually broken stone, with which cement or bituminous material is mixed to form a mortar or concrete.

*Alabaster:* a fine-grained, compact variety of gypsum.

*Alumina:* aluminum oxide. Occurs crystalline in nature as corundum, sapphire and ruby; as a silicate and in combination with other metals it is of common occurrence, especially as clay.

*Aluminum:* a bluish silver-white metal, malleable and ductile. After magnesium, it is the lightest of the metals in general use commercially. About half our consumption comes from bauxite mined domestically (chiefly in Arkansas); the remainder is imported, especially from Surinam.

*Amalgamation:* the process by which mercury is alloyed with some other metal to produce an amalgam. Used at one time for the extraction of gold and silver from pulverized ores, now superseded by the cyanide process.

*Amphibole:* see *Asbestos.*

*Andalusite:* consists of aluminum silicate, as does dumortierite, in association with which it is found. Used in the manufacture of spark plug cores, and sometimes as a semiprecious stone. Produced in Nevada and California.

*Anthracite:* see also *Coal.* Consumed largely for domestic heating. Besides being produced in Pennsylvania, anthracite and semi-anthracite are mined in small quantities in Virginia, Arkansas, Colorado and New Mexico. Production from these other states is included in the statistics for bituminous coal.

*Antimony:* an element of metallic appearance and crystalline structure, tin-white in color, hard and brittle. Used in metallic form in conjunction with lead in the manufacture of storage batteries and antifriction bearings. Antimony compounds are employed extensively in paints and sanitary enamelware. Small amounts of antimony are mined as ore in this country, or are recovered as byproducts in the smelting of other nonferrous metals; but much larger amounts are imported, chiefly from Mexico and Bolivia.

*Arrastra* or *Arrastre:* apparatus for grinding and mixing ores by means of a heavy stone dragged around upon a circular bed. Chiefly used for ores containing free gold, which were treated by amalgamation combined with grinding.

*Arsenic:* a solid brittle element of tin-white to steel-gray color and metallic luster, occurring free and also combined in various minerals. Used almost entirely for insecticides and weed killer. Small amounts are employed in the manufacture of glass and as a wood preservative; less than 1 percent is used in the drug trade. Arsenic is recovered in this country entirely as a byproduct of the smelting of other nonferrous metals, but a third to a half of our consumption is imported, chiefly from Mexico and Sweden.

*Asbestos:* a white, gray or green-gray fibrous variety of amphibole, a class of bisilicate mineral. Used for thermal insulation; also as a roofing material and for brake linings. Small quantities are produced domestically, chiefly in Vermont, but supplies come mainly from Canada.

*Asphalt:* a complex of various hydrocarbons, some of which are oxygenated; brown or brownish black in color. Used for highway construction and the manufacture of roofing. Natural asphalt or bituminous rock is produced in Texas, Oklahoma, California, New Mexico, Missouri, Kentucky and Alabama. Asphalt manufactured from petroleum competes with the natural product. Some lake asphalt is imported from Trinidad.

*Ball mill:* a short tube mill (see below) of relatively large diameter, in which grinding is done with steel balls instead of pebbles.

*Barite:* barium sulfate, known also as heavy spar because of its high specific gravity. Used as an ingredient of paint, especially in place of white lead. Mined in Missouri, Georgia, Tennessee and other states.

*Barium:* alkaline earth metal, yellowish-white, somewhat malleable, fusible at high temperatures, burning easily when heated in air. Used in metallic form in small quantities in radio and X-ray tubes.

*Barium minerals:* see *Barite; Witherite.*

*Barrel:* liquid measure containing 42 gallons.

*Barytes:* see *Barite.*

*Basalt* or *Trap rock:* includes porphyritic and felsitic rocks consisting of angite, olivine and plagioclase with varying amounts of glassy base which may disappear; and generally all the dark, basic volcanic rocks. Used especially in crushed form for concrete aggregate, road metal and railroad ballast. Produced in most states.

*Bauxite* or *Aluminum oxide:* the principal source of aluminum. Used also for the manufacture of abrasives, as an absorbent in the oil and sugar refining industries and, to a small extent, as a refractory and flux in the steel industry. It is mined chiefly in Arkansas, but almost half our requirements are imported from Surinam.

*Bench:* a single level of operations in quarrying and open pit mining. The mineral is removed in successive layers, each of which is a bench. Several benches may be in operation simultaneously in different parts of the mine.

*Beneficiating:* a term originally signifying the reduction of ores to metal; now employed, especially in the case of iron ore, to mean the breaking and concentrating of the ore before shipment.

*Bentonite:* see *Clay.*

*Beryllium:* a silver-white, malleable metal also known as glucinum; almost as light as magnesium. Used in alloy with copper where resistance to fatigue and corrosion is desired. Obtained from beryl (beryllium aluminum silicate) imported from Argentina and Brazil.

*Bismuth:* a brittle, reddish-white metal. Used in pharmaceuticals and, in metallic form, in conjunction with lead, tin and cadmium as a low melting point alloy which has many technical applications. Small amounts of bismuth are recovered in the smelting of other nonferrous metals, but most of the supply is imported from Peru.

*Bitumen:* a generic name for various solid and semisolid, tarlike hydrocarbons. See *Asphalt; Bituminous coal.*

*Bituminous coal:* see also *Coal.* Used as fuel and for the manufacture of gas coke and numerous byproducts. The following states, in descending order of importance, produced more than 10 million tons each in 1940: West Virginia, Pennsylvania, Illinois, Kentucky, Ohio, Indiana, Alabama, Virginia.

*Black lead:* see *Graphite.*

*Block caving:* a method of mining metallic ores in which gravity is used for breaking and loading. Each block is undercut over the greater part of its bottom area and the supporting pillars are then blasted out.

*Bog ore:* an iron hydroxide ore from marshy places, much used by the early iron industry of New England.

*Bootlegging:* mining, especially of anthracite, without the consent of the owner of the mineral rights.

*Borates:* see *Boron minerals.*

*Borax* or *Sodium biborate:* see *Boron minerals.*

*Boron minerals:* used chiefly by manufacturers of heat-resisting glass and vitreous enamelware; also employed as fertilizer. The United States produces 90 percent of the world supply.

*Breaker:* in anthracite mining, the structure in which the coal is broken, sized, and cleaned for market.

*Breast:* section of the coal face in a coal mine.

*BTU:* British thermal unit, the quantity of heat required to raise a pound of water one degree Fahrenheit.

*Bromine compounds:* used chiefly in the production of antiknock gasolines. Derived from sea water at Wilmington, N. C. and from natural brine in Michigan.

*Brucite:* a magnesium hydroxide which has been mined in recent years in Nevada for use as a refractory.

*Bucking iron* or *Bucking plate:* an iron plate on which ore is ground by hand by means of a muller. Extensively used for the final reduction of ore samples for assaying.

*Cable drill:* see *Churn drill.*

*Cadmium:* a tin-white, malleable, ductile metal, capable of a high polish. Used for electroplating, for the manufacture of bearings and of low melting point alloys (with lead, tin and bismuth). Cadmium compounds are important as pigments and in the chemical industry. From domestic ores cadmium is obtained mainly as a byproduct in the smelting of zinc; substantial quantities are derived from Mexican or other foreign ores.

*Cage:* a frame with one or more platforms for cars, used in hoisting in a vertical shaft. It is steadied by guides on the sides of the shaft.

*Calcine:* to expose to heat, with or without oxidation; to roast. Applied to ores for the removal of water and sulfur, and to disintegrate the mass; to limestone for the expulsion of its carbon dioxide; etc.

*Calcium:* a silver-white, rather soft metal of the alkaline earth group. Employed in metallic form in small quantities for fine-grain alloy steels and for magnesium alloys.

*Calcium chloride:* used in refrigeration and for the control of dust and ice in highway construction. Produced from natural brines.

*Carbon black:* see *Natural gas.*

*Caving:* a system of mining, developed originally in Lake Superior mines. The support is removed from a great block of ore, which then caves or falls, being broken in this manner sufficiently to permit handling.

*Cement:* a substance used in a soft pasty state to join stones or brick, and which afterwards becomes hard as stone; especially a strong mortar made with lime or a calcined mixture of clay and limestone. Being a manufactured product, cement is not treated in this volume. Statistics for cement rock, or limestone used in cement manufacture, will be found in Appendix A.

*Chalcocite:* a copper sulfide, the chief source of copper in the Ray and Miami districts of Arizona.

*Channeling machine:* used in dimension stone quarries for cutting rock where smooth sides are desired. Operates by progressively deepening a groove by percussion.

*Chats:* a waste product obtained in concentrating lead and zinc ores.

*Chert:* a compact, flint-like, siliceous rock used for grinding.

*Chrome ore* or *Chromite:* a chromate of iron. The steel industry consumes more than three fourths of the supply either in refractories or in the production of chrome alloys, and especially stainless steel; the mineral is used also for tanning leather and for chemical manufacture. Small amounts are mined in California, but 99 percent of our supply is imported, chiefly from South Africa, Cuba and the Philippines.

*Chromium:* a brilliant, tin-white, comparatively rare metal, hard, brittle and refractory. Occurs chiefly as chromite. See *Chrome ore.*

*Chrysotile:* a form of asbestos.

*Churn drill,* also called *Cable drill* or *Well drill:* portable drilling equipment usually mounted on four wheels and driven by gasoline, electricity or steam. Also applied to a stationary drill operated from a derrick, as in oil well drilling. The drill head is raised by means of a rope or cable and allowed to drop, thus striking successive blows by means of which the rock is pulverized and the hole deepened.

*Cinnabar:* a vermilion-colored mercuric sulfide, the principal ore of mercury, occurring as hexagonal crystals.

*Clay:* a substance which, when finely ground and mixed with water, forms a pasty moldable mass that preserves its shape when air dried; the particles soften and coalesce when highly heated and form a stony mass upon cooling. Clays are composed mostly of aluminum silicate. Statistics for common clay, used for bricks and heavy clay products, were not available until 1939. The five chief varieties of fine clay are: kaolin or china clay, ball clay, fire and stoneware clay, bentonite, and fuller's earth. The first three are used for pottery and stoneware, high grade tile and linoleum manufacture. In addition, kaolin and fire clay are used for rubber and as refractories; kaolin is used as a filler and coating for paper, and in the manufacture of paints and cements; fire clay for architectural terra cotta. Bentonite is used in foundry molding; as a filter and bleaching agent in the oil refining industry, and as mud for the rotary drilling of oil and gas wells. Fuller's earth, like bentonite, is used in the oil refining industry; also for clarifying solvents in the dry cleaning industry.

*Coal:* a carbonaceous substance formed from the remains of vegetation by partial decomposition. The vegetal matter appears to have first taken the form of peat, then lignite, and finally, bituminous coal. The latter by the loss of its bitumen has in some places been converted into anthracite or hard coal. See *Anthracite; Bituminous coal.*

*Coal gas:* see *Manufactured gas.*

*Cobalt:* a tough, lustrous, nickel-white metal, related to and occurring with iron and nickel. Used in oxide form by the ceramic industry; as cobalt salts in the paint, varnish and linoleum industries; and as metallic cobalt in alloy steels for drills and cutting tools, and for catalytic purposes. Domestic production is negligible; imports come mainly from the Belgian Congo.

*Coke:* bituminous coal from which the volatile constituents have been driven off by heat, so that the fixed carbon and the ash are fused together. Although occasionally found in nature, coke is commercially available only as a manufactured product, and is therefore outside the scope of this volume.

*Columbium:* a metallic element of steel-gray color and brilliant luster, closely associated with tantalum. Used for special purpose ferrous alloys. Imported from Nigeria.

*Concentrate:* to increase the strength by diminishing the bulk of an ore; to separate metal or ore from the gangue or associated rock. Crushing or grinding is usually the first step, followed by wet or dry physical or chemical processes of separation. The word is used also as a noun to describe the products of a concentration process.

*Concrete:* a mixture of sand, gravel, pebbles, crushed stone, or other aggregate, with cement (or occasionally with tar); used for roads, foundations and other construction purposes.

*Copper:* a common metal of reddish color, ductile and malleable; has its widest application in the manufacture of electrical apparatus. Often mined in association with gold and silver, it comes partly from deep mines (especially in Michigan) and partly from large scale surface workings (as in Utah).

*Corundum:* natural alumina abrasive, not mined in the United States.

*Cradle:* a wooden box, longer than wide, provided with a movable slide and hopper, and mounted on two rockers. Used at placer workings for washing gold-bearing earths.

*Crosscut:* a small passageway in a mine driven at right angles to the main entry to connect it with a parallel entry or air course.

*Cryolite:* a fluoride of sodium and aluminum, used in the metallurgy of aluminum, the manufacture of glass and enamels, and insecticides. All supplies are imported from Greenland.

*Culm:* the waste or slack of the Pennsylvania anthracite mines, consisting of fine coal of varying purity, and coal dust and dirt.

*Cut-and-fill:* a method of mining in which the excavation is filled with waste material to support the walls and roof.

*Cyanide process:* a method of extracting gold from finely crushed ores, concentrates and tailings by means of potassium cyanide in dilute solutions. The gold is dissolved and subsequently recovered by deposition upon metallic zinc or by other means.

*Cyanite:* see *Kyanite.*

*Derrick:* framework or tower over a deep drill hole, such as that of an oil well, for supporting the tackle for boring, hoisting or lowering. At first made of wood, now usually of steel.

*Diamond:* a very hard, crystalline form of carbon, occurring in nature. Valuable as a precious stone and as an abrasive. Industrial diamonds are imported from Brazil and South Africa.

*Diatomaceous earth:* see *Diatomite.*

*Diatomite:* a powdered form of silica consisting essentially of the remains of microscopic plants called diatoms. Used in the manufacture of dynamite, pottery glaze, abrasives and filters. California and Oregon are the chief producing states.

*Dimension stone:* quarried or cut in accordance with required dimensions. Includes building stone, paving blocks and stone for sea walls and dock facings.

*Dinkey:* a small locomotive used to move cars in and about mines and quarries.

*Dolomite:* a carbonate of calcium and magnesium, often contained in limestone. Used in making refractory materials; also, recently, for the production of metallic magnesium.

*Dragstones:* see *Millstones.*

*Dressing:* originally referred to the picking, sorting and washing of ores preparatory to reduction. The term now includes more elaborate processes of milling and concentration of ores; also the shaping of dimension stone.

*Drift:* a horizontal passage underground. A drift follows the vein; it is to be distinguished from a crosscut, which intersects it, or a level or gallery, which may do either.

*Dry hole:* a well, drilled for oil or gas, in which none is found.

*Ductile:* capable of being permanently drawn out or hammered thin.

*Dumortierite:* a bright bluish, lavender or reddish translucent aluminum silicate. Like andalusite, with which it is found, it is used chiefly for the manufacture of spark plug cores. Produced in Nevada.

*Emery:* natural alumina abrasive, an impure form of corundum, mined in small quantities near Peekskill, N. Y. Supply comes mainly from abroad, and the mineral has lost ground to artificial abrasives.

*Entry:* a passage or haulage way in a coal mine.

*Fatigue:* the weakening of a metal bar by the repeated application and removal of a load considerably less than the breaking weight of the bar.

*Feldspar:* a mineral consisting of complex aluminum silicates. Used in the glass and ceramic industries and in the manufacture of soap and abrasives. Produced in many states. Small amounts are imported from Canada.

*Flint:* a dense, fine-grained, form of silica which is very tough and yields a cutting edge on fracture. Used especially as grinding pebbles for tube mills in the concentration of metallic ores. Chiefly imported from France, Belgium and Denmark, flint pebbles are now being produced in several states in this country.

*Flotation process:* a concentration process for ores of the nonferrous metals which takes advantage of the principles of surface tension and colloid chemistry to separate mineral from gangue. The mineral is induced to float on the surface of water or other liquid, while the gangue is induced to sink through the surface and settle separately. Classified as film flotation and froth flotation.

*Fluorspar:* calcium fluoride; purple, green or white mineral. Chiefly consumed as a flux by the steel industry; also for glass and enamel. Produced principally in Illinois and Kentucky, partly as a byproduct of lead-zinc ores. Small quantities are imported.

*Flush production:* the yield of an oil well during the early period of production.

*Fuller's earth:* see *Clay.*

*Gangue:* the nonmetalliferous, or nonvaluable metalliferous, minerals in an ore; the mineral associated with the ore in a vein.

*Garnet:* a group of silicate minerals used as abrasives. Produced in New York, North Carolina and Vermont.

*Gas:* see *Manufactured gas; Natural gas.*

*Gasoline:* see *Natural gasoline; Petroleum.*

*Gems:* see *Precious stones.*

*Gold:* a metallic element of characteristic yellow color. The most malleable and ductile of all metals, and one of the heaviest substances known. Today it is purchased chiefly by the Treasury. Mined partly from "lode" or deep mines, and partly from "placer" or surface workings, it comes largely from mixed ores which also contain copper or silver.

*Granite:* a granular igneous rock, composed essentially of quartz, orthoclase or microcline, and mica; also small quantities of apatite, zircon and magnetite. Used commercially, the term includes other compact igneous rocks resembling true granite. As dimension stone, granite is produced chiefly in Pennsylvania, Maryland, Georgia, Massachusetts, Maine, and Vermont. As crushed stone, it is quarried in most states.

*Graphite:* a soft, steel-gray to black, more or less impure, native form of carbon. Called also black lead or plumbago, because it is used for marking, although lead does not enter into its composition. Used for foundry facings and crucibles, especially in the manufacture of copper-alloy castings; also in the manufacture of lubricants and paint. Small production in New York and Nevada; imported from Ceylon and Madagascar.

*Gravel:* small stones and pebbles, or a mixture of sand and small stones; any fragments of rock, worn by the action of air and water, but larger than sand. Used chiefly for construction purposes. Produced in every state.

*Greensand* or *Marl:* a mixture of clay and sand, sometimes containing chalk; used almost exclusively in water-softening compounds. Produced in New Jersey.

*Grindstones:* made of tough sandstone of fine and even grain, composed almost entirely of quartz (silica), mostly in angular grains. Must have sufficient cementing material to hold the grains together, but not enough to fill the pores and cause the surface to wear smooth. Used for sharpening tools. Produced in Ohio and West Virginia.

*Ground sand and sandstone:* a form of silica used for pottery, porcelain and tile manufacture, and as an abrasive. Produced in Illinois, New Jersey, Ohio, and other states.

*Gypsum:* hydrous calcium sulfate. Used, after calcining, for making lath, wallboard and other building materials. Mined in New York, Michigan, Iowa, Texas, California, Nevada, Oklahoma, and other states. Considerable quantities are imported from Canada.

*Hammer drill:* a development of the piston drill in which the drill steel is not attached to the piston, but remains in the hole, the piston delivering a rapid succession of light hammer blows. The drill steel is frequently hollow so that air or water may be driven through to cool the bit and clean the hole. Rotation of the bit is automatic. Also known as jackhammer.

*Helium:* an inert, monatomic, gaseous element occurring in the atmosphere of the sun and stars, in small quantities in the earth's atmosphere, and in certain minerals and mineral waters. The U. S. Government produces helium from natural gas at Amarillo, Texas, for its own use in meteorological and military balloons; small amounts are sold also for medical and scientific use.

*Hydraulic mining:* a method of mining in which a bank of gold-bearing earth or gravel is washed away by a powerful jet of water and carried into sluices, where the gold separates from the earth by its specific gravity. Also used for other metallic ores, anthracite, phosphate rock. Hydraulic mining has been made unlawful and prohibited in certain river systems where it obstructs navigation or injures adjoining properties, particularly in California.

*Ilmenite* or *Menaccanite:* iron titanium oxide, the principal titanium ore.

*Indium:* a soft, white, malleable, easily fusible metallic element, found combined in very small quantities in many ores. Used for bearing, low melting and dental alloys, to improve the tarnish resistance of silverware, as a glass colorant, and for electrical contacts. Indium-bearing ores have been mined experimentally in Arizona, but current production is chiefly from metallurgical residues.

*Infusorial earth:* a form of silica related to *Diatomite*.

*Iodine:* a black, nonmetallic element, used for photographic chemicals and pharmaceuticals. Produced from sea water in California and imported from Chile.

*Ionium:* a radio-active element, present in Canadian radium ores. Has no current commercial applications.

*Iridium:* see *Platinum metals*.

*Iron:* a silver-white metallic element, malleable and ductile, rusting easily in moist air. It has the widest application of any metal. Most iron ore comes today from Minnesota; other states with iron mines are Alabama, Michigan and Wisconsin.

*Ironstone:* any ore of iron from which the metal may be smelted commercially. The term is usually restricted to stratified ores.

*Jack:* a name given to zinc ores.

*Jig:* a machine in which ore is concentrated, or coal is separated from slate, on a screen or sieve in water by a reciprocating motion of the screen, or by the propulsion of water through the screen.

*Jigging:* separating ores according to specific gravity with a sieve agitated up and down in water. The apparatus is called a jig or jigger.

*Kaolin:* see *Clay*.

*Kyanite* or *Cyanite:* identical in composition with andalusite (aluminum silicate) but differs in crystalline form. Used as a refractory material, and sometimes as a gem. Imports come from India; California and Virginia produce the mineral domestically.

*Leaching:* the process of separating metal from waste by treatment with a solvent. Used especially in recovering copper from oxide ores and old tailings.

*Lead:* a metallic element, heavy, pliable and inelastic, having a bright, bluish color, but easily tarnished to a dull gray. Used for storage batteries, cable covering, paint, roofing, bearings and typesetting. It is mined in association with gold and silver in the Mountain states and with zinc in the Mississippi Valley.

*Level:* a horizontal passage or drift into or in a mine. It is customary to work mines by levels at regular intervals in depth, numbered in order. Rarely applied to coal mining.

*Lignite:* see also *Coal*. Used largely for electric power production in the localities where it is mined. Produced in North Dakota and Texas, and in smaller quantities in South Dakota and Montana.

*Lime:* calcium oxide, a light, earthy, white substance obtained by calcining limestone (calcium carbonate). When made from dolomitic limestone it also contains magnesia. A manufactured product, and therefore outside the scope of this report.

*Limestone:* general term for sedimentary rocks composed essentially of calcium carbonate. Produced for building purposes chiefly in Texas, Indiana and Kansas. Employed in crushed form for lime and cement manufacture, fluxing, concrete aggregate, road metal, railroad ballast, agricultural purposes, and a wide range of other uses, and produced for these purposes locally in practically all states.

*Litharge:* lead monoxide, made by heating lead moderately in a current of air. It is straw-yellow, and is used as a pigment, in making storage batteries and insecticides, and for glazing pottery.

*Lithium minerals:* used in glass making and ceramics. Mined in North Carolina and South Dakota.

*Lithopone:* a mixture of zinc sulfide and barium sulfate, used extensively as a pigment, and in the manufacture of linoleum and rubber.

*Lode:* a vein of metalliferous material. A deposit of ore with more or less definite boundaries, fixed in place between deposits of nonmetalliferous rock and so distinguished from a placer deposit. As originally used the term meant simply a formation by which the miner could be led or guided (from the verb "lead"). The meaning is now restricted to the ore body itself.

*Long ton:* measure of weight containing 2,240 pounds.

*Magnesia:* magnesium oxide, a light, earthy, white substance. A constituent of lime made from dolomitic limestone.

*Magnesite:* magnesium carbonate. Used as a refractory and in the manufacture of cement and fertilizers; also, recently, for the production of metallic magnesium. Mined in California and imported from Asia.

*Magnesium:* a silver-white metallic element, malleable, ductile and very light in weight (specific gravity, 1.74). In metallic form it is now used chiefly as an alloy metal in aircraft construction; also in the manufacture of incendiary bombs, tracer bullets, and flares for military use. Until recently it was produced entirely by the electrolysis of magnesium chloride obtained from brine, but magnesite and dolomite now also supply the metal. Brine is pumped from wells (as in Michigan) or is simply sea water (as in Texas). No magnesium is imported.

*Malleable:* capable of being shaped by beating or rolling.

*Manganese:* a hard, brittle metallic element having a grayish-white color tinged with red. Rusts easily like iron. An essential constituent of open-hearth steel. Although there are large deposits of manganese ore in the United States they are mostly of low grade, and practically the whole supply is imported. Cuba, India, the Gold Coast, Russia and Brazil are the chief sources of supply.

*Manufactured gas:* a mixture of gaseous hydrocarbons produced from coal or oil; not discussed in this volume, which excludes manufactured products.

*Marble:* strictly a metamorphosed and recrystallized limestone; used commercially for any limestone which will take a polish. Produced as dimension stone chiefly in Vermont, Tennessee and Georgia.

*Marl:* see *Greensand.*

*Meerschaum:* a clay used for smokers' pipes which has not been mined in the United States since about 1914. Several tons a year are imported from Turkey.

*Menaccanite:* see *Ilmenite.*

*Mercury* or *Quicksilver:* a heavy, silver-white, liquid, metallic element. Used for the manufacture of detonators; in antifouling paint for ships; for high temperature boilers; and for various types of lamps. The metal is mined in many states, but especially in California, Oregon and Nevada. In normal times considerable quantities are imported, chiefly from Spain and Italy.

*Mica:* a hydrous silicate having a very fine basal cleavage that renders it capable of being split into thin, tough, transparent plates. Used for electrical insulation. Produced in North Carolina, Connecticut, New Hampshire and other states. Largely imported from India.

*Milling:* the process whereby metallic ores are ground, concentrated, separated and otherwise prepared for the smelter.

*Millstones:* usually a form of sandstone, used for grinding cereals, cement rock (limestone) and other materials. Quarried underground in Virginia; also produced in New York and (of granite) in North Carolina.

*Molybdenum:* a metallic element of the chromium group, malleable, white in color. It is one of the foremost steel hardening materials, and, owing to abundant domestic supplies, has been largely substituted for nickel and tungsten. It is also used in ceramics. Besides coming from the molybdenum mine at Climax, Colo., it is obtained as a byproduct in copper mining.

*Monazite:* composed mainly of cerium phosphate, but containing up to 18 percent of thorium oxide. Formerly monazite was valued for its thoria content, used in the manufacture of gas mantles. Recently salts of cerium and the other rare earths have found application in glass; searchlight, motion picture and therapy lamp carbons; and for water- and mildew-proofing. Monazite was mined in the United States from 1893 to 1910 and from 1915 to 1917. About 1 ton was produced in Florida in 1925. At present the mineral is imported from Brazil and India.

*Natural gas:* a mixture of gaseous hydrocarbons found in the earth, chiefly in association with petroleum deposits. Used as fuel for domestic purposes, power production, cement manufacture, and other industrial purposes; also as a raw material for the manufacture of carbon black used in the rubber industry. The following states, in descending order of importance, each produced more than 100 billion cubic feet in 1940: Texas, California, Louisiana, Oklahoma, West Virginia.

*Natural gasoline:* a mixture of liquid hydrocarbons produced from natural gas. Used for mixing with refinery gasoline. In descending order of importance, Texas, California, Oklahoma and Louisiana each produced more than 100 million gallons in 1940.

*Nickel:* a hard, malleable, ductile, metallic element of the iron group, nearly silver-white, capable of a high polish and resistant to oxidation. Used for alloy steels and for plating. Produced in insignificant amounts in the United States (as a byproduct of froth flotation of talc); practically the whole of our supply comes from Canada.

*Oilstones:* natural stones, usually of silica, used for sharpening tools. Produced in Arkansas, Indiana, New Hampshire and Ohio.

*Opal:* a hydrous form of silica. When opalescent it is regarded as a precious stone.

*Open pit,* or *open cut, mining:* a form of operation designed to extract minerals that lie near the surface. Waste, or overburden, is first removed, and the mineral is then broken and loaded, as in a stone quarry. Important chiefly in the mining of ores of iron and copper.

*Osmium:* see *Platinum metals.*

*Overburden:* the waste which overlies the good stone in a quarry, or the ore in an open pit mine. Stripping is the operation of removing the overburden prior to the working of the mineral.

*Palladium:* see *Platinum metals.*

*Paraffin-base petroleum:* crude oil which carries solid paraffin hydrocarbons and practically no asphalt.

*Peat:* see also *Coal.* A dark brown or black residuum produced by the partial decomposition and disintegration of mosses, sedges, trees and other plants that grow in marshes. Consists principally of carbon, hydrogen and oxygen in varying proportions. Because of its high carbon content, it will ignite and burn freely when dry. Used almost entirely for soil improvement and as fertilizer; small quantities are also used for packing fragile articles. It is not produced commercially in this country for use as fuel.

*Pennsylvania anthracite:* see *Anthracite.*

*Pennsylvania rottenstone:* see *Rottenstone.*

*Petroleum:* an oily, inflammable, liquid mixture of numerous hydrocarbons, chiefly of the paraffin series, found in the earth. The petroleums found in different areas vary widely in composition and appearance. They occur naturally, oozing from crevices in rocks, floating on the surface of water, or in subterranean deposits. When crude petroleum is refined the principal resulting products are as follows: gasoline, kerosene, fuel oil, lubricating oil, wax, coke, asphalt, still gas and road oil. The following states, in descending order of importance, each produced more than 10 million barrels of crude petroleum in 1940: Texas,

California, Oklahoma, Illinois, Louisiana, Kansas, New Mexico, Wyoming, Arkansas, Michigan, Pennsylvania.

*Phosphate rock:* a sedimentary rock containing calcium phosphate. Produced almost entirely in Florida and Tennessee, it is used for the manufacture of superphosphates (fertilizer) and, to a lesser extent, as raw material by the chemical industry.

*Piston drill:* a percussive drill in which the cutting steel is attached to a piston actuated back and forth within a cylinder by compressed air. The drill usually provides for automatic rotation of the bit. Now superseded by varieties of the hammer drill.

*Placer:* a place where gold is obtained by washing; an alluvial or glacial deposit, as of sand or gravel, containing particles of gold or other valuable material.

*Platinum:* a heavy, almost silver-white metallic element, ductile and malleable, but very infusible and resistant to most chemical reagents. Used in the chemical industry, especially as a catalyst, and for handling corrosive liquids; in the manufacture of electric lamp bulbs, temperature measuring instruments, spark plug electrodes and magneto contacts; and by jewelers and dentists. Some platinum is recovered from placer mines in Alaska and in California. Most of the supply is imported from Canada and Colombia, or as scrap from the United Kingdom.

*Platinum metals:* the group of metallic elements which in their chemical and physical properties resemble platinum. They are rhodium, ruthenium and palladium, whose specific gravities are about 12; and osmium, iridium and platinum, whose specific gravities are over 21. The other five metals are used for similar purposes, either alone or alloyed with platinum. They are also found in the same deposits.

*Plumbago:* see *Graphite.*

*Polonium:* radio-active element, used in small quantities for spark plug alloys. Extracted from Canadian radium ores.

*Porphyry:* any igneous rock in which relatively large conspicuous crystals are set in a finer-grained and glassy groundmass. Colloquially the word is used to mean almost any igneous rock, occurring in sheets or dikes, particularly one that is spotted, soft, or light colored.

*Potash:* used as fertilizer and as a raw material for the chemical industry. Produced from natural brine and saline deposits in California, New Mexico and Utah.

*Precious stones* (chiefly of the agate family): produced domestically in Oregon and Washington. Some turquoise is produced in Nevada and Colorado. Most precious stones used in making jewelry, and for industrial purposes, are imported. See also *Diamonds.*

*Pulpstones:* very large grindstones, up to 72 inches in diameter, employed in pulp mills for crushing or grinding wood into fiber. Artificial pulpstones of silicon carbide and aluminum oxide are sometimes used. Natural pulpstones are quarried from sandstone in Washington and West Virginia. See also *Grindstones.*

*Pumice:* an excessively cellular, glassy lava, a sort of solidified volcanic froth, composed of silicates. Generally light gray in color; will float on water. Used as an abrasive, and for the manufacture of acoustic plaster, lightweight concrete block and roofing tile. Produced in many Western states.

*Pyrite:* a hard, heavy, shiny, yellow sulfide of iron, generally in cubic crystals. Used for making sulfuric acid and produced in Tennessee and other states.

*Pyrophyllite:* a hydrous aluminum silicate, similar in character and uses to talc, with which its production statistics are combined. See *Talc.*

*Quartz:* a crystalline form of silica. Amethyst and rock crystal are varieties. Used as an abrasive. Produced in California and many other states.

*Quicksilver:* see *Mercury.*

*Radium:* a radio-active element derived ultimately from uranium. Used (in minute quantities) for medical purposes, luminous paints and metal radiography (the examination of castings and forgings). United States consumption is supplied entirely from Canada and the Belgian Congo.

*Raise:* a mine shaft driven from below upward.

*Rank:* the degree of metamorphism through which coal has passed from its original deposition to the present. Corresponds, in a rough fashion, to the concept grade of ore in metal mining.

*Red lead:* an oxide of lead, used as a pigment.

*Rhodium:* see *Platinum metals.*

*Riffle:* from the Danish "rifle," a groove or channel in the bottom of an inclined trough or sluice, for arresting gold contained in sands or gravels. Also describes the lining of the bottom of a sluice, made of blocks or slats of wood, or stones, arranged in such a manner that chinks are left between them. The whole arrangement at the bottom of the sluice is usually called "the riffles." In smaller gold-saving machines, as the cradle, the slats of wood nailed across the bottom are called "riffle-bars," or simply "riffles." See also *Sluice.*

*Rig:* a derrick, with its engine house, etc.; used for boring, and afterwards pumping, an oil well. The term refers also to the derrick itself.

*Riprap:* nondimension stone used for foundations and sustaining walls.

*Road metal:* rock suitable for surfacing macadamized roads and for foundations for asphalt and concrete roadways.

*Rocker:* a short trough in which auriferous sands are agitated by oscillation, in water, to collect their gold. Used at placer workings.

*Rolls:* cast-iron cylinders, either plain or fitted with steel teeth, used to break coal and other materials into various sizes.

*Room and pillar:* a system of mining in which the distinguishing feature is the winning of 50 percent or more of the coal or ore in the first working. The material is mined in rooms separated by walls or pillars left to support the roof. The material in the pillars is obtained by subsequent working, in which sections of roof are successively allowed to cave. The first working in rooms is an advancing, and the winning of the ribs or pillars a retreating, operation. This method is applicable to coal, iron ore, lead and zinc, where the mineral occurs in flat deposits.

*Rottenstone:* a soft, light, earthy substance consisting of fine-grained silica, resulting from the decomposition of siliceous limestone. Usually combined with tripoli for statistical purposes.

*Rubble:* water-worn or rough broken stones, usually with only one good face, used for foundations and coarse masonry. Commonly classed as a form of dimension stone.

*Ruthenium:* see *Platinum metals.*

*Rutile:* titanium dioxide; see *Titanium.*

*Salt:* sodium chloride. Used in the food industry and for livestock. Produced from brine (especially in Michigan) and mined also as rock salt.

*Salt cake:* sodium sulfate, used primarily in paper manufacture. Obtained from brine by solar evaporation in California, and manufactured from various materials by the chemical industry.

*Sand:* any hard, granular rock material, finer than gravel and coarser than dust. Common sand is used mainly for building purposes. Special sands are glass sand (98 percent silica) and molding or foundry sand, for glassmaking and casting metal, respectively. Produced in every state. See also *Ground Sand and sandstone.*

*Sandstone:* an indurated sedimentary rock formed of coherent or cemented sand. As dimension stone it is produced chiefly in Ohio, New York and Pennsylvania. As crushed stone it is used for refractory purposes, concrete aggregate, road metal and railroad ballast, especially in Pennsylvania, and in most other states as well. See also *Ground Sand and sandstone.*

*Scabbling:* the removal of surface irregularities from dimension stone.

*Scythestones:* see *Oilstones.*

*Selective mining:* a method whereby mining is deliberately confined to the richer portions of a mineral deposit; commonly at least a partial separation between broken mineral and waste occurs in the mine itself, rather than in a processing plant on the surface.

*Selenium:* an element related to tellurium and sulfur. Used in glassmaking, to improve the machining qualities of copper, and in the manufacture of rectifiers. It is obtained domestically as a byproduct in the electrolytic refining of copper; some is also imported.

*Shale:* a fine-grained sedimentary rock, rather fragile and uneven in character, yielding a somewhat splintery fracture. Often incorrectly called slate.

*Shale oil:* a crude oil obtained from bituminous shales, especially in Scotland, by subjecting them to destructive distillation in special retorts.

*Short ton:* see *Ton.*

*Shrinkage stoping:* a method of mining in which part of the ore is used as a support for the walls and as a working platform.

*Silica:* silicon oxide; especially quartz, flint, opal, diatomite, sandstone.

*Silicates:* salts of the silicic acids. One of the largest classes of minerals, and of very common occurrence, e.g., as clay. As pumice and garnet, silicates are used as abrasives. See also *Talc; Pyrophyllite; Soapstone.*

*Silicon:* next to oxygen, the chief elementary constituent of the earth's crust. It has industrial applications as ferrosilicon in the manufacture of steel alloys: as silica (silicon oxide) it is a natural abrasive, and as silicon carbide it is an artificial abrasive.

*Silver:* a white metallic element, ductile, very malleable, and capable of a high degree of polish. Used for jewelry and decorative purposes, and for coinage. Mined in association with gold, copper, lead and zinc, it can frequently be described as a byproduct of the output of other metals.

*Skip:* a large hoisting bucket, constructed of boiler plate, which slides between guides in a shaft, so arranged that it may be automatically dumped at the surface.

*Slate:* a dense, fine-textured metamorphic rock whose separate minerals are indistinguishable to the unaided eye, and which has an excellent parallel cleavage, so that it breaks into thin plates or pencil-like shapes. Used for roofing, electrical insulation, sanitary construction, grave vaults, blackboards, billiard tables, school slates and flagstones. Produced chiefly in Pennsylvania and Vermont.

*Sluice:* a long, inclined trough, usually on the ground, for washing auriferous earth. In gold mining such a contrivance is paved with riffles to hold the quicksilver for catching the gold. See also *Riffle.*

*Soapstone:* a metamorphic rock composed of talc and related minerals. See *Talc.*

*Soda ash:* sodium carbonate; used chiefly in glass making and in the manufacture of caustic soda. Obtained both naturally and from chemical sources.

*Sodium carbonate:* see *Soda ash.*

*Sodium chloride:* see *Salt.*

*Sodium sulfate:* see *Salt cake.*

*Spelter:* the zinc of commerce, more or less impure, in slabs, plates or ingots cast from molten metal.

*Square set:* a set of timbers, used to support the roof and walls of a mine, composed of a cap, girt and post. These members meet so as to make a solid right angle. They are so framed at the intersection as to form a compression joint, and join with three other similar sets. The posts are 6 to 7 feet high, the caps and girts 4 to 6 feet long.

*Stone:* see *Basalt; Granite; Limestone; Marble; Sandstone; Slate;* also *Precious stones.*

*Stope:* an excavation from which the ore has been extracted, either above or below a level, in a series of steps, especially where veins are inclined. Frequently used, perhaps incorrectly, as a synonym of room, which is a wide working place in a mine where the veins are nearly level.

*Strip mining:* see *Open pit mining.*

*Stripping:* the operation of removing the overburden prior to working the mineral in a quarry or open pit mine.

*Strontium minerals:* used in the chemical and rayon industries, and occasionally for metallurgical purposes; also for railroad and military flares. Known chiefly as celestite. Domestic production has been unimportant.

*Sublevel caving:* a method of mining whereby intermediate levels are opened at short distances above the main level, and the ore is won by caving; the ore body is worked from the top down in successive slices.

*Sulfur:* a nonmetallic element occurring naturally in large quantities either native or in various sulfides. Native sulfur occurs in yellow orthorhombic crystals, in masses, crusts, and powder. It is the chief ingredient of sulfuric acid, a heavy chemical used as raw material for the manufacture of fertilizers, refining of petroleum, pickling of steel, processing of textiles and manufacture of explosives. Sulfur is mined in Texas and Louisiana.

*Tailings:* parts of any incoherent or fluid material separated as refuse, or separately treated as inferior in quality or value. In metallurgy, the part rejected in washing an ore that has passed through the screens of a stamp mill; the worthless slimes left after the valuable portion has been separated by dressing or concentration.

*Talc:* a hydrous magnesium silicate, which has a greasy or soapy feel and is easily cut. Used in paint, ceramics, roofing, paper, rubber and toilet preparations. Produced in New York and many other states. Talc also is imported, mainly ground, from Italy, France, Canada, China, and other countries.

*Tantalum:* a rather brittle lustrous white metal, closely associated with columbium. Alloyed with tungsten it is used in fountain pens, alloyed with nickel in radio tubes. As metal it is also used for corrosion resistant apparatus in chemical plants; as carbide it is employed in wire drawing dies and steel cutting tools. Imported from Australia, Brazil and the Belgian Congo.

*Tar:* a thick, brown-to-black viscous liquid, obtained by the distillation of wood, coal, peat and other organic materials.

*Tellurium:* an element related to selenium and sulfur. Occasionally found native as a crystalline substance of tin-white metallic luster, but usually in combination, as with gold and silver. Used in small quantities to toughen rubber, lead and copper, and in vapor form in "daylight" lamps.

*Terneplate:* a variety of tinplate coated with an alloy of tin (one third) and lead (two thirds).

*Tin:* a soft, lustrous white, crystalline metal, malleable at ordinary temperature but brittle when hot. Used for tinplate (especially in the manufacture of food containers); as solder, for bearings, and in the manufacture of brass; and for collapsible tubes and foil. A few tons of tin are mined annually in Alaska, but practically none in the continental United States. Before its occupation by the Japanese in 1942, Malaya supplied most of our tin; with the construction of a smelter in Texas, it is expected that an important part of our supply will be derived from Bolivia in the form of concentrates.

*Titanium:* a metallic element found in nature in combined form only, and isolated as an infusible, iron-gray, crystalline powder. Used extensively as ilmenite (iron titanium oxide) and rutile (titanium dioxide) for pigments, ceramics, paper-making and cosmetics. Metallic titanium is used in conjunction with vanadium in steel alloys. Ilmenite comes from India; rutile is mined in Virginia and Arkansas, and is imported from Australia.

*Ton:* measure of weight containing 2,000 pounds. See also *Long ton.*

*Trap rock:* see *Basalt.*

*Tripoli:* an incoherent, highly siliceous sedimentary rock composed of the shells of diatoms or radiolaria. Used as a polishing powder, and for filters. Produced in several states, especially Illinois.

*Tube mill:* a revolving cylinder nearly half filled with glacial or water-worn flints, used for fine grinding of ore prior to concentration.

*Tungsten:* a metal of the chromium group, found combined in certain minerals as wolframite and scheelite, and isolated as a hard, brittle, white or gray metal. Used for making high-speed tool steels and electric light filaments. Substantial amounts of tungsten ore are produced domestically (chiefly in California and Nevada); but, like the rest of the world, this country is in part dependent on imports from eastern Asia, particularly China. Because of this dependence, there has been some tendency to substitute molybdenum for tungsten in alloy steels, but there is apparently nothing that can well be substituted in the manufacture of lamp filaments.

*Turquoise:* hydrous aluminum phosphate, colored by traces of copper. Produced in small quantities in Nevada and Colorado.

*Uranium:* a heavy, hard, nickel-white metal of the chromium group. It does not at present have commercial applications, but has been proposed as a source of atomic power. Obtainable as a byproduct of vanadium.

*Vanadium:* a grayish-white metallic powder; does not occur in native form, but is combined in several ores. Used as a steel-hardening material, especially in conjunction with molybdenum in tool steels in which tungsten has been replaced by the latter; also in small quantities as a catalyst in the manufacture of sulfuric acid; and in the ceramic industries. Although vanadium ores (which often also contain uranium) are mined in this country, chiefly in Colorado, a substantial portion of our supply has to be imported, mainly from Peru.

*Vein:* an occurrence of ore, usually disseminated through a gangue, and having a more or less regular development in length, width and depth. When metalliferous, a vein is described as a lode.

*Vermiculite:* a hydrated silicate related to mica, used for heat insulation and as a refractory. It has been mined in this country since 1924, chiefly in Montana.

*Walking beam:* an oscillating beam or lever for transmitting power, especially from engine to drill tool in a cable or churn drill of the sort used for drilling oil wells.

*Water level:* the level at which, by natural or artificial drainage, water is removed from a mine or mineral deposit.

*Well drill:* see *Churn drill.*

*Whetstones:* see *Oilstones.*

*Whim:* a large capstan or vertical drum turned by horse or steam power, for raising coal, ore or water from a mine. Called also whimsey, whim gin, horse gin.

*White lead:* a pigment composed of approximately 75 percent lead carbonate and 25 percent hydrated lead oxide.

*Windlass:* a roll or drum with handles, used in winding or hoisting from shallow pits.

*Witherite:* mineral composed of barium carbonate. Uses same as for barite. Small quantities are mined in California.

*Zinc:* a bluish-white, crystalline, metallic substance, used chiefly for galvanizing and the manufacture of brass. Mined in association with gold and silver in the Mountain states and with lead in the Mississippi Valley.

*Zirconium:* a grayish, crystalline metallic element found in combination only. As zircon (zirconium silicate) used in refractories, specialized porcelains and heat resisting glass; other compounds are used as enamels. In metallic form zirconium is used in flash bulbs, radio tubes and electrodes for welding.

# Index

Abrasives
  artificial, 409
  bauxite, 410
  diamonds, 413
  employment, 65, 67n
  mine value, 306
  output, 293
  prices, 293
  sandstone, 53, 293, 303, 355n
  (see also Corundum; Emery; Feldspar; Garnet; Pumice; Silica abrasives)
Accident bulletins, 272–75, 315–25, 327–41, 369, 385–91 (see also individual publications, e.g., "Coal-Mine Accidents in the United States")
Accident rates, 180n, 276
"Accidents at Metallurgical Works in the United States," 316, 317n, 318n, 319, 321, 322n, 323
Accuracy of data, 275–76, 351n (see also Bias in indexes; Coverage of data)
Acoustic plaster, 418
Active period average employment, 64–65, 67n, 68n, 273–75, 315, 319, 325–27, 331, 367
  defined, 273–74
Actual copper content
  concentrates, 396–401, 403–05
  ores, 231n, 396–401, 403 (see also Grade of ore)
Adams, William W., 316, 317n, 322n, 325, 339n, 388n
African copper, 31, 260, 264
Agate, 409 (see also Precious stones)
Age of mining industries, 5–6, 39–40, 56, 58, 184, 193, 252
Agglomeration of iron ore, 149
Aggregate, 409 (see also Concrete aggregate)
Agricultural interests, opposition to sluicing, 100–01
Agricultural occupations, 60n
Agricultural use of limestone, 55, 415
Agriculture, 4, 5, 249
  diminishing returns, 251
  employment, 79–80
  jointly pursued with mining, 99, 100
  labor force, 60

Agriculture (cont.)
  output, 14–17, 79–80
  productivity, 79–80, 85–86
Air separation, 148, 270
Alabama, 52, 149, 209, 220n, 410, 415
Alabaster, 409
Alaska
  exclusion of, 201n, 228n, 269n, 299, 307n, 316, 317n, 318, 321, 322n, 376
  tin mines, 421
Alcohol as fuel, 256–57
Alkali works, limestone used by, 55
Alloy metals 24–27 (see also individual metals, e.g., Manganese; Molybdenum)
Alloy steels, 24–27
  calcium, 411
  cobalt, 412
  columbium, 412
  in mine locomotives, 132
  in mining tools, 118, 203
Alloys, nonferrous
  copper, 37 (see also Beryllium; Selenium)
  dental (see Indium)
  low melting point (see Bismuth; Cadmium; Indium)
  magnesium, 416
  platinum, 418
Alternative indexes of output
  copper, 394–405
  dimension stone, 379–82
Alumina, 409 (see also Artificial abrasives; Corundum; Emery)
Aluminum, 21, 39, 45, 409
  cryolite, 413
  (see also Alumina; Andalusite; Bauxite; Clay; Dumortierite; Feldspar; Kyanite; Pyrophillite)
Amalgamation process, 98n, 151–52, 155, 409
Amarillo, Tex., 415
American Bureau of Metal Statistics, 359n, 360n
American Economic Association, 175n
American Economic Review, 175n
American Iron and Steel Institute, 406
American Petroleum Institute, 325, 366n

Milling *(cont.)*
efficiency *(see* Mill recovery; Ratio of concentration)
employment, 316–19, 321–23
included in mining, 8, 269–71
iron ore, 148–49, 209, 214–16
metallic ores, 89–90, 93, 107–10, 114, 146, 153–57, 263, 269–70
*(see also* Stone crushing)
Milling ores *(see* Concentrating ores)
Mills
cement *(see* Cement mills)
ore dressing *(see* Milling)
Millstock, 300
Millstones, 67n, 306, 409, 416
Mine lighting, 134–35
Mine locomotives, 131–32, 138
Mine output *(see* Output)
Mine railroads, 130–32, 138, 141, 144, 171
Mine temperatures, 135
Mine value of minerals, 8, 271, 278–79, 283–95, 305–09, 369–70, 373–75
determination, 373
quarrying, 380–82
Mineral enrichment *(see* Milling)
*Mineral Industry, The,* 302, 308n
"Mineral Market Reports," 74n
Mineral pigments, 70n *(see also* Paint)
Mineral reserves, 249–50, 257, 259–61
coal, 167–69, 257, 261–62
copper, 262
natural gas, 258, 261
petroleum, 198, 254, 257, 261, 366
*Mineral Resources of the United States,* 31n, 46n, 162n, 296, 298, 303, 307n, 359n, 370n, 372n, 374n *(see also Minerals Yearbook)*
Mineral waters, 306, 309n
Mineral wool from limestone, 55n
*Minerals Yearbook,* 26n, 41n, 46n, 55n, 56n, 68n, 82n, 175n, 179n, 181n, 185n, 187n, 189n, 196n, 215n, 219n, 228n, 296, 301, 303, 305, 307n, 308n, 321, 324, 325, 326n, 333n, 336n, 339n, 342n, 356n, 359n, 360n, 361n, 362n, 363n, 365n, 369, 370, 373n, 381n, 386n, 388–89, 402n, 403n, 405n, 406, 409
Mines, Bureau of, 11, 13, 64–65, 66n, 67n, 74n, 77n, 175n, 181, 240, 273–74, 276, 296–99, 302, 304, 307n, 315, 316, 317n, 319, 321, 322n, 324, 325, 327, 336n, 339n, 366n, 369, 371, 376, 378n, 379–81, 384–88, 392, 402n, 403n, 405n, 407
Mining
defined, 4

Mining *(cont.)*
distinguished from manufacturing, 7–8, 269–71, 307n, 377–86
history, 5–6, 98–105
share of labor force, 60–62
share of national income, 5
Mining, Census of *(see* Census of Mining)
Mining methods
and grade of ore, 106–10, 114
and mechanization, 117–18
underground metal mining, 110–14
*(see also* Block caving; Cut-and-fill mining; Open pit mining; Shrinkage stoping; Square-set timbering; Sublevel caving; Top slicing; Underground mining)
*Mining and Scientific Press,* 115n
Minnesota, 5, 52, 137, 149, 209, 218n, 259n, 300, 415
Minor nonmetals, 55–58
Mississippi, state of, 259
Mississippi Valley, 9n, 99, 100, 281, 305, 323, 342, 369, 371, 373–75, 415, 422
defined, 297, 373
Missouri, 6, 126, 129n, 297, 320n, 342n, 353n, 371n, 373–75, 410
Mixed ore mining, 369, 371–72, 374–75
employment, 323
mine value, 305
output, 280–81, 297
*(see also* Complex ores)
Mobile loaders, 128, 132
Mobility of labor, 61
Molding
clay, 412
sand, 419
Molybdenum, 20, 25–27, 64, 66n, 70n, 77n, 223n, 284, 298, 305, 354n, 371, 416–17, 422
Monazite, 65, 68, 306, 309n, 417
Monroe county, Ind., 300
Montana, 102, 222, 227n, 228n, 298, 402n, 403n, 405n, 415, 422
Monumental stone, 299, 378–79, 381
Morenci copper mine, 402, 403n, 404–05
Mortar, 409, 411
Mosier, McHenry, 126n, 127n, 139n, 140n, 141n
Motor trucks, 141, 144
and bootlegging, 181
Mud for well drilling, 203–04
clay, 412
Mules, 130–31
Multiple-bench quarries, 141, 142

National income
share of mining, 5

# Publications of the
# National Bureau of Economic Research

   * Out of print.

The Social Sciences and the Unknown Future, a reprint of the introductory
chapter to Dr. Macaulay's volume: 35 cents; in orders of 10 or more, 25 cents.

*34 COMMODITY FLOW AND CAPITAL FORMATION, I (1938)
   Simon Kuznets

*35 CAPITAL CONSUMPTION AND ADJUSTMENT (1938)
   Solomon Fabricant

*36 THE STRUCTURE OF MANUFACTURING PRODUCTION, A CROSS-SECTION VIEW  (1939)
   C. A. Bliss

37 THE INTERNATIONAL GOLD STANDARD REINTERPRETED, 1914–34 (1940)
   William Adams Brown, Jr.                              2 vol., 1420 pp., $12.00

38 RESIDENTIAL REAL ESTATE, ITS ECONOMIC POSITION AS SHOWN BY VALUES, RENTS,
   FAMILY INCOMES, FINANCING, AND CONSTRUCTION, TOGETHER WITH ESTIMATES FOR
   ALL REAL ESTATE (1941)
   D. L. Wickens                            320 pp., 8¼ x 11¾, $3.50

39 THE OUTPUT OF MANUFACTURING INDUSTRIES, 1899–1937 (1940)
   Solomon Fabricant                                    700 pp., $4.50

40 NATIONAL INCOME AND ITS COMPOSITION, 1919–1938 (1941)
   Simon Kuznets                                   2 vol., 980 pp., $5.00

41 EMPLOYMENT IN MANUFACTURING, 1899–1939: AN ANALYSIS OF ITS RELATION TO
   THE VOLUME OF PRODUCTION (1942), Solomon Fabricant          360 pp., $3.00

42 AMERICAN AGRICULTURE, 1899–1939: A STUDY OF OUTPUT, EMPLOYMENT AND
   PRODUCTIVITY (1942), Harold Barger and Hans H. Landsberg      435 pp., $3.00

43 THE MINING INDUSTRIES, 1899–1939: A STUDY OF OUTPUT, EMPLOYMENT AND
   PRODUCTIVITY (1944), Harold Barger and Sam H. Schurr          447 pp., $3.00

## FINANCIAL RESEARCH PROGRAM

  I A Program of Financial Research
  1 REPORT OF THE EXPLORATORY COMMITTEE ON FINANCIAL RESEARCH (1937)
                                                          91 pp., $1.00
  2 INVENTORY OF CURRENT RESEARCH ON FINANCIAL PROBLEMS (1937)    253 pp., $1.50

  II Studies in Consumer Instalment Financing

  1 PERSONAL FINANCE COMPANIES AND THEIR CREDIT PRACTICES (1940)
    Ralph A. Young and Associates                         170 pp., $2.00
  2 SALES FINANCE COMPANIES AND THEIR CREDIT PRACTICES (1940)
    Wilbur C. Plummer and Ralph A. Young                  298 pp., $3.00
  3 COMMERCIAL BANKS AND CONSUMER INSTALMENT CREDIT (1940)
    John M. Chapman and Associates                        318 pp., $3.00
  4 INDUSTRIAL BANKING COMPANIES AND THEIR CREDIT PRACTICES (1940)
    R. J. Saulnier                                        192 pp., $2.00
  5 GOVERNMENT AGENCIES OF CONSUMER INSTALMENT CREDIT (1940)
    J. D. Coppock                                         216 pp., $2.50
  6 THE PATTERN OF CONSUMER DEBT, 1935–36 (1940)
    Blanche Bernstein                                     238 pp., $2.50
  7 THE VOLUME OF CONSUMER INSTALMENT CREDIT, 1929–38 (1940)
    Duncan McC. Holthausen in collaboration with
    Malcolm L. Merriam and Rolf Nugent                    137 pp., $1.50
  8 RISK ELEMENTS IN CONSUMER INSTALMENT FINANCING (1941)
    David Durand          101 pp., $1.50; Technical edition, 160 pp., $2.00
  9 CONSUMER INSTALMENT CREDIT AND ECONOMIC FLUCTUATIONS (1942)
    Gottfried Haberler                                    230 pp., $2.50
 10 COMPARATIVE OPERATING EXPERIENCE OF CONSUMER INSTALMENT FINANCING
    AGENCIES AND COMMERCIAL BANKS, 1929–40, Ernst A. Dauer        (In press)

* Out of print.

III *Studies in Business Financing*

TERM LENDING TO BUSINESS (1942)
*Neil H. Jacoby* and *R. J. Saulnier*  163 pp., $2.00
FINANCING SMALL CORPORATIONS IN FIVE MANUFACTURING INDUSTRIES, 1926–36
(1942), *Charles L. Merwin*  172 pp., $1.50
ACCOUNTS RECEIVABLE FINANCING (1943)
*R. J. Saulnier* and *Neil H. Jacoby*  157 pp., $2.00
THE FINANCING OF LARGE CORPORATIONS, 1920–39 (1943)
*Albert R. Koch*  141 pp., $1.50
FINANCING EQUIPMENT FOR COMMERCIAL AND INDUSTRIAL ENTERPRISE (1943)
*R. J. Saulnier* and *Neil H. Jacoby*  104 pp., $1.50
FINANCING INVENTORY ON FIELD WAREHOUSE RECEIPTS (1944)
*Neil H. Jacoby* and *R. J. Saulnier*  104 pp., $1.50

## CONFERENCE ON RESEARCH IN INCOME AND WEALTH

STUDIES IN INCOME AND WEALTH
I (1937), 368 pp., $2.50; II * (1938); III (1939), 500 pp., $3.50; IV: OUTLAY AND
INCOME IN THE UNITED STATES, 1921–1938 (1942), *Harold Barger*, 391 pp., $2.50;
V: INCOME SIZE DISTRIBUTIONS IN THE UNITED STATES, PART I (1943), 125 pp., $1.00;
VI: (1943), 276 pp., $3.00

## CONFERENCE ON PRICE RESEARCH

1 REPORT OF THE COMMITTEE ON PRICES IN THE BITUMINOUS COAL INDUSTRY (1938)
144 pp., $1.25
2 TEXTILE MARKETS—THEIR STRUCTURE IN RELATION TO PRICE RESEARCH (1939)
304 pp., $3.00
3 PRICE RESEARCH IN THE STEEL AND PETROLEUM INDUSTRIES (1939)  224 pp., $2.00
4 COST BEHAVIOR AND PRICE POLICY (1943)  356 pp., $3.00

## CONFERENCE ON RESEARCH IN FISCAL POLICY

FISCAL PLANNING FOR TOTAL WAR (1942)
*W. L. Crum, J. F. Fennelly, L. H. Seltzer*  361 pp., $3.00

## OCCASIONAL PAPERS

1 MANUFACTURING OUTPUT, 1929–1937 (December 1940), *Solomon Fabricant*  .25
2 NATIONAL INCOME, 1919–1938 (April 1941), *Simon Kuznets*  .25
3 FINISHED COMMODITIES SINCE 1879, OUTPUT AND ITS COMPOSITION (August
1941), *William H. Shaw*  .25
4 THE RELATION BETWEEN FACTORY EMPLOYMENT AND OUTPUT SINCE 1899
(December 1941), *Solomon Fabricant*  .25
5 RAILWAY FREIGHT TRAFFIC IN PROSPERITY AND DEPRESSION (February 1942)
*Thor Hultgren*  .25
6 USES OF NATIONAL INCOME IN PEACE AND WAR (March 1942)
*Simon Kuznets*  .25
7 PRODUCTIVITY OF LABOR IN PEACE AND WAR (September 1942)
*Solomon Fabricant*  .25
8 THE BANKING SYSTEM AND WAR FINANCE (February 1943)
*Charles R. Whittlesey*  .25

* Out of print.

TECHNICAL PAPERS

---

NATIONAL BUREAU OF ECONOMIC RESEARCH

1819 Broadway, New York 23, N. Y.

European Agent: Macmillan & Co., Ltd.

St. Martin's Street, London, W.C.2